Physics of Thin Films
Advances in Research and Development

Volume 4

CONTRIBUTORS TO THIS VOLUME

H. E. Bennett

J. M. Bennett

C. R. Crowell

J. P. Hirth

D. R. Kerr

K. R. Lawless

J. W. Matthews

K. L. Moazed

J. A. Perri

W. A. Pliskin

S. M. Sze

Physics of Thin Films

Advances in Research and Development

Edited by

GEORG HASS

Night Vision Laboratory
U. S. Army Electronics Command
Fort Belvoir, Virginia

and

RUDOLF E. THUN

Raytheon Company
Missile Systems Division
Bedford, Massachusetts

VOLUME 4

1967

ACADEMIC PRESS
NEW YORK AND LONDON

COPYRIGHT © 1967, BY ACADEMIC PRESS INC.
ALL RIGHTS RESERVED.
NO PART OF THIS BOOK MAY BE REPRODUCED IN ANY FORM,
BY PHOTOSTAT, MICROFILM, OR ANY OTHER MEANS, WITHOUT
WRITTEN PERMISSION FROM THE PUBLISHERS.

ACADEMIC PRESS INC.
111 Fifth Avenue, New York, New York 10003

United Kingdom Edition published by
ACADEMIC PRESS INC. (LONDON) LTD.
Berkeley Square House, London W.1

LIBRARY OF CONGRESS CATALOG CARD NUMBER: 63-16561

PRINTED IN THE UNITED STATES OF AMERICA

Contributors to Volume 4

Numbers in parentheses indicate the pages on which the authors' contributions begin.

H. E. BENNETT (*1*), Michelson Laboratory, China Lake, California

JEAN M. BENNETT (*1*), Michelson Laboratory, China Lake, California

C. R. CROWELL (*325*), Departments of Materials Science and Electrical Engineering, University of Southern California, Los Angeles, California

J. P. HIRTH (*97*), Ohio State University, Columbus, Ohio

D. R. KERR (*257*), Components Division, International Business Machines Corporation, East Fishkill Facility, Hopewell Junction, New York

KENNETH R. LAWLESS (*191*), Department of Materials Science, School of Engineering and Applied Science, University of Virginia, Charlottesville, Virginia

J. W. MATTHEWS (*137*), Department of Physics, University of the Witwatersrand, Johannesburg, South Africa

K. L. MOAZED (*97*), Ohio State University, Colombus, Ohio

J. A. PERRI (*257*), Components Division, International Business Machines Corporation, East Fishkill Facility, Hopewell Junction, New York

W. A. PLISKIN (*257*), Components Division, International Business Machines Corporation, East Fishkill Facility, Hopewell Junction, New York

S. M. SZE (*325*), Bell Telephone Laboratories Inc., Murray Hill, New Jersey

Preface

This being the fourth volume of *Physics of Thin Films*, it might be appropriate to reminisce for a moment on the development of this serial publication and the field it covers. In all volumes we followed essentially the program outlined in the Preface to Volume 1, in which we stated that the series would contain comprehensive survey articles dealing with fundamental and applied research on the preparation, properties, and applications of thin films. For this reason each volume contains articles on various aspects of thin film physics, instead of focusing on a single area such as optics, electronics, or any other topic. This may be a disadvantage, since many specialists are only interested in a few of the subjects treated. There are, however, many reasons for continuing the present organization of this book series, such as having the flexibility of covering new developments more timely, and of persuading the right authors at the right time. In addition, there exist so many cross links between the different areas of thin film physics that it should be of interest to most workers in this field to have a convenient opportunity to look over the fence of their narrow speciality.

The first article in Volume 4, by H. E. Bennett and Jean M. Bennett, discusses precision measurements in thin film optics. This should find a wide interest beyond the boundaries of thin film optics, since it describes many convenient methods of general utility in the characterization of films. The following three articles deal with nucleation, growth, and structure of thin films, which may be considered common ground for the entire field of thin film physics. J. P. Hirth and K. L. Moazed give in their article on nucleation processes in thin film formation a review of today's theoretical models and their comparison with actual experimental findings. J. W. Matthews follows with a review article on evaporated single-crystal films, covering their growth and structure, and K. R. Lawless discusses the growth and structure of electrodeposits, giving the reader an opportunity to compare structural behavior as a function of deposition processes. The next article, on thin glass films, by W. A. Pliskin, D. R. Kerr, and J. A. Perri should be of great interest to those concerned with microelectronic research and development, since such glass films have gained increasing importance in this field. The last article of this volume, on hot-electron transport and electron tunneling by C. R. Crowell and S. M. Sze, discusses one of the currently most exciting fields of solid state electronics.

Volume 5 will cover such areas as the preparation and properties of semiconductor films, film applications in monolithic circuit technology, and various topics of thin film optics.

We hope that *Physics of Thin Films* will find in the future the same kind of acceptance it has received in the past, and we wish to thank the contributors and Academic Press who deserve most of the credit for this success.

October 1967

GEORG HASS
RUDOLF E. THUN

Contents

CONTRIBUTORS TO VOLUME 4 v
PREFACE vii
CONTENTS OF PREVIOUS VOLUMES xi
ARTICLES PLANNED FOR FUTURE VOLUMES xiii

Precision Measurements in Thin Film Optics
H. E. Bennett and Jean M. Bennett

I. Introduction 1
II. Substrate Preparation 2
III. Film Preparation 8
IV. Surface Roughness... 12
V. Film Thickness 21
VI. Transmission Measurements... 41
VII. Normal Incidence Reflection Measurements......................... 57
VIII. Nonnormal Incidence Reflection Measurements 69
IX. Ellipsometric Measurements... 79
X. Absolute Phase Change on Reflection Measurements................. 84
    References 90

Nucleation Processes in Thin Film Formation
J. P. Hirth and K. L. Moazed

I. Introduction... 97
II. Heterogeneous Nucleation Theory 89
III. Experimental Results.. 114
IV. Heterogeneous Nucleation and Epitaxy.............................. 128
    References 134

Evaporated Single-Crystal Films
J. W. Matthews

I. Introduction 137
II. Modes of Film Growth... 138
III. Monolayer Growth of Single-Crystal Films 138
IV. Film Formation by the Generation, Growth, and Coalescence of Nuclei .. 150
V. Annealing of Thin Films 186
    References 187

The Growth and Structure of Electrodeposits
Kenneth R. Lawless

I. Introduction	191
II. The Nucleation and Growth of Electrodeposits	192
III. The Structure of Electrodeposits	217
References	251

Thin Glass Films
W. A. Pliskin, D. R. Kerr, and J. A. Perri

I. Introduction	257
II. Preparation	259
III. Evaluation of Physical and Chemical Properties	270
IV. Electrical Properties of Glass Films	289
V. Applications of Glass Films to Semiconductor Devices	316
References	320

Hot-Electron Transport and Electron Tunneling in Thin Film Structures
C. R. Crowell and S. M. Sze

I. Introduction	325
II. Hot-Electron Scattering Processes in Metals	327
III. Collection of Hot Electrons	330
IV. Photoemission Experiments	341
V. Tunnel Emission	350
VI. Schottky (Thermionic) Emission	354
VII. Discussion and Summary	368
References	369

AUTHOR INDEX	373
SUBJECT INDEX	386

Contents of Previous Volumes

Volume 1

Ultra-High Vacuum Evaporators and Residual Gas Analysis
 Hollis L. Caswell

Theory and Calculations of Optical Thin Films
 Peter H. Berning

Preparation and Measurement of Reflecting Coatings for the Vacuum Ultraviolet
 Robert P. Madden

Structure of Thin Films
 Rudolf E. Thun

Low Temperature Films
 William B. Ittner, III

Magnetic Films of Nickel-Iron
 Emerson W. Pugh

AUTHOR INDEX · SUBJECT INDEX

Volume 2

Structural Disorder Phenomena in Thin Metal Films
 C. A. Neugebauer

Interaction of Electron Beams with Thin Films
 C. J. Calbick

The Insulated-Gate Thin-Film Transistor
 Paul K. Weimer

Measurement of Optical Constants of Thin Films
 O. S. Heavens

Antireflection Coatings for Optical and Infrared Optical Materials
 J. Thomas Cox and Georg Hass

Solar Absorptance and Thermal Emittance of Evaporated Coatings
 Louis F. Drummeter, Jr. and Georg Hass

Thin Film Components and Circuits
 N. Schwartz and R. W. Berry

AUTHOR INDEX · SUBJECT INDEX

Volume 3

Film-Thickness and Deposition-Rate Monitoring Devices and Techniques for Producing Films of Uniform Thickness
  Klaus H. Behrndt

The Deposition of Thin Films by Cathode Sputtering
  Leon I. Maissel

Gas-Phase Deposition of Insulating Films
  L. V. Gregor

Methods of Activating and Recrystallizing Thin Films of II-VI Compounds
  A. Vecht

The Mechanical Properties of Thin Condensed Films
  R. W. Hoffman

Lead Salt Detectors
  D. E. Bode

AUTHOR INDEX · SUBJECT INDEX

Articles Planned for Future Volumes

The Optical Properties of Metallic Films
  F. Abelès

The Preparation and Properties of Semiconductor Films
  M. H. Francombe

Thin Films in Transistor and Monolithic Circuit Technology
  R. Glang, A. E. Lessor, and R. E. Thun

Interference Photocathodes
  Deutscher, Hirschberg, and Kossel

Oxide Layers Deposited from Organic Solutions
  H. Schroeder

Design of Multilayer Interference Filters
  A. Thelen

Physics of Thin Films
Advances in Research and Development

VOLUME 4

Precision Measurements in Thin Film Optics

H. E. BENNETT AND JEAN M. BENNETT

Michelson Laboratory, China Lake, California

I.	Introduction	1
II.	Substrate Preparation	2
	1. Choice of Substrate	2
	2. Glass Substrates	3
	3. Crystalline Substrates	7
III.	Film Preparation	8
IV.	Surface Roughness	12
	1. Gaussian Surface Roughness	13
	2. Non-Gaussian Surface Roughness	17
	3. Correction of Reflectance Measurements for Surface Roughness	17
	4. Measurement of Surface Roughness	18
V.	Film Thickness	21
	1. Methods of Measurement	21
	2. Fizeau Interferometric Method	24
	3. Feco Interferometric Method	31
	4. Measurement of Thin Oxide Films	37
VI.	Transmission Measurements	41
	1. Transmittance of a Thin Film on a Nonabsorbing Substrate	42
	2. Systematic Errors Caused by Sample	44
	3. Instrumental Sources of Systematic Error	47
VII.	Normal Incidence Reflection Measurements	57
	1. Types of Reflectometers	59
	2. Double-Reflection Spherical Mirror Reflectometer	61
	3. Single-Reflection Movable Detector Reflectometer	65
VIII.	Nonnormal Incidence Reflection Measurements	69
	1. Types of Polarimetric Measurements	69
	2. Attenuated Total Reflection	74
	3. Brewster Angle Measurements	76
IX.	Ellipsometric Measurements	79
X.	Absolute Phase Change on Reflection Measurements	84
	1. Methods of Measurement	85
	2. Sources of Error	86
	3. Feco Interferometric Method	88
	References	90

I. Introduction

The optical properties of thin films are of importance both in basic and applied research. In addition to the wide use of thin films in optical devices as mirror coatings, interference filters of various kinds, absorption filters, antireflection coatings, and protective coatings to prevent oxidation or abrasion of optical surfaces, thin films have also been used to control the temperature of objects in outer space, and as optical and thermal detectors. In all these applications, accurate knowledge of the optical properties of the films is essential. Even more stringent requirements are placed on thin films used to determine the optical properties of solids. Films are much easier to use than bulk samples since surface films, surface roughness, and lattice disorder are more easily avoided and large, optically flat samples can be prepared. Very careful sample preparation techniques are required, however, if the film is to have optical properties representative of the bulk material.

Another application of precision optical measurements on thin films is the determination of such nonoptical properties as film thickness, density, roughness, or uniformity. The ease and accuracy with which such measurements can be made using optical techniques is often not appreciated by scientists in fields other than optics, and antiquated and inaccurate techniques such as determining film thickness by weighing are still widely used. The nonoptical film properties mentioned above are of interest in virtually all thin film applications, but the usefulness of optical techniques for determining them is probably least recognized by those investigating the electrical and mechanical properties of thin films.

All studies involving optical measurements on thin films may be divided into three categories: (1) sample preparation, (2) measurement techniques, and (3) interpretation of results. If either of the first two has not been adequately performed, the interpretation of results is likely to be erroneous. Unfortunately, optical measurements often appear deceptively simple. It is also very difficult to tell from a published description of the experimental procedure whether or not the experiment was properly done. In this chapter some useful procedures for making good optical measurements will be described, and some factors which can affect the accuracy or interpretation of the measurements will be pointed out.

II. Substrate Preparation

1. Choice of Substrate

Optical instruments can be designed to minimize the effect of a rough sample on the validity of the measurements, but usually a loss in accuracy results. Thus for precision optical measurements it is desirable to have samples whose surfaces are both smooth and flat. Since evaporated films contour the substrate surface even to atomic dimensions (1, 2), to obtain flat, smooth, thin film samples one must have flat, smooth substrates. Fused quartz and some other glasses can be polished to give such surfaces (3), and hence these materials are popular as substrates for evaporated films. Their major disadvantage is that large strains often occur in films evaporated on these substrates (4), which can affect both the optical and the mechanical properties of the films. In order to minimize these strains one can use a substrate having the same thermal expansion coefficient as that of the film, ideally a bulk sample of the same material. If epitaxial films are desired, the substrate must be crystalline instead of amorphous. Electropolished or cleaved single crystal substrates of materials such as germanium or silicon, cleaved sodium chloride or other alkali halide crystals, and cleaved mica surfaces are thus often used as substrates. Surfaces cleaved in vacuum are initially clean and free of adsorbed gas molecules, and hence are often used as substrates in studies of film formation and growth. Cleaved surfaces which are atomically smooth and free from cleavage steps over areas of many square centimeters have been reported (5, 6). However, in most cases cleaved surfaces are neither flat nor free from cleavage steps even on a microscopic scale (7), and hence cannot be used for most kinds of precision optical measurements. Large area, single crystal surfaces which are optically flat, smooth, and have virtually no "surface damage," or lattice distortion at the surface resulting from mechanical polishing, can sometimes be produced (8), and may be used instead of cleaved surfaces as substrates for epitaxial single crystal thin films (9).

2. Glass Substrates

Glasses are amorphous materials and thus ideal to use as substrates for many thin film experiments. Microscope slides are fire polished during their manufacturing process so they are often fairly smooth, with rms roughnesses of 10 A or so. However, they are not optically flat and thus are not suitable as substrates for optical measurements of the highest precision. Optical flats may be purchased which, depending on size and price, may be flat to almost any specified degree (down to hundredths of a fringe over areas of several square centimeters). However, most of these flats are not smooth, i.e., they show irregularities in the microstructure of the surface, so that they may exhibit surface roughnesses of the order of 25 to 30 A rms. In Fig. 1a are shown interference fringes formed by a typical, high-quality commercial optical flat. The rms roughness, 25 A, may be estimated from the fringe irregularities. The technique for making such measurements is discussed in Section IV,4,b. Most commercial optical flats are produced by the fresh feed technique in which new slurry is added to the lap periodically and then allowed to drop off as the polishing proceeds. Much smoother surfaces may be produced, however, by a modification of the polishing procedure, called the bowl feed technique (3). Equal chromatic order fringes of one such surface are shown in Fig. 1b. The rms roughness of this optical flat is less than 7 A.

a. Bowl-Feed Polishing Technique. A bowl-feed setup for polishing optical surfaces is shown in Fig. 2. A standard optical polishing machine with an eccentric arm is used, but in addition a bowl is placed under the lap so that the polishing compound is in a water solution, forming a slurry. This slurry

(a) FRESH FEED POLISH

$\sigma_{rms} = 25$ A

(b) BOWL FEED POLISH

$\sigma_{rms} < 7$ A

FIG. 1. Fringes of equal chromatic order for (a) a commercial optical flat polished using the fresh-feed technique, and (b) a supersmooth optical flat polished with the bowl-feed method. The roughness on the two fringes in (a) or in (b) is identical although the spectrograph dispersion and varying reflectivity of the silver overcoating film make the fringes look different.

is constantly stirred by an agitator placed at the edge of the bowl, and covers the lap to a depth of about 10 to 15 mm when it is not rotating. The stroke is adjusted to produce a flat surface as in the standard optical polishing procedure. However, when the final figure has been attained, the slurry is removed, the lap and bowl carefully washed with water, and the polishing continued with pure water (and any remaining abrasive which has become imbedded in the lap). An alternate method for the final polishing is to remove the stirrer to let the abrasive settle to the bottom, and continue polishing until the water covering the lap becomes clear. This polishing procedure produces surfaces which are extremely smooth. On fused quartz, surfaces have been produced which have an rms roughness of approximately 3 A (10).

The harder the glass, the smoother the optical surface which can be produced on it. Thus, fused quartz can be given a smoother polish than can a softer glass such as dense flint, which may have an rms roughness of 40 A or more. Bowl-feed polishing can reduce this value to about 15 A. It is interesting to observe that the ordering of glasses in terms of surface roughness after optical polishing is the same as that obtained for these same glasses after grinding (10–13).

Fig. 2. Photograph of bowl-feed polishing apparatus.

b. Cleaning Procedure. In order to produce evaporated films having uniform optical properties, the substrates must be properly cleaned. Films deposited on dirty substrates will frequently show streaks or blemishes, or in some cases will look uniform but have too low a reflectance or transmittance. Thin oil films are particularly difficult to remove completely. In commercial applications film adhesion is of great importance, and various types of controlled surface contamination are used to improve it. However if the intrinsic optical properties of a film are to be measured, it seems best to keep the number of uncertain factors to a minimum and to concentrate on getting the substrates as clean as possible. Film adherence is often also improved in this way. The procedure used in this laboratory for cleaning fused quartz optical flats, which has been found to consistently enable blemish-free films to be produced, is as follows: (1) The previous film is removed from the substrate using solutions of appropriate chemicals (for example, nitric acid for silver, sodium hydroxide for aluminum, potassium cyanide in water solution for gold, hydrogen peroxide for germanium, copper sulfate in hydrochloric acid followed by a rinse in nitric acid for silicon monoxide coated aluminum, etc.). Care should be taken not to soak quartz or glass substrates in chemical reagents for more than a few minutes, since etching may occur. After repeated cleanings the flats must eventually be repolished. (2) After chemical treatment the substrates are washed by hand using a cotton pad and a solution of a detergent (such as Alconox). (3) The flats are then rinsed in distilled water, and (4) placed in an ultrasonic cleaner where they are agitated for 15 min in a solution of detergent and distilled water. (5) A second agitation in distilled water follows, and (6) the flats are given a final rinse in conductivity water in a weir washer (14). The water in this washer is continuously recirculated after passing through various filters, and is monitored to determine the amount of contamination present. After the substrates no longer add contamination to the water, the rack holding the substrates, all of which are on edge, is placed in a vacuum tank, and (7) the flats are vacuum dried. When this cleaning procedure is used no water marks on the substrates or blemishes on the evaporated films are observed.

Many experimenters advocate the use of a glow discharge as a necessary part of the cleaning procedure. Since aluminum has the lowest sputtering rate of any common metal, it is frequently used as the high-voltage electrode. However, even when an aluminum anode is used, and the dc glow discharge is restricted to the immediate area around the substrates, a thin layer of aluminum is sputtered onto the substrates (15). It has been found that silver will adhere better to a glow discharged surface than to a perfectly clean one, but for transmission or phase change measurements the effect of the barely visible sputtered film must not be ignored.

It is very difficult to prevent dust particles from settling on the substrate before it is loaded in the vacuum chamber. To eliminate pinholes caused by such particles, a technique of stripping collodion from the substrate in vacuum is sometimes employed. The technique used at the Naval Research Laboratory (16) is to pour collodion[1] over the surface, drain off the excess, and, after drying, stick 2-in.-wide Scotch tape to the entire surface. A narrow ($\frac{5}{8}$ in.) strip of tape is then placed over the wide tape leaving a tail which is then attached to an alligator clip and rotary arm assembly in the vacuum system. After pumping down the system to a roughing pressure of about 200 μ, a glow discharge is initiated which tends to decrease the adhesion between the quartz and collodion film. The collodion can then be easily stripped off by using the rotary arm assembly. Care must be taken, however, to prevent the glow discharge from contaminating the freshly stripped surface.

If the film is deposited in ultrahigh vacuum, additional cleaning occurs

---

[1] Mallinkrodt collodion, catalog number 4560, diluted with anhydrous ether until its viscosity is approximately that of water. If the collodion layer wrinkles off the substrate prematurely, the layer is probably too thick so that internal strains are set up in the film. In such cases the collodion should be further thinned.

during bakeout. Film adherence may sometimes be improved in this way. For example, the adherence of gold films deposited under standard vacuum conditions is notoriously bad. However if the films are deposited in ultrahigh vacuum on quartz substrates which have gone through our standard cleaning procedure followed by a vacuum bakeout at 200°C for about 3 hr, they show unusual adherence, and, after aging for a week or so, cannot be removed with Scotch tape.

3. Crystalline Substrates

Unless epitaxial films are desired, crystalline substrates may often be polished using more or less conventional optical polishing techniques. Mechanical grinding or polishing does, however, introduce surface damage. A rough rule of thumb is that the damage (lattice distortion) extends below the surface a distance between one and two times the diameter of the grinding or polishing particles used (17, 18). It is important, therefore, to determine the rate at which material is being removed, and to continue each stage of grinding or polishing long enough that material is removed to a depth which exceeds the distortion depth of the previous stage.

Lattice disorder can seriously affect the optical properties of materials (see Section III). Thus, if the penetration depth of light is large enough that the optical properties of the substrate are important, distortion-free surfaces may be required. Furthermore, if epitaxial films are being prepared lattice distortion in the substrates is important. One then has the very difficult problem of making the substrate surfaces smooth, flat, and undistorted. One solution is to reduce distortion as much as possible by mechanical polishing, and then complete the surface preparation by electropolishing. If the mechanically polished surface has a good figure and one is fortunate, the sample may be electropolished using a cloth-covered lap without losing the figure. In one technique (8) the electrolyte is dripped onto a rotating metal polishing wheel covered by a well-broken-in polishing cloth. A small current is passed from the substrate through the electrolyte-saturated cloth to the metal wheel. In this way the orange-peel effect usually present on electropolished surfaces is avoided.

The major difficulty in electropolishing is to keep the surface flat and at the same time prevent orange-peel effects. An ideal method for accomplishing this would be to pass current through a pitch lap on a standard optical polishing machine, so that the lap could be used to preserve the figure. Thus far, however, a conducting pitch having the right mechanical properties has not been found.

Electron diffraction patterns and multiple-beam interference fringes of germanium surfaces prepared by mechanical polishing, electropolishing, and etching are shown in Fig. 3. Since the fringes of equal chromatic order for

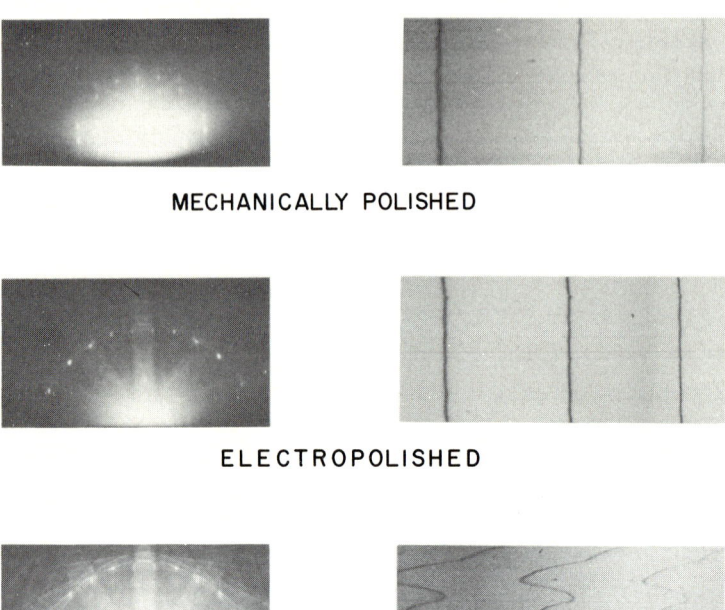

FIG. 3. Electron diffraction patterns and Feco interference fringes of various germanium surfaces [after Donovan and Seraphin (8)]. The rms roughness of the mechanically polished surface is 25 A and that of the electropolished surface 12 A.

the electropolished sample are quite straight, the figure has been maintained during the electropolishing process. Furthermore, the electropolished sample is quite smooth, having an rms roughness of about 12 A. The etched surface is much too rough for precise optical measurements, although it too appears shiny to the eye. The Kikuchi lines in the electron diffraction pattern for the electropolished sample show that it is nearly as free from lattice disorder as is the etched sample. However, the mechanically polished surface, which was polished in the final stage with a very fine grit, $\frac{1}{4}$-μ diamond powder, fails to show any Kikuchi lines and thus has much lattice distortion remaining.

III. Film Preparation

Thin films can be produced by various techniques such as chemical deposition, vapor decomposition, electrolysis, cathode sputtering, and vacuum evaporation. Chemical deposition is often used for forming films such as lead sulfide which decompose on evaporation, making it difficult to maintain stoichiometry. Vapor decomposition (*19*) has been used to produce semiconductor films whose mobility and Hall coefficient are nearly equal to single crystal values. Anodizing, one form of electrolysis, is widely used for forming oxide films of accurately controlled thickness (*20*). Cathode sputtering (*21*) is particularly useful for depositing materials which are not easily evaporated: for example, platinum (*22*), rhodium, and some metal oxides such as titanium dioxide and tin oxide (*23*). However, the sputtering process introduces occluded gas into the films, and hence is less satisfactory than vacuum evaporation for producing high-quality compact films (*22*). Vacuum evaporation in as high a vacuum as possible is the cleanest method for preparing films. If an electron gun is used for thermal heating, the material being deposited forms its own crucible. This technique is particularly useful for evaporating very reactive materials such as silicon,[2] or high melting point oxides such as aluminum oxide or silicon dioxide (*24*). Contamination is normally not a problem even if tungsten filaments or tantalum or molybdenum boats are used, since the partial pressure of these materials and their compounds is very low at normal evaporation temperatures (*25, 26*). A new evaporation technique which may prove useful for producing ultraclean films is a pulsed laser source (*27*). Although no materials have yet been found which can be evaporated more easily by the laser than by other techniques, it is hoped that stoichiometric films of semiconductor compounds can be evaporated in this way.

The optical and structural properties of evaporated films are often sensitive to the pressure at which the evaporation is made. At a chamber pressure of 10^{-5} Torr, for example, kinetic theory calculations show that in an aluminum evaporation if a moderately fast deposition rate (7 A/sec) is achieved, the number of aluminum and residual gas atoms striking the surface per second is about equal (*26*). If the probability of sticking is near unity, a monolayer coverage of residual gas atoms then forms in less than one second at 10^{-5} Torr (*28*). To minimize the effect of the residual gas, one is thus forced to go either to extremely high deposition rates or to ultrahigh vacuum. To illustrate how sensitive the optical properties of films may be to pressure, Table I gives the spectral emittances of silver, gold, and aluminum deposited under high vacuum (10^{-5} Torr) and under ultrahigh vacuum (10^{-9} Torr) conditions. The high vacuum values are of course only representative, and may vary depending on the type of vacuum system used, the evaporation rate, and the composition of the residual gas. However, it is clear that the infrared emittance can vary by more than a factor of two. It may be mentioned in passing that it had long been concluded from measurements made on metal

---

[2] Silicon tends to explode if too small an amount is evaporated too rapidly. The evaporation rate must therefore be carefully controlled, and as large an amount of silicon as possible must be used.

films deposited in high vacuum that the observed infrared emittance of good conductors did not fit the predictions of the free electron theory. However, the agreement between the theoretical values and those obtained from films deposited in ultrahigh vacuum is excellent (32), thus illustrating the crucial importance of adequate sample preparation if meaningful fundamental measurements are to be made.

TABLE I

Spectral Emittance of Materials Evaporated under High Vacuum and Ultrahigh Vacuum Conditions

Wavelength $\lambda (\mu)$	Silver		Gold		Aluminum	
	HV[a]	UHV[b]	HV[a]	UHV[b]	HV[a]	UHV[c]
0.6	1.9×10^{-2}	1.4×10^{-2}	8.1×10^{-2}	8.8×10^{-2}	8.9×10^{-2}	8.8×10^{-2}
0.7	1.5	1.1	3.0	3.1	10.1	10.2
0.8	1.4	0.8	2.3	2.1	13.7	13.2
0.9	1.3	0.7	2.0	1.6	11.1	10.9
1.0	1.1	0.6	1.8	1.4	6.1	6.0
1.5	1.1	0.6	1.8	1.0	3.2	2.6
2.0	1.1	0.6	1.7	0.9	2.8	2.2
5.0	1.1	0.5	1.7	0.6	2.3	1.6
10.0	1.1	0.5	1.6	0.6	2.0	1.2

[a] Hass and Hadley (29). [b] Bennett and Ashley (30). [c] Bennett et al. (31).

The purity of the starting material is important if reproducible optical properties are to be obtained. The importance of high purity for semiconductor and dielectric materials has long been granted, but not for metal films. A study of the effect of impurities on the reflectance of aluminum has shown that when aluminum of cp purity (99.5%) is used, the reflectance at 1600 A is 10% lower than that obtained using aluminum of 99.99% purity (33). In the visible region, the decrease in reflectance is about 0.5%, still an appreciable amount for this high-reflectance material (33). Since purities of 99.999% or 99.9999% are now available for many materials, there is little excuse for reporting erratic results caused by impure starting material.

Impurities may also be present on the surface of the material to be evaporated. For this reason, it is good practice to use a shutter between the substrate and evaporant. After the evaporation is well started, the shutter is opened and coating begins. A Japanese fan-type shutter (34) has been found to be convenient for this purpose when very fast evaporations are made. An additional advantage of allowing the evaporation to begin before the actual coating starts is that the freshly evaporated material may act as a getter, decreasing the residual gas pressure during the evaporation.

Lattice disorder can affect the optical properties of evaporated films as well as bulk material. Figure 4 shows the reflectance in the interband region of various germanium films produced under different evaporation conditions (9).

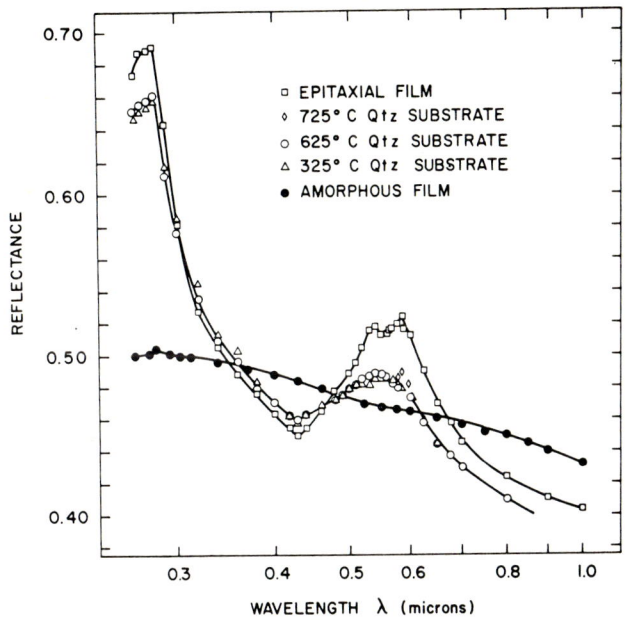

FIG. 4. Reflectance of germanium films prepared under different evaporation conditions [after Donovan and Ashley (9)]. The epitaxial film has essentially the same reflectance as electropolished bulk germanium.

The same high-purity starting material was used in each case, the only differences being in the temperature and type of substrate used. The solid circles show the reflectance of a germanium film deposited on a fused quartz substrate at room temperature. X-ray diffraction measurements have shown such films to be amorphous. As the substrate temperature is increased, structure begins to appear in the reflectance spectrum, and at a substrate temperature of 725°C the reflectance peak at about 5400 A splits into two components. At 800°C, a germanium film deposited on an electropolished germanium substrate becomes epitaxial, and has the same structure in the reflectance spectrum as does bulk undistorted single crystal germanium (35).

When precision measurements are to be made on semitransparent films, a uniform thickness across the substrate is essential. A survey of techniques available for obtaining films of uniform thickness has been given by Behrndt

(*36*). In our experience, long source-to-substrate distances (of the order of 18 in. or more) should be used, and the substrates should be rotated during the evaporation. In the system used in this laboratory, the substrates are mounted on a turntable, and each substrate spins on its own axis as the turntable rotates. Films have been produced in this way which are uniform in thickness to better than 10 A over a ½-in.-diam surface.

IV. Surface Roughness

When precise optical measurements are to be made, surface roughness can be very important. Irregularities having an rms height of only one hundredth of a wavelength may introduce an error of over 1% into measurements of normal incidence reflectance (*10*). Since it is extremely difficult to prepare surfaces which are atomically smooth over extended areas, surface roughness becomes important for all but the very smoothest samples, particularly if reflectance measurements are to be made in the ultraviolet or vacuum ultraviolet. Surface roughness must also be considered when infrared reflectance measurements are made on good conductors. Although scattered light at infrared wavelengths may be negligible, surface roughness causes the conduction electrons to be diffusely scattered at the film surfaces, thus decreasing the dc surface conductance and hence the reflectance (*32*).

Figure 5 shows the optical scattering which occurs when light is reflected from a rough metal surface. Part of the incident beam is reflected in

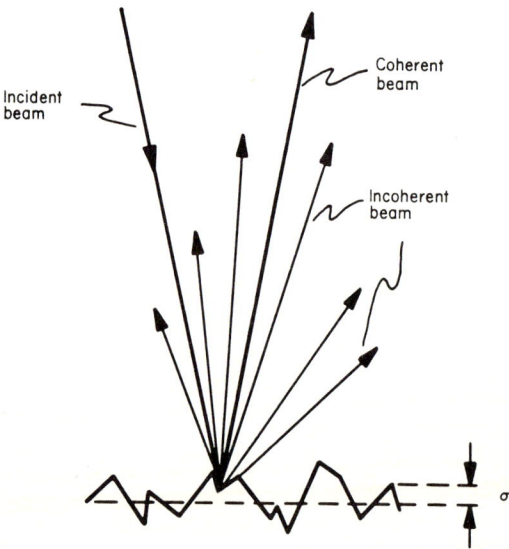

FIG. 5. Schematic representation of reflectance from a rough surface.

the specular direction, while the remainder is diffusely scattered around the specular direction. The fraction which is scattered depends on the ratio of the size of the irregularities to the wavelength. When the irregularities are large relative to the wavelength, they act as little mirrors reflecting light in various directions. The resultant intensity distribution is then determined purely by geometrical optics and all the reflected light is incoherent in phase. Furthermore, the total reflectance of the surface may be smaller than that of a perfectly smooth surface of the same material because of multiple reflections between surface facets.

If the surface irregularities become comparable in magnitude to the wavelength, diffraction effects become important. It is then no longer possible to predict what will happen from geometrical optics and, as is typical in problems involving diffraction, exact solutions have been given for only a few special cases. A prerequisite for an exact solution is that the surface character be known in great detail. As the irregularities become very small relative to the wavelength, a simplification occurs. The observed specular reflectance is then no longer affected by the shape of the irregularities, but only by their heights above and below the mean surface level. Also the reflected light develops a coherent component which comes from the surface as a whole, while the remaining incoherently reflected light is uncorrelated in phase and consists of beams which have been scattered from different parts of the surface into a cone about the specular direction. The *total* reflectance (specular plus diffuse) of the rough surface remains essentially constant in the diffraction region even for surfaces whose rms roughnesses are as much as 0.15 of the wavelength (*37*).

1. Gaussian Surface Roughness

The theory relating surface roughness to specular reflectance when the height of the surface irregularities is small compared to the wavelength of light incident on the surface has been given by Bennett and Porteus (*10, 13, 38*) and will be summarized here. If light is normally incident on a surface whose irregularities have a Gaussian distribution of heights and other restrictions, the observed reflectance R in the specular direction is given by

$$R/R_0 = \exp\{-(4\pi\sigma/\lambda)^2\} + [1 - \exp\{-(4\pi\sigma/\lambda)^2\}][1 - \exp\{-2(\pi\sigma\alpha/m\lambda)^2\}]$$

(1)

where R_0 is the reflectance of a perfectly smooth surface of the same material, σ the rms height of the surface irregularities, λ the wavelength, m the rms slope of the irregularities, and α the half acceptance angle of the instrument. In Eq. (1), which holds when $\sigma/\lambda \ll 1$, the first term gives the coherent reflectance, and the second term that part of the incoherently reflected light which is recorded by the instrument. As λ increases the incoherent term decreases more rapidly than the coherent term because of the $1/\lambda^4$ dependence. A similar wavelength dependence is found in Rayleigh scattering. The second term also decreases as the mean slope becomes larger and as the acceptance angle of the instrument becomes smaller. Thus, for steep-sided irregularities such as those found in ground glass, the incoherent term may be negligible even for values of $\sigma/\lambda > 0.1$. For polished metal surfaces where the irregularities have small mean slopes, however, the incoherent term cannot be neglected. In our experience, if $R/R_0 \geq 0.9$, the incoherent term may usually be assumed to be negligible for an instrumental acceptance angle of 0.03 sr.

To get an approximate relation valid for small values of σ/λ, the first term in Eq. (1) can be expanded. Letting $R_0 - R = \Delta R$ (the decrease in reflectance caused by surface roughness) one obtains

$$\Delta R/R_0 = (4\pi\sigma/\lambda)^2 \qquad (2)$$

Figure 6 illustrates how well Eq. (2) fits the experimental data. The theoretical value for the relative reflectance of an aluminized ground glass sample (i.e., the sample reflectance divided by the reflectance of a perfectly smooth surface of the same material) is shown by the solid line, while the circles represent the

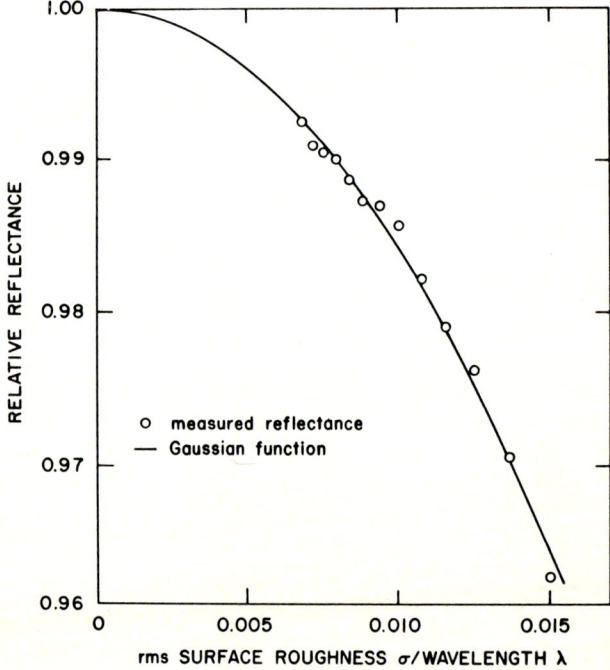

FIG. 6. Relative reflectance R/R_0 versus σ/λ for small values of surface roughness.

experimental points. At the longest wavelength, the value of σ/λ is less than 0.01, but $\Delta R/R_0$ (i.e., $1 - R/R_0$) is about 1% as predicted by theory. Thus if reflectance measurements are to be accurate to $\pm 0.1\%$, as is possible if good equipment is used, and if the instrument has a small acceptance angle, the decrease in reflectance caused by surface roughness should be less than 0.05%. Then σ/λ should be 0.0018 or less, or, in the visible region at about 5000 A, $\sigma \leq 9$ A; i.e., the surface must be nearly atomically smooth.

Not only does the observed reflectance fit the predicted curve for small values of surface roughness, but surfaces can be found which fit a Gaussian function all the way down to nearly zero reflectance. Figure 7 shows the

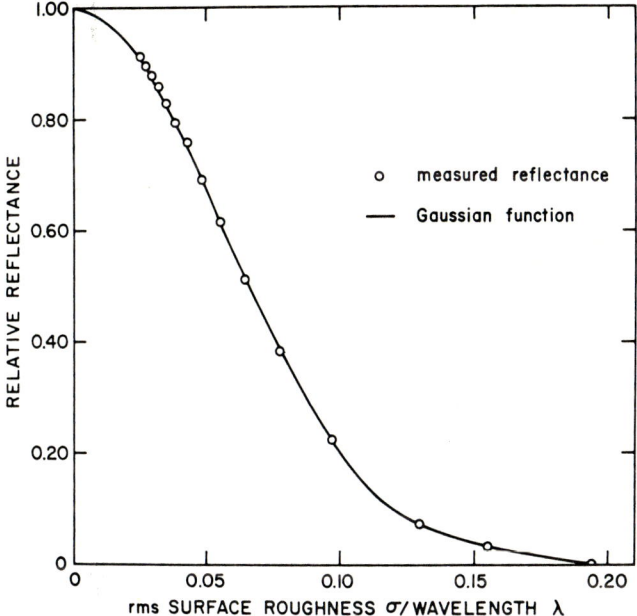

FIG. 7. Relative reflectance R/R_0 versus σ/λ for larger values of surface roughness.

measured and calculated reflectances for one such sample, an aluminized ground glass surface. Note that the relative reflectance R/R_0 is nearly zero when $\sigma = 0.2\ \lambda$. Thus, surfaces which have peak-to-peak irregularities of the order of half a wavelength or more exhibit practically no specular reflection.

A graph of the error in the measured specular reflectance caused by surface roughness is shown in Fig. 8. The abscissa is the rms roughness in angstroms, and the ordinate the wavelength region, extending from the far ultraviolet to the near infrared. The diagonal error lines indicate the wavelengths and roughnesses for which the errors in the specular reflectance will be 0.1, 1, and

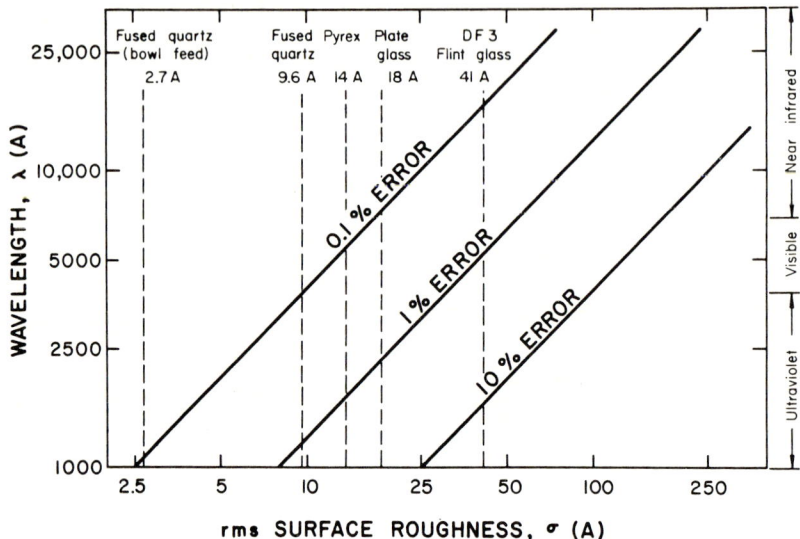

Fig. 8. Error in the measured reflectance caused by surface roughness.

10%. The dashed lines indicate the approximate surface roughnesses which can be expected on various types of optical glass polished using the fresh-feed technique. An unusually good fused quartz bowl-feed value is also included for comparison. If surfaces as smooth as the bowl-feed surface could be used routinely, surface roughness effects could be ignored even in the vacuum ultraviolet. As an experimental test of this conclusion, no scattered light could be detected from this type of surface even at a wavelength of 584 A in the vacuum ultraviolet (39).

Unfortunately, most optical surfaces are not as smooth as the bowl-feed fused quartz sample mentioned above. Also, although evaporated films can be deposited so that there is virtually no increase in surface roughness, epitaxial films normally do increase the surface roughness. Films having a surface roughness of 80 A or more are not uncommon, and appear slightly milky when viewed at a small angle to the normal. If the reflectance of such a sample were measured in the visible region using a reflectometer having a small acceptance angle, Fig. 8 shows that the observed reflectance would be about 5% too low, while at a wavelength of about 1 μ, it would be only 1% too low. In the infrared at wavelengths longer than 2.5 μ, the decrease caused by diffraction effects would be less than 0.1%, but surface roughness may still be important when measuring the reflectance of good conductors. A rough surface will cause electrons to be diffusely reflected at the air-metal boundary, resulting in a decrease in the surface conductance and thus in the observed reflectance (32).

The preceding discussion dealt entirely with the reflection of light which was normally incident on a rough surface. At nonnormal incidence, the coherent reflectance term in Eq. (1) becomes

$$R(\theta) = R_0(\theta) \exp\{-(4\pi\sigma \cos \theta/\lambda)^2\} \qquad (3)$$

where $R_0(\theta)$ is now the specular reflectance of a perfectly smooth surface of the same material at an angle of incidence θ. Also, $\sigma \cos \theta$ has replaced σ in Eq. (1). As the angle of incidence increases, the effective size of the surface irregularities, $\sigma \cos \theta/\lambda$, decreases and therefore the coherent reflectance increases. As a result, a surface which exhibits no specular reflectance at normal incidence may be a good reflector at grazing incidence.

2. Non-Gaussian Surface Roughness

Although some ground glass surfaces have a Gaussian distribution of surface irregularities, other very finely ground surfaces and many evaporated film samples do not. Bennett and Porteus (13, 38) have investigated the reflectance of various types of abnormal surfaces and have found that in some cases the relative reflectance values for a surface with a nearly Gaussian roughness distribution can be fitted by using an expression containing an exponential of the form of Eq. (1) multiplied by a polynomial correction term (13). Another example, a fictitious surface having two different scales of roughness superimposed which differ by an order of magnitude, is shown in Fig. 9. It is seen that the reflectance of this surface does not follow an exponential behavior at all as σ/λ approaches 0.

If the height distribution function for a surface is not Gaussian, the relative reflectance values cannot be used directly to determine the rms surface roughness. However, if the coherent and incoherent contributions to the reflectance can be separated, for example, by changing the acceptance angle of the instrument and extrapolating back to zero acceptance angle, the height distribution function for the surface can be characterized. In this way the roughness of filmed surfaces can be determined even if the vertical dimension of the roughness is only a few lattice spacings.

3. Correction of Reflectance Measurements for Surface Roughness

It is not necessary to determine the height distribution function in order to correct observed reflectance values for the effect of surface roughness. This correction may be made in the visible and infrared by overcoating the rough surface with an opaque film of aluminum and measuring its reflectance relative to that of a very smooth surface aluminized in the same evaporation. The reflectance is then corrected by dividing the observed values by the relative reflectance of the rough surface. Since both the roughness correction

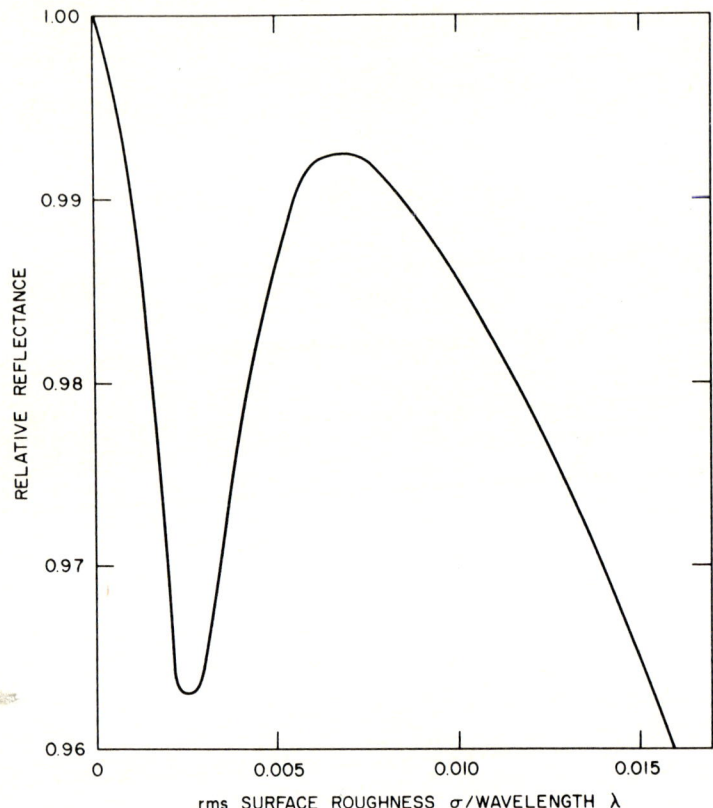

FIG. 9. Relative reflectance versus σ/λ for an abnormal surface [after Porteus (38)].

measurements and the original reflectance measurements are made on the same instrument with the same acceptance angle, the roughness correction should be complete no matter what kind of distribution function the surface has.

4. Measurement of Surface Roughness

For surfaces with a Gaussian height distribution function, the rms roughness may be determined by measuring the relative reflectance of the surface with an instrument having as small an acceptance angle as possible, and then using the first term in Eq. (1). This technique integrates the roughness over the entire portion of the surface illuminated to give a resultant value, and for this reason should be a useful method for applications involving quality control (40). It is sometimes desirable, however, to obtain the profile of the individual surface irregularities as well as a statistical average value. Measurements of this type may be made with stylus-type instruments when the irregularities are of machine-shop dimensions, but for the irregularities associated with thin films one must in general rely on interferometry and the electron microscope. These two techniques are complementary in that interferometry gives a high resolution in depth, perhaps 2 or 3 A, but poor lateral resolution (of the order of 1 μ), while the electron microscope has high lateral resolution, 10 A or less in the best cases, but poor depth resolution. By using shadowing techniques, the electron microscope can measure irregularities as small as 60–70 A in height. Because of the different capabilities of the two techniques, polished surfaces having rather widely spaced irregularities are best measured by interferometry, while surfaces composed of fine crystallites may be better studied with the electron microscope, although they are difficult to measure by either technique if quantitative roughness values are desired. When surfaces having widely spaced irregularities are investigated, the values of surface roughness obtained using reflectance techniques are in good agreement with those obtained using interferometric methods or stylus-type instruments (*10*).

There are two interferometric methods which can be used to observe surface profiles, the Fizeau method and the Feco (fringes of equal chromatic order) method. Both employ multiple-beam interference fringes and make use of a very smooth, highly reflecting reference flat. With the Fizeau method, monochromatic light is used and various areas of the rough surface may be observed simultaneously (wherever an interference fringe occurs). It is not generally possible to cause a fringe to fall exactly at a particular place on the surface and, furthermore, the most information about the roughness in a particular area is obtained when the Fizeau fringes are spaced far apart. Fringes of equal chromatic order, on the other hand, are formed by a small area on the rough surface which can be chosen at will. White light is used which is subsequently dispersed by a spectrograph to give the interferogram. The lateral resolution possible with the Fizeau method depends on the wedge angle between the two interfering surfaces and the resolution of the objective lens in the microscope. With the Feco method, the lateral resolution depends not only on the resolution of the microscope objective, but also on the width of the slit of the spectrograph which is used to disperse the white light.

a. Fizeau Method. In using Fizeau fringes to study surface profile, the surface under investigation should be carefully cleaned to remove all traces of grease and dirt (see the cleaning procedure in Section II,2,b), and then coated with an opaque layer of silver prepared by rapid evaporation in a good vacuum. The reference surface should be a high-quality optical flat having a polished back and an extremely smooth surface (see Section II,2,a) so that the resulting inteference fringes, which contour irregularities on both surfaces, will give a true picture of the rough surface. The reference flat should be coated with a partially transparent, highly reflecting film: for example, nearly opaque silver or a multilayer film. The Fizeau interferometer is formed by placing the rough surface and reference surface carefully in contact so that they are only separated by the dust particles on the two surfaces. The interference fringes may then be observed with the naked eye by illuminating the reference surface with diffuse monochromatic light: for example, from a sodium vapor lamp or a low-pressure mercury arc. A schematic view of this arrangement is shown in Fig. 11a on p. 25, Section V,2,a where the Fizeau method is described in greater detail. Alternatively, the interferometer may be placed in a low-power microscope, again illuminated with monochromatic light, and the magnitude of the irregularities on the interference fringes measured with a Filar micrometer eyepiece. The peak-to-peak roughness σ_{pp} may be obtained from the relation

$$\sigma_{pp} = \frac{\Delta x}{x_i - x_j} \frac{\lambda}{2} \tag{4}$$

where Δx is the maximum fringe width including all the irregularities, $x_i - x_j$ the separation between adjacent fringes, and λ the wavelength of the monochromatic light. To a first approximation

$$\sigma_{rms} \approx \frac{\sigma_{pp}}{2\sqrt{2}} \tag{5}$$

where σ_{pp} can be determined from Eq. (4) if it is less than one fringe (one-half wavelength). If σ_{pp} becomes larger than $\lambda/2$, adjacent parts of the fringe may overlap and make accurate measurements difficult. As an example of Fizeau fringes from a rough surface, Fig. 13 (see p. 30) shows an interferogram of a microscope slide. Certain regions of the surface are quite smooth even though the waviness is very pronounced. A second example is found in the work of Tolansky (41) who has published interferograms of polished diamonds. His pictures clearly show the polishing marks on the diamond surfaces.

b. Feco Method. When Feco fringes are used to study surface profile, the interferometer, composed of the rough surface and reference surface, is similar to that used for the Fizeau method (Section IV,4,a). The rest of the apparatus consists of a low-power microscope objective and a spectrometer, as shown schematically in Fig. 14 (see p. 32). The general procedure for aligning the interferometer is described in detail in Section V,3,b, but the important factor for roughness measurements is that the order of interference be as low as possible in order to show the greatest amount of detail on the Feco fringes. A good range of values is 4–10 (or approximately 1–2.5 μ plate separation) for studying the profile of surfaces under 50 Å in roughness. These small orders of interference are possible if both surfaces are free from dust

and their area of contact is no larger than $\frac{1}{2}$ in. in diameter. T
surface roughness is now

$$\sigma_{pp} = \frac{M}{2}\Delta\lambda = \frac{\lambda' \Delta\lambda}{2(\lambda - \lambda')}$$

where M is an integer determined from Eq. (10) in Section V,3,c, $\Delta\lambda$ the extreme width of the fringe having a mean wavelength λ, and λ' the mean wavelength of the adjacent fringe on the *short wavelength* side. For surfaces having a Gaussian profile, the relation between σ_{pp} and σ_{rms} is again given by Eq. (5). Feco interferograms of fresh feed and bowl feed polished glass surfaces are shown in Fig. 1, and of various germanium surfaces in Fig. 3. It should be remembered that all Feco fringes on a given interferogram have the same roughness contours, since they all contour the same small area on the surface of the interferometer plates. Thus, measurements on any Feco fringe will give information about the surface profile, and no new information will be gained by making measurements on more than one fringe.

V. Film Thickness

1. Methods of Measurement

In the analysis of most optical measurements on thin films, it is necessary to know the thickness of the film. In some cases, as in the preparation of multilayer films, the thickness must be monitored during the evaporation process, while in other cases the thickness need only be measured after the film has been prepared. Behrndt (*36*) has thoroughly discussed methods of monitoring and controlling film thickness during the evaporation process. In addition he has listed eleven survey articles reviewing various methods for measuring film thicknesses. Of these, the articles by Greenland (*42*) and Heavens (*43–45*) are especially helpful. Some methods for measuring film thickness give the mechanical thickness alone, others the optical thickness (mechanical thickness times the refractive index) for nonabsorbing films, while still others give the mechanical thickness along with the optical constants for absorbing films. At first glance there seem to be a multitude of methods for measuring film thickness, but simple, accurate methods for obtaining the mechanical thickness alone are few. Furthermore, several of the good methods have been either omitted or inadequately described in the survey articles. For this reason, selected frequently used methods for measuring film thickness will be mentioned here, along with comments about their advantages and disadvantages.

There are two main types of films whose thicknesses need to be determined:

those which can be formed on only part of a surface, and those which cannot, such as naturally occurring oxide films on metals and semiconductors. The thickness of the first type is rather easily measured, but it is very difficult to measure the thickness of thin, naturally occurring oxide films. Also, the mechanical thickness of the oxide films normally cannot be obtained independently of some other parameter such as the refractive index or dielectric constant. Methods for measuring the thickness of thin oxide films will be discussed in detail in Section V,4.

Interferometric methods are the best ones to use for measuring the thickness of films which can be evaporated on part of a surface so that a step, or sharp discontinuity is formed at the film boundary. These methods include: (1) a wavefront shearing interferometer (45, 46), (2) multiple-beam interferometer using Fizeau fringes (47–49), and (3) multiple-beam inteferometer employing fringes of equal chromatic order, or Feco fringes (50). Method (1) has been adequately described in the literature and is capable of very high accuracy, of the order of ± 1 A, if the film is deposited on a very smooth and flat optical surface, and high-quality, rigidly mounted optical components are used. Method (2) is the one most widely used for measuring film thickness, and is capable of accuracies in the range from 5 to 40 A depending on the smoothness of the substrates used and other experimental conditions. Although method (3) requires somewhat more elaborate instrumentation, it is inherently more accurate than the Fizeau method since it is not as limited by the irregularities on the interferometer surfaces. With care the Feco method can give thicknesses which are accurate to 1 or 2 A. Since both the Fizeau and Feco methods have many subtleties which have not been adequately discussed in the literature, the methods will be described and critically evaluated in Sections V,2 and 3.

Stylus-type instruments are also sometimes used to measure film thickness by tracing over the step at the edge of the film. However, these instruments are generally unsatisfactory for film thickness measurements because the stylus tip digs into the film and dose not give a true reading of the step height. Silver and Chow (51) have overcome this difficulty by evaporating a hard, thick layer of silicon monoxide over the area of the step. In this way they have been able to obtain reproducible readings for films in the 300–3000-A thickness range with uncertainties of 100–200 A in the thickness measurements.

Nonoptical methods for determining film thickness where a step is not required are (1) weighing, (2) piezoelectric quartz crystal oscillator, and (3) X-ray techniques. In the weighing method the film thickness is determined from a ratio of the weight of the film divided by the product of the density times the area. This method is one of the oldest, simplest, and least accurate methods, but it has the advantage that it gives average values for film thickness. It is thus useful for films which are nonuniform in thickness or are too rough to produce good interference fringes. Microbalances are now available which are accurate to fractions of a microgram (36). Thus, as long as the substrates are light enough (of the order of 100 mg or less) so that they don't overload the balance, it is possible to determine the weight of thicker films with an accuracy of a few per cent. The film density must be accurately known to use the weighing method for determining film thickness. In some metal films for example aluminum, gold, silver, chromium, and copper, the density is within 5% of bulk in the thickness range 200–5000 A (52, 53), but many dielectrics, such as lithium fluoride (54), are porous and may have densities considerably different from the bulk values. If the film thickness is determined by another method, the weighing method may be used to determine film density. In one experiment performed in this laboratory, five silver films ranging in thickness from 600 to 3700 A were found to have an average density of 10.51, in excellent agreement with the reported value of 10.49 for bulk silver (55).

Piezoelectric quartz crystal oscillators, sometimes called "quartz microbalances," have become so widely used for monitoring film thickness during evaporation that they are commonly termed "thickness monitors." The shift in the resonant frequency of the crystal is proportional to its change in mass (36), so that with proper calibration crystal oscillators may be used to measure either film thickness (assuming that the film density is known) or film density (if the film thickness is determined independently). The relation between frequency shift and film thickness is linear to better than 1% for films up to thicknesses of several thousand angstroms (36). Figure 10 shows a plot of the frequency shift versus interferometrically measured film thickness for a series of silver films prepared in this laboratory. The average deviation of the points from the straight line is ± 17 A for film thicknesses ranging from 200 to 3500 A. Thus, with proper calibration, the crystal oscillator is capable of giving accurate values for film thickness, particularly for materials whose film densities are reproducible. The easiest way to calibrate a crystal oscillator is to prepare a series of films, measure their thicknesses by another means, such as the Feco interferometric method, and make a graph similar to that in Fig. 10. The calibration graph should then hold for all subsequent evaporations using quartz crystals having the same resonant frequency and area.

X-ray emission spectroscopy (51), and X-ray inteference (56, 57) have also been used to measure film thickness. With X-ray emission spectroscopy Silver and Chow (51) have obtained a precision of about ± 6 A for nickel-iron films in the thickness range from 300 to 3500 A, but their accuracy was limited to about ± 25 A because of the accuracy of their standards. Two grazing incidence X-ray interferometric techniques have been used by Sauro et al. (56) to measure the thickness of evaporated copper films. They obtained accuracies of about 5% for films from 250–1000 A thick. A more specialized X-ray

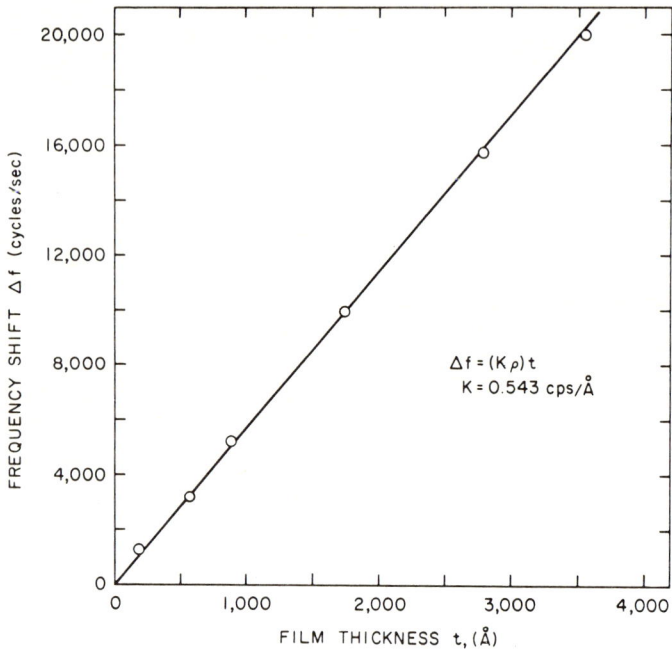

Fig. 10. Relation between frequency shift and thickness of evaporated silver films for a quartz crystal oscillator.

interference technique has been used by Croce et al. (57) to measure the thickness of gold films up to 500 A thick composed of highly oriented crystallites.

2. Fizeau Interferometric Method

Nearly all of the previously discussed methods for measuring film thickness are integrating methods which give average values of the film thickness over the area being sampled. The Fizeau and Feco interferometric methods, on the other hand, give the thickness at specific points on the film. For this reason, the requirements on film uniformity, substrate smoothness, and, to a lesser extent, substrate flatness are much more stringent than with the other methods. These factors will be further discussed in Section V,2,d.

a. Conditions for Producing Sharp Fizeau Fringes. The experimental setup for observing Fizeau fringes is shown schematically in Fig. 11a and a drawing of a Fizeau interferogram in Fig. 11b. The interferometer plates should be two optical flats, one of which is coated with a uniform, highly reflecting, semitransparent film. The other flat is partially coated with the film whose thickness is to be measured, leaving an uncoated channel across the surface. The entire flat is then overcoated with an opaque, highly reflecting material such as silver. The two flats are placed carefully in contact and are inclined at a slight wedge angle to each other. It is important that the air film between the surfaces be as small as possible, preferably only a few wavelengths, in order to give sharp, well-defined fringes (*48, 58, 59*). When the interferometer is illuminated by monochromatic light from an extended source, narrow, black-line Fizeau fringes are observed on a bright background. These fringes contour regions of constant thickness between the two surfaces, and are separated by integral multiples of half wavelengths of the monochromatic light. The film thickness is then obtained by measuring the displacement of the fringes in the channel from those on the rest of the surface by a method which will be described in more detail in Section V,2,c. In order to accurately

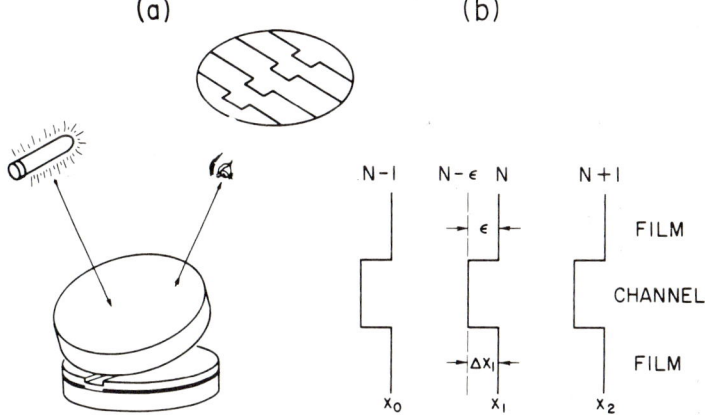

FIG. 11. (a) Experimental arrangement for observing Fizeau fringes. Diffuse monochromatic light is used and the wedge angle between the two surfaces has been greatly exaggerated. (b) Schematic representation of a Fizeau interferogram.

measure fringe displacement, a low-power microscope (of approximately 5–20 times magnification) with a Filar eyepiece may be used. Alternatively, if more accurate settings are desirable, or if the fringes drift rapidly, the pattern may be photographed and the resulting interferogram measured using a photoelectric scanning comparator (*60, 61*). It is important that the microscope magnification not be too high because, apart from the incidental difficulty of adequately illuminating the sample, the wedge angle between the two interfering surfaces must be increased so that a reasonable number of fringes may appear in the field of view. The lateral displacement of the multiply reflected beams is then increased, sometimes giving rise to bright ghost fringes alongside the dark Fizeau fringes and other complicating effects. These effects have been discussed in detail by Heavens (*48*) and Tolansky (*58, 59*).

For maximum measurement accuracy, both the semitransparent film on the first surface and the overcoating film should have reflectances as high as possible (48). If the semitransparent film has a higher reflectance than the overcoated surface, the fringes will have very poor contrast. On the other hand, if the first surface has a much lower reflectance than the overcoated surface, the fringes will have good contrast but will not show detailed surface features. Care must also be taken to have the overcoating film completely opaque to eliminate errors caused by differences in the phase change on reflection in the channel and filmed region of the second surface (15). Silver is a convenient overcoating material to use and, when rapidly evaporated in a good vacuum, has a reflectance in the green of about 98 % (30). The silver film should be at least 1000 A thick to be opaque. Semitransparent silver films with reflectances of 90–95 % in the green and relatively low absorptions are convenient for first-surface films. Multilayer dielectric films of zinc sulfide and cryolite (62) or ceric oxide and magnesium fluoride (63) also make excellent first-surface films since they are durable and can be made with a high reflectance and low absorption. However, their reflectance must be carefully peaked at the wavelength of the monochromatic illumination. Although silver films are softer and age with time, they are much easier to prepare and will last for a few days if stored in vacuum or in dry nitrogen. It is important that the semitransparent film have as low an absorption as possible since the absorption in this film sets the limit to the sharpness of the multiple-beam Fizeau fringes (48).

Another factor affecting the sharpness of the Fizeau fringes is the monochromaticity of the light illuminating the interferometer (59). The common laboratory 100-W H100-A4 mercury lamp,[3] which operates at about 8 atm pressure, has too much broadening in the spectral lines to give sharp fringes. Low-pressure mercury lamps such as a mercury electrodeless discharge tube, mineral lamp without the black-light filter,[4] or uncoated fluorescent lamp may be used to give good fringes providing that a filter is used to pass only the mercury green line. One of the best sources is a low-pressure thallium lamp which emits a single line in the visible at 5350 A and thus requires no isolation filter.[5] Since the eye is most sensitive to green light, monochromatic sources of other colors are not as useful for visual measurements.

In order to produce a sharp step between the film and the channel on the second flat, an opaquing bar is required which can be pressed tightly against the surface of the flat during the evaporation process. A bar of triangular cross

---

[3] Obtained from the General Electric Company, Cleveland, Ohio.

[4] Pen-Ray quartz mercury lamp obtained from Ultra-Violet Products, Inc., San Gabriel, California.

[5] Osram Spectral Lamp obtained from Edmund Scientific Co., Barrington, New Jersey. Thallium has a strong line at 3776 A which must be eliminated by a filter if interference fringes are photographed.

section with about a 45° bevel is best to prevent shadowing of the step. The bar is usually mounted in a holder into which the flat is inserted. It is convenient to be able to observe Fizeau fringes from both sides of the channel simultaneously in order to eliminate errors due to fringe misalignment. Thus the higher the magnification the narrower the bar must be. These bars are difficult to make and must be handled with care.

b. Procedure for Interferometer Alignment. After the interferometer plates have been coated, the two plates are placed carefully in contact so that they are at a slight angle to each other and are separated only by the dust particles on the two surfaces. It is usually helpful to blow all loose dust particles off the surfaces before they are placed in contact by using a glass tube with a rubber squeeze bulb attached to one end. With care, $\frac{1}{2}$-in.-diam flats can be separated by as little as 6 orders of interference, or about 1.5 μ, so that sharp, well-defined Fizeau fringes may be obtained. With a smaller reference flat, even smaller separations may be obtained. With larger flats, of the order of $1\frac{1}{2}$ in. in diameter, the plate separation can be of the order of 5 μ, still adequate to give sharply defined Fizeau fringes. If both surfaces are high-quality optical flats, the Fizeau fringes appear as a series of parallel, narrow black lines on a bright background. They contour all irregularities on the silvered surfaces, so that a jog in the fringes such as that shown in Fig. 11 occurs at the position of the channel on the lower flat. Also, surface roughness and nonflatness on either surface appear as hash and curvature in the fringes, so it is important to prevent these effects from interfering with the film thickness measurements. The orientation and separation of the fringes may be changed by pressing gently on the upper flat. In this way the direction and size of the wedge angle separating the two surfaces can be changed. The desired alignment is attained when the fringes are perpendicular to the channel and are spaced far enough apart to enable good measurements of fringe position to be made. In practice it is difficult to align the fringes exactly perpendicular to the channel, so that one adjusts the fringes until they are as near perpendicular as possible (within about 10 to 20°) and then the interferometer is carefully rotated as a whole until the fringes are strictly parallel to the cross hair in the eyepiece. In making this alignment it is helpful if the microscope stage can be independently rotated and translated in two directions. The parallelism of the fringes and cross hair can then be checked by turning the appropriate stage micrometer and seeing that the fringe and cross hair do not diverge.

c. Analysis of Fizeau Interferogram. In most cases the determination of film thickness from the Fizeau interferogram is straightforward. Figure 11b, p. 25 shows a schematic representation of such an interferogram where the wedge angle increases from left to right. The orders of interference of the fringes (number of half wavelengths separating the two surfaces) are given by the N's, while the fringe positions in the filmed region are given by the x's. The absolute order of interference is not determinable for Fizeau fringes unless the two surfaces are in optical contact at the apex of the wedge angle, a difficult feat. However, the difference in orders of interference between fringes is known. The fringe system in the channel where there is no film is displaced by an amount Δx from the fringe system in the filmed region. If the film thickness $t < \lambda/2$, the method for determining it is as follows. The basic interference equation is (15)

$$N\lambda = 2nd - (\beta_1 + \beta_2)\lambda/2\pi \tag{7}$$

where N, the order of interference, is an integer for each fringe, λ, the wavelength of monochromatic light illuminating the interferometer, d the thickness of the air film separating the two silvered surfaces, n the refractive index of air (taken to be 1), and β_1 and β_2 the phase changes on reflection occurring at the two silvered surfaces. Since β_1, β_2, and λ are all constant for this interferometer, the term containing the phase changes is a constant. At the position on the interferogram indicated by the dashed line, the separation of the surfaces covered with the film whose thickness is desired is less by the amount t (the film thickness) than the separation in the unfilmed region. Two equations of the form of Eq. (7) can be written for this position on the interferogram, and their difference gives

$$t = \varepsilon \frac{\lambda}{2} = \frac{\Delta x_1}{x_1 - x_0} \frac{\lambda}{2} = \frac{\Delta x_i}{x_i - x_{i-1}} \frac{\lambda}{2} \tag{8}$$

In Eq. (8), ε is the fractional order of interference by which the fringes in the filmed region are displaced from those in the unfilmed region. In other words, the order of interference in the filmed region at the position of the dashed line is $N - \varepsilon$. If the film is more than a half wavelength thick, the order of interference in the channel will be different from that on the film by an integer and a fraction. For example, if $\lambda/2 < t < \lambda$, the order of interference at the position of the dashed line will be $N - 1 - \varepsilon$; if $\lambda < t < 3\lambda/2$, it will be $N - 2 - \varepsilon$, and so on. Thus, in general the film thickness is given by

$$t = (K + \varepsilon)\frac{\lambda}{2} = \left(K + \frac{\Delta x_i}{x_i - x_{i-1}}\right)\frac{\lambda}{2} \tag{9}$$

where K is the integral difference in orders of interference between the fringes in the channel and those in the filmed region. If the approximate film thickness is unknown, the value of K must be determined by using monochromatic light of another wavelength, or if necessary two other monochromatic wavelengths (63a). The fact that K cannot be uniquely determined in a single Fizeau interferogram is one serious drawback of the Fizeau method for determining film thickness.

d. Effect of Surface Roughness on Thickness Measurements. Another major disadvantage of the Fizeau method is its sensitivity to surface roughness. The effect of surface roughness is to make the Δx's and $x_i - x_{i-1}$ differences vary slightly. Figure 12 shows the results of a series of measurements of Fizeau

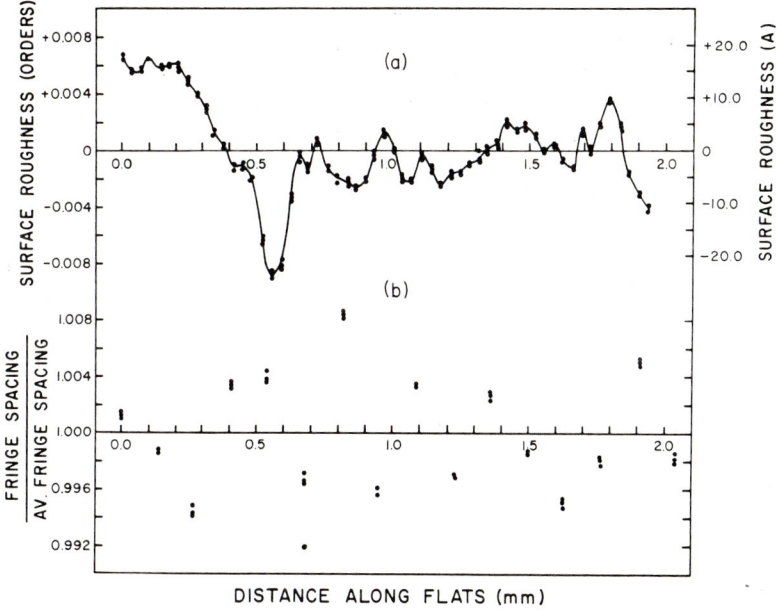

FIG. 12. (a) Surface roughness measured along 2 mm of one Fizeau fringe. (b) Variation in Fizeau fringe spacing in a 2-mm distance on the interferometer.

fringes formed by a very smooth set of interferometer plates. These plates were polished using the bowl-feed technique described in Section II,2,a. In Fig. 12b the normalized spacing between adjacent Fizeau fringes is plotted versus distance along the flat. Three separate settings were made on each fringe and are all plotted. It is seen that the spacings of the sixteen interference fringes scatter by as much as ±0.008 orders of interference over a 2mm distance on the interferometer plates, and that this scatter is not caused by setting errors on the fringes. When the scatter in fringe spacing is averaged and converted into an uncertainty in film thickness, a value of about ±8 Å is obtained. To discover the relation between the scatter in fringe spacing and the roughness on the interferometer surfaces, measurements were made at various positions along one Fizeau fringe. The results of these measurements are plotted in Fig. 12a, where again three settings were made at each position on the fringe. Note that the deviation in straightness of this one fringe corresponds to a peak-to-peak roughness of about ±20 A, or an rms roughness of about 6 A over the smoother portion of the fringe. This rms roughness is very nearly the same as the scatter in fringe spacing found in Fig. 12b. One may conclude that surface roughness on the interferometer flats causes an uncertainty in film thickness when Fizeau fringes are used. Since the roughness on the 6 A rms optical flats produced an uncertainty of ±8 A in film thickness, one would expect the 25–30 A rms roughness on commercially available optical flats to give an uncertainty of 35–40 A in film thickness.

Microscope slides, although frequently used as substrates in Fizeau film thickness measurements, are unsatisfactory for this purpose. Figure 13 shows

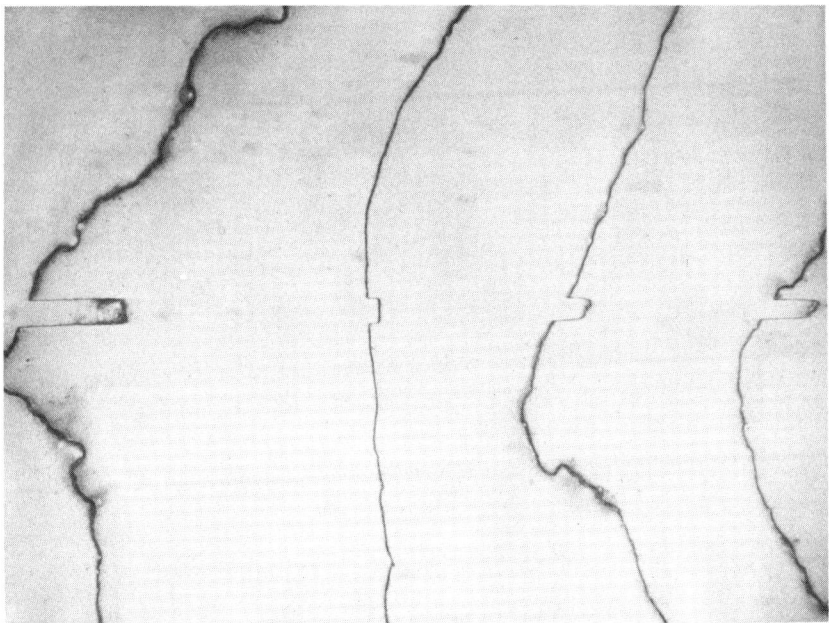

FIG. 13. Photograph of Fizeau fringes formed between a microscope slide and an optical flat. The steps in the center are from an uncoated channel left in a 401 A aluminum film deposited on the microscope slide.

the interference fringes formed between an optical flat and a microscope slide. The slide was covered with a 401 A aluminum film except for a 0.3-mm-wide channel left uncoated down the center of the slide. The Fizeau fringes show jogs where the film is missing. It is clear that an accurate film thickness measurement cannot be obtained from this interferogram even though one fringe is sharp and reasonably straight close to the step. If the fringes were spaced closer together, they might appear somewhat straighter, but an erratic scatter in fringe spacing much larger than that shown in Fig. 12b would limit the accuracy of the measurements. Microscope slides are fire polished during their manufacturing process, producing surfaces that are microscopically smooth (sometimes as smooth as 10 A over limited areas), but very wavy. Although small, locally smooth areas can sometimes be selected so that reasonably good Feco inteferograms such as that shown in Fig. 16c (see p. 35) can be obtained, microscope slides are not satisfactory for precise film thickness measurements using either Fizeau or Feco fringes.

3. Feco Interferometric Method

The advantages of measuring film thickness using fringes of equal chromatic order rather than Fizeau fringes are: (1) the orders of interference may be determined uniquely in both the filmed and unfilmed regions on the flat, and (2) the Feco method is much less sensitive to surface roughness. No variations in fringe spacing such as those found for Fizeau fringes can occur since each Feco fringe contours the *same* areas of the two optical flats forming the interferometer. In addition, especially smooth areas of the flats can be chosen for Feco measurements while it is nearly impossible to make such a selection for Fizeau measurements. As a result, the effect of surface roughness can be reduced by at least a factor of 5. The thickness of a film deposited on a bowl-feed polished substrate can thus be determined with an accuracy of 1 or 2 A using the Feco method.

a. Instrumentation and Interferometer Preparation. A schematic view of the instrumentation used for observing Feco fringes is shown in Fig. 14. White light from point source Z (zirconium arc or carbon arc) is collimated by lens L_1 and reflected to interferometer I by beam splitter B. The light reflected from the interferometer passes through the beam splitter, and lens L_2 focuses a magnified image of I on entrance slit S of a spectrograph. The white light is dispersed by the spectrograph (consisting of slit S, lenses L_3 and L_4, and prism P) and a spectrum containing interference fringes is formed in the focal plane F. Since an image of the interferometer surfaces is being formed in the focal plane (rather than an image of the source, as in conventional Fabry–Perot inteferometry) the fringes contour variations on the interferometer surfaces. Thus, if one of the flats is partially coated with a film whose thickness is desired, leaving an uncoated channel, the fringes will contour the channel, as is shown in Figs. 14 and 16 (Fig. 16 on p. 35). By measuring the wavelengths of the fringes in the two regions, the film thickness may be accurately determined. The method of analysis will be described in detail in Section V,3,c.

The requirements for producing high-contrast Feco fringes which show all the detail on the interferometer surfaces are similar to those for producing high-quality Fizeau fringes. Both interferometer plates must be coated with highly reflecting films, and the semitransparent film should have a slightly lower reflectance than that of the overcoating film on the second flat. However, a multilayer film may not be used for the semitransparent layer because: (1) multilayer films cannot easily be peaked for maximum reflectance over the entire visible wavelength range, and (2) the dispersion of the phase change on reflection with wavelength is large and introduces complications in the analysis

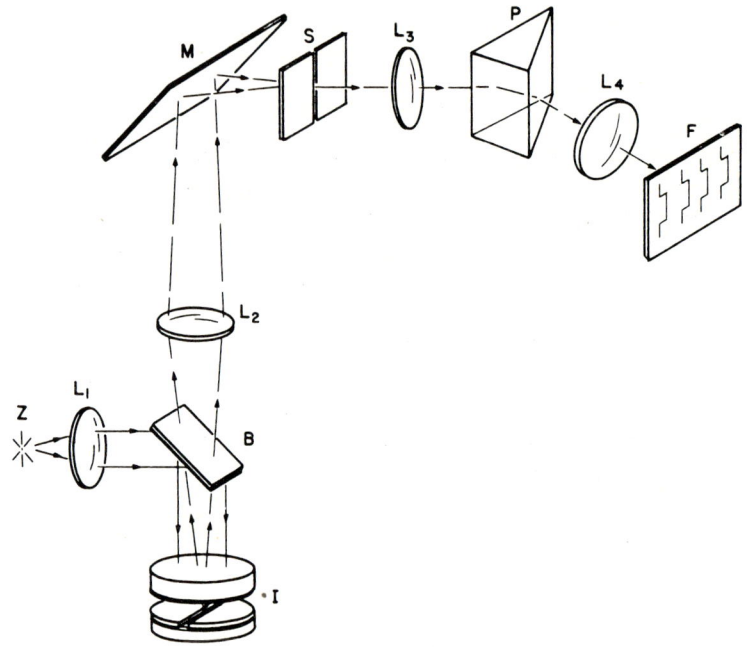

FIG. 14. Schematic view of apparatus for producing Feco fringes.

of the Feco interferogram. Here it is even more important to have the overcoating film on the second surface opaque so as not to introduce problems because of different phase dispersions on the filmed and channeled regions on the flat. Problems associated with the size of the wedge angle do not arise since the two flats are very nearly parallel. Thus, there are no ghost images on the fringes even at high magnifications. The size of the air gap also is not critical as long as the plates are nearly parallel; the definition of the Feco fringes will not deteriorate as the air gap is increased. However, it will be shown in Section V,3,d that the accuracy of the film thickness measurement is increased by using lower orders of interference, so that the air gap is generally kept as small as possible.

The preparation of the interferometer for Feco film thickness measurements is identical to that for Fizeau measurements. One optical flat is partially coated with the film whose thickness is desired, leaving an uncoated channel down the center, and is subsequently entirely overcoated with an opaque layer of silver 1000–2000 A thick. The other optical flat is coated with a semitransparent silver film of 90–95% reflectance in the green. The reflectance of silver decreases toward the blue, but is still adequate to give good Feco fringes and is higher than that of aluminum even at a wavelength of 4000 A. Generally the interferometer is placed on the stage of a low-power microscope (of 5–20 times magnification). In order to form a real image of the interferometer on the spectrograph slit, the objective-eyepiece separation must be increased, or, in some instruments, the eyepiece may be removed entirely. Lens L_2 in Fig. 14 represents the objective lens in this latter situation. To facilitate alignment and to make rapid thickness measurements it is convenient to have an eyepiece with cross hairs on the spectrograph and a direct wavelength readout.

b. Procedure for Interferometer Alignment. The interferometer alignment is somewhat more delicate than with the Fizeau method. The two flats are placed carefully in contact, being separated by the dust particles on their surfaces. The edge of the evaporated film on the second flat is aligned so that its image is perpendicular to the spectrograph slit. Ideally, the air film separating the two flats should be of constant thickness, but, since this is experimentally difficult, the small residual wedge angle should be oriented so that it is parallel to the direction of the channel. The spectrograph is then seeing a constant-thickness air film in the channel and a different constant-thickness air film in the coated region. This part of the alignment is critical since the wavelengths of the Feco fringes need to be constant in order to obtain a good value for the film thickness.

A convenient holder for the interferometer plates, which has been used in this laboratory, is shown in Fig. 15. In this holder each flat is held on the edges by Teflon bars which are controlled by tightening the small adjusting screws seen near the center of the holder. The four outer screws on the holder control the tension on springs which allow the flats to be paralleled and at the same time have any desired separation up to several millimeters. The four inner screws are available for leveling the interferometer if necessary.

A Feco interferogram of a 401 A-thick aluminum film is shown in Fig. 16b. The film was deposited everywhere on the second flat except in a channel 0.3 mm wide down the center of the flat. Note that the Feco fringes are very straight and are parallel to the spectral lines photographed as references for the wavelength calibration. Over this carefully selected rectangular area of the interferometer surfaces, approximately 1 mm by 0.0033 mm, the surface roughness is about 5 A rms as determined from the width of the Feco fringes. For comparison, the same 401 A thick aluminum film was deposited on a microscope slide, and the thickness interferogram is shown in Fig. 16c. Note that the fringe width is somewhat wider, corresponding to a surface roughness of about 10 A rms, but, more importantly, the fringes are not straight so that it would be difficult to obtain precise measurements of the film thickness from this interferogram. In addition, it was much more difficult to align the fringes produced by the microscope slide, even to the degree of parallelism shown in the photograph, than it was to align the fringes produced by the optical flat in Fig. 16b. The extreme waviness of the microscope slide surface makes alignment very difficult and working with it is a frustrating experience.

FIG. 15. Photograph of interferometer holder.

c. Analysis of Feco Interferogram. The determination of film thickness from a Feco interferogram is accomplished as follows: First, the wavelengths of the Feco fringes must be determined. They may be measured visually by using a direct-reading spectrograph, or photoelectrically by measuring the interferogram with a photoelectric scanning comparator (*60, 61*) and converting the measured distances into wavelengths using the Hartmann formula programmed for a computer (*64*). The former method gives an accuracy of about 1 A for fringe wavelengths, while with the latter method it is possible to determine wavelengths to better than 0.1 A (*15, 64*). Figure 16a is a schematic

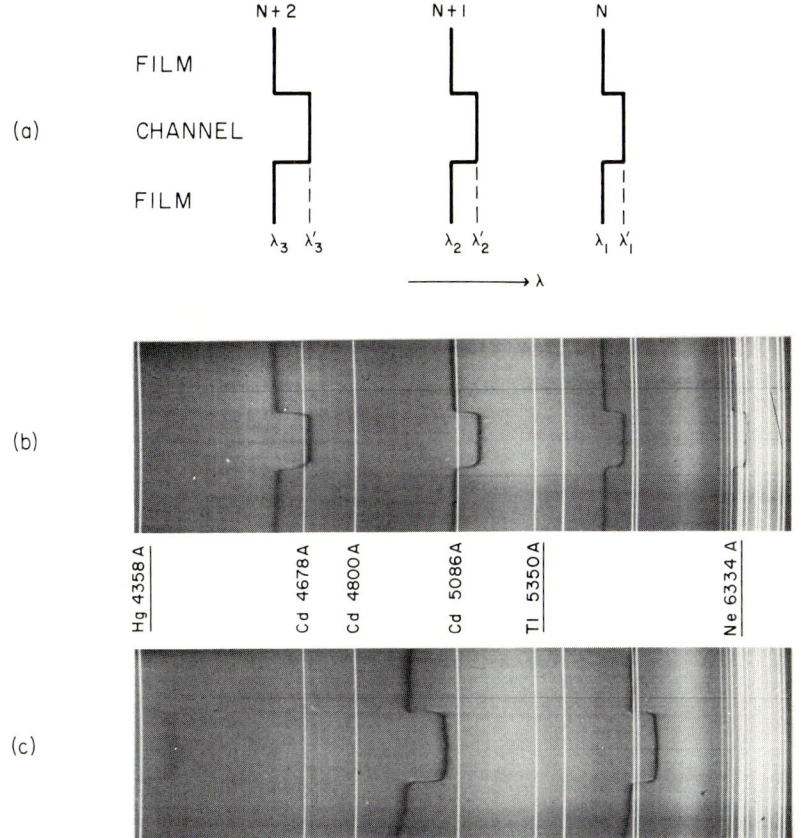

FIG. 16. (a) Schematic representation of Feco interferogram. (b) Feco interferogram for measuring thickness of 401 A aluminum film using high-quality optical flats. (c) Same as (b) except 401 A aluminum film was deposited on a microscope slide.

representation of the interferogram shown in Fig. 16b. The orders of interference can be obtained from a relation derived from Eq. (7)[6]:

$$M \equiv N + 1 = \frac{\lambda_j \, \Delta N}{\lambda_1 - \lambda_j} \tag{10}$$

where N is the order of interference (an integer) for the fringe occurring at wavelength λ_1, and λ_j is the wavelength of the fringe of *shorter* wavelength

[6] In deriving Eq. (10) it has been assumed that the phase change on reflection for both air–silver reflections is of the form $\pi - \delta$, where δ is small, and furthermore, that the quantity $\delta\lambda/\pi$ is nearly independent of wavelength for wavelengths between λ_j and λ_1. The assumption that the dispersion of the phase change is negligible allows the film thickness to be calculated from an equation such as Eq. (11).

differing by ΔN orders of interference from the fringe at wavelength λ_1. Because of the dispersion of the phase change on reflection, if λ_1 and λ_j are very difficult, the calculated value of M may not be quite an integer. However, the value to use is the integer closest to the number calculated from Eq. (10). When the dispersion of the phase change is small, as is true for rapidly evaporated, freshly prepared silver films, the film thickness may be calculated from the relation (again derived from Eq.(7))

$$t = \frac{M}{2}(\lambda' - \lambda) \tag{11}$$

for $t < \lambda/2$ and $\lambda' > \lambda$. If the film is thicker than $\lambda/2$, the value of M for the fringe in the channel will be different from that for the closest fringe in the filmed region. However, there is no ambiguity, as was the case for Fizeau fringes, since the value of M for the fringe in the channel may again be calculated from Eq. (10). For this case the film thickness may be calculated from the relation

$$t = \tfrac{1}{2}(M_j'\lambda_j' - M_j\lambda_j) \tag{12}$$

where M_j' is the value for the fringe of wavelength λ_j' in the channel. For very thick films, the thickness may be calculated using the method of coincidences described by Koehler (*65*).

At first glance it would seem that large errors would be made by ignoring the dispersion of the phase change on reflection. It is shown (*15*, Appendix) that in some cases errors in film thickness made by using the approximate relations (11) and (12) are less than 2 Å. However, one should always show that the phase dispersion is small before ignoring it. The film thickness analysis may be done graphically to eliminate the effect of phase dispersion completely. In this analysis $M_j\lambda_j$ and $M_j'\lambda_j'$ are plotted versus wavelength on two separate pieces of graph paper. Both graphs will have exactly the same shape because the phase dispersion is the same for both. When the graphs are superposed, the difference in their ordinates is exactly twice the film thickness. One such plot is shown in Fig. 9 of Bennett (*15*). Since this graphical method is exact and simple to use, it should always be employed unless one has shown that there is no loss in accuracy when using approximate equations (11) and (12).

d. Effect of Various Errors on Thickness Measurements. In determinining the accuracy in film thickness measurements possible with the Feco method, it is seen from Eq. (11) that, assuming the integer M is correct, errors in t are proportional to errors in the wavelength difference $\lambda' - \lambda$ with the proportionality constant being $M/2$. For $1\tfrac{1}{2}$-in.-diam optical flats, M's of about 20 or less can be achieved so that, if the error in $\lambda' - \lambda \sim 1$ Å, the error in t will be ~ 10 Å. However, if the error in $\lambda' - \lambda \sim 0.1$ Å, as is possible with photoelectric setting in the Feco interferogram, the error in t will be ~ 1 Å. Of course, if lower orders of interference are used, for example, by going to smaller optical flats, the error in t may theoretically be further reduced. Orders of interference of less than 10 have been obtained using $\frac{1}{2}$-in.-diam optical flats. However, surface roughness, by causing fringe irregularities, finally limits the accuracy of Feco thickness measurements. The fringes broaden and become ragged, as was shown in Fig. 1a for a commercially polished optical flat. Thus it is doubtful if thickness measurements even on very-low-order fringes can be considered accurate to better than 1 or 2 A. One may conclude that (1) if very smooth optical flats are used, (2) if the films are carefully evaporated with sharp steps at their edges, (3) if the interferometer plates are carefully aligned, and (4) if the wavelengths of the fringes are accurately measured, then it is possible to measure film thickness with an accuracy of 1 or 2 A.

4. Measurement of Thin Oxide Films

All metals except possibly gold tend to form oxides (66) and many also form nitrides, sulfides, etc., on exposure to air. Even in vacuum, oxide film formation is usually quite rapid, as is shown in Fig. 17 for iron oxide on iron. At

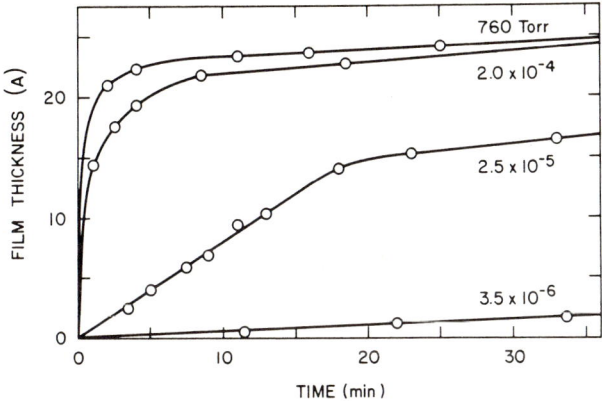

Fig. 17. Growth of iron oxide films on iron at various pressures of oxygen [after Kruger and Yolken (68)].

room temperature the limiting thickness of these films is small, usually less than 50 A, but they can have a profound effect on the observed optical properties of materials in some wavelength regions. Their effect in the vacuum ultraviolet has been described by Madden (67) in an earlier article in this series. At longer wavelengths the effect of oxide films can often be corrected for theoretically if their optical thickness is known. Figure 18 shows the calculated decrease in the reflectance of aluminum caused by aluminum oxide films of various thicknesses. The thickness of the oxide film which forms at room

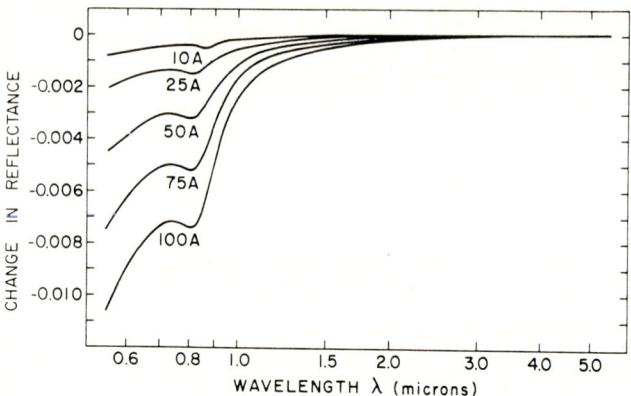

FIG. 18. Decrease in the reflectance of aluminum caused by various thicknesses of aluminum oxide films.

temperature is about 30 A. At infrared wavelengths the decrease in reflectance caused by such a film is negligible. In the visible and ultraviolet regions, however, a correction should be applied. If measurements of both the reflectance and the phase difference Δ between the p and s components of the electric vector are made, as is often the case when optical constants are determined, the surface oxide film cannot be neglected even in the infrared.

Since normally occurring oxide films are so thin, the major uncertainty in making an oxide film correction is caused by the uncertainty in film thickness. One very sensitive method for measuring this thickness is ellipsometry, which is discussed in Section IX. Since in general, however, only *changes* in film thickness can be determined using this technique, the initial measurement must be made on a film-free surface. The iron data shown in Fig. 17 were obtained ellipsometrically by Kruger and Yolken (*68*), who started with an oxide-free bulk iron surface in ultrahigh vacuum and admitted controlled amounts of oxygen.

If approximate values for the refractive indices of the film and substrate are known, ellipsometric measurements of film thickness are greatly simplified. One can then use a linear approximation to the exact equations to relate the change in Δ to film thickness. The approximation proposed by Archer for the change in Δ caused by a nonabsorbing film of thickness t on an absorbing substrate is (*69*)

$$\Delta - \bar{\Delta} = \frac{-720(t/\lambda) \cos\theta \sin^2\theta (1 - n_1^2) \times \{(a - 1/n_1^2)[\cos^2\theta - a + \sin^2\theta (a^2 - a'^2)] - a'^2\}}{[\cos^2\theta - a + \sin^2\theta (a^2 - a'^2)]^2 + a'^2} \tag{13}$$

where $\bar{\Delta}$ is the value for the unfilmed surface, λ the wavelength, θ the angle of incidence, n_1 the film index, $n - jk$ the complex index of the substrate, $a = (n^2 - k^2)/(n^2 + k^2)^2$, and $a' = 2nk/(n^2 + k^2)^2$. A comparison of the exact theory with Archer's equation and the more commonly used Drude equation is shown in Fig. 19 for (a) aluminum oxide on aluminum, and (b) silicon

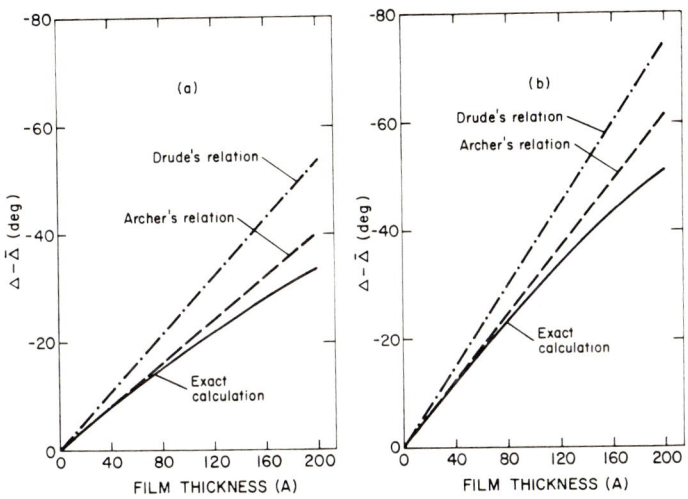

FIG. 19. Comparison of Archer's and Drude's approximate relations with the exact theory for (a) aluminum oxide on aluminum, and (b) silicon oxide on silicon.

dioxide on silicon for $\theta = 70°$ and $\lambda = 5461$ A. The errors introduced by the linear approximations are small compared to the change in Δ. If the oxide film is slightly absorbing, serious errors can result (70) if the approximate equations for a nonabsorbing film are used to compute both n_1 and t. Even for a nonabsorbing film, the linear approximation for the change in ψ, the other ellipsometric parameter, may be in error by a factor of 2 for films as thin as 10 A (69). However, if one only uses the ellipsometer to determine film thickness and uses independently determined values of n_1, n, and k, good thickness values can be obtained from Eq. (13) even if some absorption is present in the oxide film (70).

The thickness of thin oxide films may also be determined by measuring the reflectance and transmittance of semitransparent metal films in air, and the reflectance of opaque metal films in vacuum and subsequently in air. This method has been successfully used by Hass and co-workers (71–73), who found that the stable, naturally occurring oxide film on aluminum is about 30 to 40 A and that on titanium about 35 A.

A combination interferometric-capacitance method (74) for determining film thickness has been used to measure the thickness of aluminum oxide on aluminum. A condenser is formed making an aluminum film one plate of the condenser and a second aluminum film the other plate. The dielectric spacer layer ideally should be just the naturally occurring oxide film, but in practice dielectric breakdown occurs with this thin a film. Hence, various thicknesses of aluminum oxide are added to the natural film and the capacitance of the resulting condenser is measured. Since the capacitance C is inversely proportional to film thickness, a graph of the thickness of the added aluminum oxide film versus $1/C$ gives a straight line, as is shown in Fig. 20. The x intercept

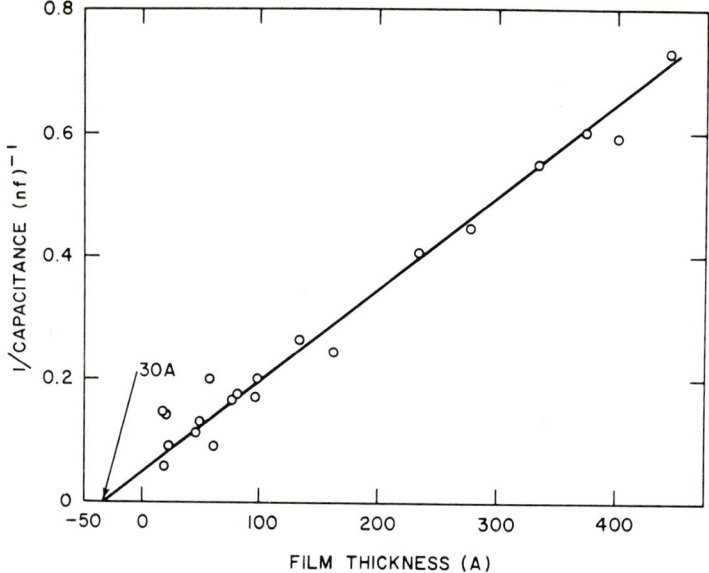

FIG. 20. Determination of the thickness of the naturally occurring oxide film on aluminum using the capacitance method.

gives the thickness of the naturally occurring film and the value, 30 A, is in good agreement with the value obtained by Hass and co-workers (72, 73).

A determination of oxide film thickness has also been made by integrated absolute intensity measurements of X rays. The thickness of copper oxide films on single crystal copper was measured in this way by Borie and Sparks (75). In another proposed X-ray technique (76), oxide film thickness may be measured from the change in shape of the reflection curve near the critical angle caused by the oxide film. This method has not yet been demonstrated experimentally. Other sensitive techniques are slow electron diffraction (77) and the reflectance of materials in the vacuum ultraviolet. If light is incident at 45° on a single interface, $R_s^2 = R_p$ where R_s and R_p are the reflectances for light polarized in the s and p directions, respectively. Although this relation is not very sensitive to surface films in the visible region (69), at 735 A where the oxide is absorbing a 5-A oxide film on aluminum would be sufficient to cause R_s^2 to be lower than R_p by the ratio of 2 : 3 (78).

VI. Transmission Measurements

Transmission measurements are undoubtedly the most common type of optical measurements made. They may be made easily, conveniently, and with moderately good accuracy, and the results are easy to interpret. Equipment for transmission measurements is commercially available from various manufacturers. Many of the instruments are completely automated and sufficiently reliable that one apparently needs to know no optics whatever to operate them. However, if one wishes to make really accurate measurements, one must take into consideration many sources of systematic error, some associated with the sample (discussed in Section VI,2) and others only with the instrument (covered in Section VI,3). Both kinds of errors may be of importance when making transmission measurements on thin films, and the instrumental errors are also important for reflection measurements.

Spectrometers used for transmission measurements may be either single-beam or double-beam instruments. In double-beam systems a chopper alternately passes light from the sample beam and from the reference beam to the detector. Either single- or double-beam instruments may be single-pass (the light passes through the dispersing system once), double-pass (twice), or double (two dispersing systems, the exit slit of the first acting as the entrance slit of the second). Double-beam instruments are usually of the ratio-recording or optical-null type. In ratio-recording instruments, signals from the sample and reference beams are both amplified and are then combined to give the ratio. For example, the reference signal may be fed across the slide wire of a strip chart recorder and the sample signal to the pen. Various other more sophisticated techniques are also used. In optical-null instruments an optical wedge is inserted into the reference beam and driven to equalize sample and reference signals. The detector is then used simply to determine the null, and the wedge position determines the transmittance. An advantage of optical-null instruments is that nonlinearity in the detector or amplifier has no effect on the accuracy of the data. Both types of double-beam instruments are insensitive to changes in source intensity, slit width, or atmospheric absorption. Thus it is possible to make a wavelength scan and plot out transmittance directly.

When precise transmittance measurements are to be made, single-beam instruments are often preferred to double-beam instruments. The instrument design is simpler and therefore there is less to go wrong. In double-beam instruments of the optical-null type, the balance position is the point at which the signal on the servo drive is zero, so that near balance the system has minimum sensitivity to small changes in signal. Also, the accuracy of the instrument depends on the construction of the optical wedge and whether or not it is uniformly illuminated. For maximum accuracy, transmittance measurements should be made point by point and the signals integrated over a period of time to eliminate noise. A zero signal should also be taken. Most double-beam instruments do not lend themselves to this technique, however. Finally, since the chopper is used to separate the sample and reference beams in a double-beam instrument, it cannot be used to chop the light between the first and second passes of a *double-pass* monochromator. This latter technique is very effective for eliminating scattered light, particularly in the infrared (see Section VI,3,b).

1. Transmittance of a Thin Film on a Nonabsorbing Substrate

Measurement of the transmittance of a thin film is usually complicated by the fact that the film is deposited on a substrate. The quantity which is desired is T_f, the transmittance of light through the film and into the substrate. The measured transmittance, however, must be corrected for the reflectance of the back side of the substrate. In addition, in order to minimize errors resulting from defocusing of the beam by the substrate, the transmittance of the film-coated substrate is usually measured relative to that of an uncoated substrate of the same thickness and material. The quantity actually recorded by the spectrophotometer is then T_{obs}, where

$$T_{obs} = T_{fs}/T_{ss} \tag{14}$$

T_{fs} is the transmittance of the film-coated substrate and T_{ss} that of the uncoated reference blank.

If the substrates are nonabsorbing, T_{ss} is given by (*79*)

$$T_{ss} = \frac{T_s^2}{1 - R_s'^2} \tag{15}$$

where T_s is the transmittance and R_s' the reflectance at a single interface, as is shown in Fig. 21a. Equation (15) takes into account multiple reflections within the reference blank, but assumes that the blank is thick enough so that interference effects can be ignored. The transmittance of the film-coated substrate is

$$T_{fs} = \frac{T_f T_s}{1 - R_f' R_s'} \tag{16}$$

where T_f and R_f', the transmittance of the film and reflectance at the film–substrate interface, are indicated in Fig. 21b.[7] If the substrate is transparent,

---

[7] Note that R_f' is the resultant reflectance caused by the semitransparent film, and not merely the intensity reflection coefficient at the film–substrate boundary.

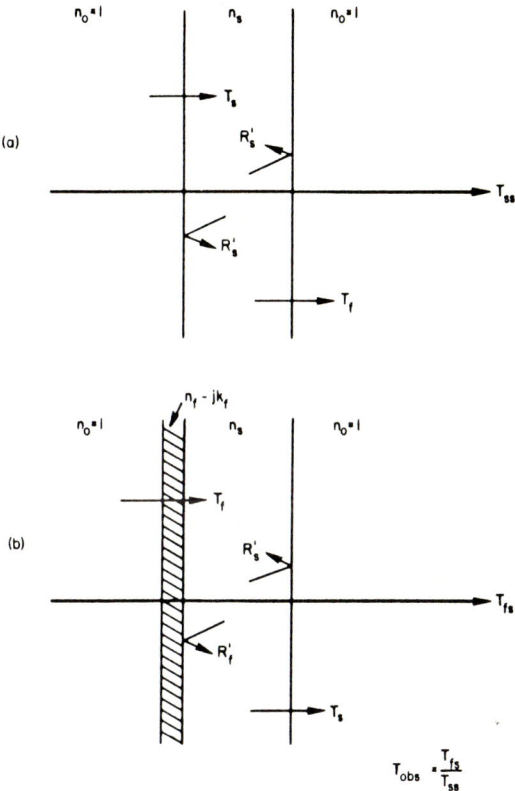

FIG. 21. Transmittance of an absorbing film on a nonabsorbing substrate measured relative to the transmittance of an identical uncoated substrate (see footnote 7).

$T_s = 1 - R_s'$. Also $T_f = 1 - R_f' - A_f'$, where A_f' is the energy which would be absorbed by the film if light were incident on it from the substrate side. The above relationships hold since from Kirchhoff's law $T_f' = 1 - R_f' - A_f'$, and the transmittance of a *nonabsorbing or absorbing* film between two nonabsorbing media is independent of the side from which the light is incident. If the film is absorbing, $R_f' \neq R_f$, where R_f is the external film reflectance, and $A_f' \neq A_f$, so that the primes on R_f' and A_f' indicate that the light is incident on the film from the substrate side. Substituting into Eqs. (14)–(16) one obtains for T_f, the air-film-substrate transmittance,

$$T_f = T_{\text{obs}} \frac{(1 - R_s' + R_s' A_f')}{1 + R_s'(1 - T_{\text{obs}})} \qquad (17)$$

Equation (17) is the general expression for the transmittance of a film on a nonabsorbing substrate measured relative to an uncoated substrate of the same material and thickness. If the film is only slightly absorbing so that $R_s'A_f' \approx 0$, T_f can be calculated directly since

$$R_s' = \frac{(n_s - 1)^2}{(n_s + 1)^2} \tag{18}$$

where n_s is the index of refraction of the substrate. Similarly, if the film is strongly absorbing so that $A_f \approx 1$, then $T_{\text{obs}} \ll 1$ and T_f is given by

$$T_f = \frac{T_{\text{obs}}}{1 + R_s'} \tag{19}$$

If neither approximation is valid, T_f cannot be determined from a single measurement since there are then two unknowns, T_f and A_f'; i.e., neither of the optical constants of the film may be neglected. If two independent measurements are made, for example, the transmittances of two films differing in thickness by a known amount, or the transmittance and reflectance of a single film of known thickness, then T_f, and hence the optical constants of the film, can be calculated by iteration.

2. Systematic Errors Caused by Sample

In the preceding section the sample was assumed to be a uniform, isotropic, optically stable film which did not scatter light and which was deposited on a plane, parallel-sided substrate thin enough to minimize defocusing of the beam but thick enough so that interference effects in the substrate could be ignored. Many transmittance samples do not meet all of these specifications. It is thus necessary to consider how important deviations from the ideal situation are and how they affect transmittance measurements made using actual instruments. Among the most important sample-related sources of error are (1) nonparallelism of the sample surfaces, (2) defocusing effects of thick samples, (3) light scattered by the sample, (4) birefringent samples, and (5) sample irradiation. These sources of error will be covered in Sections VI,2,a–e.

a. Nonparallelism of Sample Surfaces. Even though the substrate surfaces may be very nearly parallel so that multiple reflections occur with very little "walk-off," there may still be errors in the measured transmittance caused by the very slight beam shift in the instrument. The effect of nonparallelism of sample surfaces may be more or less important depending on the sample position and design of the instrument. In some cases when the source optics overfill the entrance pupil of the monochromator, a slight beam shift may cause no adverse effect. However, in other cases the parallelism requirements can be rather stringent. Figure 22 shows the error in transmittance as a function of wedge angle and refractive index measured for one of the best commercial spectrophotometers (*80*). As an example, if the transmittance of an evaporated film on an indium antimonide substrate of refractive index 3.5 were measured, and if the substrate were a disk 1 in. in diameter, Fig. 22 indicates that a difference in thickness across this disk of 0.003 in. could cause an error in transmittance of over 10%. Not all instruments are as sensitive to

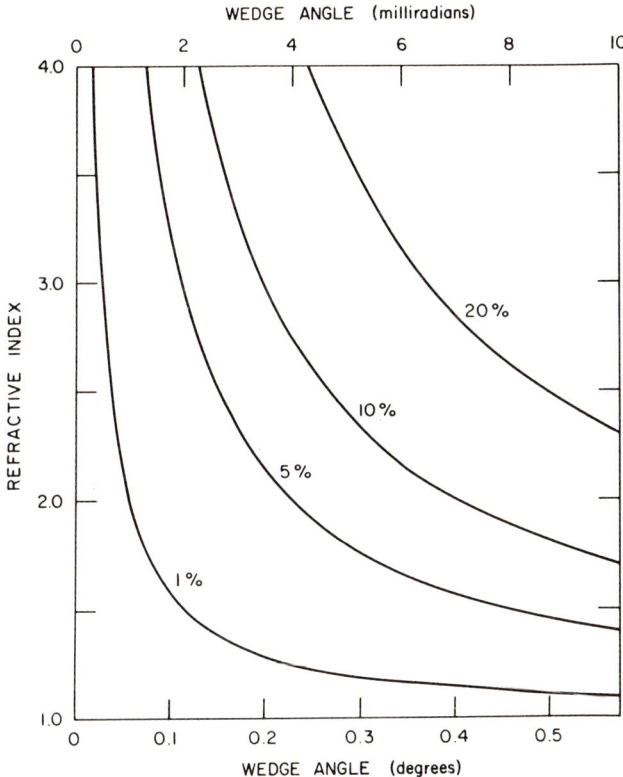

FIG. 22. Error in measured transmittance caused by various wedge angles on the substrate as a function of the refractive index of the substrate [after Olsen *et al.* (*80*)].

sample nonparallelism as this one, but it is clear that, to avoid errors, the substrate should have as low a refractive index as possible and should be paralleled to optical, not machine-shop, tolerances. If an error caused by substrate nonparallelism is suspected, it can be checked by rotating the sample about the beam axis and observing whether or not the observed transmittance changes.

b. Defocusing Effects of Thick Samples. In spite of the advantages to be gained by positioning the sample after the monochromator in the optical train, in many instruments the sample is placed in front of the entrance slit. The primary reason is that in this position defocusing errors caused by the sample, and beam shift resulting from sample nonparallelism, are reduced to a minimum. If the sample were placed on the detector side of the monochromator, any defocusing or image shift would cause a change in the detector output. Small area detectors such as thermocouples and some lead sulfide cells are understandably sensitive to this effect, but even large area detectors such as photomultipliers may be affected, since most large area detectors do not have a uniform response over their sensitive areas. By positioning the sample in front of the entrance slit, such effects are minimized. There can be no defocusing on the detector since the slit itself, or occasionally the exit pupil of the monochromator, is the object imaged on the detector. The image of the source may be defocused by the sample, but since the area of the source imaged on the slit in any well-designed instrument overfills the slit both in height and width, the detector signal is insensitive to source defocusing.

c. *Light Scattered by the Sample.* Light scattered by the sample will look like absorption when one is making transmittance measurements. This source of error, although obvious, is rather difficult to eliminate in any way except by getting better samples. Fortunately, since scattering is often very wavelength dependent, samples which scatter strongly in the visible and ultraviolet regions may be perfectly adequate in the infrared (*81*). A significant amount of scattering may occur in the film itself (*82*), or it may arise from surface roughness on the film or substrate surfaces, or from body scattering in the substrate material. A useful estimate of the magnitude of surface and body scattering for optical glass has been given by Kozawa (*83*). He measured 1-cm-thick samples of optically polished borosilicate crown, dense flint, and extradense flint optical glasses and also fused silica, and found that the fraction of the incident light which was scattered from the two surfaces at a wavelength of 5461 A was about 0.06–0.09%, except for the fused silica sample where the fraction was only 0.013%. Fused silica probably has this lower value because it takes a smoother polish than optical glasses (*10*). The body scattering from the 1-cm-thick samples was over two orders of magnitude smaller than the surface scattering, ranging from 0.0002 to 0.0009%. Both surface and body scattering would be expected to increase at shorter wavelengths approximately as $1/\lambda^4$ (*10, 84*). Surface and body scattering in the substrate, however, will usually not be a source of error in thin film measurements. Surface scattering may be eliminated in precise transmittance measurements on bulk samples by placing the sample in an absorption cell filled with a nonabsorbing liquid of the same refractive index. To make the sample-out measurement, the sample is simply lifted out of the cell, letting the liquid fill the void. In this way the optical path length and interfaces seen by the beam remain essentially unchanged in the sample-in and sample-out positions (*85*).

d. Birefringent Samples. If the light incident on a spectrometer is unpolarized, it will generally emerge partially polarized. Thus, if a birefringent sample is measured at normal incidence, its observed transmittance will vary as it is rotated about the axis of the beam. The observed transmittance at some orientations may even exceed 100%. The true transmittance of such a sample may be obtained by measuring the apparent transmittance as the sample is turned through 360°, and then averaging the results. If a good linear polarizer is available, the amount of sample birefringence may be determined by mounting the polarizer in front of the entrance slit and orienting its plane of polarization either parallel or perpendicular to the slit. Practically no ellipticity will be introduced by the spectrometer in this case.

If the sample has a wedge angle, the observed transmittance may also vary as the sample is rotated about the beam axis. The two effects may be separated by observing whether the periodicity of the signal is 180° (birefringence) or 360° (wedge angle).

e. Sample Irradiation. Erroneous transmittance values may result from sample irradiation. One good example is the measurement of F-center decay, where ultraviolet irradiation can drastically affect the results. In some instruments the sample is located in front of the entrance slit so that the full, partially focused intensity of the source is incident on it. Usually the sample will heat up somewhat, possibly changing its transmittance. The positions of interference maxima may also shift with increasing temperature. If the material is a semiconductor, careful measurements will show a shift in the band edge as the temperature increases. Solarization, a nonthermal effect, occurs when glass is subjected to intense ultraviolet irradiation and may also cause a significant change in the transmittance (*86, 87*). None of these problems occur if the sample is positioned following the monochromator so that only a narrow band of wavelengths is incident on it.

3. INSTRUMENTAL SOURCES OF SYSTEMATIC ERROR

Although most commercially available instruments for measuring transmission are well designed and engineered, it is well nevertheless to be aware of some sources of systematic error which may be caused by the instrument. Particularly when making precision measurements, checks can be made to see that no unsuspected errors are present. The most common instrumental sources of systematic error are (1) instrumental nonlinearity, (2) scattered light, (3) shutter and sample emission, (4) wavelength calibration errors, and (5) too large a spectral slit width. These topics will be discussed in Sections VI,3,a–e.

a. Instrumental Nonlinearity. Photometric nonlinearity is a problem encountered in many kinds of precision optical instruments. The electronics themselves may be nonlinear, the mechanical linkage in double-beam systems may be faulty, or the detector may be nonlinear. Spurious zero signals causing an incorrect zero level may arise from stray dc voltages. One common source of trouble is feedback from the balancing system of a potentiometric-type recorder. The electronics and recording system may be conveniently checked in many instruments by introducing a known series of signals into the preamplifier or amplifier input and monitoring the output signal. A block diagram of such a system in use at Michelson Laboratory is shown in Fig. 23.

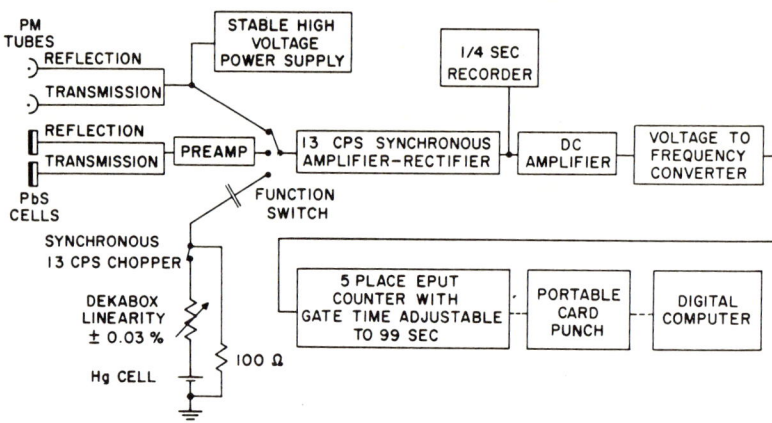

FIG. 23. Block diagram of the electronics, including Dekabox linearity checking circuit, for the double-reflection absolute reflectometer.

A precision resistance box linear to $\pm 0.03\%$ is used to introduce the test voltages. The signal is amplified, synchronously rectified, filtered, amplified again, and then passes through a voltage to frequency converter where the output voltage is transformed into a frequency which can be measured on a five-place counter. By choosing the gate time of the counter, one may integrate the signal over any desired time interval up to 99 sec. Using a series of test voltages this electronic system has been shown to be free from zero-level errors and linear to better than $\pm 0.05\%$. The test circuit can also be conveniently used for troubleshooting in case of electronic malfunction.

Although the electronics may be linear, the detector may not. For example, Fig. 24 shows the nonlinearity of a typical 5-cm-diam end-on photomultiplier tube used at a low light level. Photomultipliers must be individually selected if linearities of better than 1% are desired. Thus, it is important not only to check the linearity of the electronics, but also that of the over-all system. The usual method for checking system linearity is to introduce filters of known absorption into the optical path. However, even if considerable care is used, it is difficult to determine linearity in this way to better than 1% (88). By using three high-quality polarizers in series, keeping the axes of the outer two parallel

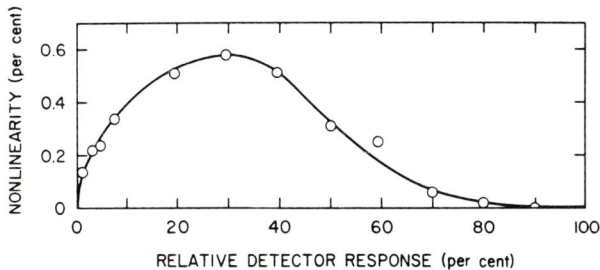

FIG. 24. Nonlinearity curve for a photomultiplier tube.

and rotating the middle polarizer, as is illustrated in Fig. 25, it is possible to eliminate most sources of error and to determine photometric linearity to better than 0.1% (*88*).

b. Scattered Light. A major source of error both in precise transmittance and reflectance measurements is scattered light of wavelengths other than that being measured. Scattered light is difficult to correct for and is particularly troublesome when measurements are made in the ultraviolet and infrared regions. The intensities of most sources are highest in the visible and near infrared, and generally decrease rapidly both to longer and to shorter wavelengths. Thus, one is often faced with the problem of discriminating against scattered light from a wavelength region where the source intensity is orders of magnitude greater than that in the region where measurements are being made.

The amount of scattered light may be determined by either of two methods: (1) by interposing a filter known to be opaque at the given wavelength but

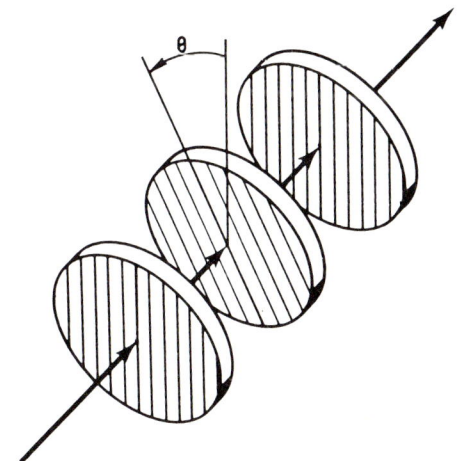

FIG. 25. Schematic diagram of three-polarizer system.

transparent at other wavelengths, or (2) by determining the deviation from Lambert's law (*89*), which states that the transmittance is proportional to $\exp(-\alpha t)$ where t is the thickness and α the absorption coefficient of the material. If the absorbing material is a solution, the concentration can be changed and the deviation from Beer's law checked. However, it is first necessary to verify that Beer's law holds. In solutions where the equilibrium conditions between two components are a function of concentration, it frequently does not. Useful materials for measuring scattered light by either of the above methods are given by McCarthy (*90*), Slavin (*91*), and Koller (*92*).

Many techniques can be used to reduce scattered light. The choice of an appropriate monochromator is probably the most important. Prisms produce less scattered light than do most gratings, and good *double* monochromators are better than single monochromators, although a single-beam, double-pass monochromator in which the light is chopped between passes is nearly equivalent to a double monochromator when used in the infrared region. As an example, the signal from a Perkin–Elmer model 83 monochromator, a single-pass, single-prism instrument, contains about 10% scattered radiation at 15 μ when a globar source is used (*93*). When this instrument is double-passed, the scattered light at 15 μ is undetectable, and even at 30 μ is less than 0.1% (*26*).

Once the basic instrument has been selected, several techniques can be used to further decrease scattered light. Among these are the use of (1) sources whose energy is concentrated in the wavelength region to be investigated, for example, a globar source in the infrared or a hydrogen or rare gas arc in the ultraviolet, (2) spectrally selective detectors such as the "solar blind" photomultipliers, (3) absorption filters (*94–101*), (4) interference-type transmission filters (*102–105*), (5) interference-type reflection filters (*106–108*), (6) Christiansen filters (*109–111*), (7) frustrated total reflection filters (*112*), (8) aluminized ground-glass scatter plates in the infrared (*13*), (9) powder filters in the infrared (*113*), (10) *restrahlen* selective reflection plates in the infrared (*114*), (11) choppers transparent except in the desired wavelength region (*115, 116*), (12) zone plates (*117*), (13) focal isolation (*118, 119*), (14) materials in the ultraviolet which do not fluoresce, (15) gratings used in first order in the ultraviolet (a technique which also minimizes the intensity of ghosts), and (16) finely ruled gratings as mirrors in the infrared (*120*). Unless otherwise noted, these various methods for reducing scattered light can be used both in the infrared and in the ultraviolet. One should of course not overlook the use of properly placed baffles and stops, and the use of flat black paint to coat the inside of the instrument.

A slightly different unwanted light problem may arise if a saturable detector is used in a chopped system, and an appreciable amount of unmodulated light of wavelengths other than that desired is incident on it. This situation can arise if choppers transparent to wavelengths other than those being utilized are used with a photomultiplier as a detector, or if a single-beam, double-pass monochromator is used in the ultraviolet and the single-pass light is not blocked out. Although the unwanted light gives rise to a dc signal which can be eliminated by use of a blocking condenser, its intensity may be high enough to make the photomultiplier unstable or at least nonlinear. In a double-pass system such as the Perkin–Elmer model 99 monochromator, this problem can be largely corrected by masking the top halves of the entrance slit and exit slit. Since the double-pass exit slit image is erect and the single-pass image is inverted, only light which has been double-passed gets through the optical system.

Another unwanted light problem arises when gratings are used in the first order and no provision is made for blocking out the shorter second-order wavelengths. This situation, which often occurs in vacuum ultraviolet instruments may be remedied by using blocking filters such as LiF, fused quartz, or glass behind the entrance slit of the instrument. These filters also prevent material in a windowless light source from depositing on the grating.

c. Shutter and Sample Emission. Shutter, chopper, sample, or mirror emission may cause significant systematic errors in precise transmission or reflection measurements made in the far infrared. For point-by-point measurement, one usually measures the signals for (1) sample-out, (2) sample-in, and (3) zero. The zero reading is obtained by cutting off the beam from the source by means of a shutter. Assume for the moment that the shutter is mounted in the beam following the sample but directly in front of the chopper, which itself is in front of at least some of the dispersive elements of the monochromator. Then, for a transmission measurement,

$$I_{\text{sample-out}} = I_0 - I_c + Z, \qquad I_{\text{zero}} = I_s - I_c + Z$$
$$I_{\text{sample-in}} = I_0 T + E - I_c + Z \tag{20}$$

where I_0 is the signal from the incident light, T the true transmittance of the sample, E the signal resulting from sample emission, I_s the signal from the shutter, and Z the electronic zero signal. I_c, the signal from the chopper blades, is subtracted since the output signal is proportional to the difference between the flux falling on the detector when the chopper blade is in and out of the beam. The measured transmittance T' is then

$$T' = \frac{I_{\text{sample-in}} - I_{\text{zero}}}{I_{\text{sample-out}} - I_{\text{zero}}}$$
$$= \frac{I_0 T + E - I_s}{I_0 - I_s} \tag{21}$$

or

$$T' \approx T + \frac{E}{I_0} - \frac{I_s}{I_0}(1 - T) \qquad (22)$$

Sample emission will thus increase the observed transmittance, and the signal from the shutter will reduce it. These corrections may be sizeable. For example, at a wavelength of 30 μ the spectral radiance from a black body at 300°K, room temperature, is over 10% of that from a globar source at 1400°K (*121*). If the sample, shutter, and monochromator are all at about the same temperature, the corrections tend to cancel in the above experimental arrangement. However, if the sample is placed *following* rather than preceding the chopper, for example, after the exit slit of the monochromator, sample emission will not affect the measurement, and the signal from the shutter will become increasingly important.

The shutter signal is composed of two parts, the energy emitted by the shutter and the energy radiated by the surroundings which is reflected by the shutter into the optical train. The spectral radiance is greatly reduced if the radiating body is at liquid-nitrogen temperature; for example, at a wavelength of 30 μ it is decreased by two orders of magnitude. Therefore, the energy reflected by the shutter may be virtually eliminated by mounting a black body at liquid-nitrogen temperature in a position so that its aperture is reflected by the shutter into the optical train. In this way energy radiated by the train back to the shutter is absorbed, and the energy reflected by the shutter back to the optical train is made negligible. If a glass shutter coated with a low-emittance material such as aluminum is used, shutter emission is also reduced by two orders of magnitude and the shutter correction becomes negligible.

If the chopper follows the shutter in the optical train, the chopper emission term cancels, as has already been shown [see Eqs. (20) and (21)]. If the shutter had been located following the chopper, I_c would replace I_s in Eq. (22). It is important to locate the chopper and shutter reasonably close together in the optical train since the emission of all mirrors located between the two also contributes to I_s in Eq. (22). Finally, both chopper and shutter should be located near the entrance slit of the monochromator so that emission from either element can be dispersed by the monochromator and only a narrow band of wavelengths will reach the detector. If the chopper and shutter follow the exit slit, their emitted radiation will be undispersed so that the resulting signal is greatly enhanced.

The preceding discussion holds for reflection as well as transmission measurements if the reflectances R and R' are substituted for T and T' in Eq. (22).

d. Wavelength Calibration Errors. Many commercial spectrophotometers have a direct wavelength readout. The readouts on grating instruments are the most reliable since the relation between wavelength and grating angle is a sinusoidal function, and is nearly linear over restricted grating rotation angles. Direct-reading prism instruments, on the other hand, must employ either a nonuniform wavelength scale or a cam shaped to match the nonlinear prism dispersion curve. The wavelength accuracy thus depends on how well the scale, or cam, is made. A correction curve for one direct-reading commercial spectrophotometer employing a rock-salt prism is shown in Fig. 26.

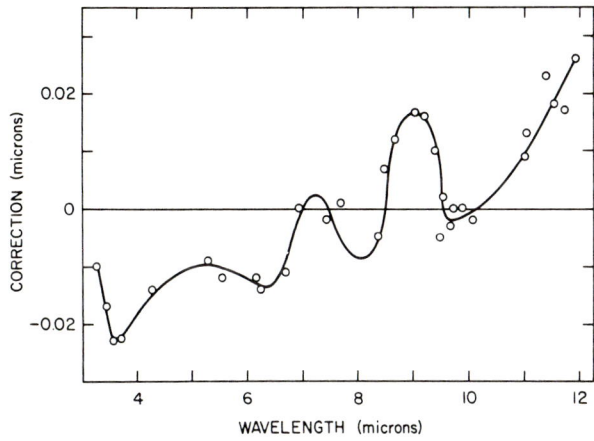

Fig. 26. Wavelength calibration curve for a direct-reading prism instrument.

Note that the wavelength readout is good to about $\pm 0.02\,\mu$, which is perfectly adequate for most routine measurements. However, it is difficult to calibrate this instrument to achieve greater wavelength accuracy, since the error curve is not a uniform function. If a lever rather than a cam is employed in a prism instrument, and if the readout is on a drum having equally spaced divisions, a uniform function relating wavelength to drum reading is generated. A mathematical expression can then be used to fit the data by means of least squares (122), achieving a greater wavelength accuracy than was possible with the cam or direct-reading wavelength scale. Using the mathematical least squares fitting technique, the accuracy of the wavelength calibration is limited primarily by the repeatability of the instrumental settings (typically 0.001–0.002 drum revolutions on our Perkin–Elmer model 99 monochromator) and the accuracy with which the wavelengths are known for the prism resolving power used. Calibrations good to a few thousandths of a micron in the infrared or a fraction of an angstrom in the visible and ultraviolet can be achieved if the prism is thermostatted so that its temperature varies by less than $\pm 0.1^\circ$C. Figure 27 shows the deviations of the experimental points from one such calibration curve (122).

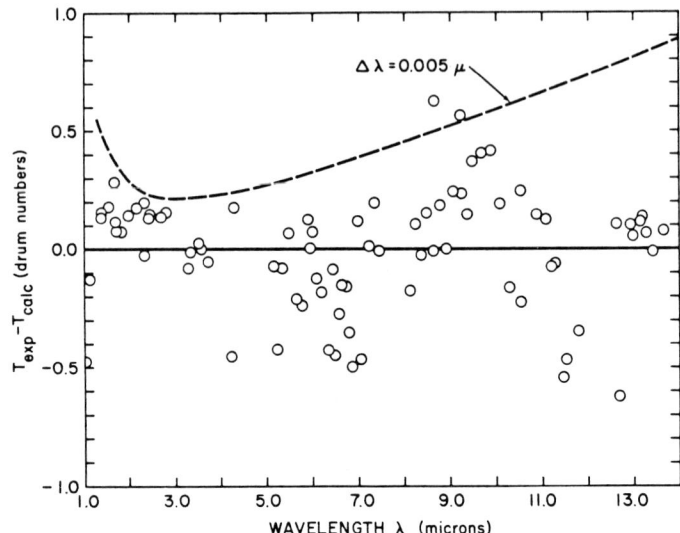

FIG. 27. Deviation of measured points from a computed calibration curve for NaCl. One drum revolution equals 100 drum numbers [after Fryer (*122*)].

Although the method for determining wavelengths precisely using a strip chart recorder is well known to spectroscopists, it may bear repeating here. A portion of the spectrum is scanned, preferably using a fixed slit width, at a speed slow enough that no distortion of the line shape occurs because of time constants in the detection system. The spectra are drawn on a strip chart recorder whose rate of paper travel has been checked and found to be constant. Pulses corresponding to every drum revolution (or other convenient interval) are fed into the output signal and are recorded as pips on the chart paper along with the spectra. Next, the centers of the lines are marked, and vertical rulings are drawn through the line centers and calibration pips with the aid of a plastic triangle which is slid along a metal bar laid at the bottom of the trace. The distances between rulings are measured and the drum positions corresponding to the line centers computed.

At first glance it would seem that a wavelength calibration which is more accurate than the smallest $\Delta\lambda$ which can be resolved by the spectrometer is unnecessary. This would be true if one were studying gases and measuring the wavelengths of many-lined rotation-vibration bands. However, in the study of solids, materials have rather broad absorption bands, and no additional structure is revealed by further increasing the resolving power. The wavelengths at which peaks occur may, nevertheless, need to be accurately known. Wavelengths of interference maxima or minima formed by thin films may also need to be known rather accurately, although the fringes themselves are broad, symmetric, and frequently widely spaced so that they do not need to be traced out with high resolving power. For these and other applications high resolution is unnecessary, but a good wavelength calibration is essential.

e. Too Large a Spectral Slit Width. Although high resolution is not always required, in some cases it is essential. If too low a resolution is used, instrumental broadening will increase the width of sharp transmission lines or bands and reduce their height. Also, if the structure is asymmetric, the apparent wavelengths of maxima or minima may be shifted. This situation is particularly important when measuring the transmission of spike interference filters, or wavelength positions of steep absorption band edges. The band of wavelengths passed by a spectrometer is determined to a large extent by the slit width settings. Since the advent of spectrometers with automatic slit width controls, little attention has been given to the problem of determining band widths, and some instrument manufacturers are not even able to furnish the data required for calculating spectral slit widths of their instruments. Since the relations for calculating spectral slit widths from instrumental parameters are not readily available, they will be briefly presented here.

The maximum energy for a given bandwidth is obtained when the entrance and exit slits are of equal width in an optical system symmetric about the dispersing element. Most instruments are designed in this way. The theoretical resolving power in a diffraction limited system is achieved for infinitely narrow slits. If $\Delta\lambda_{min}$ is the minimum wavelength separation which two very sharp spectral lines of equal intensity may have and still be distinguished, then, using the Abbé resolution criterion[8] for a grating (*123*),

$$\Delta\lambda_{min} = 0.873\lambda/\eta mn \tag{23}$$

where λ is the wavelength, m the grating order, n the total number of rulings, and η the number of times the grating is used. For a prism,

$$\Delta\lambda_{min} = \frac{0.873\lambda}{\eta b\ dn/d\lambda} \tag{24}$$

where b is the length of the effective prism base (that length seen by the light), and n the refractive index of the prism material. The prism is assumed to be in air or vacuum. As the slit width is increased, there is little increase in $\Delta\lambda_{min}$ until the "normal slit width," $\lambda f/4d$ (*125*), is reached. Here f is the focal length of the collimating lens or mirror if a plane grating or prism is used (or the focal length of a concave grating), and d the width of the projection of the

---

[8] The more stringent Abbé resolution criterion has been found to better describe the observable resolution limit for high-quality diffraction gratings and other optical systems than the Rayleigh criterion which is used in most textbooks. When using the Rayleigh criterion the factor 0.873 in Eqs. (23) and (24) is replaced by 1. For a discussion of the two criteria, see Rank *et al.* (*123*) and Conrady (*124*).

grating or prism on the collimating element. At wider slit widths the spectral purity, or per cent of theoretical resolution which can be achieved, falls rapidly until, at 8 times the normal slit width, it is only 43% of Abbé theoretical (*126*). At still wider slit widths, which are the ones usually used if high resolution is not necessary, diffraction effects may be neglected and $\Delta\lambda_s$, the spectral slit width, may be computed from geometrical optics. If the intensity of light passing through the exit slit when the entrance and exit slits are equal is plotted as a function of wavelength, a triangle will result, as is shown in Fig. 28. The spectral slit width is the wavelength interval at half height and is

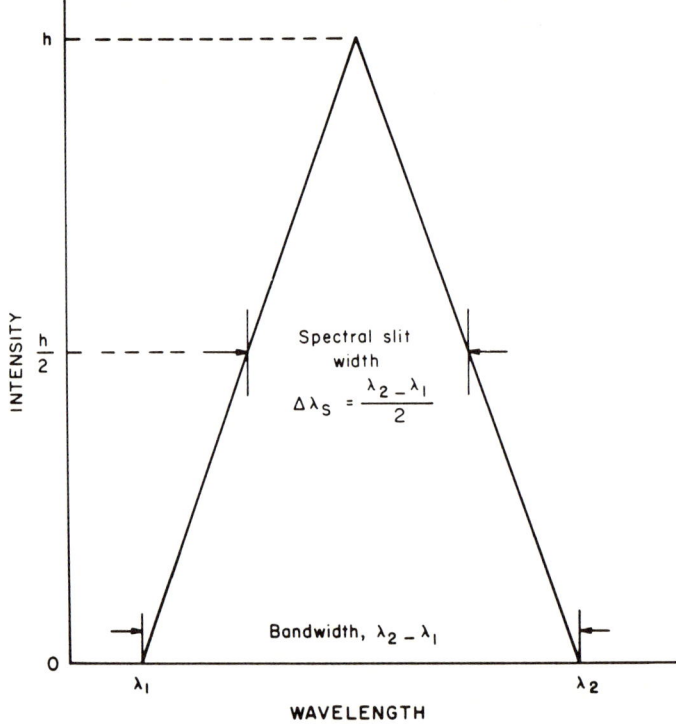

FIG. 28. Energy distribution curve when entrance and exit slits are equal.

nearly equal to the wavelength separation of two just-resolved spectral lines.[9] It may be computed for a grating by differentiating the grating equation. Assuming a Littrow mounting, where the angles of incidence and diffraction are equal, the grating equation is

$$m\lambda = 2a \sin \theta \qquad (25)$$

[9] If the Rayleigh rather than the Abbé resolution criterion is used, the spectral slit width is exactly equal to the wavelength separation of two just-resolved lines.

where a is the grating constant and θ the angle of incidence. The spectral slit width is then

$$\Delta\lambda_s = \left[\frac{(4a^2 - m^2\lambda^2)^{1/2}}{\eta m f}\right] s \tag{26}$$

where s is the physical width of the slits. As before, η gives the number of times the grating is used; for a double-pass system $\eta = 2$. The term in the parentheses is called the "linear dispersion of the monochromator."

To reduce astigmatism, prism monochromators are usually designed so that their prisms are used near the angle of minimum deviation. The angle δ through which the light is deviated by the prism can be calculated from the expression

$$n = \frac{\sin\frac{1}{2}(\alpha + \delta)}{\sin\frac{1}{2}\alpha} \tag{27}$$

where α is the apex angle of the prism and n its refractive index. After differentiating Eq. (27) and including the parameter η to take into account the number of times the prism is traversed, the expression for the spectral slit width of a prism monochromator is obtained:

$$\Delta\lambda_s = \left[\frac{(1 - n^2\sin^2\frac{1}{2}\alpha)^{1/2}}{2\eta f(dn/d\lambda)\sin\frac{1}{2}\alpha}\right] s \tag{28}$$

which holds for $s \geq 2\lambda f/d$. The apex angle α for glass, SiO_2, NaCl, and KBr prisms is usually 60°, but for CsBr, CsI, CaF_2, and LiF prisms other angles are more common and can be found by consulting the manual for the particular monochromator used. For Littrow prism mountings the light traverses the prism twice for each pass, so that $\eta = 4$ for a double-pass system. It should be pointed out that Eqs. (26) and (28) are derived assuming that the monochromator optics introduce no additional broadening. In well-designed instruments this condition can often be very nearly achieved, but any aberrations or out-of-focus conditions will make the instrumental spectral slit width larger than the calculated value.

VII. Normal Incidence Reflection Measurements

Although transmittance measurements at normal incidence are the most common type of optical measurements made on thin films, normal incidence reflectance measurements are more versatile and can be made with greater accuracy. Reflectance measurements can be made on opaque as well as transparent materials throughout the spectrum, and, in the 0.3 to 30 μ

wavelength region, can be made with an accuracy of about ±0.001 (*127*). By using differential reflectance techniques such as electroreflectance or piezoreflectance, one can detect changes as small as 5×10^{-6} in the relative reflectance (*128*). Advantages of making reflectance measurements at nearly normal incidence are: (1) the data analysis is relatively easy, (2) the reflectance in most cases is insensitive to any polarization introduced by the monochromator, and (3) the reflectance is insensitive to angle of incidence for angles within about 10° of normal incidence (*127*). For nearly all materials the average of R_p and R_s, the reflectances measured parallel and perpendicular to the plane of incidence, differs by less than 0.001 from that at normal incidence even for angles as large as 10°. Thus, reflectance measurements made at nearly normal incidence are insensitive to both the convergence angle of the incident radiation and the average angle of incidence.

In spite of the advantages to be gained by measuring reflectance at normal incidence, this type of measurement has not developed the popularity which transmittance measurements have. One reason is that there are additional sources of systematic error which may be difficult to overcome. Besides the instrumental sources of systematic error which were discussed in Section VI,3, there is the additional problem of sample tilt which may be difficult to eliminate. In reflectance measurements the beam is shifted through twice the angle by which the sample is tipped, so that a very small sample tilt, such as might be caused by a speck of dirt, may cause the beam to shift on the detector and give an incorrect reading. Another potential source of systematic error which can occur in instruments employing a reflectance standard is the chance for an error in the reflectance value of the reference mirror. Even if the mirror had been measured at a previous time, one is never sure that its reflectance has not changed in the meantime.

Sample preparation requirements are more stringent for reflectance measurements than they are for transmittance measurements, particularly when absorbing materials are being studied. The amplitude penetration depth δ of light into a material is given by

$$\delta = \lambda/2\pi k \qquad (29)$$

where k, the extinction coefficient, is the imaginary part of the complex refractive index $\bar{n} = n - jk$. For materials studied by reflectance techniques k is often large. If the material is a good conductor, k/λ is approximately constant over an extended wavelength region in the infrared and visible, and the penetration depth may be only a few hundred angstroms over the entire region. Thus, one is measuring a surface property when measuring the reflectance of such a material, rather than a mainly volume effect as is the case with transmittance measurements. For this reason, surface defects such as lattice distortion, strain, surface oxide films, and surface roughness are all very important when making reflectance measurements. The effect of surface oxide films has already been mentioned in Section V,4, while surface roughness was discussed in detail in Section IV. A 10 A aluminum oxide film on aluminum, or a surface roughness of only 13 A rms will decrease the measured specular reflectance at 5000 A by 0.1 %.

1. Types of Reflectometers

Various methods for measuring specular reflectance at normal incidence are shown in Fig. 29. In Fig. 29a is shown a double-beam relative reflectometer of the kind available in some commercial instruments. This type of reflectometer is convenient to use if high accuracy is not necessary. The autocollimation system for eliminating sample tilt illustrated in Fig. 29b is particularly useful when precise relative reflectance measurements are desired. Before making the measurement the beam splitter B is turned to the dashed position, and the sample and reference surfaces are paralleled by autocollimation. Errors resulting from sample tilt are thus eliminated. Uncertainties of 1% of the reflectance of a glass standard, or ± 0.0006, have been reported (129)

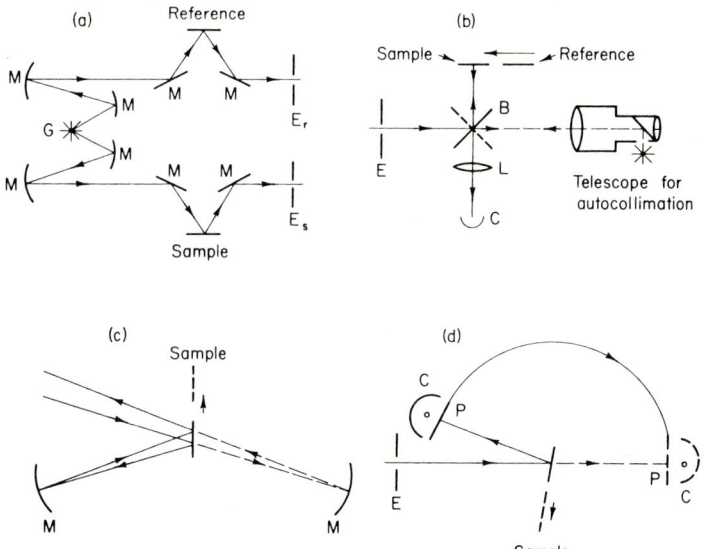

FIG. 29. Reflectometer designs for measuring normal incidence specular reflectance. (a) Double-beam system where reference surface is used in one beam; (b) sample and reference surface are interchanged in a single-beam system—the autocollimation feature helps eliminate errors due to tilt of sample or reference surfaces; (c) double-reflection absolute reflectance system; and (d) single-reflection movable detector system—this system can also be used at nonnormal incidence.

using this technique. A method for measuring absolute reflectance is illustrated in Fig. 29c. The principle is similar to that of the Strong absolute reflectometer (*127, 130*), but spherical instead of plane mirrors are used. In this way errors caused by sample tilt can be eliminated without using an integrating sphere. A reflectometer based on this principle will be described in detail in Section VII,2. Another type of reflectometer for measuring absolute reflectance is shown in Fig. 29d. This system is particularly useful in the vacuum ultraviolet where the number of reflecting surfaces must be kept to a minimum. In one type of instrument (*131*) a light pipe is used between phosphor P and detector C. Ultraviolet radiation striking the phosphor is transformed into visible radiation which then passes down the light pipe to the detector. This system has the advantage that the detector can stay fixed, and all the movement is done by the light pipe. An alternate approach is to mount the detector immediately behind the phosphor and move it from the reflected beam position to the straight-through position (*34, 132–135*), or to optically move it by a mirror interchange (*136, 137*). The single-reflection, movable detector reflectometer will be discussed in more detail in Section VII,3.

If the reflectance to be measured is near unity, it may be more advantageous to measure the absorptance, which is equal to $1 - R$, rather than R itself. An uncertainty of 1.4% of the absorptance has been achieved (*138*) by using a quartz oscillator to detect temperature differences as small as 6×10^{-5} °K. For aluminum this uncertainty corresponds to ± 0.0004 at $2\ \mu$. At liquid-helium temperature a carbon resistance thermometer or similar device (*139*) may be used in place of the quartz oscillator to measure $1 - R$.

Various other techniques for measuring specular reflectance at normal incidence might be mentioned: (1) The number of reflections can be changed to obtain absolute reflectance values (*140*). (2) Fourier transform spectroscopy can be used to eliminate the effect of scattered light when reflectance measurements are to be made in the far infrared (*141*). (3) If the sample is rough, the total reflectance rather than the specular reflectance may be measured. As long as the σ/λ ratio is 0.15 or less, the total reflectance at normal incidence is equal to that of a perfectly smooth surface of the same material (*37*).

Many types of reflectometers have been used to measure the absolute reflectance of diffusely reflecting samples at normal or nearly normal incidence. Among these are (1) the integrating sphere reflectometer (*142–144*), (2) the Coblentz hemisphere reflectometer (*145–147*), which has been modified by substituting an ellipsoid (*148–150*) or a double paraboloid (*151, 152*) for the hemisphere, and (3) the Gier–Dunkle heated cavity reflectometer (*153–155*). Unfortunately, the reflectance values obtained with these instruments appear to have uncertainties of 2 to 10% or more, over an order of magnitude larger than those which can be obtained if smooth samples are used.

2. Double-Reflection Spherical Mirror Reflectometer

The reflectometer principles illustrated in Figs. 29c and 29d are probably the most accurate ones yet devised for measuring absolute specular reflectance with minimized systematic errors. Together they furnish a means for making accurate normal incidence reflectance measurements from the far infrared to the vacuum ultraviolet. The system illustrated in Fig. 29c involves a double reflection from the sample, which allows all the sources of systematic error which are normally present in reflectance measurements to be either minimized or eliminated. Not only is the difficult problem of sample tilt present in most other reflectometer designs eliminated, as shown below, but also the problems of beam reversal and change in the plane of polarization are eliminated. These latter problems will be discussed in Section VII,3. Measurements having an average deviation of ± 0.0004 and an absolute accuracy of ± 0.001 are possible, making reflectance the most accurately measurable spectrophotometric quantity.

The way in which sample tilt is eliminated is illustrated in Fig. 30. After the first reflection from the tilted sample at position S', the light follows the dashed line to spherical mirror M. A spherical mirror, however, has the property that it forms an image at the same point regardless of where on the mirror surface the light strikes. On the second reflection from the sample, the

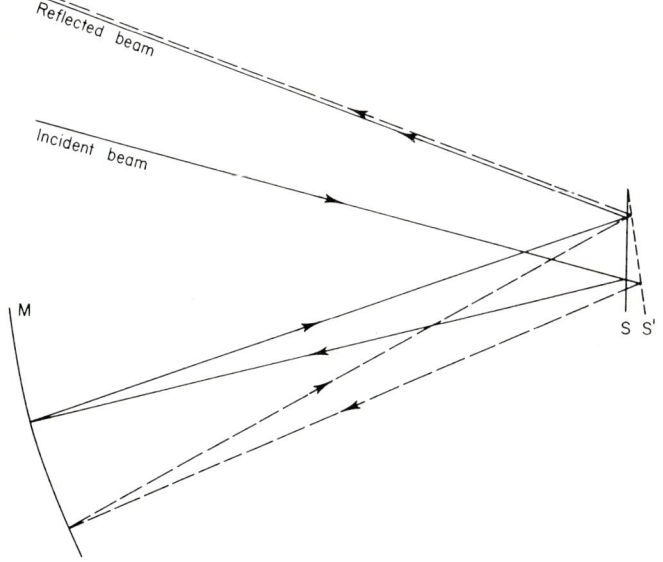

Fig. 30. Diagram showing how effect of sample tilt is eliminated by double reflection from sample.

beam deviation is exactly cancelled and the light follows the same path as it does when S is in the undeviated position. This freedom from lateral motion is particularly important when a small area detector such as a thermocouple is used.

A schematic diagram of an absolute reflectometer based on the double-reflection principle (*127*) is shown in Fig. 31. Light sources, mounted at A and G, are imaged on entrance slit E_1 of the monochromator by lens L or mirror M_{32}. For the ultraviolet and visible regions xenon, mercury-xenon, or

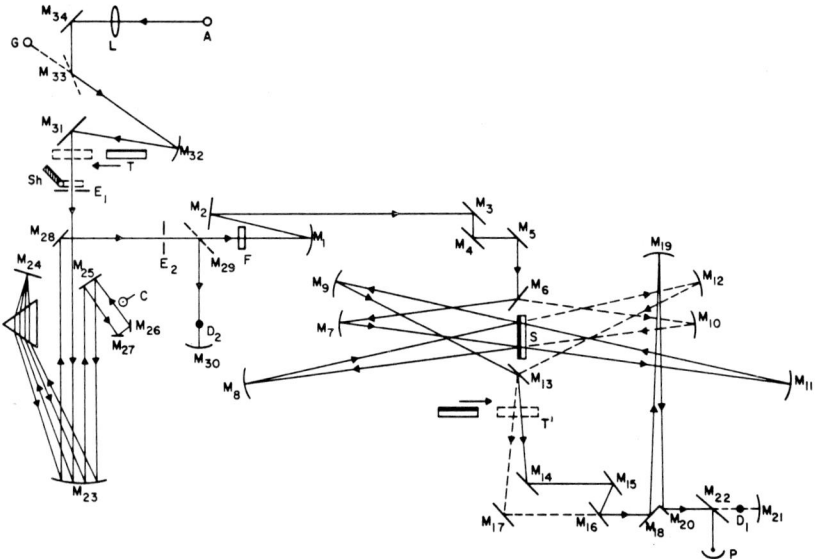

FIG. 31. Schematic diagram of double-reflection absolute reflectometer (see text).

tungsten strip or ribbon filament lamps are used, while a globar source is used in the infrared. A Perkin–Elmer model 99 single-beam double-pass monochromator disperses the light. In this laboratory a CaF_2 prism is usually used to cover the wavelength range from 0.25 μ in the ultraviolet to 7 μ in the infrared, and a CsBr prism to extend the range to 32 μ. The monochromator is double-passed so that scattered light is almost completely eliminated in the visible and infrared regions. In the ultraviolet a filter F, located near exit slit E_2, is inserted to block out further scattered light. Corning 9863 glass is used for the filter in the near ultraviolet, and is combined with single crystal nickel sulfate hexahydrate for measurements below 0.3 μ (*98*). When a photomultiplier is used (for wavelengths shorter than 0.7 μ) the single-pass radiation in the monochromator is blocked out by masking the top halves of the entrance slit and exit slit. This prevents overloading the photomultiplier with a large amount of unchopped radiation which may cause saturation effects and nonlinearity (see Section VI,3,a).

The instrument can be used for measuring either reflectance or transmittance. When transmittance measurements are desired, the sample may be placed in transmission slide T, located in front of entrance slit E_1, or slide T' following the reflectometer portion of the instrument. In either position an identical uncoated reference flat is measured along with the sample to eliminate possible defocusing effects caused by the thickness of the sample. Wavelength scans at constant background intensity can also be made by inserting pickoff mirror M_{29} behind exit slit E_2 to direct some of the radiation to auxiliary detector D_2. The signal from this detector drives a servomotor which provides automatic slit control, so that a record of reflectance or transmittance as a function of wavelength can be made. More accurate measurements, however, are made point by point with a manually controlled slit.

The optical system of the reflectometer shown in Fig. 31 can be explained as follows. After leaving the monochromator the light strikes spherical mirrors M_1 and M_7 which form a reduced image of the monochromator exit pupil on sample S. The area of S illuminated is a rectangle about $\frac{1}{4}$ by $\frac{3}{8}$ in., and is independent of the monochromator slit setting. When the sample is in the beam, light is reflected to M_8, which reimages the exit pupil on the sample. The beam then strikes M_9 which, together with M_{19} and M_{21}, demagnifies the exit slit and images it on thermocouple detector D_1. For measurements in the visible and ultraviolet regions, the light can be reflected to photomultiplier P by inserting mirror M_{22}. The sample is mounted on a vertical slide and can be completely removed from the beam. When S is out of the beam the light passes to M_{11}, a mirror identical to M_8, which reimages the exit pupil in the plane formerly occupied by the sample surface. The light then passes to M_9 and through the rest of the optical system as before. In the sample-in and sample-out positions the path length of the beam is the same, the beam strikes the same areas of the same mirrors (except for M_8 and M_{11}), and there is no beam reversal or change in the plane of polarization. If M_8 and M_{11} are identical, the ratio of sample-in to sample-out readings with the electrical zero subtracted gives the square of the absolute sample reflectance. If M_8 and M_{11} are not identical, the potential systematic error can be eliminated by optically interchanging the mirrors and taking the product of the measurements in the two configurations. Since the reflectance of each mirror appears in both numerator and denominator of the product, it cancels, and the fourth root of the product gives the absolute reflectance of the sample. In practice the optical interchange of the two mirrors is made by rotating the sample holder M_6 and M_{13} by 180° so that the light follows the dashed lines. M_{16}, which is on a slide, must of course be moved to allow the light to pass to M_{18}.

After the signal from either thermocouple D_1 or photomultiplier P in Fig. 31 has been obtained, it is recorded using an electronic system similar to that shown in Fig. 23 and described in Section VI,3,a. The linearity of the electronics in this system has been checked and found to be better than 0.05%. The over-all system linearity also has been checked using the three-polarizer technique (88) and is normally of the same order of magnitude as the linearity of the electronics.

The procedure for taking reflectance data is as follows: First, the aluminized shutter located in front of the monochromator entrance slit is closed to obtain the zero signal. The shutter is then opened and the sample-out and sample-in signals are recorded. Finally, the zero is remeasured and the entire process is repeated three times. Thus, four reflectance measurements are taken in each configuration. All readings are punched on IBM cards which are subsequently fed into a computer that calculates and prints out the reflectance values. The scatter in the points about a smooth curve plotting reflectance versus wavelength is usually about ±0.0004.

As an example of the accuracy of data taken with this reflectometer, the reflectance of gold evaporated in ultrahigh vacuum is shown in Fig. 32 (32).

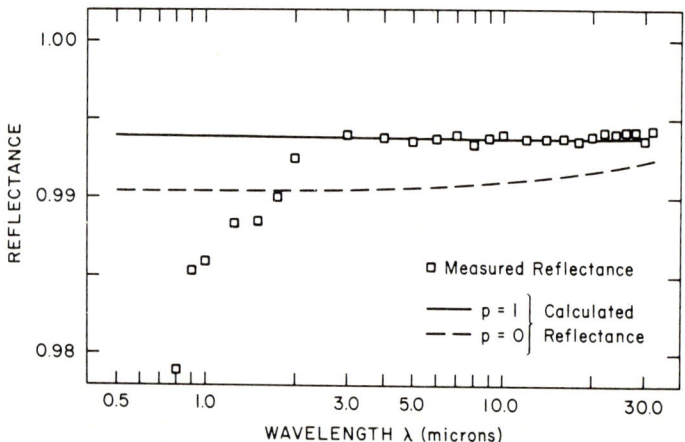

FIG. 32. Reflectance of gold deposited in ultrahigh vacuum and comparison with anomalous skin effect theory.

The solid line is the theoretical infrared reflectance of gold calculated from the dc conductivity by taking the effective mass of the conduction electron to be equal to that of a free electron. Specular electronic reflection from the surface was assumed since the substrate was a supersmooth fused quartz optical flat. No optical data were used in the calculations. The decrease in the observed reflectance at shorter wavelengths is caused by the onset of interband transitions and is not yet completely understood. However, the excellent agreement with theory at longer wavelengths where only free electron effects should be important is good evidence both of the correctness of the experimental measurements and of the validity of the theory. The dashed line shows the calculated theoretical reflectance if diffuse rather than specular reflection of electrons from the surface had occurred. It has been found experimentally that if a rough substrate is used the infrared reflectance does fall to the diffuse value (32). The agreement with the specular value provides additional evidence for the conclusion, already inferred from interferometric measurements and from reflectance measurements in the vacuum ultraviolet (39), that the sample surface is nearly atomically smooth.

3. SINGLE-REFLECTION MOVABLE DETECTOR REFLECTOMETER

The single-reflection moving detector or light-pipe reflectometer shown in Fig. 29d can give very accurate results, although some sources of systematic error which were eliminated in the double-reflection instrument discussed in Section VII,2 are still present in this optical system. The reflectometer can be used both at normal and nonnormal incidence, and is particularly well suited for measurements in the vacuum ultraviolet where sources are weak and the number of reflecting surfaces must be kept to a minimum. The one reflecting surface in this reflectometer is the sample. Even if the sample is slightly rough so that it scatters an appreciable amount of light around the specular direction, the detector can be placed close enough to the sample to intercept most of this scattered light. Also a large detector acceptance angle will help minimize any error due to sample tilt. Another advantage of the reflectometer is that it is simple enough to be mounted in a vacuum system, thus allowing measurements to be made on a film immediately after it is evaporated (156). In this way the surface oxide film, which can greatly affect reflectance measurements in the vacuum ultraviolet (67), does not have a chance to form. An alternative to measuring reflectance in ultrahigh vacuum is to encapsulate the surface with a transparent, nonreactive film of known thickness and optical constants.

Two principal difficulties associated with the single-reflection moving detector reflectometer are: (1) when the light beam is reflected from the sample it is reversed left for right, so that a given part of the beam strikes one side of the detector or light pipe on reflection and the other side in the direct-beam position (see Fig. 29d), and (2) if the incident beam is polarized, the plane of polarization can be rotated on reflection even at normal incidence. The reversal of the beam is important since the intensity distribution across the beam in grating monochromators is in general neither uniform nor symmetric, and may also be wavelength dependent (157). Thus, the photomultiplier or other detector should have a uniform response across its photosensitive surface. Uniformity of response can be checked by stopping down the effective aperture of the grating to give a beam with a convergence angle of about ½ degree, and then scanning that beam across the detector. If a phosphor coating is used either directly on the photomultiplier or on the end of a light pipe, it too must have a uniform response. Sodium salicylate can be applied by spraying and with care can be made sufficiently uniform to give the desired response.

The detector response should also be insensitive to the state of polarization of the light. A systematic error may be introduced in reflectance measurements both at normal and at nonnormal incidence if a polarization-sensitive detector is used. The problem is obvious at nonnormal incidence since even if the light incident on the sample is unpolarized it will become polarized upon reflection. However, at nearly normal incidence where the reflectances of the s and p components of the incident light are effectively equal, it is harder to see why a polarization-sensitive detector should cause trouble. To illustrate how this generally unrecognized problem arises, assume that light incident on a dielectric is polarized at 45° to the plane of incidence, as shown in Fig. 33. Both the s and p components undergo a phase change of 180° on reflection, but since the plane of polarization is always measured looking against the direction of the beam, it appears that the phase of the p component in the plane of

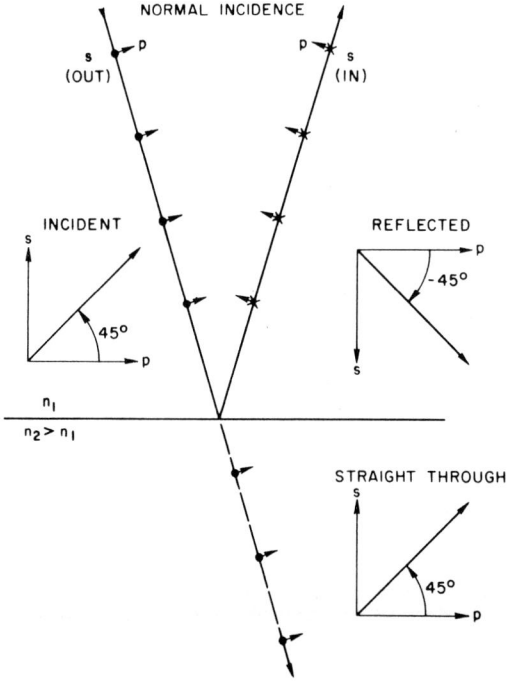

FIG. 33. Rotation of the plane of polarization upon reflection at normal incidence.

the paper is unchanged. Since the phase of the s component is changed by 180°, the resultant polarization vector is rotated by 90°, and an analyzer oriented to pass the incident beam would, if swung around to intercept the reflected beam at nearly normal incidence, extinguish it. Thus if a polarization-sensitive detector is used, its response to the reflected beam will in most cases be either too low or too high, and an error in the measured normal incidence reflectance will result.

Usually light emerging from the exit slit of a monochromator is partially polarized in a direction either parallel or perpendicular to the exit slit. If *only* normal incidence measurements are made and if the detector in a single-reflection movable detector reflectometer is rotated about an axis parallel to the slit, this problem will not occur. However if nonnormal incidence measurements are now made, a correction for instrumental polarization is essential. This correction may be eliminated by letting the axis about which the sample and detector rotate be at 45° to the slit (*158*). In this case if light from the slit is partially polarized either parallel or perpendicular to the slit, the components along the s and p direction are equal, and no correction for instrumental polarization is required. It is now essential, however, that the detector be insensitive to polarization since, if it is not, errors will be made in the normal incidence as well as in the nonnormal incidence reflectance measurements. Possible sensitivity of a detector to polarization may be checked by turning the sample rotation axis about the beam direction and observing whether or not the measured reflectance at nearly normal incidence changes.

Because of the various polarization effects described above, it is important to be able to measure the degree and plane of polarization produced by a monochromator. Figure 34 shows the polarization ratio $I_\parallel / I_\perp$ for a 1-meter normal incidence vacuum ultraviolet monochromator determined using a pile of lithium fluoride plates for an analyzer (*159*). Here $I_\parallel$ and $I_\perp$ are the intensities observed when the polarizer is oriented to pass light polarized parallel

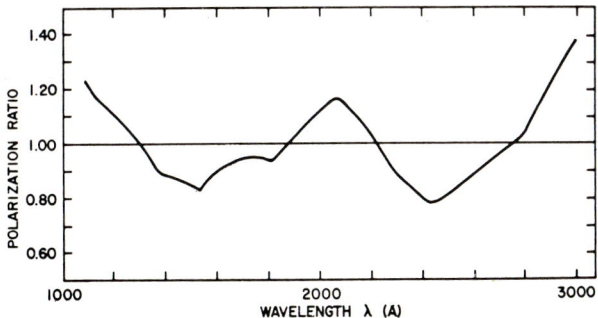

FIG. 34. Polarization ratio $I_\parallel / I_\perp$ for a normal incidence vacuum ultraviolet monochromator [after Hinson (*159*)].

or perpendicular to the slit. Note that the amount of polarization is strongly wavelength dependent, and that the plane of polarization changes from parallel to perpendicular over the wavelength range studied. A simple method of determining instrumental polarization without using an analyzer has been described by Madden and co-workers (*78*). It utilizes the Abelès relation which states that, at 45° for a single interface, $R_s^2 = R_p$, and is independent of the optical constants of the two media. This method can be used at any wavelength, is independent of the reflecting surface as long as no film is present, and, in addition to determining the magnitude of the polarization, will also give the plane of polarization. Since even a very thin oxide film will affect the results in the vacuum ultraviolet, Madden and co-workers used evaporated gold, which apparently does not form an oxide, and polished fused silica for their test surfaces. Good agreement between the polarizations determined using these two surfaces was found.

Of the various detectors which may be used for making precision reflectance measurements in the vacuum ultraviolet, the combination of sodium salicylate phosphor and conventional photomultiplier appears to be the most satisfactory. Unlike windowless photomultipliers sodium salicylate is insensitive to polarization. When properly prepared it has a uniform response. Unfortunately this combination has a considerably lower sensitivity than either conventional photomultipliers with uv-sensitive phosphors or windowless photomultipliers. An additional loss occurs if a light pipe is used. This loss may be kept to a minimum by optically polishing the sides of the pipe as well as the ends, and by keeping the bends in the pipe reasonably gradual. A further improvement, which becomes more important for large-diameter light pipes, may be effected by using fiber optics. An 8-in.-long fiber optic pipe bent in the form of a question mark, and having a numerical aperture of about 0.60 and a packing fraction of 86%, will transmit about 40% of the light emitted into a hemisphere by a sodium-salicylate–coated plate (*160*). By using a fiber optic bundle having a larger numerical aperture and packing fraction, this efficiency may be increased.

The entire ultraviolet wavelength range may be covered by using sodium salicylate since its quantum efficiency is close to unity from the extreme to the near ultraviolet where it becomes translucent (*161–163*). The fluorescence is peaked at about 4250 A, near the maximum sensitivity of conventional photomultipliers. Since sodium salicylate is sensitive to such a wide wavelength range, it is much more sensitive to scattered light than "solar blind" photomultipliers. In the extreme ultraviolet at wavelengths shorter than 900 A, aluminum films may be used as filters to block out longer wavelengths (*96, 164*) or a predisperser may be used (*165*). A correction for longer-wavelength scattered light may be made by measuring the reflectance, blocking out the desired radiation with a filter near the entrance slit of the monochromator, and measuring the reflectance again. Since the fraction of the signal which is scattered light and the reflectance of the sample for this light is known, a correction to the initial reflectance reading can be made. An error in ultraviolet reflectance measurements will also occur if a single grating monochromator is used in first order, and higher orders are not blocked out. Short-wavelength cutoff filters such as LiF, fused quartz, and various glasses can be used for this purpose. Filters should be mounted near the entrance slit to eliminate problems caused by fluorescence.

VIII. Nonnormal Incidence Reflection Measurements

Nonnormal incidence measurements may be divided into two general categories: (1) those in which only the reflectance or the reflectance ratio R_p/R_s is measured, and (2) those in which the phase difference Δ between the p and s components is also determined. The first category, a form of polarimetry, will be covered in this section, while the second, ellipsometry, will be discussed in Section IX. When polarimetric measurements are made on absorbing materials, two measurements are necessary to determine both optical constants n and k. Although external reflection measurements (described in Section VIII,1) are more common, internal reflection measurements (covered in Section VIII,2) are in some cases much more sensitive to changes in n and k. In the case of dielectrics, Brewster angle measurements are a good way of getting accurate values of n either for nonabsorbing films or dielectric substrates. These techniques will be discussed in Section VIII,3.

1. Types of Polarimetric Measurements

A survey of possible ways for making polarimetric measurements on absorbing materials has been given by Humphreys-Owen (*166*). He finds that the best methods are measurement of (1) the pseudo-Brewster angle θ_B' at which R_p reaches a minimum, and R_p or the ratio R_p/R_s, (2) R_s alone at θ_B' if k is small, (3) the ratio R_p/R_s or the value of R_p at two angles of incidence, (4) the value of R_p and R_s at one angle of incidence, and (5) the reflectance of unpolarized light at two angles of incidence. Other possible methods, such as measuring R_s at two angles of incidence, are insensitive to changes in n or k.

Figure 35 (*167*) shows R_s (upper curves) and R_p (lower curves) as a function of angle of incidence for various values of n and k. Also shown is R_a, the average of R_s and R_p. When $k \sim 0$ and $n \sim 1$, the normal incidence reflectance is low and the minimum defining θ_B' barely discernible. As n or k increases, the normal incidence reflectance increases, and the minimum becomes more pronounced, moving to larger angles of incidence. Also, R_a remains essentially constant to larger and larger angles of incidence. For

$n = k = 2.3$, for example, R_a changes by less than 1% from normal incidence up to 65°. If materials have even moderately large n or k values, one must work at such high angles of incidence to use method (5) that it becomes unattractive. Better sensitivity is achieved with any of the methods utilizing measurements of R_p alone, or as a ratio with R_s, but even in this case at least one measurement must be made near the pseudo-Brewster angle. In the

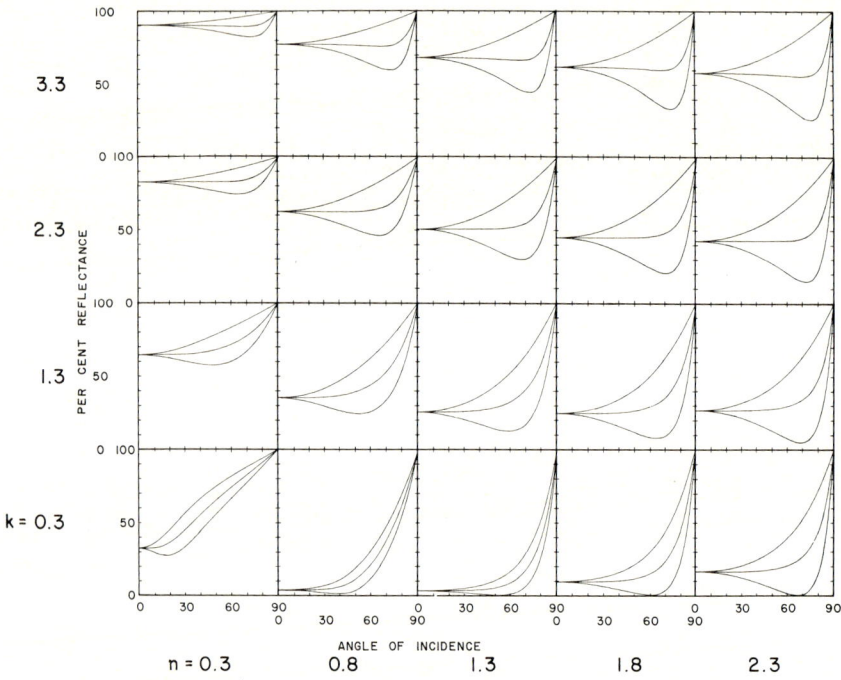

FIG. 35. R_s (upper curves), R_p (lower curves), and $R_a = (R_s + R_p)/2$ as a function of angle of incidence for various values of n and k [after Hunter (*167*)].

infrared region, n and k for metals rise to values in the 10's and 100's, $\theta_B{}'$ is close to 90° and unreachable experimentally. Hence for these materials polarimetry is useful primarily in the visible and ultraviolet regions of the spectrum.

a. Polarized Light. Reflectance measurements using polarized light are usually made at predetermined angles of incidence which include $\theta_B{}'$. In these measurements it is better to measure the ratio R_p/R_s rather than R_p or R_s alone, since only a relative measurement is required and effects of source fluctuations and amplifier drift are thereby minimized. Also, the projected area of the sample normal to the beam direction need not be the same at various angles of incidence. If carefully made, reflectance measurements using polarized light can be quite accurate. The number of measurements should always be in excess of the number required for determining n and k. One useful check measurement is the ratio R_p/R_s at 45° angle of incidence. At this angle the ratio equals R_s, and, since R_s can also be calculated from the polarimetrically determined optical constants, an estimate of the uncertainty in the measurements can be obtained. Reflectometers employing polarized light have been successfully used to measure optical constants of evaporated films and bulk samples with precision. Potter (*168, 169*) has recently achieved accuracies of a few tenths of a per cent in reflectance measurements with an instrument of sophisticated design incorporating several internal reflections which increase the measurement precision and allow the sample to be mounted in a cryostat.

There are several potential sources of errors which should be guarded against when making reflectance measurements with polarized light. First and foremost, the polarizer should be a good one. Not only should it have a high extinction ratio, not deviate the beam as it is rotated (so as not to shift the image on the detector), but it should also give the same signal in all positions 180° apart. Most polarizing prisms do deviate the beam. Even if they do not, they may not meet the last requirement. Several years ago in our laboratory two large new Glan Thompson prisms of the highest quality were obtained. Neither defocused the beam nor deviated it by as much as 1 minute of arc. However, when either one was used in a photometric system with the beam stopped down so that the prism was not the limiting aperture of the system, it did not give the same signal when it was rotated by 180°. The reason for this is not understood, but it does emphasize the fact that a problem exists. High-quality sheet polaroid encapsulated in glass can be purchased which does satisfy all the above requirements.

Other common sources of systematic error in polarimetric measurements are polarization originating in the light source, the use of a polarization sensitive detector, and the presence of other polarizing elements such as mirrors used at nonnormal incidence. The polarimeter should thus be designed so that the signal may be recorded for different polarizer positions when the sample is removed from the beam. Most light sources are slightly polarized, tungsten lamps being a good example. Although a new strip filament lamp may be unpolarized, with use it develops a partial polarization amounting to several per cent. Polarizations of 6% are common with coiled filament lamps, and values as high as 15% are theoretically possible (*170*). The effect of polarization in the light source can sometimes be eliminated by mounting an auxiliary linear polarizer set at 45° between the source and the primary polarizer. The transmitted intensities when the primary polarizer is set at 0° and 90° are then independent of source polarization.

It should be mentioned here that the generally accepted convention for measuring polarizer and analyzer angles is to measure them from the plane of incidence, i.e., the plane containing the incident beam and the normal to the surface, when the observer is looking *against* the beam. Positive angles are measured in a counterclockwise direction starting from the right-hand half of the plane of incidence.

b. *Unpolarized Light.* Although nonnormal incidence reflectance measurements using polarized light are inherently more sensitive than those made using unpolarized light, in some spectral regions it is difficult to obtain good polarizers, and unpolarized light must be used. One such region is the vacuum ultraviolet. Although Walker (*171*) has shown that a lithium fluoride pile of plates polarizer can be used down to 1200 Å, most reflectance measurements in this region are made without polarizers. In order to determine both optical constants for absorbing materials, the reflectance must be measured at two angles of incidence. For maximum sensitivity one is usually near normal incidence and the other in the neighborhood of the principal angle, which coincides with the Brewster angle for $k = 0$. The reason for this choice of angles can be seen from the isoreflectance plots in Fig. 36 (*167*). At a given angle of incidence the various values of n and k which give a constant value of $R_a = (R_s + R_p)/2$ lie on one of the 8 lines in each of the small graphs. For example, in the square at the lower right-hand end of the array the isoreflectance curve for an 80° angle

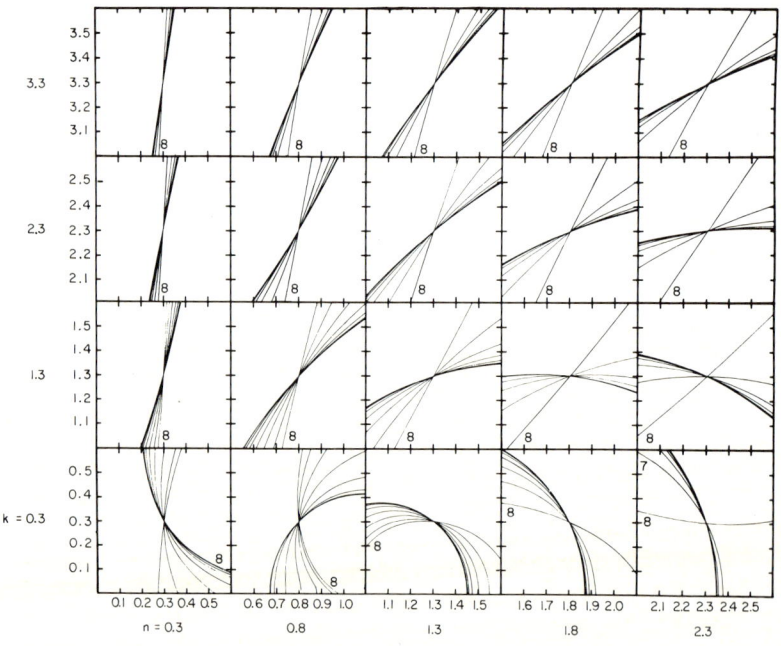

FIG. 36. Isoreflectance curves for R_a for various values of n and k [after Hunter (*167*)].

of incidence is the nearly horizontal curve. In this same graph isoreflectance curves for other angles of incidence from 10 to 70° are also shown, and all intersect at the values $n = 2.3$, $k = 0.3$. Thus, if the average reflectance were measured at two angles of incidence for a material having these optical constants, the intersection of the two isoreflectance curves would uniquely determine the optical constants of the material. The maximum sensitivity of this method occurs when the angle of intersection of the two curves is the largest, i.e., when one measurement is near normal incidence and the other near the principal angle. It is also clear from the graphs that the sensitivity of the method is highest when $n \geq k$ and lowest when $k \gg n$.

Another way of showing how the sensitivity of the method depends on the values of n and k is illustrated in Fig. 37 (*167*). In these graphs for R_a and

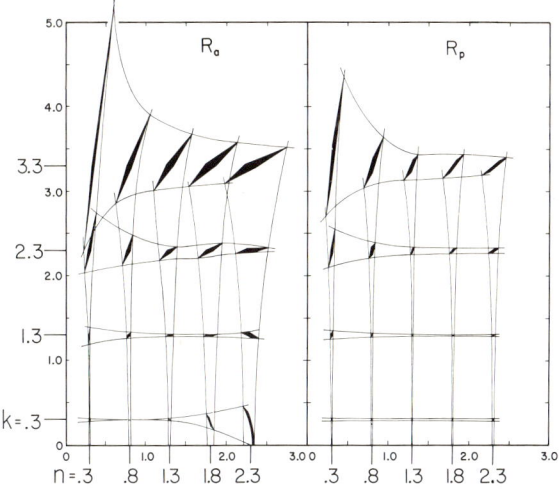

FIG. 37. Effect of a 1% reflectance error on the determination of n and k. Angles of incidence of 20° and 70° were used [after Hunter (*167*)].

R_p a $\pm 1\%$ error in the measured reflectances at 20° and 70° has been assumed. The errors in n and k produced by these measurement errors are shown as blackened parallelepipeds, and the extreme uncertainties in n and k by the connecting lines. It is clear that large uncertainties in k occur when $k \geq 4$ and, if the graph were extended in the n direction, it would show a similar result when $n \geq 4$ (*172*). Thus, absolute reflectance measurements at nonnormal incidence give the most precise results when n and k are fairly small, i.e., in the visible and ultraviolet regions.

The preceding discussion concerning measurements of R_a has assumed that the beam of light incident on the sample is unpolarized. However, as was mentioned in Section VIII,1,a, some sources may be partially polarized so that the above assumption is not always correct. Three different approaches have been taken to solve this problem. One is to let the polarization of the incident beam be a third variable, and determine n, k, and the degree of polarization for each wavelength studied. Computer programs for carrying out such calculations have been described in the literature (*167, 173*). Another solution is to orient the source polarization at 45° to the s and p directions. This equalizes the magnitudes of the s and p components in the beam incident on the sample. A third solution is to make two series of measurements at the same angles of incidence but with the sample rotated by 90° for the second series. The average of the two sets of measurements for each angle of incidence gives R_a, and the effect of beam polarization is cancelled.

There are some experimental difficulties associated with measurements of reflectance at nonnormal incidence. If the material has a low k value, the reflectance at the principal angle may be too low to measure accurately. Also, at large angles of incidence beam convergence and setting errors may become important. Using angles of incidence of 20° and 70° Hunter (*167*) has calculated the effect of a convergence half angle of 2°, approximately that obtained from a standard 1-meter normal incidence vacuum ultraviolet monochromator, on the accuracy of the measurements. He concluded that this convergence angle does not appreciably affect the accuracy unless n is fairly large ($n \sim 1.8$) and k small ($k \sim 0.3$). Finally, the area of the sample illuminated increases rapidly as the angle of incidence becomes large. The sample area changes by a factor of three in going from 0 to 70° angle of incidence, but then doubles in going from 70 to 80°. Thus, if the principal angle is near 80°, as will be the case for materials with large k values, the sample size may have to be rather large.

2. Attenuated Total Reflection

Measurements of light reflected internally from the substrate side of a film have the great advantage that the film surface is protected, and therefore cannot oxidize or adsorb gas. If, in addition, the film has a lower index than the substrate and an angle of incidence greater than the critical angle for the film-substrate combination is used, either total reflection or attenuated total reflection occurs depending on whether the extinction coefficient of the film is zero or nonzero. In either case, no light is transmitted through the film. If $n - jk$ is the complex refractive index of the film and n_s the substrate index, the critical angle θ_c is given by

$$\sin \theta_c = n/n_s \qquad (30)$$

where $n < n_s$. When $k = 0$, an abrupt change in the internal reflectance occurs at the critical angle; this is the principle on which the Pulfrich and Abbé refractometers operate (*174*). If $k \neq 0$, the rate of change of reflectance with angle of incidence is not a step function at θ_c, but the critical angle can still be determined and is the angle where the function has its maximum slope. An analysis of this method for determining θ_c including sources of systematic error has been given by Hunter (*175*). Alternately, the film optical constants can be determined from reflectance measurements for different angles of incidence or kinds of polarization. Methods for producing single and multiple internal reflections at fixed or variable angles of incidence, and for analyzing the results, are described in the literature (*175–185*). An analysis of the advantages to be gained by making ellipsometric internal reflection measurements has also been given (*186*).

Attenuated total reflection is of particular importance in the ultraviolet and vacuum ultraviolet. In this region $n < 1$ for many materials, so that a critical angle exists even when measurements are made on the side of the film which is exposed. The same phenomenon exists in the soft X-ray region, although here θ_c is nearly at grazing incidence.

The sensitivity of internal and external reflectance measurements to small changes in the film optical constants is shown in Fig. 38. The incident light is assumed to be unpolarized. In Fig. 38a external reflectance versus angle of incidence curves are given for a film having $k = 0.1$ and various values of n, deposited on a substrate of index 2.4. This substrate could be $KTaO_3$, since it has an index varying from 2.2 to 2.4 in the visible (*187*), or KRS-5 which has an index of around 2.4 in the near infrared where it becomes transparent (*188*). Internal reflectance curves for the same film-substrate combination are shown in Fig. 38b. External and internal reflectance versus angle of incidence curves for a film with $n = 1.5$ and various values of k, deposited on a substrate of index 2.4, are plotted in Figs. 38c and 38d, respectively. It is seen from these figures that the internal reflectance is much more sensitive to small changes in n and k for the film than is the external reflectance. For example, at an angle of 60° the change in internal reflectance on going from $n = 1.4$ to $n = 2.2$ is 6 times as much as that for external reflection. The changes in reflectance per unit change in k are even more impressive. At a 40° angle of incidence the change in attenuated total reflectance is 0.829 as k goes from 0 to 0.4, which is 32 times that for external reflectance.

Some of the other experimental advantages of attenuated total reflection measurements are: (1) the penetration depth of light into the less optically dense medium varies from about 0.1 wavelength near grazing incidence to indefinitely large values near the critical angle (*185*). However, although energy may be absorbed from the standing wave at the surface, interference does not occur. Thus the optical constants of semitransparent films may be determined by attenuated total reflection without having to contend with interference fringes. Scattering in the film is probably also unimportant.

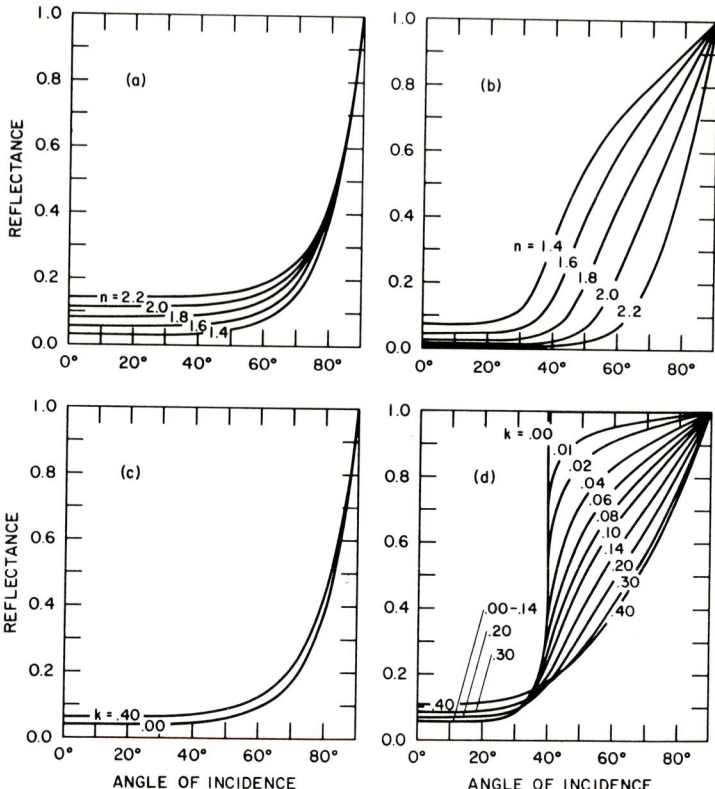

FIG. 38. Comparison of sensitivity for determining optical constants using external (a, c) and internal (b, d) reflectance measurements. (a, b) $k = 0.1$; (c, d) $n = 1.5$ for the film. The refractive index of the substrate is 2.4 in all cases.

(2) There is no decrease in the intensity of the incident light except by absorption in the film. Therefore multiple reflections in the substrate are possible, and the absorption of very thin or weakly absorbing films may be measured. As much as 10^4 times as much sensitivity as in conventional transmission measurements has been reported (*189*). (3) The angle of incidence for maximum sensitivity is reduced, often making the experimental measurements easier to make. Angles of 45 to 50° or less are common as compared to angles of 65 to 70° or more for external reflection measurements. (4) The sample surface is encapsulated so that if a film is deposited on a clean, chemically inert surface in ultrahigh vacuum the surface oxide problem is eliminated.

3. Brewster Angle Measurements

Sections VIII,1 and 2 have dealt with measurements made on absorbing materials such as metals and semiconductors. However it is frequently also necessary to measure the refractive indices of transparent materials. Measurement of the Brewster angle is a sensitive way of determining n either for a nonabsorbing film or for the substrate on which it is to be deposited. At the Brewster angle θ_B, given by

$$\tan \theta_B = n_1/n_0 \tag{31}$$

where n_1 and n_0 are the refractive indices of two media separated by a single interface (the incident medium having index n_0), the p component of the reflected light has zero intensity. Thus by measuring the angle at which the reflectance minimum of the p component occurs for an unfilmed transparent substrate one can determine its refractive index. Unfortunately, the reflectance minimum is rather broad. If a computer is available, θ_B may be determined quite accurately by measuring the relative reflectance photoelectrically in the vicinity of the minimum and fitting it to a cubic equation using a least-squares calculation (190). The derivative of this cubic is a quadratic, and the positive root gives the angle at which the reflectance is a minimum, i.e., the Brewster angle. This method is not only more sensitive than graphing the reflectance versus angle of incidence, but it also reduces the effect of scatter in the experimental points. With care n can be determined to about ± 0.0001 (190).

An alternate method first suggested by Pfund (191) has nearly as good sensitivity if photoelectric setting is used and does not require a computer. Both a polarizer and analyzer are required. The polarizer is set at 1–4° so that nearly all the light incident on the sample is polarized in the plane of incidence, i.e., in the p direction. The analyzer is then set for extinction at several angles of incidence near the Brewster angle. Most of the reflected light is polarized in the p direction unless the angle of incidence is within a few degrees of the Brewster angle. The analyzer setting is thus near 90°. However, since at the Brewster angle none of the p component will be reflected unless a film is present, the analyzer setting here is 0°. If the amount of the s component in the incident beam is quite small, the rotation of the plane of polarization of the reflected light will occur very abruptly. By plotting the analyzer angle versus the angle of incidence, the Brewster angle can thus be determined quite accurately.

The Abelès Brewster angle method for measuring the refractive index of a thin dielectric film (192–195) has gained wide popularity because of its accuracy and simplicity both experimentally and theoretically. If a film-covered surface is illuminated with p component light, at the Brewster angle for the film no light is reflected from the air-film interface, so the reflectivity of the film-covered substrate is the same as that of an uncoated substrate. Equation (31) then gives the refractive index of the film. Experimentally one partially coats a substrate with the film whose index is desired, and then determines the angle where the reflectances from both parts of the surface are equal. Either visual or photoelectric setting may be used and in theory either a metal or dielectric substrate is possible. Visual setting is adequate when the reflectances of the filmed and unfilmed surfaces are very different and low-reflectance substrates such as glass or fused quartz are used. Photoelectric setting is preferable when the substrate has a higher reflectance and the contrast is poorer. Kelly and Heavens have used a photoelectric technique (*195, 196*) to measure the index of anodic oxide films on tantalum where the substrate reflectance was about 16% at the Brewster angle. If the substrate reflectance is very high, as would be the case for a silvered or aluminized surface, the contrast between filmed and unfilmed regions is too poor to enable the Brewster angle to be determined. When the refractive index of the film is within ± 0.3 of that of the substrate, an accuracy of ± 0.002 is possible (*194*).

The requirements for films measured using the Abelès method are that they be homogeneous, isotropic, and nonabsorbing. Film thickness is not important, although the method is most sensitive when the optical film thickness is an odd multiple of $\lambda/4$ near the Brewster angle (*194, 195*). If the films are inhomogeneous so that the refractive index varies with film thickness, erroneous results will be obtained using the Abelès method (*197*). Anisotropy in the film is readily revealed by rotating the specimen in the plane of its surface. If a small amount of absorption is present in the film, the Brewster angle will be lowered causing an error in the derived refractive index of approximately the same magnitude as the value of k (*198*). However, if k is measured in another experiment, the amount of the shift in θ_B can be calculated (*198*) and corrected for.

The limitation that for good accuracy the film index be within ± 0.3 of the substrate index is eliminated by using a modification of the Pfund method (*191*) proposed by Hacskaylo (*199*). In this method the sample, consisting of a dielectric film covering part of a dielectric substrate, is illuminated with light polarized parallel to the plane of incidence with the polarizer offset by about 1° to admit a small amount of *s*-component light. The analyzer is set so that the reflected light from the filmed and unfilmed regions is equal. At the Brewster angle for the film, the reflected intensity from the two regions is equal only if just the parallel component is incident on the sample. Thus, the analyzer must be set to pass only the *p* component. At other angles of incidence, the analyzer settings will be different so that a plot of analyzer angle versus angle of incidence will accurately give the Brewster angle of the film. Hacskaylo (*199*) estimates that, by using a spectrometer having a circle good to $\pm 0.005°$, one should be able to determine the refractive index of a film of index 1.2 to ± 0.0002, and of index 2.3 to ± 0.0006, regardless of the index of the dielectric substrate.

IX. Ellipsometric Measurements

Although transmittance and reflectance measurements are both conceptually simpler and more widely used, ellipsometric techniques are a powerful tool for making precision measurements on thin films. A feature distinguishing these techniques from those previously discussed is that here angles, phase differences, and amplitude ratios are the measured quantities rather than the intensity of transmitted or reflected light. Ellipsometric techniques provide one of the most sensitive methods yet devised for measuring film growth. Changes in film thickness of 0.07 A, or less than 0.03 monolayer, can be observed (*200, 201*). Refractive indices of films can also be measured although, if the film is absorbing, either several film thicknesses must be used, or the film must be prepared on different substrates or immersed in liquids of different indices of refraction (*202*). If the absorbing film is thick enough to be opaque, its optical constants can again be determined by making ellipsometric measurements on a single sample.

Various ellipsometric parameters including ψ and Δ are illustrated in Fig. 39. Figure 39a shows the vectors for a reflection at an angle of incidence less than the principal angle, and Fig. 39b those for a reflection at an angle greater than the principal angle. If the horizontal axis represents the plane of

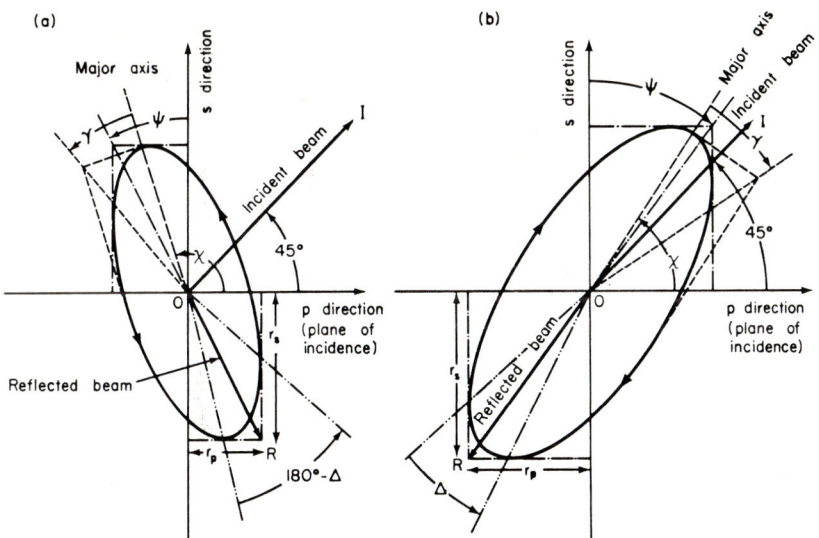

FIG. 39. Graphical representation of various ellipsometric parameters for (a) reflection at an angle of incidence less than the principal angle, and (b) one greater than the principal angle.

incidence, and if light striking the sample surface is initially polarized at 45° to that plane, the amplitude of the incident electric vector may be represented by *OI*. When the sample is a dielectric and no surface film is present, the amplitude of the reflected vector is *OR*, and the reflected light is plane polarized. The ratio of r_p, the reflected amplitude polarized parallel to the plane of incidence, to r_s, that polarized perpendicular to it, gives the tangent of the ellipsometric parameter ψ:

$$\tan \psi = r_p/r_s \tag{32}$$

If there is a surface film, or if the substrate itself is absorbing, however, r_s and r_p will no longer be in phase, and the reflected light will be elliptically polarized in the direction shown by the arrows on the ellipses in Figs. 39a and 39b, respectively. The phase difference between r_p and r_s is then Δ, the second ellipsometric parameter:

$$\Delta = \delta_p - \delta_s \tag{33}$$

where δ_p and δ_s are the phases of r_p and r_s, respectively. Two other ellipsometric parameters, χ and γ, are also indicated in the figure.

A phase angle diagram showing δ_p and δ_s for an absorbing solid is given in Fig. 40. At normal incidence δ_p and δ_s are 180° apart because of the "mirror

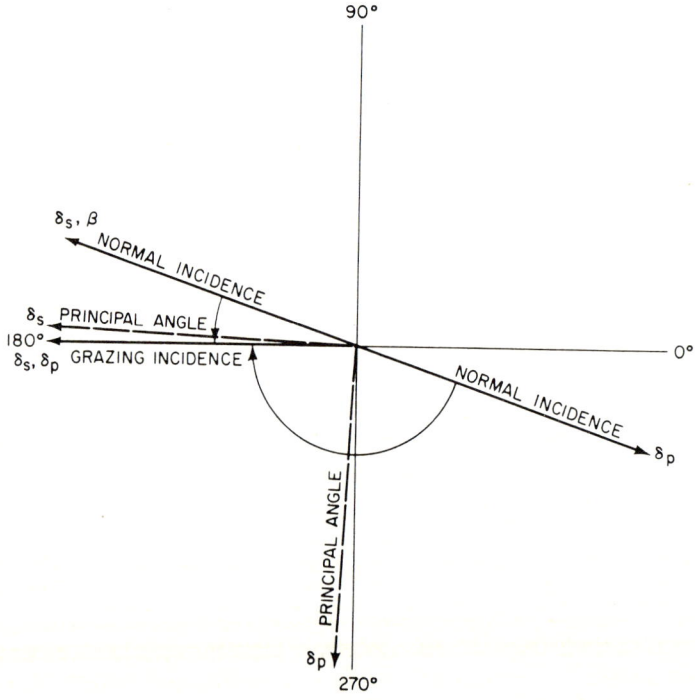

FIG. 40. Rotation of δ_s and δ_p with angle of incidence.

image effect" which was explained in Section VII,3 and illustrated in Fig. 33. As the angle of incidence increases, δ_p and δ_s approach each other and, at the principal angle, they differ by only 90°. At grazing incidence they coincide. Figure 41 has a different representation of δ_p, δ_s, and Δ as a function of angle of incidence. At the principal angle $\bar{\theta}$, $\Delta = 90°$, and near this angle is the region where maximum sensitivity in ellipsometric measurement is achieved. If the material is a dielectric with no surface film, $\bar{\theta} = \theta_B$, the Brewster angle where $r_p = 0$. For absorbing materials r_p does not reach zero,

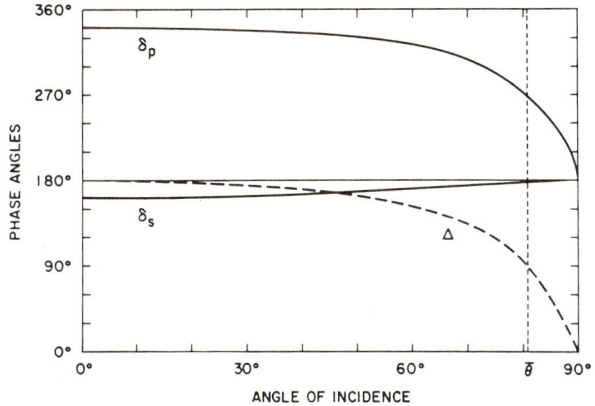

FIG. 41. δ_s, δ_p, and Δ as a function of angle of incidence. The principal angle $\bar{\theta}$ is also shown.

but the angle where it is a minimum is called the pseudo-Brewster angle, θ_B'. In general θ_B' does not coincide with $\bar{\theta}$ although their difference is usually only a fraction of a degree. The light reflected from an absorbing material is elliptically polarized, and at $\bar{\theta}$ the semimajor and semiminor axes of the ellipse are along the s and p directions. The mathematical relations are also considerably simplified at this angle. When the sample is coated with a dielectric or absorbing film, the reflected light is elliptically polarized even if the substrate is a dielectric. The sample behaves, however, much as a single interface with an appropriate pseudoindex (69). There is still a principal angle near which r_p passes through a minimum, and methods for determining ψ and Δ are the same as those for a single interface.

Two experimental setups used for ellipsometric measurements are shown in Figs. 42 and 43. Briefly they consist of a collimated source of radiation (composed of a source, slit, and collimating lens), polarizer, sample mount, quarter wave plate compensator, analyzer, focusing lens, and detector, all usually mounted on a divided circle spectrometer. Either visual or photoelectric detection may be used. Various additional components such as half-shade

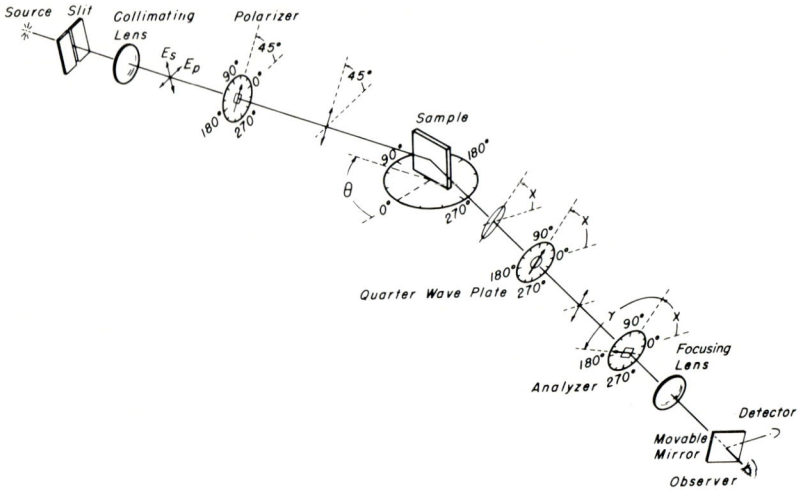

FIG. 42. Ellipsometric apparatus for measuring ψ and Δ with polarizer set at 45°.

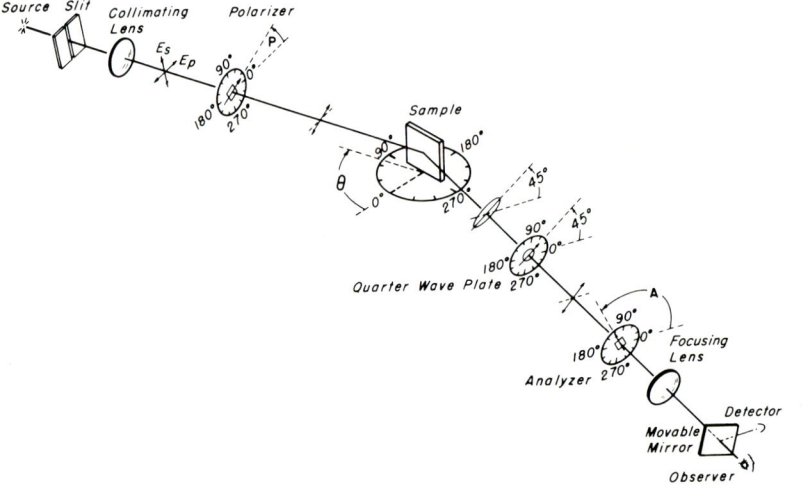

FIG. 43. Ellipsometric apparatus for measuring ψ and Δ with quarter-wave plate set at 45°.

devices to increase visual setting precision (*203, 204*) or Faraday cells for extremely precise photoelectric setting (of the order of 1 second of arc) (*205*) may also be added. Although there may appear to be an unlimited number of ways in which ellipsometric measurements can be made, they all fall into five general categories:

(1) The retardation of the compensator is varied and either the polarizer or analyzer is rotated to produce extinction. The compensator retardation thus determines Δ and the analyzer (or polarizer) setting ψ (*205a*). The measuring precision obtainable by this method using Babinet–Soleil compensators is low, but if an electro-optic retarder is used, this method becomes very attractive.

(2) The polarizer is set at 45° and the compensator and analyzer rotated to produce extinction, as is shown in Fig. 42. Major drawbacks of this technique are that the determination of the position for extinction is difficult since the settings of the compensator and analyzer are interdependent, and that an exact quarter-wavelength compensator must be used. The measurement may be made at any angle of incidence, but angles near the principal angle usually give the greatest sensitivity. If the angle between the fast axis of the compensator and the plane of incidence is χ, and that between the fast axis of the compensator and the analyzer is γ, as shown in Fig. 42, then ψ and Δ are obtained from the relations

$$\cos 2\psi = \cos 2\gamma \cos 2\chi, \quad \tan \Delta = \tan 2\gamma / \sin 2\chi \qquad (34)$$

The optical equivalent of the above arrangement may also be used. In this case the analyzer is set at 45°, and the polarizer and compensator rotated to produce extinction. The compensator is then mounted between the polarizer and sample instead of between the sample and analyzer as shown in Fig. 42.

(3) The fast axis of the quarter-wave plate compensator is fixed at 45° (or 135°) to the plane of incidence, and the polarizer and analyzer are rotated to produce extinction (Fig. 43). An advantage of this arrangement is that the compensator need not be exactly a quarter wavelength, and can be mounted on either side of the sample. If the compensator is set at 45°, ψ and Δ are obtained from the relations

$$\tan \psi = \cot L \tan(-A), \quad \tan \Delta = \sin \delta \tan(90° - 2P),$$
$$\cos 2L = -\cos \delta \cos 2P \qquad (35)$$

where P and A are the polarizer and analyzer angles measured from the plane of incidence, and δ is the retardation of the compensator. A good description of the experimental procedure to be followed when using this method has been given by McCrackin *et al.* (*206*), while others have described methods for making and testing quarter-wave compensators (*207, 208*). Procedures for calibrating compensators are also available (*209–211*).

(4) The polarizer or analyzer, and quarter-wave plate compensator are set so that extinction will occur at the principal angle, where $\Delta = \pi/2$. The angle of incidence is then changed until the principal angle is found.

(5) No compensator is used and ψ and Δ are obtained from ratios of the

reflected intensities for different polarizer-analyzer orientations rather than from an extinction measurement. This method is most sensitive if the measurements are made at the principal angle (*211a*), but can also be used at other angles of incidence. The method was initially used in the infrared by Beattie (*212*) and Roberts (*213*), and has been employed successfully out to wavelengths of 22 μ (*214*). At 1 μ a monolayer coverage can be detected (*213*).

Ellipsometry is often used to measure optical constants of materials. It can give excellent results (*215*) *provided* that corrections for surface films are properly made. Δ in particular is very sensitive to surface films, and the 30 to 40 Å thick oxide film which typically forms on metal surfaces causes Δ to change by several degrees (*69*). Contrary to the hopes often expressed in the literature, these films cannot be detected by making measurements at various angles of incidence (*69, 202*). Thus, if the film thickness is not measured and corrected for, the optical constants derived from ellipsometric measurements in air will almost certainly be in error. Methods for measuring the thickness of such films have been given in Section V,4, but oxide film corrections for ellipsometric optical constant measurements should be made using the exact ellipsometric equations, and not the linear approximations (*69*). If the film thickness is not known, both the film index and thickness may be measured by immersing the sample in liquids having a range of refractive indices (*202, 216*). If the film index is known, the effect of the film can be eliminated by measuring the sample while immersed in a liquid whose index matches that of the film (*217*). Even if a metal does not oxidize in air, thin adsorbed water or oil films may effect the measurements (*206*). The most elegant method for determining optical constants of metal films ellipsometrically is to prepare and measure them in ultrahigh vacuum. For example, if a vacuum of 10^{-9} Torr or better is used, it takes at least half an hour for a monolayer of contaminants from the residual gas to form on a freshly evaporated or cleaned surface (*28*). However, if the vacuum is 10^{-6} Torr, a film could form in as little as 2 sec (*28*), too short a time to complete a series of measurements. One common problem which arises when making measurements in vacuum is strain birefringence in the windows, since a considerable force is exerted on them when the system is under vacuum.

X. Absolute Phase Change on Reflection Measurements

When light is reflected from a single interface, the ratio of reflected to incident electric vectors can be written $re^{i\delta}$, where r is the amplitude reflectance and δ the absolute phase change on reflection. The quantity most often measured is r^2, the reflected intensity. In Section IX various combinations of r_s and r_p, the two components of r at nonnormal incidence, were measured, but only the phase difference $\Delta = \delta_p - \delta_s$, not the absolute phase change, could be determined ellipsometrically. Even in interferometry the quantity usually determined is the phase dispersion or variation of phase change with wavelength. The object is usually to eliminate it when, for example, making precision wavelength measurements with a Fabry–Perot interferometer. Thus, in contrast to the wealth of information obtained from phase angles in the electrical portion of the electromagnetic spectrum, in the optical region phase change information is nearly untapped.

At normal incidence the absolute phase change on reflection is usually represented by β, where by convention $\beta = \delta_s$ as illustrated in Fig. 40. If light is reflected from a dielectric in air, $\beta = 180°$. For a reflection from an absorbing material $\beta < 180°$ and is given by (15)

$$\tan \beta = \frac{2k}{1 - n^2 - k^2} \tag{36}$$

where, as before, $\bar{n} = n - jk$ is the complex refractive index of the absorbing material, and the index of air is 1. Since the denominator is negative for $n^2 + k^2 > 1$, β will always lie in the second quadrant if the reflection is from a single interface and the light is incident from the air side. However, if light is reflected from one or more dielectric or semitransparent absorbing films, β may lie either in the second or third quadrants. If light is incident from the more optically dense medium and is reflected from a single interface, $\beta = 0°$ if k for the material is 0, but will lie in the fourth quadrant if $k \neq 0$. If a film is present β will lie in the first or fourth quadrants.

In the above discussion β has been taken to be a positive angle (measured in the counterclockwise direction), or phase advance. Since from electromagnetic theory a phase advance equals $2\pi/\lambda$ times a path difference, a phase advance is equivalent to reflection from a fictitious surface in front of the actual physical surface.

1. Methods of Measurement

Nearly all phase change measurements are made on semitransparent films. Relative phase change measurements can be made rather easily using either fringes of equal chromatic order (*218*) or a combination of Feco and Fizeau fringes (*219*). Frequently the purpose of such measurements is to correct for effects caused by the phase dispersion when making precision wavelength measurements with a Fabry–Perot interferometer. In such cases it is usually better to eliminate the phase dispersion by using two different spacers (*220, 221*). Absolute phase change measurements may be made by several methods, all experimentally difficult. Among these are the use of (1) a Fabry–Perot etalon with circular Haidinger fringes (*222–225*), (2) two Fabry–Perot etalons in series (*226*), (3) Michelson interferometer (*224*), (4) Koester interference comparator (*227*), (5) mica interference filter (*228, 229*), (6) three-slit interference (*230, 231*), (7) Fizeau fringes with a wedge interferometer (*225, 232–235*), and (8) fringes of equal chromatic order with a parallel plate interferometer (*15*). Method (1) is the classical method of Rouard (*222*) in which diameters of the circular fringes formed by filmed portions of the plates are compared to ring diameters from uncoated portions. Since the light is focused on a small portion of the interferometer surface, a convergent rather than parallel beam is used and the equation for the angular diameters of the rings (*236, 237*) is slightly different than that for the true Fabry–Perot rings formed in parallel light. The most popular method for measuring absolute phase change is method (7) where straight-line Fizeau fringes contouring the interferometer surfaces are employed. Many of the same problems arise here that occur when film thickness is measured using Fizeau fringes (see Section V,2). In addition, the reference two-beam fringe system from uncoated portions of the interferometer plates is of low contrast and difficult to measure accurately unless photoelectric setting techniques (*60, 61*) are employed. One of the most precise methods for measuring absolute phase change is method (8) which will be described in detail in Section X,3.

2. Sources of Error

A major problem in measuring the absolute phase change on reflection is the inability of many investigators to use a consistent set of sign conventions in interpreting their data. Many examples in the literature could be cited to illustrate this failing, which frequently leads to incorrect results. Other more physical problems are concerned with (1) film structure, purity, and uniformity, (2) flatness and smoothness of the interferometer plates, (3) reference fringe system, and (4) interpretation of the interference pattern.

The discussion of the importance of sample preparation given in Section III is particularly cogent when absolute phase change measurements are to be made. The phase change is much more sensitive to small changes in the optical constants than is either the reflectance or transmittance (*238*). The flatness and smoothness of the interferometer plates are also more critical, since to determine the phase change interference fringes from one area of the interferometer plates are compared with fringes from an adjacent area a fraction of a millimeter to a few millimeters away. It is always assumed that over these distances the interferometer surfaces are flat, so that their separation is constant. It is clear that this assumption definitely is not valid for microscope slides which are smooth but very wavy (see Fig. 13), and even commercially polished optical flats are rough enough (see Fig. 1) that the roughness may obscure longer-range surface irregularities. Thus, precision phase change measurements should only be made using the highest-quality smooth and flat optical surfaces.

In all measurements of absolute phase change, the positions of fringes formed between filmed interferometer surfaces are compared with a reference fringe system formed between surfaces whose phase change is known. These reference surfaces are usually the uncoated interferometer plates, in which case the phase change is assumed to be exactly 180° for an air-dielectric reflection. If adsorbed gas, water, or other films are present on the plates this assumption may be incorrect. In another type of reference fringe system, one interferometer surface is coated with an opaque film of the material being studied and its phase change is calculated from optical constants reported in the literature for the bulk material. This procedure is very risky since there is no guarantee that the bulk optical constants will be the same as those for an opaque evaporated film, particularly if it is deposited under poor vacuum conditions.

The equations used for the phase change calculations should be carefully scrutinized to be sure that a consistent set of sign conventions is followed. Since there are numerous ways of writing the Fresnel equations (*239*), upon which the sign and magnitude of the phase change at the boundary between two media are based, confusion can easily occur. The main problem is how to write the amplitude reflection coefficient for reflection from an air-metal interface. Equation (36) is based on a sign convention that assumes a phase change of 180° for reflection in air at an air-dielectric interface. In addition, one must write the interference equation for the particular type of interferometer used in a manner consistent with the conventions chosen for the Fresnel equations (*240*). Many authors do not make clear what sign conventions they have chosen, so that it is difficult to interpret their results.

Once the sign conventions have been chosen and the measurements made, the interference patterns need to be correctly interpreted in terms of the particular form of the interference equation used. Usually one guesses what the approximate phase change will be, computes the positions of the interference fringes, and then recomputes the phase change by substituting values of the measured fringe positions. This approach is valid if measurements are made on interferometers where light is transmitted through the thin absorbing films whose phase change is being measured. Trouble can arise, however, if Fabry–Perot or Fizeau interferometers are used in reflection and the first surface is coated with an absorbing film. In such cases the reflected fringe pattern is not always the inverse of the transmitted pattern, i.e., interference maxima in transmission do not necessarily occur at the same positions as do the interference minima in reflection Anomalies have been observed in the reflected Fizeau fringe patterns when the first surface is coated with a very thin silver or other metal film (*232, 241*). Fringes of equal chromatic order observed in this laboratory also show this anomalous behavior when silver or aluminum films are used on the first surface. The anomalies do not occur when the first surface is bare quartz or is coated with a dielectric film. The theory for the intensity distribution in the reflected multiple-beam interference system has been given by Holden (*242*), but when values of the optical constants for bulk silver are substituted into his equations, the calculated shifts in the reflection fringes relative to the transmission fringes are fractions of a degree rather than the 90° observed when the maxima in transmission coincide with maxima in reflection. Even when one is working in transmission, it is not always easy to correlate the experimentally measured phase shifts with the predicted ones. Hence, extreme care should be taken in analyzing interferograms to obtain the correct values of the phase change.

3. FECO INTERFEROMETRIC METHOD

It is possible to make precise absolute phase change measurements if the factors mentioned above are properly dealt with. Method (8) employing fringes of equal chromatic order has been successfully used in our laboratory and will be briefly described here, although a more complete account can be found in the literature (*15*). The interferometer consists of two super-smooth fused quartz optical flats polished using the bowl-feed technique described in Section II,2,a and coated with the film whose phase change is to be measured. An uncoated channel is left across each flat for the reference fringe system. The two flats are placed in a specially designed holder, shown in Fig. 15, in which they are supported on edge and can be accurately paralleled and separated by any desired amount. The uncoated channels on the two flats are carefully superimposed (with the aid of a low-power microscope) and the interfering surfaces are accurately paralleled using Fizeau fringes and a low-pressure thallium lamp. The experimental setup used to photograph the fringes of equal chromatic order is nearly identical with that shown in Fig. 14. The interferometer is oriented so that the image of the channel is perpendicular to the spectrograph slit. Fringes of equal chromatic order are then photographed in transmission by moving the light source Z and lens L_1 to a position where light can pass through interferometer I. The two-beam reference fringe system from the uncoated portions of the interferometer is photographed in reflection to increase the contrast. To take the two different exposures, v-shaped and inverted v-shaped draw slides are used over entrance slit S of the spectrograph. Finally, the spectra of mercury, cadmium, thallium, and neon are photographed to provide calibration lines for wavelength measurements of the interference fringes. The resulting interferogram for the phase change measurement of a pair of 128 A aluminum films is shown in Fig. 44a. Wavelengths can be determined by measuring the positions of both interference fringes and reference lines using a photoelectric scanning comparator (*60, 61*) and a modified Hartmann formula programmed for a computer (*64*). In this way wavelengths of both multiple-beam fringes and two-beam reference fringes can be measured with an accuracy of approximately ± 0.05 A (*15, 64*).

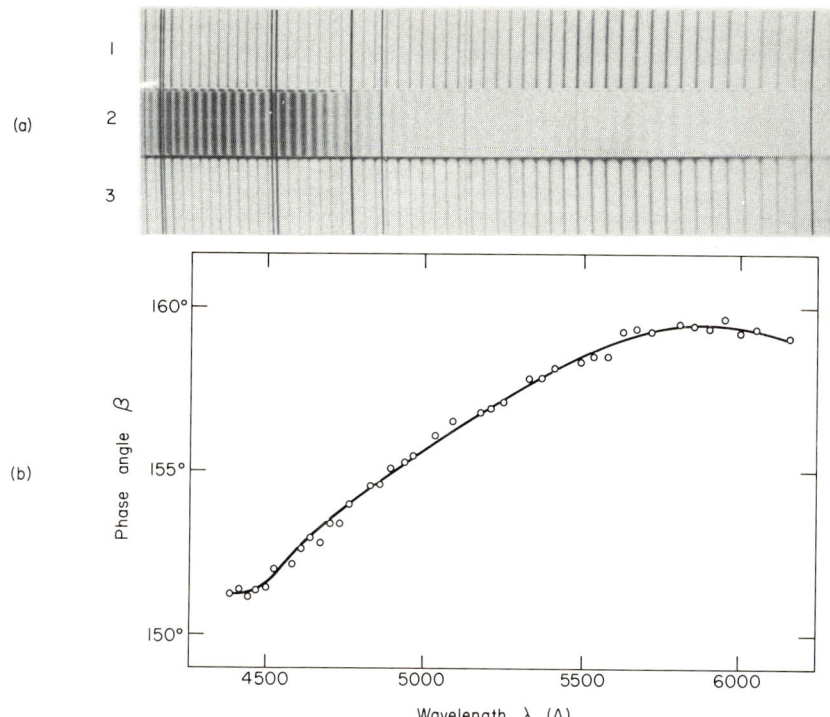

FIG. 44. (a) Feco interferogram for measuring phase change of 128 A thick aluminum film, and (b) measured phase change for 128 A aluminum film.

The interpretation of the interferogram and the determination of the phase change can be done as follows. First, the sign convention used for Fresnel's equations is that the phase change for an air-dielectric reflection is 180° and for an air-metal reflection a value in the second quadrant given by Eq. (36). Second, the interference equation is written as (*15*)

$$N\lambda = 2nd - (\beta_1 + \beta_2)\lambda/2\pi \qquad (37)$$

where N is the order of interference (an integer) for each maximum in transmission, λ the wavelength of the maximum, n the refractive index of air (or other medium) separating the two interfering surfaces, d the physical separation of the surfaces, and β_1 and β_2 the phase changes on reflection (measured in radians) of the two films. The minus sign in Eq. (37) is required to make the definition of β here consistent with those in the Fresnel equations. β is measured in the positive (counterclockwise) direction and the effect of the minus sign is to show that the optical separation of the interfering surfaces is smaller than their physical separation. The value of d is obtained from the reference two-beam fringe system in region 2 of Fig. 44a. Since both β's are π in this region and $n = 1$, N can be determined unambiguously using Eqs. (10) and (37),[10] and the $(N + 1)\lambda$ products for each fringe give several values of d which when averaged can give a value good to ± 2 A (*15*). In the multiple-beam region, N can be determined relative to that in the two-beam region in a preliminary experiment by following the fringes in transmission from the two-beam to multiple-beam region using a film of gradually increasing thickness. The value of d in the multiple-beam region is equal to d in the two-beam region minus twice the film thickness, which is measured interferometrically using the method described in Section V,3. Then the measured wavelengths of the interference maxima will give unambiguous values for $\beta = \beta_1 = \beta_2$ for the thin metal film. The measured values of the phase change for a 128 A aluminum film are shown in Fig. 44b for wavelengths from 4300 to 6000 A. Note that the values are very smooth with almost no scatter. When all the systematic errors have been assessed, the accuracy of the measurements is probably better than $\pm 1°$ in phase angle. It should be remembered that the measured value of β is for the semitransparent film and is a result of both the film and substrate. The expression for tan β in terms of n and k for the film, n for the substrate, and the thickness of the film is given by Eq. (5) by Bennett (*15*). This rather formidable expression can be most tractably handled by a computer. In order to extract the two optical constants of the film, another experimental parameter such as the reflectance or transmittance must be determined. The two experimentally measured quantities may then be used to solve for the two unknowns, n and k.

References

1. W. F. Koehler and A. Eberstein, *J. Opt. Soc. Am.* **43**, 747 (1953).
2. S. Tolansky, *Lab. Pract.* **12**, 722 (1963).
3. R. W. Dietz and J. M. Bennett, *Appl. Opt.* **5**, 881 (1966).
4. A. E. Ennos, *Appl. Opt.* **5**, 51 (1966).
5. A. I. Bailey and J. S. Courtney-Pratt, *Proc. Roy. Soc.* **A227**, 500 (1955).
6. H. H. Soonpaa, Private communication (1965).
7. S. Tolansky, "Multiple-Beam Interferometry of Surfaces and Films," pp. 55–57, 104–107. Oxford Univ. Press, London and New York, 1948.
8. T. M. Donovan and B. O. Seraphin, *J. Electrochem. Soc.* **109**, 877 (1962).
9. T. M. Donovan and E. J. Ashley, *J. Opt. Soc. Am.* **54**, 1141 (1964).
10. H. E. Bennett and J. O. Porteus, *J. Opt. Soc. Am.* **51**, 123 (1961).
11. W. F. Koehler, *J. Opt. Soc. Am.* **43**, 743 (1953).
12. W. F. Koehler and W. C. White, *J. Opt. Soc. Am.* **45**, 1011 (1955).
13. H. E. Bennett, *J. Opt. Soc. Am.* **53**, 1389 (1963).
14. J. P. Reames, *Rev. Sci. Instr.* **30**, 834 (1959).
15. J. M. Bennett, *J. Opt. Soc. Am.* **54**, 612 (1964).

[10] Note that Eq. (10) now gives an exact value for N since $\beta_1 = \beta_2 = \pi$.

16. D. W. Angel, Private communication, (1966).
17. L. E. Samuels, *in* "The Surface Chemistry of Metals and Semiconductors" (H. C. Gatos, ed.), p. 82. Wiley, New York, 1960.
18. T. M. Buck, *in* "The Surface Chemistry of Metals and Semiconductors" (H. C. Gatos, ed.), p. 107. Wiley, New York, 1960.
19. *RCA Rev.* **24**, 499–573 (1963).
20. L. Young, "Anodic Oxide Films." Academic Press, New York, 1961.
21. L. I. Maissel, *Phys. Thin Films* **3**, 61 (1966).
22. J. Yarwood, "High Vacuum Technique," p. 160. Wiley, New York, 1956.
23. L. Holland, "Vacuum Deposition of Thin Films," p. 517. Wiley, New York, 1958.
24. J. T. Cox, G. Hass, and J. B. Ramsey, *J. Phys. (Paris)* **25**, 250 (1964).
25. J. Strong, *Astrophys. J.* **83**, 401 (1936).
26. H. E. Bennett, J. M. Bennett, and E. J. Ashley, *J. Opt. Soc. Am.* **52**, 1245 (1962).
27. H. M. Smith and A. F. Turner, *Appl. Opt.* **4**, 147 (1965).
28. R. W. Roberts and T. A. Vanderslice, "Ultrahigh Vacuum and Its Applications," p. 4. Prentice-Hall, Englewood Cliffs, New Jersey, 1963.
29. G. Hass and L. Hadley, *in* "American Institute of Physics Handbook" (D. E. Gray, ed.), 2nd ed., p. 6–119. McGraw-Hill, New York, 1963.
30. J. M. Bennett and E. J. Ashley, *Appl. Opt.* **4**, 221 (1965).
31. H. E. Bennett, M. Silver, and E. J. Ashley, *J. Opt. Soc. Am.* **53**, 1089 (1963).
32. H. E. Bennett and J. M. Bennett, *in* "Optical Properties and Electronic Structure of Metals and Alloys" (F. Abelès, ed.), p. 175. North-Holland Publ., Amsterdam, 1966.
33. G. Hass, W. R. Hunter, and R. Tousey, *J. Opt. Soc. Am.* **47**, 1070 (1957).
34. G. Hass, W. R. Hunter, and R. Tousey, *J. Opt. Soc. Am.* **46**, 1009 (1956).
35. T. M. Donovan, E. J. Ashley, and H. E. Bennett, *J. Opt. Soc. Am.* **53**, 1403 (1963).
36. K. H. Behrndt, *Phys. Thin Films* **3**, 1 (1966).
37. H. E. Bennett, *in* "Symposium on Thermal Radiation of Solids" (S. Katzoff, ed.), NASA SP-55, p. 145. NASA, Washington, D.C. 1965.
38. J. O. Porteus, *J. Opt. Soc. Am.* **53**, 1394 (1963).
39. R. G. Johnston and R. P. Madden, *Appl. Opt.* **4**, 1574 (1965).
40. H. E. Bennett, *Ind. Quality Control* **20**, No. 8, 18 (1964).
41. S. Tolansky, "Multiple-Beam Interferometry of Surfaces and Films," pp. 89–90. Oxford Univ. Press, London and New York, 1948.
42. K. M. Greenland, *Vacuum* **2**, 216 (1952).
43. O. S. Heavens, "Optical Properties of Thin Solid Films," pp. 96–154. Butterworths, London, 1955.
44. O. S. Heavens, *Rept. Progr. Phys.* **23**, 1 (1960).
45. O. S. Heavens, *Phys. Thin Films* **2**, 193 (1964).
46. J. Dyson, *Physica* **24**, 532 (1958).
47. S. Tolansky, "Multiple-Beam Interferometry of Surfaces and Films," pp. 147–150. Oxford Univ. Press, London and New York, 1948.
48. O. S. Heavens, "Optical Properties of Thin Solid Films," pp. 106–111. Butterworths, London, 1955.
49. L. Holland, "Vacuum Deposition of Thin Films," pp. 224–227. Wiley, New York, 1958.
50. G. D. Scott, T. A. McLauchlan, and R. S. Sennett, *J. Appl. Phys.* **21**, 843 (1950).
51. M. D. Silver and E. T-K. Chow, *J. Vacuum Sci. Technol.* **2**, 203 (1965).
52. A. R. Wolter, *J. Appl. Phys.* **36**, 2377 (1965).
53. T. E. Hartman, *J. Vacuum Sci. Technol.* **2**, 239 (1965).
54. L. G. Schulz, *J. Chem. Phys.* **17**, 1153 (1949).

55. H. M. Trent, D. E. Stone, and R. Bruce Lindsay, in "American Institute of Physics Handbook" (D. E. Gray, ed.), 2nd ed., p. 2-21. McGraw-Hill, New York, 1963.
56. J. Sauro, I. Fankuchen, and N. Wainfan, *Phys. Rev.* **132**, 1544 (1963).
57. P. Croce, M. Gandais, and A. Marraud, *Rev. Opt.* **40**, 555 (1961).
58. S. Tolansky, "Multiple-Beam Interferometry of Surfaces and Films," pp. 14-19. Oxford Univ. Press, London and New York, 1948.
59. S. Tolansky, "Surface Microtopography," pp. 19-25, 37-41. Wiley (Interscience), New York, 1960.
60. J. M. Bennett and W. F. Koehler, *J. Opt. Soc. Am.* **49**, 466 (1959).
61. J. M. Bennett, *Appl. Opt.* **2**, 1330 (1963).
62. R. Belk, S. Tolansky, and A. Turnbull, *J. Opt. Soc. Am.* **44**, 5 (1954).
63. J. C. Kelly, *Opt. Acta* **5**, 75 (1958).
63a. S. J. Lins, in "1961 Trans. 8th Natl. Vacuum Symp." (L. E. Preuss, ed.), Vol. II, p. 846. Pergamon, New York, 1961.
64. W. F. Koehler and F. K. Odencrantz, *J. Opt. Soc. Am.* **47**, 862 (1957).
65. W. F. Koehler, *J. Opt. Soc. Am.* **48**, 55 (1958).
66. O. Kubaschewski and B. E. Hopkins, "Oxidation of Metals and Alloys," 2nd ed., p. 1. Academic Press, New York, 1962.
67. R. P. Madden, *Phys. Thin Films* **1**, 123 (1963).
68. J. Kruger and H. T. Yolken, *Corrosion* **20**, 29t (1964).
69. D. K. Burge and H. E. Bennett, *J. Opt. Soc. Am.* **54**, 1428 (1964).
70. D. W. Peterson and N. M. Bashara, *J. Opt. Soc. Am.* **55**, 845 (1965).
71. G. Hass and A. P. Bradford, *J. Opt Soc. Am.* **47**, 125 (1957).
72. P. H. Berning, G. Hass, and R. P. Madden, *J. Opt. Soc. Am.* **50**, 586 (1960).
73. G. Hass, in "Applied Optics and Optical Engineering" (R. Kingslake, ed.), Vol. III, p. 309. Academic Press, New York, 1965.
74. H. E. Bennett, J. M. Bennett, and E. J. Ashley, *J. Opt. Soc. Am.* **55**, 597 (1965).
75. B. Borie and C. J. Sparks, *Acta Cryst.* **14**, 569 (1961).
76. N. J. Scott, "Study of Thin Vacuum Deposited Copper Films by X-Ray Total Reflection," Tech. Rept. No. 11, Cornell Univ., Doc. No. AFOSR TN-57-779 and ASTIA AD 148 010 (Dec. 1957).
77. J. J. Lander, in "Recent Progress in Solid-State Chemistry" (H. Reiss, ed.), Vol. II, p. 26. Pergamon, New York, 1965.
78. K. Rabinovitch, L. R. Canfield, and R. P. Madden, *Appl. Opt.* **4**, 1005 (1965).
79. P. H. Berning, *Phys. Thin Films* **1**, 69 (1963).
80. A. L. Olsen, K. B. LaBaw, and L. W. Nichols, *J. Opt. Soc. Am.* **54**, 813 (1964).
81. A. L. Olsen and W. R. McBride, *J. Opt. Soc. Am.* **53**, 1003 (1963).
82. J. M. Bennett, E. J. Ashley, and H. E. Bennett, *Appl. Opt.* **4**, 961 (1965).
83. S. Kozawa, *Proc. Conf. Opt. Instrs. Tech. London, 1961* (K. J. Habell, ed.), p. 410. Chapman & Hall, London (1962).
84. R. D. Maurer, *J. Chem. Phys.* **25**, 1206 (1956).
85. Wilbur Kaye, Private communication (1966).
86. E. A. Boettner and L. J. Miedler, *J. Opt. Soc. Am.* **51**, 1310 (1961).
87. L. R. Koller, "Ultraviolet Radiation," 2nd ed., pp. 169-171. Wiley, New York, 1965.
88. H. E. Bennett, *Appl. Opt.* **5**, 1265 (1966).
89. A. C. Hardy and F. H. Perrin, "The Principles of Optics," pp. 24-25. McGraw-Hill, New York, 1932.
90. D. W. McCarthy, *Appl. Opt.* **2**, 591 (1963).
91. W. Slavin, *Anal. Chem.* **35**, 561 (1963).
92. L. R. Koller, "Ultraviolet Radiation," 2nd ed., pp. 158-188. Wiley, New York, 1965.

93. "Model 99 Double Pass Monochromator," Bull. 101. The Perkin–Elmer Corp., Norwalk, Connecticut.
94. G. R. Harrison, R. C. Lord, and J. R. Loofbourow, "Practical Spectroscopy," p. 484. Prentice-Hall, Englewood Cliffs, New Jersey, 1948.
95. Y. Yamada, A. Mitsuishi, and H. Yoshinaga, *J. Opt. Soc. Am.* **52**, 17 (1962).
96. C. H. Shaw and W. T. Foreman, *J. Opt. Soc. Am.* **49**, 724 (1959).
97. R. Lincke and G. Palumbo, *Appl. Opt.* **4**, 1677 (1965).
98. H. E. Bennett and W. R. McBride, *Appl. Opt.* **3**, 919 (1964).
99. W. C. Walker, O. P. Rustgi, and G. L. Weissler, *J. Opt. Soc. Am.* **48**, 1017 (1958).
100. P. T. Scharf, *in* "Applied Optics and Optical Engineering" (R. Kingslake, ed.), Vol. I, p. 111. Academic Press, New York, 1965.
101. W. R. Hunter, D. W. Angel, and R. Tousey, *Appl. Opt.* **4**, 891 (1965).
102. P. Baumeister, *in* "Applied Optics and Optical Engineering" (R. Kingslake, ed.), Vol. I, p. 285. Academic Press, New York, 1965.
103. K. F. Renk and L. Genzel, *Appl. Opt.* **1**, 643 (1962).
104. C. B. Childs, *J. Opt. Soc. Am.* **51**, 895 (1961).
105. J. Grant, E. Michel, and J. Thielen, *Infrared Phys.* **2**, 123 (1962).
106. G. Hass, *J. Opt. Soc. Am.* **39**, 539 (1949).
107. G. Hass, *in* "Applied Optics and Optical Engineering" (R. Kingslake, ed.), Vol. III, pp. 325–327. Academic Press, New York, 1965.
108. R. P. Madden, *Phys. Thin Films* **1**, 175–177 (1963).
109. R. L. Sinsheimer and J. R. Loofbourow, *Nature* **160**, 674 (1947).
110. R. A. Sawyer, "Experimental Spectroscopy," 2nd ed., pp. 296–297. Prentice-Hall, Englewood Cliffs, New Jersey, 1951.
111. R. A. Smith, F. E. Jones, and R. P. Chasmar, "The Detection and Measurement of Infra-Red Radiation," pp. 381–385. Oxford Univ. Press, London and New York, 1957.
112. R. A. Smith, F. E. Jones, and R. P. Chasmar, "The Detection and Measurement of Infra-Red Radiation," pp. 389–390. Oxford Univ. Press, London and New York, 1957.
113. R. A. Smith, F. E. Jones, and R. P. Chasmar, "The Detection and Measurement of Infra-Red Radiation," p. 380. Oxford Univ. Press, London and New York, 1957.
114. R. A. Smith, F. E. Jones, and R. P. Chasmar, "The Detection and Measurement of Infra-Red Radiation," pp. 374–378. Oxford Univ. Press, London and New York, 1957.
115. R. A. Smith, F. E. Jones, and R. P. Chasmar, "The Detection and Measurement of Infra-Red Radiation," pp. 369–374. Oxford Univ. Press, London and New York, 1957.
116. R. P. Madden, *Phys. Thin Films* **1**, 135–136 (1963).
117. A. V. Baez, *Nature* **186**, 958 (1960).
118. J. Strong, "Procedures in Experimental Physics," pp. 380–382. Prentice-Hall, Englewood Cliffs, New Jersey, 1938.
119. L. L. Scott and C. J. Bronco, *J. Opt. Soc. Am.* **55**, 300 (1965).
120. J. U. White, *J. Opt. Soc. Am.* **37**, 713 (1947).
121. M. Pivovonsky and M. R. Nagel, "Tables of Blackbody Radiation Functions." Macmillan, New York, 1961.
122. R. E. Fryer, *Appl. Opt.* **6**, 275 (1967).
123. D. H. Rank, J. N. Shearer, and J. M. Bennett, *J. Opt. Soc. Am.* **45**, 762 (1955).
124. A. E. Conrady, "Applied Optics and Optical Design," Vol. I, pp. 132–136. Dover, New York, 1957.
125. A. Schuster, *Astrophys. J.* **21**, 197 (1905).

126. D. H. Rank, *J. Opt. Soc. Am.* **42**, 279 (1952).
127. H. E. Bennett and W. F. Koehler, *J. Opt. Soc. Am.* **50**, 1 (1960).
128. B. O. Seraphin, R. B. Hess, and N. Bottka, *J. Appl. Phys.* **36**, 2242 (1965).
129. G. E. Pride, *J. Opt. Soc. Am.* **36**, 510 (1946).
130. J. Strong, "Procedures in Experimental Physics," p. 376. Prentice-Hall, Englewood Cliffs, New Jersey, 1938.
131. A. Smith, *J. Opt. Soc. Am.* **50**, 862 (1960).
132. E. O. Hulburt, *Astrophys. J.* **42**, 205 (1915).
133. H. Kuhn and B. A. Wilson, *Proc. Phys. Soc. (London)* **B63**, 745 (1950).
134. R. F. Weeks, *J. Opt. Soc. Am.* **48**, 775 (1958).
135. R. P. Madden and L. R. Canfield, *J. Opt. Soc. Am.* **51**, 838 (1961).
136. S. J. Fray, A. R. Goodwin, F. A. Johnson, and J. E. Quarrington, *J. Sci. Instr.* **40**, 387 (1963).
137. J. E. Shaw and W. R. Blevin, *J. Opt. Soc. Am.* **54**, 334 (1964).
138. W. M. Brandenberg, O. W. Clausen, and D. McKeown, *J. Opt. Soc. Am.* **56**, 80 (1966).
139. M. A. Biondi, *Phys. Rev.* **102**, 964 (1956).
140. D. M. Gates, C. C. Shaw, and D. Beaumont, *J. Opt. Soc. Am.* **48**, 88 (1958).
141. R. B. Sanderson, *J. Phys. Chem. Solids* **26**, 803 (1965).
142. A. H. Taylor, *J. Opt. Soc. Am.* **4**, 9 (1920).
143. D. M. Packer and F. H. Kierstead, *J. Opt. Soc. Am.* **35**, 806 (1945).
144. D. K. Edwards, J. T. Gier, K. E. Nelson, and R. D. Roddick, *J. Opt. Soc. Am.* **51**, 1279 (1961).
145. W. W. Coblentz, *Bull. Bur. Std.* **9**, 283 (1913).
146. F. Paschen, *Ber. Berlin Akad. Deut. Wiss.* **27** (1899).
147. T. Royds, *Phil. Mag.* **21**, 167 (1911).
148. W. M. Brandenberg, *J. Opt. Soc. Am.* **54**, 1235 (1964).
149. W. R. Blevin and W. J. Brown, *J. Sci. Instr.* **42**, 385 (1965).
150. S. T. Dunn, "Design and Analysis of an Ellipsoidal Mirror Reflectometer," Ph.D. Thesis, Oklahoma State Univ., 1965.
151. R. V. Dunkle, *in* "Surface Effects on Spacecraft Materials" (F. J. Clauss, ed.), p. 117. Symposium held at Palo Alto, California, May 12–13, 1959. Wiley, New York, 1960.
152. R. T. Neher and D. K. Edwards, *Appl. Opt.* **4**, 775 (1965).
153. J. T. Gier, R. V. Dunkle, and J. T. Bevans, *J. Opt. Soc. Am.* **44**, 558 (1954).
154. A. G. Worthing, *J. Appl. Phys.* **11**, 421 (1940).
155. C. D. Reid and E. D. McAlister, *J. Opt. Soc. Am.* **49**, 78 (1959).
156. R. P. Madden, *Phys. Thin Films* **1**, 135–141 (1963).
157. R. P. Madden, *Phys. Thin Films* **1**, 132 (1963).
158. G. H. C. Freeman, Private communication (1965).
159. D. C. Hinson, *J. Opt. Soc. Am.* **56**, 408 (1966).
160. D. K. Burge, *J. Opt. Soc. Am.* **56**, 1454A (1966).
161. K. Watanabe and E. C. Y. Inn, *J. Opt. Soc. Am.* **43**, 32 (1953).
162. D. H. Thurnau, *J. Opt. Soc. Am.* **46**, 346 (1956).
163. R. Allison, J. Burns, and A. J. Tuzzolino, *J. Opt. Soc. Am.* **54**, 747 (1964).
164. W. R. Hunter and R. Tousey, *J. Phys. (Paris)* **25**, 148 (1964).
165. H. E. Blackwell, G. S. Shipp, M. Ogawa, and G. L. Weissler, *J. Opt. Soc. Am.* **56**, 665 (1966).
166. S. P. F. Humphreys-Owen, *Proc. Phys. Soc. (London)* **77**, 949 (1961).
167. W. R. Hunter, *J. Opt. Soc. Am.* **55**, 1197 (1965).
168. R. F. Potter, *J. Opt. Soc. Am.* **54**, 904 (1964).

169. R. F. Potter, *Appl. Opt.* **4**, 53 (1965).
170. A. G. Worthing, *J. Opt. Soc. Am.* **13**, 635 (1926).
171. W. C. Walker, *Appl. Opt.* **3**, 1457 (1964).
172. A. Engelsrath and E. V. Loewenstein, *Appl. Opt.* **5**, 565 (1966).
173. D. W. Juenker, *J. Opt. Soc. Am.* **55**, 295 (1965).
174. A. C. Hardy and F. H. Perrin, "The Principles of Optics," pp. 359–364. McGraw-Hill, New York, 1932.
175. W. R. Hunter, *J. Opt. Soc. Am.* **54**, 15 (1964).
176. J. Fahrenfort and W. M. Vissner, *Spectrochim. Acta* **18**, 1103 (1962).
177. W. N. Hansen, *Spectrochim. Acta* **21**, 209 (1965).
178. W. N. Hansen and J. A. Horton, *Anal. Chem.* **36**, 783 (1964).
179. W. N. Hansen, *ISA Trans.* **4**, 263 (1965).
180. W. N. Hansen, *Spectrochim. Acta* **21**, 815 (1965).
181. W. N. Hansen, *Anal. Chem.* **37**, 1142 (1965).
182. N. J. Harrick, *Anal. Chem.* **36**, 188 (1964).
183. N. J. Harrick, *J. Opt. Soc. Am.* **55**, 851 (1965).
184. N. J. Harrick, *Appl. Opt.* **4**, 1664 (1965).
185. N. J. Harrick, *Ann. N. Y. Acad. Sci.* **101**, 928 (1963).
186. E. Passaglia and R. R. Stromberg, *J. Res. Natl. Bur. Std.* **68A**, 601 (1964).
187. V. L. Rideout and S. H. Wemple, *J. Opt. Soc. Am.* **56**, 749 (1966).
188. W. L. Wolfe, S. S. Ballard, and K. A. McCarthy, *in* "American Institute of Physics Handbook" (D. E. Gray, ed.), 2nd ed., p. 6-42. McGraw-Hill, New York, 1963.
189. N. J. Harrick, *Phys. Rev.* **125**, 1165 (1962).
190. H. E. Bennett and R. J. Stirton (unpublished results).
191. A. H. Pfund, *J. Opt. Soc. Am.* **31**, 679 (1941).
192. F. Abelès, *Compt. Rend.* **228**, 553 (1949).
193. F. Abelès, *J. Phys. Radium* **11**, 310 (1950).
194. F. Abelès, *in* "Progress in Optics" (E. Wolf, ed.), Vol. II, p. 251. North-Holland Publ. Amsterdam, 1963.
195. O. S. Heavens, *Phys. Thin Films* **2**, 210–213 (1964).
196. J. C. Kelly and O. S. Heavens, *Opt. Acta* **6**, 339 (1959).
197. G. Koppelmann and K. Krebs, *Z. Physik* **163**, 539 (1961).
198. O. S. Heavens and H. M. Liddell, *Appl. Opt.* **4**, 629 (1965).
199. M. Hacskaylo, *J. Opt. Soc. Am.* **54**, 198 (1964)
200. R. J. Archer, *in* "Ellipsometry in the Measurement of Surfaces and Thin Films" (E. Passaglia, R. R. Stromberg, and J. Kruger, eds.), p. 255. Natl. Bur. Std. Misc. Publ. 256. U.S. Govt. Printing Office, Washington, D.C., 1964.
201. R. J. Archer and G. W. Gobeli, *J. Phys. Chem. Solids* **26**, 343 (1965).
202. F. L. McCrackin and J. P. Colson, *in* "Ellipsometry in the Measurement of Surfaces and Thin Films" (E. Passaglia, R. R. Stromberg, and J. Kruger, eds.), p. 61. Natl. Bur. Std. Misc. Publ. 256. U.S. Govt. Printing Office, Washington, D.C., 1964.
203. L. Tronstad, *J. Sci. Instr.* **11**, 144 (1934).
204. A. B. Winterbottom, *J. Sci. Instr.* **14**, 203 (1937).
205. J. M. Weingart and A. R. Johnston, *in* "Ellipsometry in the Measurement of Surfaces and Thin Films" (E. Passaglia, R. R. Stromberg, and J. Kruger, eds.), p. 113. Natl. Bur. Std. Misc. Publ. 256. U.S. Govt. Printing Office, Washington, D.C., 1964.
205a. R. E. Hartman, *J. Opt. Soc. Am.* **41**, 244 (1951).
206. F. L. McCrackin, E. Passaglia, R. R. Stromberg, and H. L. Steinberg, *J. Res. Natl. Bur. Std.* **67A**, 363 (1963).
207. R. M. Emberson, *J. Opt. Soc. Am.* **26**, 63 (1936).

208. J. Strong, "Procedures in Experimental Physics," p. 388. Prentice-Hall, Englewood Cliffs, New Jersey, 1938.
209. R. C. Plumb, *J. Opt. Soc. Am.* **50**, 892 (1960).
210. F. P. Mertens and R. C. Plumb, *J. Opt. Soc. Am.* **54**, 1063 (1964).
211. R. R. Alfano and W. H. Woodruff, *Appl. Opt.* **5**, 352 (1966).
211a. A. H. Lettington, Private communication (1965).
212. J. R. Beattie, *Phil. Mag.* **46**, 235 (1955).
213. S. Roberts, *in* "Ellipsometry in the Measurement of Surfaces and Thin Films" (E. Passaglia, R. R. Stromberg, and J. Kruger, eds.), p. 119. Natl. Bur. Std. Misc. Publ. 256. U.S. Govt. Printing Office, Washington, D.C., 1964.
214. A. P. Lenham and D. M. Treherne, *J. Opt. Soc. Am.* **56**, 752 (1966).
215. G. Hass and J. E. Waylonis, *J. Opt. Soc. Am.* **51**, 719 (1961).
216. R. J. Archer, *J. Electrochem. Soc.* **104**, 619 (1957).
217. M. A. Barrett, *in* "Ellipsometry in the Measurement of Surfaces and Thin Films" (E. Passaglia, R. R. Stromberg, and J. Kruger, eds.), p. 213. Natl. Bur. Std. Misc. Publ. 256. U.S. Govt. Printing Office, Washington, D.C., 1964.
218. C. J. Koester, *J. Res. Natl. Bur. Std.* **64A**, 191 (1960).
219. C. F. Bruce and P. E. Ciddor, *J. Opt. Soc. Am.* **50**, 295 (1960).
220. K. W. Meissner, *J. Opt. Soc. Am.* **31**, 405 (1941).
221. H. Barrell and P. Teasdale-Buckell, *Proc. Phys. Soc. (London)* **B64**, 413 (1951).
222. P. Rouard, *Ann. Phys. (Paris)* **7**, 291 (1937).
223. L. G. Schulz, *J. Opt. Soc. Am.* **40**, 690 (1950).
224. L. G. Schulz and E. J. Scheibner, *J. Opt. Soc. Am.* **40**, 761 (1950).
225. G. Henderson and C. Weaver, *J. Opt. Soc. Am.* **54**, 1052 (1964).
226. P. Bousquet, R. Deleuil, and A. Gastaud, *J. Phys. (Paris)* **25**, 31 (1964).
227. N. Barakat and S. Mokhtar, *J. Opt. Soc. Am.* **53**, 1153 (1963).
228. E. Eisner, *Research* **4**, 183 (1951).
229. L. G. Schulz, *J. Opt. Soc. Am.* **44**, 357 (1954).
230. A. Lohmann, *Z. Physik* **143**, 533 (1956).
231. H. J. Bolle, *Z. Physik* **143**, 538 (1956).
232. R. C. Faust, *Phil. Mag.* **41**, 1238 (1950).
233. S. Nawata, *Sci. Rep. Res. Inst. Tohoku Univ. Ser. A* **3**, 740 (1951).
234. R. Philip, *Compt. Rend.* **241**, 559 (1955).
235. C. Weaver, R. M. Hill, and J. E. S. Macleod, *J. Opt. Soc. Am.* **49**, 992 (1959).
236. S. Tolansky, *Phil. Mag.* **34**, 555 (1943).
237. J. H. Jaffe, *J. Opt. Soc. Am.* **43**, 1170 (1953).
238. O. S. Heavens, "Optical Properties of Thin Solid Films," pp. 171–175. Butterworths, London, 1955.
239. G. Friedmann and H. S. Sandhu, *Am. J. Phys.* **33**, 135 (1965).
240. I. N. Shklyarevski and N. A. Nosulenko, *Opt. Spectry. (USSR) (English Transl.)* **14**, 127 (1963).
241. J. Holden, *J. Opt. Soc. Am.* **41**, 504 (1951).
242. J. Holden, *Proc. Phys. Soc. (London)* **B62**, 405 (1949).

Nucleation Processes in Thin Film Formation

J. P. HIRTH AND K. L. MOAZED

Ohio State University
Columbus, Ohio

I. Introduction	97
II. Heterogeneous Nucleation Theory	98
1. Classical Theory	98
2. Contact Angle Modifications	103
3. Interface Structure	106
4. Condensation Coefficient Effects	107
5. High Substrate Temperature Modifications	108
6. Low Substrate Temperatures	109
7. Substrate Imperfections	111
8. Impurity Effects	113
9. Chemical Vapor Deposition	113
10. Summary	114
III. Experimental Results	114
1. Verification of the Nucleation Model	114
2. Critical Supersaturation Measurements	121
IV. Heterogeneous Nucleation and Epitaxy	128
1. Types of Epitaxy	128
2. Theory of Epitaxial Nucleation	129
3. Discussion of Experimental Results	131
References	134

I. Introduction

In this chapter, we treat the theory of heterogeneous nucleation from the vapor phase onto a substrate, review experimental results on such nucleation and compare them with the theory, and discuss the process of growth of the nuclei, with emphasis on conditions leading to an epitaxial deposit. Since a number of recent articles deal with nucleation (*1–9*), we do not intend to develop the topic exhaustively, but will discuss the salient features of the theory, stressing recent findings.

From a pedagogical standpoint, we emphasize two aspects of the theory which appear to have been misunderstood in the general literature. Firstly, nuclei in general are described in terms of macroscopic physical parameters for a specific nucleus shape, largely as a *mathematical convenience*; in actuality the nucleus parameters are expected to differ from these, so that the macroscopic parameters must be regarded as *phenomenological* parameters describing the nucleation process. Secondly, the word *epitaxy* has been used to define implicitly a number of types of processes. We attempt to clarify this usage, in particular distinguishing between epitaxial nucleation and epitaxial growth.

II. Heterogeneous Nucleation Theory

1. CLASSICAL THEORY

Various stages in the nucleation process are depicted in Fig. 1. A substrate is exposed to either a supersaturated uniform vapor phase or a molecular beam. At usual substrate temperatures the effective pressure exceeds in either case the equilibrium vapor pressure of the extended bulk phase of the condensing substance. The nucleation process then involves the formation of a

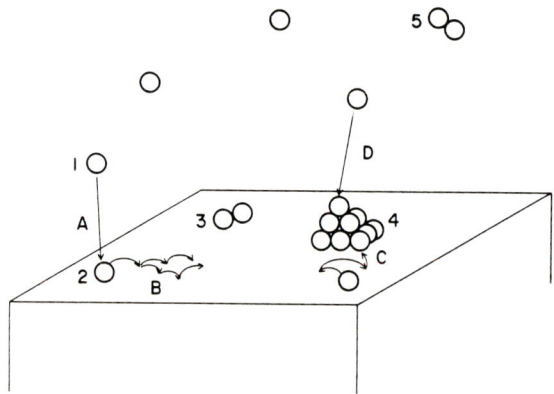

FIG. 1. Schematic illustration of interaction of vapor and substrate showing (1) monomer in vapor, (2) monomer adsorbed, (3) dimer adsorbed, (4) embryo, and (5) dimer in vapor, and the processes of (A) adsorption, (B) surface diffusion, (C) growth of embryo by surface diffusion addition, and (D) growth of embryo by vapor impingement.

critical-size nucleus, configuration 4 in Fig. 1, which can grow spontaneously with a decrease in free energy of formation. The process can be formulated in terms of a generalized diffusion flux of particles in size space (10–12), as shown in Fig. 2. There i represents the number of atoms in an ith-size cluster, i^* represents the critical-size cluster, and G_i is the free energy of the ith-size cluster.

The diffusion flux in size space, corresponding to the nucleation rate, is given by

$$J = Z \cdot \omega^* n_i^* \qquad (1)$$

Here, n_i^* is the equilibrium concentration of critical-size nuclei (Fig. 2), ω^*

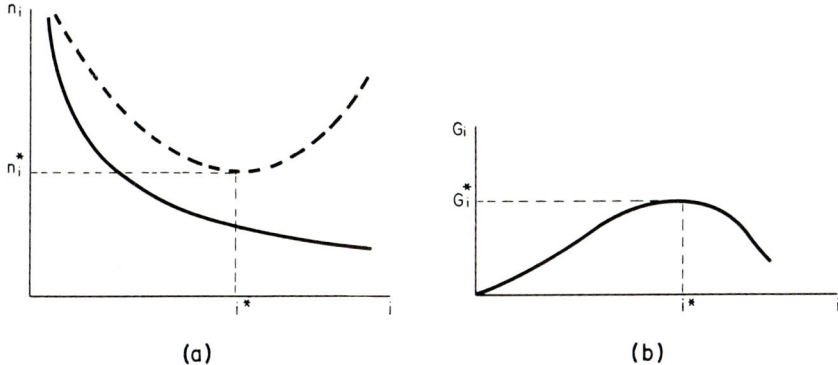

FIG. 2. (a) Equilibrium concentration of clusters as a function of size (dashed curve), and actual diffusion gradient in size space (solid curve). (b) Free energy of formation of a cluster as a function of size.

is the growth frequency of critical-size nuclei, and Z is the so-called Zeldovich nonequilibrium factor (10–12). For two-dimensional nucleation Z is given by (13, 14)

$$Z = \left(\frac{G_i^*}{3\pi k T i^{*2}}\right)^{1/2}$$

and is typically of the order of 10^{-1} to 10^{-2}. If the factor Z is neglected, Eq. (1) reduces to the classical result of the type formulated by Volmer (15),

$$J = \omega^* n_i^* \qquad (2)$$

which gives the growth flux of nuclei from an *equilibrium* population n_i^*. Equation (2) is often applied in determining the nucleation rate. This is a reasonable approximation, for Z is near unity. However, one must remember that the actual nucleation rate is given by the kinetic diffusion result of Eq. (1).

The determination of ω^* and n_i^* depends on the specific nucleation process, for which several possibilities are shown in Fig. 1. The most likely mechanism (16) for most cases of physical interest involves (i) the equilibration of critical-size nuclei with an adsorbed monomer population[1] which in turn is equilibrated with the vapor phase, and (ii) growth of the critical-size nuclei by surface diffusion of the adsorbed monomer. This process is considered in detail here. Examples of other possible mechanisms are (i) growth of the critical nuclei by monomer impingement from the vapor, and (ii) impingement of an embryo which is subcritical in the vapor phase, but which becomes

---

[1] For simplicity, we assume that the monomer is a single atom.

supercritical upon adsorption. Such possibilities are treated briefly in the following sections.

The shape of the nuclei, and hence their free energy of formation, depends on the surface energy. For crystals with isotropic (or weakly anisotropic) surface energy, the shape is that of a spherical cap (Fig. 3). Considering only

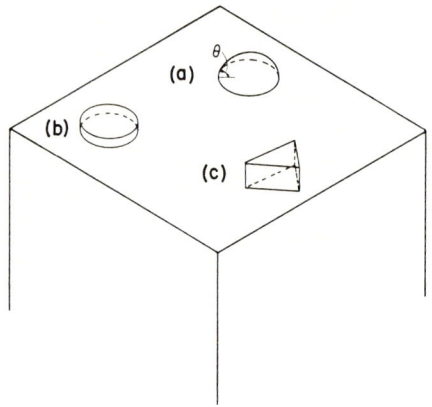

FIG. 3. (a) Spherical cap-shaped nucleus meeting the substrate at a contact angle θ. (b) Disk-shaped nucleus. (c) Polyhedral nucleus.

surface energies and assuming that the small nuclei have bulk properties, we find that the shape is determined by the contact angle θ, given by (17)

$$\sigma_{x-v} = \sigma_{c-x} + \sigma \cos \theta \qquad (3)$$

where σ_{x-v}, σ_{c-x}, and σ are, respectively, the surface energies of the substrate-vapor, substrate-condensate, and condensate-vapor interfaces. Because such a case is convenient to treat mathematically, we assume such a cap-shaped model for the nucleus in the present derivation, as is commonly done in the literature. We emphasize that this is simply a convenient assumption; failure to appreciate this point has led to confusion in the literature. For more anisotropic crystals, the critical nuclei might be polyhedral or disk-shaped, as also shown in Fig. 3. Furthermore, for small nuclei, the line tension of the periphery of the area of contact between nucleus and substrate will contribute to the formation energy (8, 18) and will also be a determining factor in fixing the equilibrium shape. Finally, it is questionable whether bulk values for surface energies or volume free energies apply to small nuclei (4–7, 19). Rather than treating all of these possibilities exhaustively, we present the cap-shaped case as a sample calculation. The result *qualitatively* resembles the result for any of these cases in the temperature and pressure dependence of the nucleation rate. If the cap-shaped model results are applied to nucleation data because of lack of knowledge of the actual physical parameters of the nucleus, the resulting values of σ, θ, etc., must be regarded as *empirical* parameters describing the nucleation potency of the system; in general, they are *not* expected to correspond closely to actual bulk values.

Let us now develop an expression for G_i^*. The free energy of formation of an *i*th-size cluster is composed of a volume term and a surface term. Summing the contributions from the various interfaces for the cap and using Eq. (3), one finds that the surface term is

$$G_s = \pi r^2 \sin^2 \theta (\sigma_{c-x} - \sigma_{x-v}) + 2\pi r^2 (1 - \cos \theta)\sigma$$
$$= 4\pi r^2 \sigma f(\theta) \tag{4}$$

Here r is the radius of curvature of the nucleus, and $f(\theta)$ is the geometric factor

$$f(\theta) = \tfrac{1}{4}(2 - 3\cos\theta + \cos^3\theta) \tag{5}$$

The volume term is

$$G_B = (4/3)\pi r^3 f(\theta)\, \Delta G_v \tag{6}$$

where ΔG_v is the free energy change per unit volume in forming the condensate from the supersaturated adsorbed monomer population[2]

$$\Delta G_v = \frac{-kT}{\Omega} \ln\left(\frac{n_1}{n_{1e}}\right) \tag{7}$$

Ω is the atomic volume, and n_1 and n_{1e} are, respectively, the actual adsorbed monomer concentration, and that which would be in equilibrium with the equilibrium vapor pressure of the condensate. ΔG_v thus expresses the degree of supersaturation in the system. In the usual case where the adatom concentration is in equilibrium with the vapor, a balance of impingement and desorption fluxes yields the relation

$$n_1/\tau_{\text{des}} = n_1 v \exp(-\Delta G_{\text{des}}/kT) = J_{\text{im}} \tag{8}$$

where τ_{des} is the relaxation time for monomer desorption, v is the vibrational frequency, and ΔG_{des} is the activational free energy for desorption. For either the case that the impingement flux J_{im} arises from a molecular beam or that it represents the flux from a uniform vapor phase, an effective vapor pressure p at the substrate temperature T_s is defined by the condition

$$J_{\text{im}} = \alpha p (2\pi m k T_s)^{-1/2} \tag{9}$$

---

[2] For concentrated adsorbates, one would have to use surface activities instead of surface concentrations.

with m the atomic mass and α the condensation coefficient (3). Since n_1 is thus directly proportional to p, the supersaturation in the adsorbed layer is equal to that of the vapor

$$n_1/n_{1_e} = p/p_e \tag{10}$$

With these definitions, the total free energy of formation is given by

$$G_i = G_s + G_B = [4\pi r^2 \sigma + (4/3)\pi r^3 \Delta G_v] f(\theta) \tag{11}$$

The maximum value of G_i occurs at a value

$$r^* = -2\sigma/\Delta G_v \tag{12}$$

and is given by

$$G_i^* = \frac{16\pi\sigma^3 f(\theta)}{3 \Delta G_v^2} \tag{13}$$

The free energy of formation of the critical-size nucleus thus decreases with an increase in driving force ΔG_v or with a decrease in θ.

Consider now the total free energy of the substrate system, ΔG, which is given by the sum of the concentrations of various-size clusters times their formation energy, and an entropy-of-mixing term arising from the distribution of the clusters on the n_0 available substrate sites per unit area:

$$\Delta G = \sum_i n_i G_i - TS_{\text{mix}} \tag{14}$$

The entropy of mixing is given by Fermi–Dirac statistics as

$$S_{\text{mix}} = k \ln \left[\frac{n_0!}{(n_0 - \sum_i n_i)! \prod_i n_i!} \right]$$

$$= -k \sum_i n_i \ln(n_i/n_0) \tag{15}$$

Minimizing ΔG with respect to the concentration of critical-size nuclei, $(\partial \Delta G/\partial n_i)_{i=i^*} = 0$, one finds that

$$n_i^* = n_0 \exp(-G_i^*/kT) \tag{16}$$

Only ω^* now remains to be determined in the expression for J, Eq. (1). The growth frequency in the surface diffusion case is given by the product of the number of adatoms adjacent to a critical nucleus, $n_1 2\pi r^* a \sin \theta$, and the diffusion jump frequency,

$$\omega^* = n_1 2\pi r^* a \sin \theta \, v \exp(-\Delta G_D/kT) \tag{17}$$

Here a is the spacing of surface sites n_0, and ΔG_D is the activational free energy for surface diffusion.

All terms in the nucleation rate equation are now evaluated. Substituting into Eq. (1), one finds

$$J = C_1 p \exp[(\Delta G_{des} - \Delta G_D - G_i^*)/kT] \tag{18}$$

C_1 is a term which can be considered to be a constant $\sim 10^{17}$ dyn^{-1} sec^{-1} over a narrow range of substrate temperatures. The nucleation rate equation (18) can be applied directly to describe nucleation rates which are measured dynamically. Often one is unable to measure J directly, however, in which case an alternative arrangement of Eq. (18) is required. Physically, the latter types of experiment involve the detection of a *minimum* observable nucleation rate. One starts with a low supersaturation in the system and gradually increases it until nucleation is observed. G_i^* in Eq. (18) is a very sensitive function of ΔG_v, decreasing rapidly as the latter "driving force" increases. Thus the nucleation rate increases rapidly from a completely negligible value to an observable value J_{crit} over a very narrow range of supersaturation about a value defined as the critical supersaturation $\Delta G_{v_{crit}}$. In terms of $\Delta G_{v_{crit}}$, Eq. (18) can be expressed in the form

$$\left(\frac{1}{\Delta G_{v_{crit}}}\right)^2 = \left[\frac{3}{16\pi\sigma^3 f(\theta)}\right]\left[kT\left(\ln\frac{C_1}{J_{crit}} + \ln p\right) + \Delta G_{des} - \Delta G_D\right] \tag{19}$$

The values of T, J_{crit}, and p are fixed by the experimental conditions, and the physical parameters in C_1 are usually known, so that the data are expressed in terms of nucleation theory by constructing a Pound plot (*16*) of $(1/\Delta G_{v_{crit}})^2$ versus $kT[\ln(C_1/J_{crit}) + \ln p]$. The slope should be a straight line, yielding the surface energy function $\sigma^3 f(\theta)$, while the intercept[3] gives $(\Delta G_{des} - \Delta G_D)$. Thus the theory is tested by determining whether such a plot is linear, and, if so, whether the parameters σ, θ, ΔG_{des}, and ΔG_D are in reasonable agreement with physical expectation.

2. Contact Angle Modifications

We have emphasized that the contact angle θ is in general a phenomenological parameter. Nonetheless, a consideration of some of the consequences of changes in θ in the idealized cap-shaped nucleus model provides physical insight into the nucleation process (*20*). In some cases, of course, the model is expected to apply exactly.

---

[3] Actually the original equation predicted an intercept of $2 \Delta G_{des} - \Delta G_D$ (*16*). The original expression was modified by Lothe and Pound (*9*); the modified formulas were presented by Hirth and Pound (*3*).

Rewriting Eq. (18) for the critical case in terms of θ, we find[4]

$$J_{crit} = \exp(A) \sin \theta \exp[-B f(\theta)] \quad (20)$$

or

$$\ln J_{crit} = A + \ln \sin \theta - B f(\theta)$$

The factor $f(\theta)$, which directly enters the free energy of formation of the critical nucleus, Eq. (13), can be considered as a measure of the catalytic potency of the substrate for nucleation, while the term $\ln \sin \theta$ is effectively a measure of the efficiency of the surface diffusion growth frequency step. Both functions are plotted in Fig. 4.

For small supersaturations, or small ΔG_v, there is no real solution to Eq. (20); i.e., the curves representing the arguments $A + \ln \sin \theta$ and $B f(\theta)$ do not intersect. As the supersaturation is increased, eventually there will be

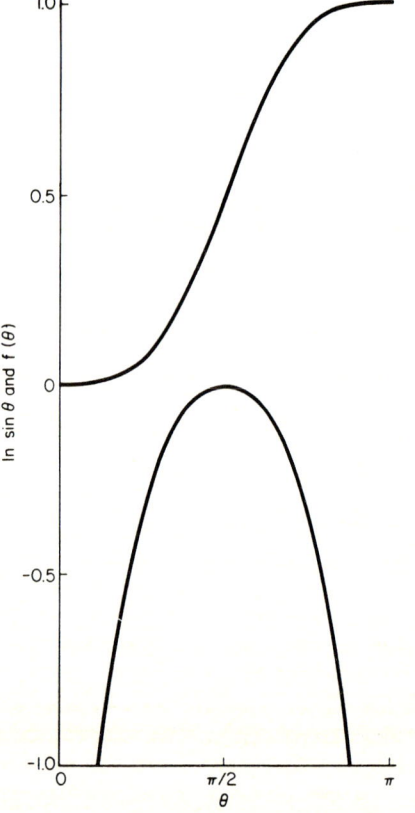

FIG. 4. The functions of $f(\theta)$ and $\ln \sin \theta$ as a function of the contact angle θ.

[4] Actually the nonequilibrium factor Z is weakly dependent on θ. However, the inclusion of this complex term does not significantly change the results (20), so that it is dropped here.

a single possible solution, namely the point representing the common tangent of the two curves. The value of θ at which the two curves are tangent is given explicitly by the solution of Eq. (20) for the condition

$$\cos \theta / \sin^4 \theta = 3B/4 \tag{21}$$

For larger supersaturations there are two possible solutions to Eq. (20) as indicated in Fig. 5.

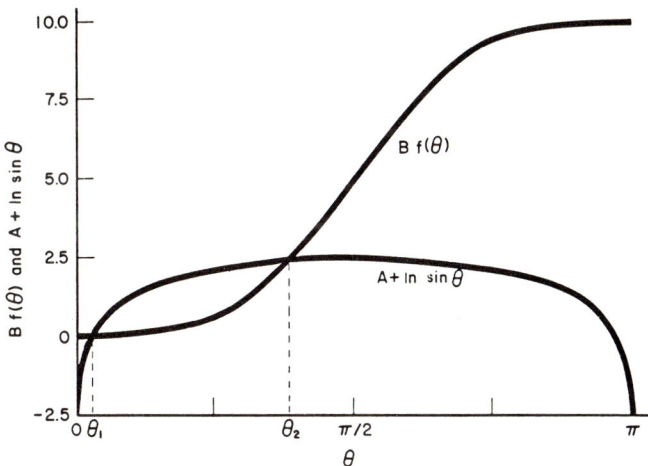

FIG. 5. The terms $A + \ln \sin \theta$ and $Bf(\theta)$ as a function of θ.

In an actual experiment, the supersaturation is increased until Eq. (20) is satisfied for the particular θ value of the studied combination of condensate and substrate materials. Thus, supposing that the curves shown in Fig. 5 correspond to an actual experimental observation of nucleation, then either θ_1 or θ_2 on Fig. 5 is a possible contact angle for the nucleus. Qualitatively, the upper value θ_2 would indicate that the principal influence of θ on the nucleation equation would be to increase G_i^* by increasing the surface area and hence the total surface energy of the critical nucleus. The lower value θ_1 would indicate that the principal influence of θ on the nucleation equation would be to reduce the circumference of the critical nucleus and thus decrease the frequency of growth of critical-size nuclei.

Thus the occurrence of nucleation as predicted by Eq. (20) will yield two possible θ solutions for all cases except the tangent case. Which of the two θ values is applicable in a given case must be decided by data or reasoning aside from that connected with the nucleation expression. Equation (21), which give the values of θ for the tangent case, provides a quantitative delineation of possible upper and lower θ values, and thus should be useful in determining which θ value is applicable in a given case. For physically realizable values of A and B, the possible values of θ for the tangency case lie in the range $10° < \theta < 40°$. Values of θ_1 below about 5 or 10° are not physically meaningful in terms of the cap-shaped nucleus model. For such low θ values the nucleus shape is more likely to be that of a disk, and the growth frequency could become that of direct impingement from the vapor. In either case Eq. (20) would not describe the nucleation rate.

In order to illustrate one other example of θ effects, and to suggest some of the additional effects associated with the disk-shaped or polyhedral nuclei of Fig. 3, we briefly discuss the contribution to G_i^* caused by ε, the energy per unit length associated with the line of contact of the three surfaces at the periphery of the nucleus (*18, 20*). The surface term in such a case is, instead of Eq. (4),

$$G_s = 2\pi r^2 (1 - \cos\theta) + \pi r^2 \sin^2\theta \, (\sigma_{c-x} - \sigma_{x-v}) + 2\pi r\varepsilon \sin\theta \quad (22)$$

The resulting expression for G_i^* is again given by Eq. (13). However θ is no longer fixed by Eq. (3), but instead is determined by

$$\cos\theta' = \frac{\sigma_{c-v} - \sigma_{x-v}}{\sigma} - \frac{\varepsilon}{\sigma r \sin\theta'} \quad (23)$$

Thus when the ε effect is important, the microscopic contact angle θ' will exceed the macroscopic value θ, r^* will become θ dependent, and Eq. (20) would become quite complicated and difficult to solve. However, the magnitude of ε in general will be determined by second- or higher-order neighbor bonds, while the σ values will be determined principally by nearest neighbor bonds. Substituting typical values of $(\sigma_{c-v} - \sigma_{x-v}) \sim 500$ ergs/cm², $\varepsilon \sim 10^{-5}$ ergs/cm, and $\theta = 90°$ one finds that the last term in Eq. (23) can be neglected until r decreases to $\sim 2a$. In the limit of $\theta \to 0°$, the line tension would be important for larger r values, but, as discussed above, the cap-shaped model itself breaks down in this limit. Hence, in the region where the cap-shaped nucleus model holds, it should be valid to neglect the line tension contribution. In cases where ε might influence the solution to Eq. (20), it would shift the solutions to higher values of θ.

3. Interface Structure

The degree of coherency of the substrate-condensate interface can affect the nucleation process in a manner related to the contact angle effects of the preceding section. These coherency effects were first treated by Turnbull and Vonnegut (*21*) and are discussed elsewhere (*3, 6*). A coherent interface is one across which there is perfect atomic matching. Usually the surface planes are of low index for both phases meeting at the interface. Semicoherent interfaces are those which have perfect matching over most of the interface, but which contain some interface dislocations (22).

When coherency effects are present, the nucleus will be elastically strained in general. The value of G_i^* will then involve a minimization in terms of the strain e. The energy of the interface is given by

$$\sigma_{c-x} = \sigma_{c-x}^0 + C_2(\Delta - e) \qquad (24)$$

where σ_{c-x}^0 is the contribution of chemical bond energy, C_2 is a factor containing the elastic constant and relating to the formation energy of an interface dislocation, and $\Delta = \Delta a/a$ is the disregistry of lattice spacings of the condensate and substrate. Thus the degree of coherency affects θ via Eqs. (24) and (3). In the presence of strains e, the bulk driving force is modified to

$$\Delta G_v' = \Delta G_v + C_3 e^2 \qquad (25)$$

Thus the e dependence of both θ and $\Delta G_v'$ must be included in ΔG, Eq. (14), which must in general be minimized with respect to e, giving a critical value e^*.

In the case of nucleation on high index planes or on surface imperfections, as is often the case, coherency effects are unlikely. When they are present, coherency effects are important at high supersaturations. When $|\Delta G_v| \gg C_3 \Delta^2$, the nucleus will form coherently such that $e^* \to \Delta$ in order that σ_{c-x} be minimized (Δ is the upper limit of e^*). When $C_3 \Delta^2 \gg |\Delta G_v|$, $e^* \to 0$ and incoherent nucleation will occur. In cases where they form, coherent interfaces are expected to relax to semicoherent interfaces under thermal activation as nuclei grow.

4. Condensation Coefficient Effects

A low value of the condensation coefficient α in Eq. (9) can have several effects. The nucleation rate itself is directly proportional to α. Also, if α is very small, the relaxation time for equilibrium between the adsorbed layer and the vapor might be of the order of or larger than the experimental observation time, so that one must consider a time-dependent concentration n_1 as discussed in Section II, 6. Both experiment and theory indicate that $\alpha \sim 1$ for condensing monatomic vapors, except in the case of very weak binding energies to the substrate (3, 23, 24). For condensing polymeric vapors, on the other hand, the requirement for the deactivation of rotational degrees of freedom can lead to low values of α, given by (3)

$$\alpha = F_R^*/F_R \qquad (26)$$

where F_R^* and F_R represent the rotational partition functions in the activated state for adsorption and in the vapor phase, respectively. Similar effects can occur in the adsorbed layer itself if rotational degrees of freedom are activated there.

As first suggested by Sears and Cahn (*25*), corrections are also required if thermal accommodation with the substrate is poor. In such a case the temperature in the adsorbed layer will exceed that of the substrate, so that the supersaturation will be less than would be the case if the temperatures were equal. Such effects are not present when the binding energy ΔG_{des} is large, as for metals depositing on metals (*26*, *27*). For cases of weak binding energy, such as metal depositing on Pyrex glass, small nonaccommodation effects are present (*27*), but not to the extent suggested by Sears and Cahn (*25*).[5]

5. High Substrate Temperature Modifications

Several phenomena can occur at high temperatures, each of which can markedly modify the nucleation rate equation. Let us first consider adatom (ad-molecule) mobility. In the classical model adatoms are considered to diffuse by discrete jumps from one local site to another. Above a critical temperature, the adatoms will translate as a two-dimensional gas instead of being localized. The critical temperature is given by the condition that the relaxation time for a diffusion jump exceed the jump distance divided by the velocity in the two-dimensional gas. A straightforward analysis of the kinetic theory of two-dimensional gases yields the condition

$$av \exp(-\Delta G_D/kT) < (2kT/m)^{1/2}$$

which for typical parameters reduces to

$$\Delta G_D < kT \qquad (27)$$

In this case, ω^* relates to the collision frequency in the two-dimensional gas, yielding (*3*)

$$\omega^* = 2r^* n_1 \sin\theta \, (\pi kT/2m)^{1/2} \qquad (28)$$

This expression replaces Eq. (17) and yields a higher nucleation rate than the latter. The activation of translational (or rotational) degrees of freedom for adsorbed monomer also causes a decrease in ΔG_{des} by an amount

$$\Delta G'_{\text{des}} = kT \ln(F_R' F_T'/F_v) \qquad (29)$$

where F_R' and F_T' represent the partition functions for the activated degrees of freedom, and F_v represents the partition function for the vibrational modes removed to conserve degrees of freedom. Thus n_1 should increase abruptly at the temperature where the rotations or translations are activated.

The critical-size nuclei themselves might be activated to translate or rotate

---

[5] Thermal effects associated with the release of the heat of condensation are a definite factor in crystal *growth* at high deposition rates (*3*); these effects are generally absent when *nucleation* is rate controlling.

in the adsorbed state. The principal effect of such activation, analogous to the case of homogeneous nucleation in the vapor (9, 14) would be to decrease G_i^* by an amount (3)

$$\Delta G_i^* = kT \ln(F_R F_T / F_v) \tag{30}$$

The pertinent partition functions in the adsorbed state are

$$F_R = (8\pi^3 IkT)^{1/2}/h, \qquad F_T = 2\pi imkT/n_1 h^2,$$
$$F_v = [1 - \exp(-hv/kT)]^{-1} \tag{31}$$

where I is the moment of inertia for one rotational degree of freedom of the nucleus in the adsorbed state. Again this effect would yield a higher value for J than would the classical result.

Other effects that can occur at high temperatures include the following. (i) Rotation of adsorbed monomer can lead to a low "condensation coefficient," analogous to Eq. (26), for the growth of a critical nucleus by monomer impingement. (ii) Bulk diffusion processes can become appreciable so that adsorbed monomer can be drained into the substrate, and the substrate-nucleus interface can become diffuse by interdiffusion, changing the value of σ. (iii) Since both the population of ith-size monomer and the number of atoms in the critical-size nucleus increase with increasing temperature, the population $\sum_1^{i^*-1} n_i$ can become so large that the approximation in Eq. (15) is no longer valid. Under these circumstances, the formation of a critical nucleus may proceed by impingement of adsorbed polymers (28, 6), and the concentration of available sites n_0 is decreased.

6. Low Substrate Temperatures

Perhaps the most important effect of low temperatures is the decrease in size i^* with decreasing temperature. Rewriting Eq. (18) for the critical value of J and substituting for G_i^*, we have

$$J_{\text{crit}} = A'(T) \exp\left(-\frac{16\pi\sigma^3 f(\theta)}{3kT \Delta G_{v_{\text{crit}}}^2}\right) \tag{32}$$

As the substrate temperature T decreases, $A'(T)$ decreases. Consequently, to achieve a given critical rate of J, the exponent in Eq. (32) must decrease, which, finally, requires an increase of $\Delta G_{v_{\text{crit}}}$. According to Eq. (12), this increase of $\Delta G_{v_{\text{crit}}}$ corresponds to a decrease in size of the critical nucleus r^*.

When r^* becomes so small that $i^* \gtrsim 50$, the aforementioned problem of describing the critical nucleus in terms of macroscopic parameters becomes severe. Statistical mechanical models have been developed (4, 7, 19) which describe such small clusters in terms of general partition functions for the range $1 < i^* < 50$. In both treatments, the difference from the classical result is that n_i^* is given by the following expression instead of Eq. (16),[6]

$$n_i^* = F_a(n_1/n_0)^{i^*} \exp(-E_i^*/kT) \tag{33}$$

where F_a is the total partition function for the critical-size cluster, E_i^* is its potential energy of formation, and the term $(n_1/n_0)^{i^*}$ is an entropy-of-mixing term. Walton and Rhodin (7, 19) consider F_a to be composed of vibrational terms and envision E_i^* as the potential energy of the cluster minus the potential energy of i^* single adsorbed monomers. Hirth (4) introduces the possibility that F_a can include translational and rotational terms for the adsorbed cluster if these degrees of freedom are activated, and considers E_i^* to be the potential energy of i^* atoms in the condensed bulk phase plus the total surface energy of the cluster minus the potential energy of i^* single adsorbed monomers, which is equivalent to the other definition. In either model, the problem of assessing E_i^* and the partition functions for such small sizes is extremely difficult. Thus these models present essentially alternate phenomenological models to the cap-shaped one for description of the nucleus. Therefore, we do not describe these statistical models here, but rather consider the phenomenological cap-shaped model to extend to small sizes, realizing the approximation involved. Of course, below the temperature where $i^* \sim 1$, the nucleation model breaks down altogether, every atom that strikes the substrate sticks there, and film formation is controlled by growth processes.

Another effect that appears at low temperatures is that the relaxation time for desorption becomes so large that equilibration between the vapor and the adatom concentration cannot occur during the time of experimental observation t. In such a case n_1 is time dependent, and is given by

$$n_1(t) = J_{\text{im}} \tau_{\text{des}}[1 - \exp(-t/\tau_{\text{des}})] \cong J_{\text{im}} t \tag{34}$$

Thus the supersaturation in the adsorbed layer increases continuously with time of exposure to a vapor source in such a case.

Also, at low temperatures, the surface mobility might be reduced to the point that equilibration *within* the adsorbed population no longer occurs (29). In this case, the adatoms remain at the point where they impinged until they re-evaporate. In such a case the concentration of critical-size nuclei is simply

$$n_i^* = (n_1/n_0)^{i^*} \tag{35}$$

[6] Frenkel (28a) much earlier suggested a formula of the type of Eq. (33) for the special case that $i^* = 2$, which he proposed as a general nucleation condition. His work was thus the precursor of both the statistical mechanical models and the treatment leading to Eq. (19).

and the growth frequency is given by the vapor impingement flux

$$\omega^* = 4\pi r^{*2} f(\theta) \frac{p}{(2\pi mkT)^{1/2}} \tag{36}$$

This mechanism of nucleation can also occur when $\Delta G_D > \Delta G_{des}$ (29), but this case is not expected to occur often for possible physical systems.

Finally, there are a number of indirect effects of decreasing temperature. For example, crystal surface energies become increasingly anisotropic with decreasing temperature (30). Thus the nucleus shape can change from a cap shape at high temperature, corresponding to an isotropic σ, to a disk shape at low temperature, the transition being accompanied by a change in the nucleation rate equation.

7. Substrate Imperfections

In the cap-shaped model of Section II,1, the substrate is supposed to be isotropic and smooth. The presence of imperfections on the substrate can affect the nucleation process greatly. There are two classes of defects, macroscopic ones such as cracks, macroscopic surface ledges and re-entrant grooves, and microscopic ones such as ledges of monatomic height and points of emergence of dislocations.

As an example of the macroscopic defects, let us consider nucleation at the 90° re-entrant groove (Fig. 6). Chakraverty and Pound (31) have analyzed this case in detail and find that G_i^* is given by

$$G_i^* = \frac{16\pi\sigma^3 K(\theta)}{3 \Delta G_v^2} \tag{37}$$

which is identical to Eq. (13) except for the function of θ. $K(\theta)$ and $f(\theta)$ are

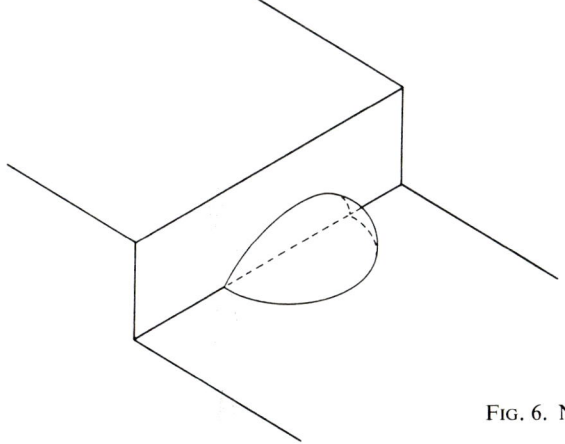

Fig. 6. Nucleus at a re-entrant groove.

plotted in Fig. 7. For all θ values, $K(\theta)$ is less than $f(\theta)$, indicating that the step is a more efficient nucleation catalyst than the flat surface. The frequency factor for this case, however, is less, being given by Eq. (17) times the factor (n_L/n_0) where n_L ($\ll n_0$) is the concentration of ledge sites. Considering both factors, the ratio of nucleation rate on ledge sites to that on the flat surface has the θ dependence shown in Fig. 8 for the typical case. Below $\sim 45°$ there is no nucleation barrier at the ledge, whereas between ~ 45 and $105°$ ledge

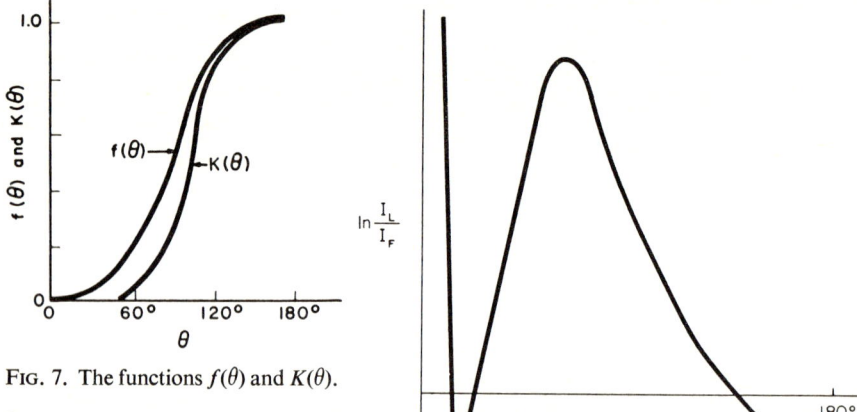

FIG. 7. The functions $f(\theta)$ and $K(\theta)$.

FIG. 8. Ratio of nucleation current on a ledge I_L to that on a flat surface I_F as a function of θ (31).

nucleation predominates. Above $\sim 105°$, the frequency factor is dominant so that nucleation on the flat becomes more rapid. Extending the above model, one can assert that any macroscopic defect which increases the area of the substrate-condensate interface for the critical nucleus will enhance the nucleation rate for contact angles below about 90°.

As an example of a microscopic imperfection, consider nucleation on a monatomic step as shown in Fig. 9. The reduction of the surface energy of the monatomic step by the amount $\Delta\sigma$ decreases $G_i{}^*$ by an amount $2r^*h\,\Delta\sigma$ for this case, again tending to enhance the nucleation rate.

Generalizing the above results, one expects that most substrates will contain a wide variety of types of nucleation sites, each of which would have a characteristic nucleation rate associated with it. In a *phenomenological* description of all such sites in terms of the cap-shaped model, each type of site is characterized by a specific θ value, which describes the efficiency of the site as a nucleation catalyst. The alternative approach of analyzing the nucleation rates based on different models for each type of site is a problem of forbidding complexity which is compounded by our present lack of knowledge of surface parameters such as ledge energies.

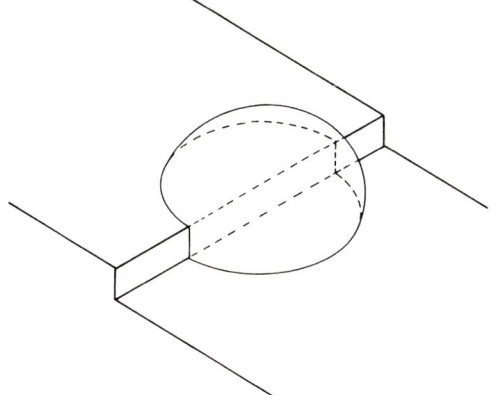

Fig. 9. Cap-shaped nucleus formed upon a monatomic step.

8. Impurity Effects

In the above analysis all surfaces are considered to be free of adsorbed impurities. Microscopically clean surfaces can be achieved by outgassing substrates in ultrahigh vacuum ($\sim 10^{-10}$ Torr or better) and maintaining them in ultrahigh vacuum for relatively short time periods (~ 1 hour), or by cleavage of the crystal in ultrahigh vacuum and maintaining the crystal under ultrahigh vacuum for short time periods. Such conditions have been achieved only recently for nucleation experiments (32). Hence it is pertinent to consider briefly the effects of impurity adsorption. A number of such effects are reviewed by Hirth and Pound (3).

The presence of a layer of adsorbed impurity on the substrate in general decreases the binding energy of adsorbed monomer (although the opposite effect is possible) and hence decreases the activation energies for both desorption and surface diffusion. Changes in these energies would, respectively, lower or raise the nucleation rate.

Adsorption of impurities to a surface also lowers its equilibrium surface energy according to the Gibbs adsorption isotherm (17). Thus, equilibrated adsorption to a critical nucleus will decrease the effective value of $f(\theta)$ and increase the nucleation rate. On the other hand, impurity trapped between the critical nucleus and the substrate in a nonequilibrium distribution will raise σ_{x-c}, increase the effective value of $f(\theta)$, and hence decrease the nucleation rate. The latter situation corresponds to "poisoning" of nucleation sites, for example the monatomic ledges of the last section, by impurity adsorption.

9. Chemical Vapor Deposition

As a final modification of the classical nucleation equations, we consider nucleation of a condensate from a multicomponent system by a chemical reaction or a dissociation reaction. As an example consider the dissociation reaction

$$AB_{(g)} \to A + B_{(g)} \tag{38}$$

where A is the nucleating species. The kinetics are found to closely resemble those discussed in Section II,1, with the following exceptions (33): The impingement flux of AB is related to the effective pressure p_{AB} of AB by Eq. (9), while the effective pressure p_B of B is related to its desorption flux by the same expression. The effective pressure of A is then given by

$$p_A = \frac{p_{AB}}{p_B} K_e \tag{39}$$

where K_e is the equilibrium constant for reaction (38) at the substrate temperature. With this definition, Eq. (10) defines the supersaturation of the system with respect to nucleation; the above definitions of effective pressures thus provide a relation between free energies of reaction in a chemical system and the supersaturation in a nucleation reaction. The other differences include the possibility that the other reactants, AB and B in the above case, can behave like impurities by adsorbing to nucleus surfaces, etc., as discussed in the preceding section, and the possibility that equilibration on the substrate involves the diffusion of adsorbed AB instead of adsorbed A. A development closely related to the above has been proposed to account for codeposition of different metals to nucleate metallic alloys or intermetallic compounds by Sigsbee and Pound (33a).

10. Summary

A large number of possible nucleation rate expressions are suggested for various possible physical situations. Sufficient data are presented to enable one to write down the appropriate rate equation for a given case. Often, however, values of the physical parameters required to evaluate such expressions are unavailable. Hence, in such cases, the classical cap-shaped nucleus is applied to describe the data via a Pound plot, Eq. (19). The parameters θ, σ, and ΔG_{des} derived from such a plot are, therefore, often simply phenomenological parameters describing the potency of the substrate as a nucleation catalyst.

III. Experimental Results

1. Verification of the Nucleation Model

a. Field Electron Emission Observations. Field electron emission microscopy (FEEM) is well suited for the study of heterogeneous nucleation of a solid from the vapor phase because of four important factors. First, ultrahigh vacua are required for the operation of FEEM. Second, with FEEM it is possible to detect substrate surface contamination much less than a monolayer in thickness. Third, the substrate surface is crystallographically well defined and all crystallographic orientations are simultaneously observed. Fourth, with FEEM it is possible to detect the onset of nucleation instantaneously. Although the over-all resolution of this technique is generally quoted as 20 A, it is possible under favorable conditions to resolve single adatoms on the surface. For nucleation studies, even the lower resolution value of 20 A is considerably better for detection of nuclei than any other technique used in the study of nucleation, because once nucleation has occurred, growth of nuclei is very rapid and hence the incubation time can be determined accurately.

The model of adsorption, equilibration within an adsorbed layer and growth by surface diffusion, was directly verified first by Moazed and Pound (*34*, *35*) in a field electron emission study of silver nucleation on tungsten. In this work, the conditions were such that the adatom concentration was time dependent, Eq. (34). At a substrate temperature of 300°K, it was found that nucleation occurred at a given concentration $n_{1_{crit}}$ (a fraction of a monolayer) *independent of beam flux*, thus indicating that equilibration did occur within the adsorbed layer, and that nucleation does occur by a surface diffusion mechanism at a critical supersaturation. Nucleation was observed to occur preferentially on the high index planes of the substrate. These planes are composed of monatomic ledges with varying ledge separation. It was also noted that once nucleation had occurred, nuclei grew rapidly at a constant vapor beam flux until impingement occurred.

There was no evidence of "liquid-like behavior" during nucleation or growth of the nuclei as has been observed by electron microscopy (to be discussed in a later section). The nuclei appeared as discrete single crystals which grew on the field emitter tip. The growth of crystallites continued in all directions until impingement occurred with other crystallites. In some cases sharp boundaries were observed between adjacent crystallites which had impinged on one another, while in other cases the boundary between adjacent crystallites disappeared following impingement (Fig. 10). Undoubtedly, the factor that determined whether the boundary remained or was eliminated was the spatial orientation of the crystallites on the substrate surface. Apparently those crystallites that had nearly the same orientation as their neighbors grew together without retaining a noticeable boundary; whereas those crystallites that did not have such a relationship maintained the boundary (*36*). Also in contrast to the electron microscope results, the boundaries did not anneal out at the temperature of the field emission observations (300°K).

Further verification of the nucleation model was provided by the work of Gretz and Pound (*18*, *37*), who studied silver, nickel, zinc, cadmium, and gold

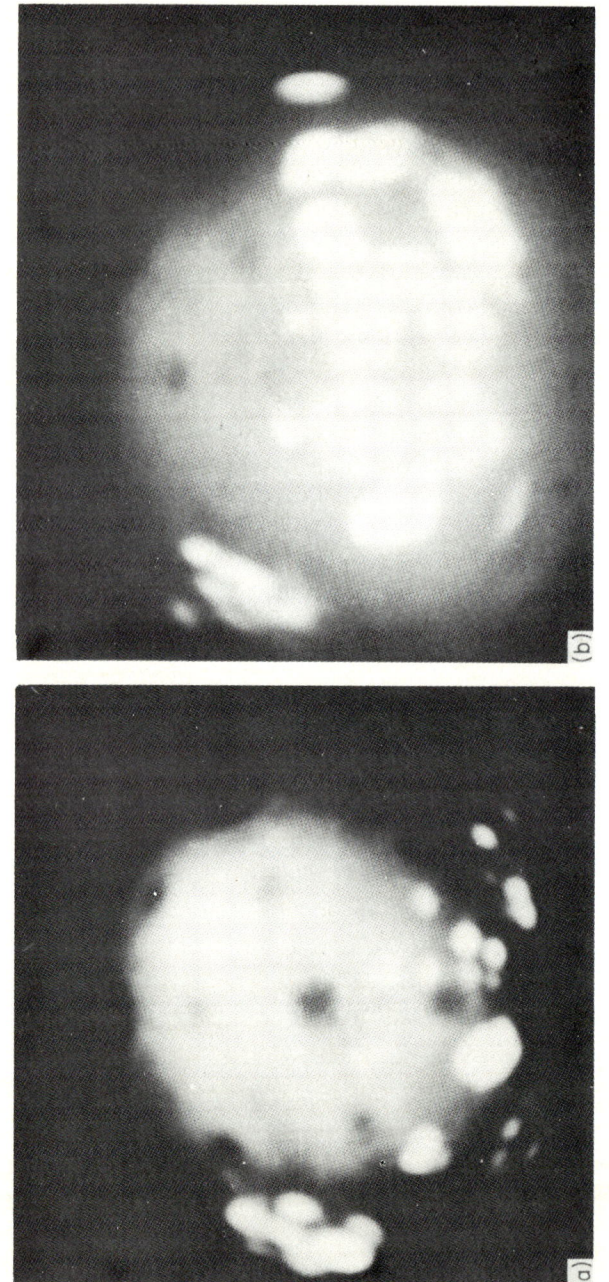

FIG. 10. Field electron emission study of nucleation of silver on tungsten at 300°K showing: (a) short time after nucleation; (b) growth of nuclei.

nucleating on tungsten. A plot of t^{-1} versus J_{im} which shows that nucleation occurs at a constant value of $n_{1_{crit}}$ is given in Fig. 11 (37). This result of Gretz (37) for cadmium on tungsten corresponds to a low-temperature region where i^* is very small and the application of classical nucleation theory is questionable. At 75°K, Eq. (19) indicates that $r^* = 9$ A. The other data (5, 37, 38) yield values of $r^* = 2$–15 A. Thus even under extreme conditions where the applicability of the theory is in question, nucleation follows the expected behavior.

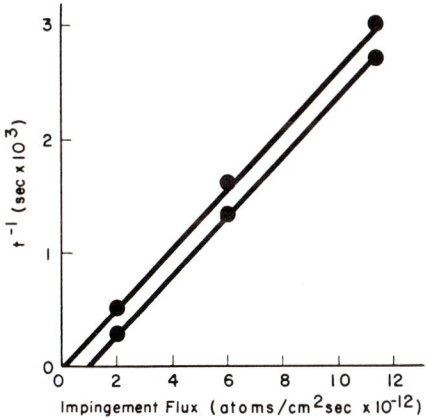

FIG. 11. Plot of reciprocal time for nucleation versus impingement flux for the case of zinc nucleating on tungsten (37).

In order to analyze these results, we must consider Eqs. (20) and (21) and the conditions which produce double θ values. For zinc, the two pertinent θ values are $\theta \sim 1°$ and $\theta \sim 44°$; for cadmium, $\theta \sim 1°$ and $\theta \sim 20°$. The macroscopic contact angles are $\geq 70°$ for zinc and cadmium (18, 37) and these are the cases with the largest r^* values (18, 37) so that the upper θ values appear to be the valid ones for these cases. For nickel the θ solutions are (18, 37) $\theta \sim 1°$ and $\theta \sim 100°$; for gold, $\theta \sim 1°$ and $\theta \sim 180°$. The macroscopic contact angles are 0° for both of these metals (18, 37). Thus for these two cases the lower θ values appear to be the valid solutions.

For such low contact angles the classical nucleation model should break down, and nucleation could now occur by some other mechanism such as the formation of a crystalline nucleus in an amorphous multiatomic film, as suggested by Gretz and Pound (18, 37).

An alternative possibility for these cases, suggested by the observed variation of the field emission patterns with time prior to and during nucleation, is that a several-atom-thick adsorbed layer of the condensate forms, completely "wetting" the substrate, and that cap-shaped nuclei subsequently form on top of this layer. Such a model is consistent with the observation that the total deposit was 3.7 monolayers and 2.8 monolayers, for nickel and gold, respectively, when nucleation occurred (*18, 37*). The corresponding total deposit for silver was 0.1 monolayer (*35, 37*).

Although this discussion indicates that the interpretation of the data is not unequivocal in these cases, it serves to illustrate the importance of considering both possible θ solutions.

There have been several other field electron emission studies of vapor deposition including the recent work of Hardy who investigated nucleation of mercury on tungsten (*38*).

The results of recent experiments on the oxidation of refractory metals using field electron and field ion microscopy (*39–41*) strongly suggests that the early stages in the oxidation of metals can be described in terms of the classical nucleation theory (*41*). Of course, in the case of oxidation the mechanistic steps leading to nucleus formation are much more complex than those discussed here, and would involve the motion of cations, anions, or both. The process of nucleation for systems where anion mobilities are rate controlling for mass transport seems to require a local supersaturation of oxygen ions in the metal matrix (at or near the oxygen gas–metal interface), leading to the precipitation of the oxide phase from the unstable supersaturated solid solution. The oxide precipitate may be the stable oxide or a transitional lattice which forms because of the factors mentioned in an earlier section (e.g., surface energy and strain energy). It should be noted that a great deal more experimental verification is required in order to have a complete understanding of oxide nucleation.

Field ion microscopy in recent years has become an important technique for the study of surface structure and of surface reactions. Although at the present time the technique is not amenable to the study of vapor deposition, it is conceivable that in the future it may be adapted for the study of solid nucleation from molecular beams. When that occurs, it will be possible to study nucleation on an atomic scale and hopefully many of the present uncertainties about nucleation from the vapor phase will be resolved.

b. Electron Microscope Observations. Bassett (*42, 43*) and Pashley, Stowell, and co-workers (*44, 45, 46*) developed the technique of direct observation of nucleation and growth upon substrates by transmission electron microscopy. Continuing work along these lines is reviewed by Pashley (*47*). The experimental conditions in these experiments differ markedly from those of the field-emission experiments. The vacuum in the electron microscope observations is generally $\gtrsim 10^{-6}$ Torr, so that impurity adsorbates are expected to be present. Also, the substrate temperatures in these in situ measurements is in the range 250–400°C, and heating in the electron beam raises the substrate temperature somewhat. These observations therefore correspond to lower ratios of binding energy to temperature and to much higher mobilities of surface adatoms than the field-emission results.

In these experiments the substrate is exposed to a continuous beam flux, nuclei are observed to appear abruptly, and growth and agglomeration processes then take place rapidly in the size range $r \sim 100$ A to $r \sim 10^4$ A. In the course of growth, nuclei are observed to translate (43), to rotate (42, 45), and to rapidly agglomerate upon contact as shown in Fig. 12. Such

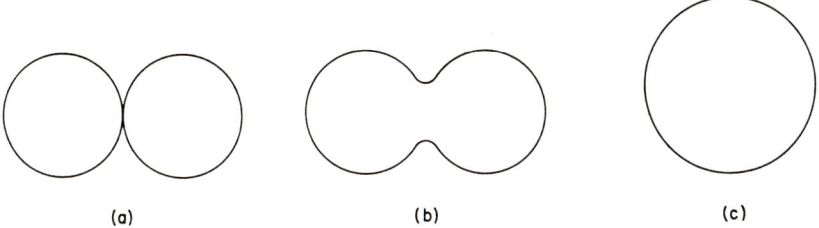

FIG. 12. Successive stages in the agglomeration of cap-shaped nuclei which have come into contact.

motion led to the concept of "liquid-like behavior" of the nuclei. However, it soon became evident that the nuclei were small single crystals in all stages of the growth process (43, 45). The translation and agglomeration can be explained by surface diffusion under the capillary driving forces produced by shapes of such small radius of curvature as the nuclei (45, 47, 48). Consider, for example, the rate of sintering of the configuration in Fig. 12. The concentration of adatoms in equilibrium with a region of local principal radii of curvature r_1 and r_2 is (17)

$$\frac{n_1}{n_{1_e}} = \exp\left[\frac{\sigma\Omega}{(r_1 + r_2)kT}\right] \tag{40}$$

where Ω is the atomic volume. For silver on graphite (43) with $\sigma = 1100$ erg/cm^2, $T = 250°$C, $r_1 = -50$ A and $r_2 = \infty$ at the neck, and $r_1 = 200$ A and $r_2 = \infty$ for the nucleus, we find that the concentration gradient is

$$-\Delta n_1/\lambda = 1.71 n_{1_e}/\lambda$$

giving a diffusion flux

$$J \cong 2D_s n_{1_e}/\lambda$$

With a diffusion distance $\lambda \sim 100$ A, $n_{1_e} \sim 10^9$/cm^2, and $D_s \sim 10^{-10}$ cm^2/sec, this gives $J \sim 10^5$ atoms/cm-sec which is completely adequate to explain the observed sintering rate. The values of n_{1_e} and D_s are estimated from the typical values for such parameters (3) since exact values are not known for silver on graphite. However, considerable changes in ΔG_{des} or ΔG_D would not change the above conclusion. Pashley et al. (45) have analyzed the rate of coalescence of gold on MoS_2 in a more detailed analysis based on the theory of sintering, and conclude that the relaxation time for coalescence by surface diffusion is 10^{-7} sec for $r = 100$ A at 400°C; hence, again surface diffusion is adequate to explain the results.

Since the electron microscopy growth results are consistent with a surface diffusion model in an equilibrated adsorbed layer, the results also support the model of nucleation by such a mechanism. These observations together with the field-emission results thus indicate that the surface-diffusion nucleation model is valid over a wide range of substrate temperatures, yet the growth processes differ markedly because of differences in surface mobility. We shall again consider the consequences of this conclusion in our later discussion of epitaxy.

c. *Role of Imperfections and Impurities.* Several studies of nucleation from the vapor phase have demonstrated that preferential nucleation sites exist in general upon substrates as discussed in Section II,7. Probably the first observations of this kind were those of Andrade and Martindale (49) who sputtered gold and silver onto quartz or glass and observed preferential nucleation at surface microcracks. A number of studies of this type are reviewed by Hirth and Pound (3) and Pashley (47).

Particularly pertinent in the present discussion is the work of Chakraverty and Pound (31). They found that gold preferentially nucleated at macroscopic cleavage steps on NaCl and LiF. Since the contact angle for these systems is $\theta \sim 95°$, the results are consistent with the theoretical results of Fig. 8. Cadmium nucleated on the flat regions of the same crystal also in a way consistent with theory since θ is about 120° in this case. Bassett (50) found that gold nuclei decorated monatomic steps on gold. An example of his results is shown in Fig. 13. This finding suggests that the critical angle for nucleation on monatomic ledges, Fig. 9, is about the same as that for macroscopic ledges, Fig. 8. Because the contact angle $\theta \sim 95°$ is near the critical angle of 105°, some nucleation is expected on the flats, consistent with the observations illustrated in Fig. 13.

Impurity adsorption has been shown both to increase and to decrease nucleation rates. Chirigos et al. (32) showed that the nucleation rate of silver on copper at 200–400°C was higher in vacua of $\sim 10^{-9}$ Torr than in vacua of $\sim 10^{-5}$ Torr. Similar results were recently obtained by Bachmann and Shin (51). On the other hand, adsorption of ferric ion was shown to increase the nucleation rate of lithium fluoride from aqueous solution, a process analogous to nucleation from the vapor, by Sears (52).

Some quite recent work that shows the effect of both impurities and imperfections has been carried out by Erb (53) on the nucleation of water onto

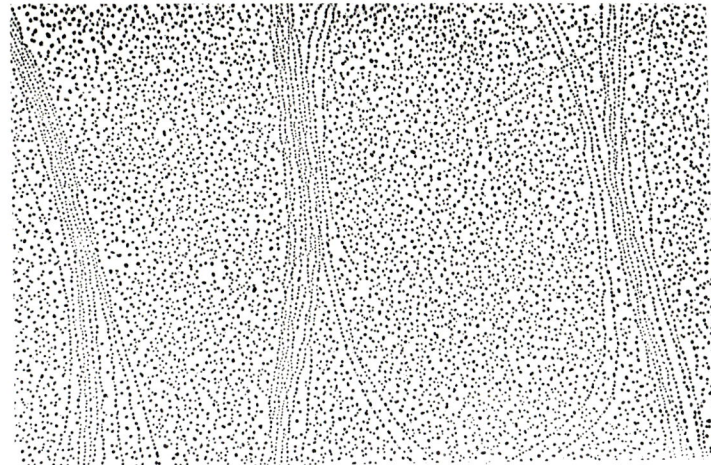

FIG. 13. Gold nuclei deposited onto a sodium chloride {100} substrate at 500°C; 150,000 × (courtesy of G. A. Bassett).

silver and gold and by Koutsky et al. (54) on the nucleation of water on a variety of substrates. Erb explicitly demonstrated that a spectrum of sites of varying catalytic potency existed on his substrates, and that each had its own critical supersaturation; i.e., on a given substrate, sites with a variety of effective values of θ exist. Koutsky et al. (54) showed directly that impurity adsorption of polar adsorbates changed the potency of the substrate gradually over a period of time. Also, in studying a wide variety of substrates, Koutsky et al. (54) found that the critical supersaturation was high for water nucleating on substances such as Teflon, where θ was large, and that the critical supersaturation decreased to a minimum at a contact angle $\theta \sim 50°$ and then increased again as $\theta \to 0$ for such substrates as cadmium sulfide. This result agrees very well with the theoretical analysis of Section II,2, and indicates the importance of considering the dependence of the pre-exponential factor on θ in analyzing nucleation data. A number of other measurements that qualitatively demonstrate preferential nucleation on imperfections and the role of impurities are reviewed by Hirth and Pound (3).

2. Critical Supersaturation Measurements

a. Existence of Critical Supersaturation. Early work on deposition from the vapor, at nominally constant beam fluxes, established that nucleation occurred below a "critical" substrate temperature (55, 56). Estermann (57) then studied the condensation of cadmium on silver and copper. He used an atomic beam vapor source and varied both the beam flux and temperature. He demonstrated that the onset of nucleation depended on a critical supersaturation, (p/p_e), which in turn depended on both beam flux and substrate temperature. Thus he provided the first semiquantitative verification of the pressure and temperature dependence of the nucleation rate as expressed in the form of Eq. (18).

Jackson et al. (58) have verified the existence of a critical supersaturation in a chemical vapor deposition system. They studied the nucleation of chromium from a chromous-iodide beam onto silica substrates. The free energy of formation in K_e in Eq. (39) was such that the supersaturation should *increase* with increasing substrate temperature for a given beam flux, opposite to the situation in a one-component system. In agreement with expectation from Eq. (19), nucleation at a constant beam flux was found to occur *above* a critical substrate temperature corresponding to a critical supersaturation $\Delta G_{v_{crit}}$ for this system.

Sigsbee and Pound (33a) showed similarly that the free energy of formation is important in the codeposition of interacting metals. They found that the nucleation rate was greatly enhanced in a system (Mg-Sb) in which a compound formed with a large free energy of formation.

b. Nucleation Data Analyzed by Using Eq. (19). Cockcroft (58a) investigated the nucleation of cadmium on copper as a function of beam flux and temperature. Pound et al. (16) showed that Cockcroft's data fit an equation similar to Eq. (19) as shown in Fig. 14. Since that time a number of such measurements have been analyzed by the use of Eq. (19). The resulting parameters are listed in Table I. In all of these cases the temperature and pressure dependence of $\Delta G_{v_{crit}}$ agreed very well with Eq. (19). However, independent

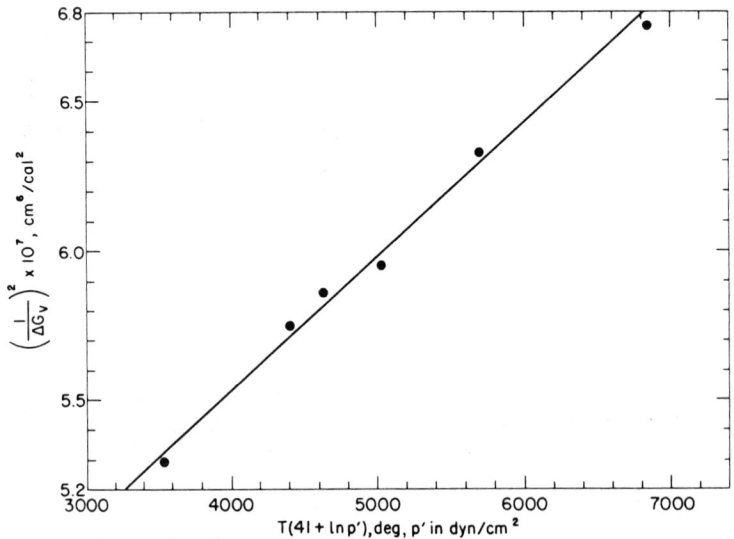

FIG. 14. Plot of nucleation data for Cd depositing on copper (58a) in the form of Eq. (19).

measurements of θ and ΔG_{des} are not available for most of these cases, so that the theory cannot be tested in detail. In all cases, the vacua were such that impurity adsorption was possible. Thus the only test for θ and ΔG_{des} is whether the values appear reasonable for a contaminated system; the values in Table I are in the expected range.

TABLE I

Nucleation Data Analyzed by the Use of Eq. (19)

System	r^* (Å)	σ (ergs/cm^2)	i^*	θ (deg)	ΔG_{des} (cal/mole)	Ref.
Na on CsCl	2.6–3.1	310	—	125	2300	(59)
Cd on Cu	7.5–8.7	700	—	141	17,200	(58a)
Zn on glass	3.3–240	750	4 to 4×10^5	~ 50	3110	(60)
H$_2$O on Hg	220	73	4×10^5	~ 15	6800	(61)

In one case, the study of water nucleating on mercury (61) the data was found to fit the form of Eq. (19). In this case sufficient data for the parameters in Eq. (19) were independently available to predict the rate theoretically. The experimental curve and the theoretical curve differed markedly in absolute value of supersaturation as shown in Fig. 15. A value of $\theta \sim 15°$, as opposed to a macroscopic value of $\theta \sim 70°$, is required to make theory and experiment agree, even though r^* is quite large, 220 Å, in this case. Again this illustrates the phenomenological nature of the nucleation parameter θ. The probable interpretation in this case (62, 63) is that nucleation is actually occurring on mercuric oxide impurities which are a more potent nucleation catalyst than mercury, accounting for the low apparent θ value.

When measurements are made over a wide temperature range, deviations from linearity arise in the plot of Eq. (19). An example is the result for Zn on glass. Hudson (60) originally fitted the curve to theory at high substrate temperatures and found a large deviation from theory at low temperatures. The analysis of Hruska (63a) and of Ruth et al. (27), however, indicates that a very good fit with theory is obtained at low temperatures if a disk-shaped nucleus model is invoked. The fact that a cap-shaped model could also describe the low temperature data, but less accurately, is an indication of the possible use of the cap-shaped model in a phenomenological description of the results. For the disk-shaped nucleus, Eq. (19) is replaced by the expression

$$\frac{1}{\Delta G_v + \sum \sigma/h} = \frac{1}{\pi \sigma^2 h}[kT(\ln C_4 + \ln p) + \Delta G_{des} - \Delta G_D] \quad (41)$$

where $\sum \sigma = (\sigma + \sigma_{c-x} - \sigma_{x-v})$ and $C_4 \cong C_1$ (3). The results are plotted in

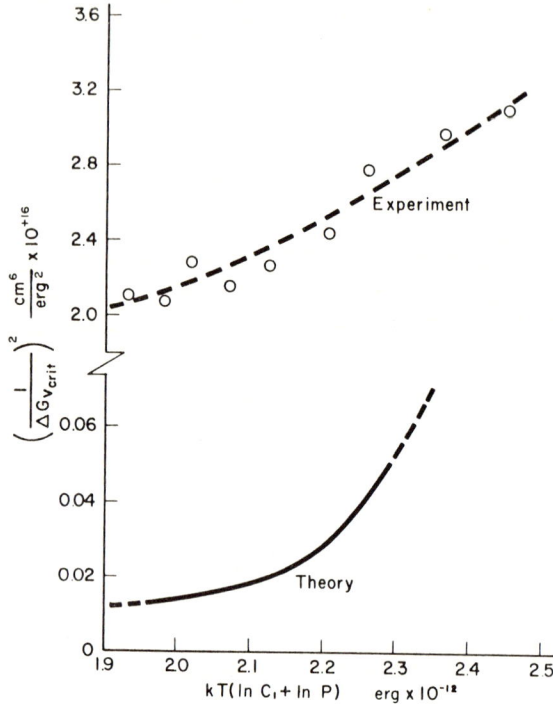

FIG. 15. Plot of nucleation data for water depositing on mercury (61) in the form of Eq. (19).

terms of Eq. (41) in Fig. 16. The change in slope at high substrate temperatures is associated with the onset of a mechanism of mutual impingement of polymeric adsorbate clusters (28, 63a) as discussed in Section II,5.

Finally, in the deposition of CrI_2 on single crystalline alumina (58), it was found that Eq. (19) did not at all describe the data, as illustrated in Fig. 17; the apparent value of θ did not lie between 0 and 180° for this experiment. In this case nucleation was found to be consistent with a mechanism of direct impingement from the vapor, the physical reason for this being the large value of ΔG_D for this system.

c. Direct Measurements of Nucleation Rate. Walton et al. (64) used the Bassett technique, illustrated in Fig. 13, to directly measure the nucleation rate of silver on NaCl at temperatures in the range of 500°K in high vacuum ($\sim 10^{-9}$ Torr). The substrates were prepared by cleavage *in vacuo*. By counting the nuclei density as a function of time they were able to determine the nucleation rate directly. They actually count clusters which have grown to supercritical sizes, so that one might expect that some agglomeration has also

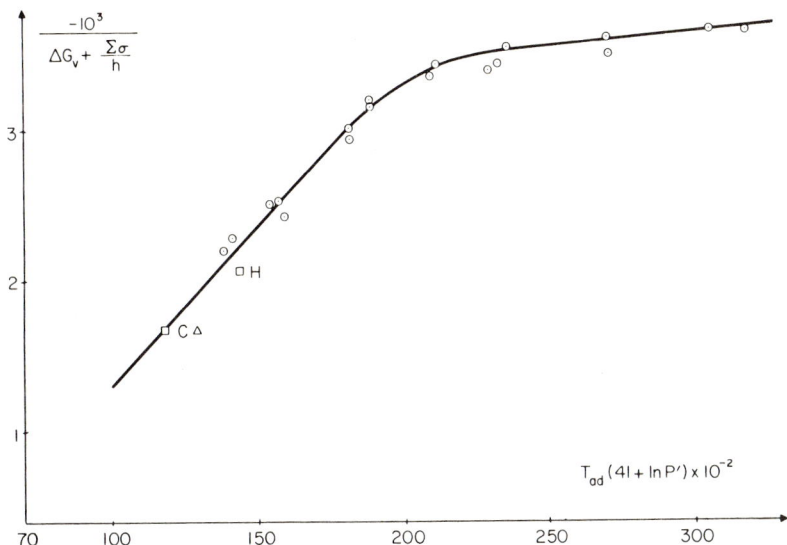

FIG. 16. Plot of nucleation data for zinc depositing on glass (27) in the form of Eq. (41).

occurred. On the other hand, the measured rate was linear with time, supporting the view that the observed rate was indeed the nucleation rate. Their results are presented in Fig. 18. They interpret the data in terms of Eq. (33) and find that $i^* = 3$, $E_i^* = 48$ kcal/gm-atom, and that the monomer desorption

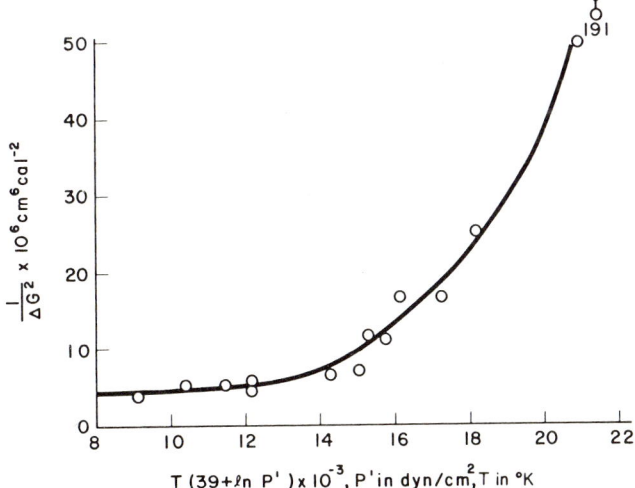

FIG. 17. Plot of nucleation data for CrI_2 depositing on single crystal alumina (58) in the form of Eq. (19).

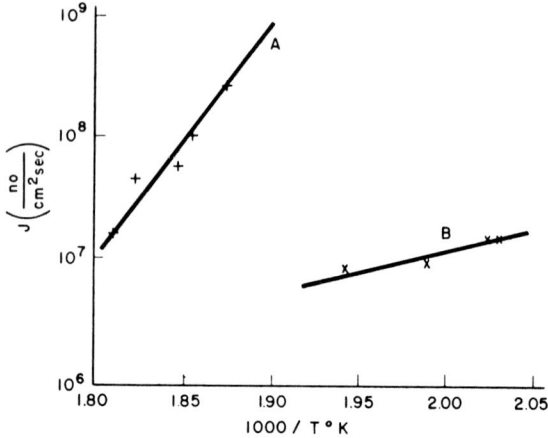

Fig. 18. Nucleation rate of silver on sodium chloride {100} surface as a function of temperature at deposition fluxes of A, 6×10^{13} atoms/cm² sec, and B, 1×10^{13} atoms/cm² sec (*64*).

energy $\Delta E_{\text{des}} = 9$ kcal/gm-atom. As indicated in Table II, their data can also be interpreted (*65*) in terms of Eq. (19) yielding the parameters θ and ΔG_{des}. Thus, the data can be analyzed in terms of either Eq. (19) or Eq. (33) and the results considered phenomenological parameters describing the nucleation efficiency of the substrate. It has been suggested that nucleation actually takes place at surface defects (surface vacancies or vacancy clusters) in this case.

Robins and Rhodin (*66*) have carried out similar experiments in the nucleation of gold on MgO. They find that the data are consistent with a model of nucleation on randomly distributed defect sites (solute impurities) with $i^* \sim 1$ or 2. Other measurements of this type have been performed by Siegel and co-workers (*51, 66a*).

d. Other Measurements of Critical Supersaturations. There have been a number of other measurements of critical supersaturations for nucleation. In many cases, the data were not obtained at a sufficient number of different substrate temperatures to analyze in terms of Eq. (19). Therefore, we have simply listed those data that are available in Table II. It is noteworthy that most of the values of r^* are in the range $r^* \gtrsim 10$ Å where the application of the classical theory is questionable. However some measurements are in the range where near-macroscopic behavior is expected.

Considering all of the results of measurements of $\Delta G_{v_{\text{crit}}}$, Eq. (19) does describe some of the data very well. However, a number of discrepancies with Eq. (19) exist, illustrating its phenomenological nature. There is a clear need for further measurements of $\Delta G_{v_{\text{crit}}}$, particularly over wide ranges of substrate temperature and *in vacua* of 10^{-10} Torr or better, with carefully characterized surfaces.

TABLE II
Summary of Nucleation Data

Consensate	Substrate	T (°K)	σ (ergs/cm²)	$(\Delta G_{des} - \Delta G_D)$ kcal/mole	θ (deg)	$-\Delta G_{v_{crit}}$ (cal/cc)	r^* (Å)	$n_{1_{crit}}$ ($\times 10^{-15}$ cm²)	Ref.
Ag	W	300	1100	—	~84	2900	2	0.17	(35)
Ag	W	300	1100	~34.5	78	3170	1.5	0.14	(37)
Ag	W	75	1100	~34.5	78	3300	1.5	0.14	(37)
Zn	W	373	750	~23	44	685	5	3.7	(18)
Zn	W	75	750	~23	44	730	5	3.7	(18)
Cd	W	75	600	~23	20	340	9	1.6	(37)
Cd	W	300	600	~23	20	350	9	1.6	(37)
Ni	W	75	1900	~46	120	8300	1.1	5.2	(18)
Ni	W	300	1900	~46	120	8390	1.1	5.2	(18)
Au	W	300	1200	~46	~180	4160	1.4	3.9	(18)
Cd	NaCl	167	600	—	~135	1208	2.2	—	(31)
Cd	LiF	167	600	—	~135	1215	2.2	—	(31)
Na	CsCl	300	310	2.3	~125	500	3	—	(59)
Cd	Cu	300	600	—	~141	410	8	—	(58a)
H₂O	Hg	300	73	6.8	~15	12	220	—	(61)
Zn	Glass	300	750	3.1	~50	1090	3.3	—	(60)
Zn	Glass	685	750	3.1	~50	15	240	—	(60)
Zn	Mica	300	750	—	—	1100	3.3	—	(27)
Zn	LiF	300	750	—	—	1120	3.3	—	(27)
Ag	NaCl	500	1200	6.6	110	2800	2	—	(27)
Mg	Glass	500	—	—	—	3000	12	—	(33a)
Sb	Mg₃Sb₂	600	—	—	—	55	51	—	(33a)
Mg₃Sb₂	Glass	770	—	—	—	500	5	—	(33a)

IV. Heterogeneous Nucleation and Epitaxy

1. Types of Epitaxy

The phenomenon of epitaxy is discussed elsewhere in this volume by Matthews (67), in two extensive review articles by Pashley (47, 68), and in a review by Gretz (29). Hence, we shall not discuss epitaxy in detail here. However, some aspects of heterogeneous nucleation theory relate directly to the theory of epitaxy; so that the interplay between these theories is discussed briefly in the following.

There are a number of types of deposits that can be classified as epitaxial. These include:

a. Coherent Epitaxial Film. Here, the atoms match perfectly across the deposit-substrate interface. Usually the deposit and substrate have the same crystal structure, but this case can also result from the matching of different $\{hkl\}$ planes of different crystal structures.

b. Semicoherent Epitaxial Film. In this case atom matching occurs over regions of the surface separated by interface dislocations (22, 69).

c. Oriented Overgrowth. For this case, the deposit is a single crystal with a specific plane oriented with respect to the substrate, but the substrate can be a randomly oriented polycrystal, or even an amorphous material such as glass.

d. Unidimensional Epitaxy. In this case, a given plane of the deposit is oriented parallel to the substrate, but different regions of the deposit do not have identical orientations of crystallographic directions within the oriented plane. This effect can arise from so-called multiple positioning, arising from the equivalency of symmetric orientations on the substrate (Fig. 19a), or it can be associated with complete randomness in two dimensions (Fig. 19b).

FIG. 19. Idealized nuclei with three-fold symmetry: (a) with double positioning; (b) with random positioning in two dimensions.

All of the above cases can arise from epitaxial nucleation. The requirements are that the surface energy of the nucleus-substrate interface be lower for the epitaxial orientation than for other orientations, so that the nucleation rate for the epitaxial orientation is greater under specific deposition conditions. However the above cases of epitaxy can also result from nuclei agglomeration or growth processes, or from recrystallization of the deposit following growth. In the next section we discuss the requirements for epitaxial nucleation only, and then briefly consider experimental evidence and the role of epitaxial nucleation compared to other epitaxial processes in a final section.

2. Theory of Epitaxial Nucleation

a. Role of Temperature. Let us again take as a typical example the cap-shaped nucleus model, with the nucleation rate expressed in terms of θ as in Eq. (19). Consider the ratio β of the nucleation rate J_1 of nuclei of a favorable epitaxial orientation characterized by the contact angle θ_1, to that J_2 characterized by θ_2. In general, there are a multiplicity of unfavorable orientations, so that the condition for epitaxial nucleation is that

$$\beta = J_1/J_2 \gg 1 \qquad (42)$$

With a given set of experimental conditions, all parameters in Eq. (19) other than those involving θ will be the same for either type of nucleation, so that the ratio of nucleation rates is given by

$$\beta = \frac{\sin \theta_1}{\sin \theta_2} \exp\{B[f(\theta_2) - f(\theta_1)]\} \qquad (43)$$

Since by assumption σ_{c-x} is less for the epitaxial orientation, $\theta_2 > \theta_1$ and $f(\theta_2) > f(\theta_1)$.

Consider first the effect of temperature on β. The pre-exponential factor A' in Eq. (32) increases with increasing temperature, largely because of the increase of required impingement flux and of the surface diffusion jump frequency. Thus, for a critical nucleation rate, B also increases with increasing temperature. Therefore, at the critical supersaturation, β increases and epitaxy is favored for increasing substrate temperatures. As the supersaturation is increased above $|\Delta G_{v_{\text{crit}}}|$, B decreases,

$$B = \frac{16\pi\sigma^3}{3\,\Delta G_v^{\,2}\, kT} \qquad (44)$$

β decreases, and epitaxial nucleation is less favored. Thus, the temperature dependence of the *preexponential factor* A' is of primary importance in determining the ratio β at the critical supersaturation. The temperature dependence of B is of importance only in determining how rapidly β decreases as the supersaturation is increased above $|\Delta G_{v_{\text{crit}}}|$; i.e., the temperature appears as a coefficient of ΔG_v in

$$\frac{\partial \ln \beta}{\partial \Delta G_v} = [f(\theta_2) - f(\theta_1)] \frac{\partial B}{\partial \Delta G_v}$$

$$= -[f(\theta_2) - f(\theta_1)] \frac{32\pi\sigma^3}{3k} \cdot \frac{1}{T} \cdot \frac{1}{\Delta G_v^{\,3}} \qquad (45)$$

Thus the decrease of β with increasing $|\Delta G_v|$ is more rapid the lower the temperature.

It is sometimes stated that epitaxy is always favored by an increase in substrate temperature. This circumstance is so for the classical nucleation model in a one-component system as discussed above. However, for a chemical vapor deposition system, the temperature dependence of K_e in Eq. (39) can be such that n_1 decreases markedly with an increase in T. In such a circumstance A' *decreases* with increasing temperature, B is less at the critical supersaturation, and β decreases with increasing temperature. Thus, in such a case epitaxy is favored by a *low* substrate temperature. Hence the dependence of epitaxial nucleation on substrate temperature is a function of the operative nucleation mechanism.

While the above treatment is presented only for the cap-shaped model, the temperature dependence of β will qualitatively be the same as that of Eq. (43) for any model of the nucleus of a one-component system. Only in chemical vapor deposition is it likely that epitaxy will be favored by low substrate temperature, independent of the nucleus model.

Walton (*19, 70*) has proposed a model for epitaxial nucleation that requires epitaxy to be the result of orienting small critical nuclei containing 2 or 3 atoms. However, for such small nuclei, ΔG_v must be large [Eq. (12)] and B must be small [Eq. (44)]. This situation, which arises at low substrate temperatures, leads to a small ratio of β, Eq. (43), and hence is *unfavorable* for epitaxial nucleation. Only when the energy factor overwhelmingly favors a particular orientation for two or three atom clusters, i.e., when the difference between the factors equivalent to $[f(\theta_2) - f(\theta_1)]$ is so large that a lowering of B still leaves $\beta \gg 1$, does Walton's mechanism become likely.

b. Role of Contact Angle. Consider now the effect of the contact angle on θ. As shown by Eq. (20), either high or low values of the contact angle lead to a low value of A and hence of B which is required for nucleation. The physical reason for this is that the nucleus periphery becomes small for a given r in either limit, so that the growth frequency by surface diffusion jumps becomes small. In addition, as shown in Fig. 4, $[f(\theta_2) - f(\theta_1)]$ will be a minimum for a given $(\theta_2 - \theta_1)$ in the limits of $\theta \to 180°$ and $\theta \to 0°$. Thus both factors in the exponent of Eq. (43) will be minimized at the high and low θ limits. Since $(\sin \theta_1/\sin \theta_2) < 1$, β will be a minimum as a function of θ in the limits of high and low θ, and hence these orientations are least favorable for epitaxial nucleation. The most favorable θ value to give epitaxially oriented nuclei is the tangent value given by Eq. (21).

We emphasize that the above discussion only applies when the nuclei are cap-shaped, and in the range $10° \gtrsim \theta$, where the model of Eq. (20) is applicable. For example, in the case of very strong binding between deposit and substrate, characterized by complete wetting and $\theta = 0°$, nucleation theory is inapplicable, corresponding to the case $i^* < 1$. In this case complete epitaxy is possible under purely growth-controlled conditions.

With this reservation in mind, we see that the θ example may be qualitatively applicable for other nucleation mechanisms, provided that a nucleation barrier exists; i.e., $i^* > 1$. Intermediate interactions between the substrate and condensate can be the most favorable case for epitaxial nucleation.

In summary, epitaxial nucleation in the usual case of one component deposition is favored by high substrate temperatures, by low supersaturations, and by a specific interaction with the substrate characterized by θ. Since θ relates to the various surface energies σ, σ_{c-x}, and σ_{x-v}, this parameter is affected by the degree of coherency of the substrate-nucleus interface, by impurity adsorption, by substrate orientation, and by the presence of substrate imperfections, all of which are discussed in Section II.

3. Discussion of Experimental Results

Experimental results on epitaxy and their relation to nucleation theory are reviewed extensively elsewhere (*3, 6, 47, 67*) so that only a few pertinent references are discussed here. Sloope and Tiller have carried out a series of experiments on the epitaxial deposition of silver on NaCl in low vacuum (*71*) and for Ge on CaF_2 and other substrates in both low and high vacuum (*72*). In each case they found, in agreement with the above predictions, that epitaxy was favored by high substrate temperatures, and that the minimum substrate temperature for epitaxy increased with increasing impingement flux, i.e. with increasing ΔG_v. However, they observed the deposits after considerable film growth and showed that the growth process itself influenced the perfection of the deposit. Hence their results only indirectly confirm the concepts of epitaxial nucleation.

In a series of experiments on the deposition of gold on NaCl in low and high vacuum, Matthews and Grünbaum (*73*) and Matthews (*67, 74*) studied the nucleation process before nuclei had agglomerated into a complete film. They clearly delineated the roles of epitaxial nucleation and of agglomeration growth processes in producing a final degree of epitaxy. From the aspect of Eq. (43), their favorable epitaxial nucleation orientation was {100}gold//{100}NaCl, while the "unfavorable" orientation was {111}gold//{100}NaCl. In agreement with theory, the density of favorable nuclei in the early stages of formation was greater at high substrate temperatures. However, the shapes were anisotropic due to the anisotropic surface energy. The periphery of the energetically less favorable {111} nuclei was larger than that of {100} nuclei so that the former grew more rapidly. Thus, in high vacuum, where the nuclei density was low, the final film consisted of a considerable fraction of {111} grains. On the other hand, in low vacuum, impurities enhanced the nucleation rate, so that for a given amount of deposit the nuclei density was greater, but the nucleus size was smaller. The surface concentration in equilibrium with the smaller particles was larger, Eq. (40), so that agglomeration processes occurred rapidly, causing the {111} nuclei to dissolve and the {100} nuclei to grow preferentially. Thus, the final degree of epitaxy was greater with the higher nucleation rate produced by impurities. This in turn suggests that, as a result of agglomeration, the final degree of epitaxy would be greater in a given vacuum the greater the nucleation rate or supersaturation, in direct contrast to the expected decrease in epitaxial *nucleation* with such an increase in nucleation rate.

FIG. 20. Transmission electron micrograph of gold nuclei on molybdenum disulfide (75), 400,000 × (courtesy of M. J. Stowell).

Also pertinent to nucleation versus agglomeration in epitaxy is the double positioning of nuclei as illustrated in Fig. 20 (75). From an epitaxial nucleation standpoint, such double positioning would correspond to perfect epitaxial nucleation. When the nuclei impinge upon one another, however, twin boundaries are formed at the contact surface and the final film is not perfectly epitaxial unless one of the orientations is consumed during film growth by agglomeration processes, as shown by Matthews (74), or by grain or twin-boundary migration, as observed by Jacobs et al. (45, 75).

The observations of agglomeration, growth, and motion of nuclei by surface diffusion under capillary driving forces (43, 44, 45) are pertinent to the model of Eq. (19) in describing epitaxial nucleation versus Walton's model of nuclei containing 2 or 3 atoms. Since even large (200 A diameter versus 2–10 A for the critical nucleus) three-dimensional, supercritical clusters rapidly reach equilibrium with respect to their orientation into positions of lowest surface energy, it can be assumed that small critical nuclei reach this orientation instantaneously. Thus, whether the initial orientation of a 3- or 10-atom cluster is determined by a quasi-macroscopic model such as the cap-shaped model, or by a statistical model (4, 7), agglomeration during the initial stages of growth should produce the same effective orientations at sizes of 200 A as if the clusters were cap-shaped from the outset.

A summary of the expected interaction of nucleation theory, epitaxial nucleation, and epitaxial growth is presented in Fig. 21 for the idealized

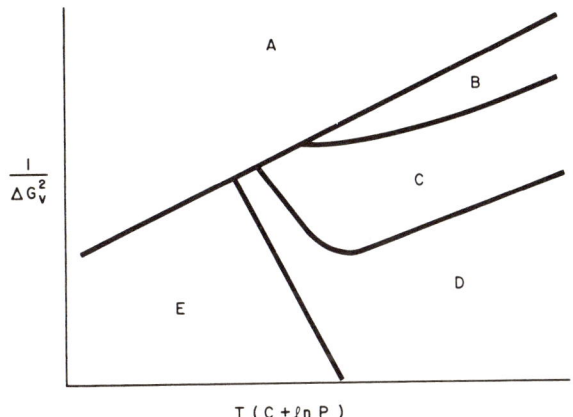

FIG. 21. Regions of nucleation, epitaxy, and epitaxial nucleation in a plot of the type of Eq. (19). See text for pertinence of the different regions.

case of a cap-shaped nucleus. In region A no nucleation takes place. The boundary between region A and regions B-C-D represents the plot of values of $\Delta G_{v_{crit}}$. Region B represents the region of epitaxial nucleation. Region C represents the region where epitaxial nucleation does not occur, but where agglomeration processes lead to a resultant epitaxial deposit. Region E represents the condition where atom mobility on the substrate becomes so limited that no rearrangements on the substrate can occur and the deposit becomes essentially amorphous. The boundary between D and E represents the temperature where the relaxation time for a surface diffusion jump equals the time for a monolayer deposition. Region D represents the region where some agglomeration occurs, but where the growth rate is sufficiently rapid compared to the agglomeration rate that complete agglomeration to an epitaxial film cannot occur.

If Fig. 21 represents nucleation in a clean system, impurity adsorption would, of course, shift all of the curves in the figure. Similarly, the onset of a different nucleation mechanism would produce shifts in the curves. However, the order of the arrangement of the different regions would still qualitatively resemble that of Fig. 21.

Acknowledgments

This research was supported in part by the U.S. Army Research Office-Durham and in part by the U.S. Office of Naval Research. We are grateful to G. A. Bassett and M. J, Stowell for contributing Figs. 13 and 20, respectively, and to R. A. Erb, J. B. Hudson, G. M. Pound, and R. A. Sigsbee for permission to present unpublished results.

References

1. G. M. Pound, in "Liquid Metals and Solidification" (B. Chalmers, ed.), p. 87. Am. Soc. Metals, Cleveland, 1958.
2. D. Turnbull, Solid State Phys. 3, 225 (1958).
3. J. P. Hirth and G. M. Pound, "Condensation and Evaporation: Nucleation and Growth Processes." Pergamon Press, Oxford, 1963.
4. J. P. Hirth, Ann. N. Y. Acad. Sci. 101, 805 (1963).
5. G. M. Pound and J. P. Hirth, in "Condensation and Evaporation of Solids" (E. Rutner et al. eds.), p. 475. Gordon and Breach, New York, 1964.
6. J. P. Hirth, S. J. Hruska, and G. M. Pound, in "Single Crystal Films" (M. Francombe and H. Sato, eds.), p. 9. Pergamon Press, Oxford, 1964.
7. T. N. Rhodin and D. Walton, in "Metal Surfaces," p. 259. Am. Soc. Metals, Cleveland, 1963.
8. J. P. Hirth and K. L. Moazed, in "Fundamental Phenomena in the Materials Sciences" (L. J. Bonis et al., eds.), Vol. 3, p. 63. Plenum Press, New York, 1966.
9. J. Lothe and G. M. Pound, J. Chem. Phys. 36, 2080 (1962).
10. J. B. Zeldovich, Acta Physiochim. U.R.S.S. 18, 1 (1943).
11. R. Becker and W. Döring, Ann. Phys. 24, 719 (1935).
12. J. Feder, K. C. Russell, J. Lothe, and G. M. Pound, Advan. Phys. 15, 1 (1966).
13. J. P. Hirth, Acta Met. 7, 755 (1959).
14. K. C. Russell, J. Lothe, and G. M. Pound, in "Condensation and Evaporation of Solids" (E. Rutner et al., eds.), p. 503. Gordon and Breach, New York, 1964.
15. M. Volmer, "Kinetik der Phasenbildung." Steinkopff, Dresden, 1939.
16. G. M. Pound, M. T. Simnad, and L. Yang, J. Chem. Phys. 22, 1215 (1954).
17. J. W. Gibbs, "Collected Works," Vol. 1. Yale Univ. Press, New Haven, Connecticut, 1948.
18. R. D. Gretz, Ph.D. Thesis, Carnegie Inst. of Tech., Pittsburgh, 1962.
19. D. Walton, J. Chem. Phys. 37, 1282 (1962).
20. K. L. Moazed and J. P. Hirth, Surface Sci. 3, 49 (1964).

21. D. Turnbull and B. Vonnegut, *Ind. Eng. Chem.* **44**, 1292 (1952).
22. J. H. Van der Merwe, *Proc. Phys. Soc. (London)* **A63**, 616 (1950); *in* "Single Crystal Films" (M. Francombe and H. Sato, eds.), p. 139. Pergamon Press, Oxford, 1964.
23. H. Eyring, F. M. Wanlass, and E. M. Eyring, *in* "Condensation and Evaporation of Solids" (E. Rutner *et al.*, eds.), p. 3. Gordon and Breach, New York, 1964.
24. B. McCarroll and G. Ehrlich, *in* "Condensation and Evaporation of Solids," (E. Rutner *et al.*, eds.), p. 521. Gordon and Breach, New York, 1964.
25. G. W. Sears and J. W. Cahn, *J. Chem. Phys.* **33**, 494 (1960).
26. S. J. Hruska and G. M. Pound, *Trans. AIME* **230**, 1406 (1964).
27. V. Ruth, K. L. Moazed, and J. P. Hirth, *J. Chem. Phys.* **44**, 2093 (1966).
28. S. J. Hruska, Ph.D. Thesis. Carnegie Inst of Tech., Pittsburgh, 1962.
28a. J. Frenkel, *Z. Physik* **26**, 117 (1924).
29. R. D. Gretz, *in* "Vapor Deposition" (C. F. Powell *et al.*, eds.), p. 149. Wiley, New York, 1966.
30. W. W. Mullins, *in* "Metal Surfaces," p. 17. Am. Soc. Metals, Cleveland, 1963.
31. B. K. Chakraverty and G. M. Pound, *Acta Met.* **12**, 851 (1964); *in* "Condensation and Evaporation of Solids" (E. Rutner *et al.*, eds.), p. 553. Gordon and Breach, New York, 1964.
32. J. N. Chirigos, Ph.D. Thesis. Carnegie Inst. of Tech., Pittsburgh, 1957; See also ref. 3, p. 59.
33. J. P. Hirth, *in* "Vapor Deposition" (C. F. Powell *et al.*, eds.), p. 126. Wiley, New York, 1966.
33a. R. A. Sigsbee and G. M. Pound (to be published).
34. K. L. Moazed, Ph.D. Thesis. Carnegie Inst. of Tech., Pittsburgh, 1959.
35. K. L. Moazed and G. M. Pound, *Trans. AIME* **230**, 234 (1964).
36. K. L. Moazed, *in* "High Temperature, High Resolution Metallography." Gordon and Breach, New York, to be published.
37. R. D. Gretz and G. M. Pound, *in* "Condensation and Evaporation of Solids" (E. Rutner *et al.*, eds.), p. 575. Gordon and Breach, New York, 1964.
38. S. C. Hardy, *J. Phys. Chem. Solids Supplement*, 287 (1967).
39. D. W. Rausch and K. L. Moazed, *Proc. Joint AIME/USAF Mat. Lab. Symp. on Oxidation of Tungsten and Other Refractory Metals*, Tech. Doc. Rept. ML-TDR-64-162, p. 53. Materials Laboratory, Wright-Patterson AFB, Ohio (1965).
40. S. S. Brenner, *in* "High Temperature, High Resolution Metallography." Gordon and Breach, New York (to be published).
41. K. L. Moazed, *in* "The Use of Epitaxial Films in Physical Investigations." Academic Press, New York, 1966.
42. G. A. Bassett, *Proc. European Regional Conf. Electron Microscopy, Delft, 1960*, p. 270. Nederlandse Vereniging Electronenmicrospie, Delft (1961).
43. G. A. Bassett, *in* "Condensation and Evaporation of Solids" (E. Rutner *et al.*, eds.), p. 599. Gordon and Breach, New York, 1964.
44. D. W. Pashley and M. J. Stowell, *Proc. 5th Intern. Conf. Electron Microscopy* (S. S. Breese, ed.). Academic Press, New York (1962).
45. D. W. Pashley, M. J. Stowell, M. H. Jacobs, and T. J. Law, *Phil. Mag.* **10**, 127 (1964).
46. M. J. Stowell and T. J. Law, *Phys. Status Solidi* **16**, 117, 479 (1966).
47. D. W. Pashely, *Advan. Phys.* **14**, 327 (1965).
48. J. P. Hirth, Discussion to ref. 43.
49. E. N. Da C. Andrade and J. G. Martindale, *Phil. Trans. Roy. Soc. London* **A235**, 69 (1935).
50. G. A. Bassett, *Phil. Mag.* **3**, 72 (1958).

51. L. Bachmann and J. J. Shin, *J. Appl. Phys.* **37**, 242 (1966).
52. G. W. Sears, *J. Chem. Phys.* **33**, 1068 (1960).
53. R. A. Erb, Ph.D. Thesis. Temple University, Philadelphia, 1965 (to be published).
54. J. A. Koutsky, A. G. Walton, and E. Baer, *Surface Sci.* **3**, 165, 280 (1965).
55. M. Knudsen, *Ann. Phys.* **50**, 472 (1916).
56. R. W. Wood, *Phil. Mag.* **32**, 314 (1916).
57. I. Estermann, *Z. Elektrochem.* **31**, 441 (1925).
58. C. S. Jackson, R. D. Gretz, and J. P. Hirth, *Surface Sci.* **6**, 171 (1967).
58a. J. D. Cockcroft, *Proc. Roy. Soc.* **A119**, 293 (1923).
59. L. Yang, C. E. Birchenall, G. M. Pound and M. T. Simnad, *Acta Met.* **2**, 462 (1954).
60. J. B. Hudson, *J. Chem. Phys.* **36**, 887 (1962).
61. J. B. Hudson and S. A. Koop (to be published).
62. J. B. Hudson, Private communication (1966).
63. G. M. Pound, Private communication (1966).
63a. S. J. Hruska, *Acta Met.* **12**, 1211 (1964).
64. D. Walton, T. N. Rhodin, and R. W. Rollins, *J. Chem. Phys.* **38**, 2698 (1963).
65. J. L. Kenty, Private communication (1966).
66. J. L. Robins and T. N. Rhodin, *Surface Sci.* **2**, 346 (1964).
66a. G. S. Yeh, J. M. M. Wills, and B. M. Siegel, in "Condensation and Evaporation: Nucleation and Growth Processes," p. 65. Pergamon Press, Oxford, 1963.
67. J. W. Matthews, this volume.
68. D. W. Pashley, *Advan. Phys.* **5**, 173 (1956).
69. G. A. Bassett, J. W. Menter, and D. W. Pashley, *Proc. Roy. Soc.* **A246**, 345 (1958).
70. D. Walton, *Phil. Mag.* **7**, 1671 (1962).
71. B. W. Sloope and C. O. Tiller, *J. Appl. Phys.* **32**, 1331 (1961).
72. B. W. Sloope and C. O. Tiller, *J. Appl. Phys.* **33**, 3458 (1962); **36**, 3174 (1965); **37**, 887 (1966).
73. J. W. Matthews and E. Grünbaum, *Appl. Phys. Letters* **5**, 106 (1964); *Phil. Mag.* **11**, 1223 (1965).
74. J. W. Matthews, *Phil. Mag.* **12**, 1143 (1965).
75. M. H. Jacobs, D. W. Pashley, and M. J. Stowell, *Phil. Mag.* **13**, 129 (1966).

Evaporated Single-Crystal Films

J. W. MATTHEWS*

*Department of Physics, University of the Witwatersrand
Johannesburg, South Africa*

I. Introduction	137
II. Modes of Film Growth	138
III. Monolayer Growth of Single-Crystal Films	138
1. Examples of Monolayer Growth	138
2. Accommodation of Misfit between Overgrowth and Substrate Lattices	139
3. Defects in Films	149
IV. Film Formation by the Generation, Growth, and Coalescence of Nuclei	150
1. Nucleation	150
2. Orientation of Nuclei	156
3. The Shape of Nuclei	161
4. Accommodation of Misfit between Nucleus and Substrate	161
5. Growth of Nuclei	163
6. Coalescence of Nuclei and the Formation of Defects	165
7. Changes in Orientation	175
8. Defects in Complete Films	180
9. Misfit Dislocations	182
V. Annealing of Thin Films	186
References	187

I. Introduction

Single-crystal films of many elements, alloys, and compounds can be made by deposition of the film materials onto single-crystal substrates. Descriptions of the techniques available for film deposition, and of the growth conditions under which single-crystal films are obtained, are given in two reviews by Pashley (*1, 2*). The second of these reviews also describes the methods currently used to study the growth and structure of the films obtained. The aim of the present article is to describe films prepared by condensation of the film materials in high (10^{-3}–10^{-6} Torr) and in ultrahigh (10^{-6}–10^{-10} Torr) vacuum onto single-crystal surfaces. Particular emphasis will be placed on films grown in ultrahigh vacuum on surfaces prepared inside the vacuum chamber. The advantage of this technique is that the contamination of substrate and film can be kept very low (*3*). The description of the films is divided into two main parts. The first (Section III) is concerned with films that exhibit monolayer or monolayer-like growth. The second (Section IV) describes films

---

* Part of this article was written while the author was on leave at the University of Virginia, Charlottesville, Virginia.

whose growth begins with the generation of three-dimensional nuclei, or islands, and proceeds with the growth and coalescence of these islands. The two parts are preceded by a discussion (Section II) of the conditions under which the two modes of film growth are expected to occur.

II. Modes of Film Growth

Studies of the early stages in film growth have been made for many overgrowth-substrate combinations. In almost every combination it has been found that growth begins with the generation of isolated three-dimensional islands (1, 2, 4). Few observations of monolayer growth have been made. The rarity of monolayer-like growth that is suggested by these results is probably misleading. Film growth is expected to begin with the generation of three-dimensional nuclei or islands if the contact angle θ between overgrowth and substrate is greater than zero. At equilibrium, the contact angle is related to σ_s, σ_0, and σ_i—the surface free energies of substrate, overgrowth, and of the interface between substrate and overgrowth—in the following way (5):

$$\sigma_s = \sigma_i + \sigma_0 \cos \theta \tag{1}$$

Clearly, the contact angle is greater than zero when $\sigma_i + \sigma_0$ is greater than σ_s. Growth as a monolayer is expected when the contact angle between overgrowth and substrate is zero. This occurs when σ_s is greater than or equal to $\sigma_i + \sigma_0$. It seems probable that there are many overgrowth-substrate combinations in which this condition is satisfied.

The above condition for monolayer growth is not the only one under which monolayer-like growth will occur. One would expect a deposit to grow approximately as a monolayer if the substrate temperature is low enough or if the rate of deposition is sufficiently high (6). Films grown under these conditions are often polycrystalline or amorphous (7, 8) but this is not invariably so (see Section III,1).

III. Monolayer Growth of Single-Crystal Films

1. Examples of Monolayer Growth

Perhaps the best-known example of monolayer growth, in which the condition $\sigma_s \geq \sigma_i + \sigma_0$ is satisfied, is the growth of lead on {111} surfaces of silver. This was discovered by Newman (8), and studied in detail by Grunbaum (9). The {111} silver surfaces were prepared by condensing a 1500-A layer of the metal onto the cleavage face of hot (270°C) muscovite mica (10). The temperature of the silver during the deposition of lead upon it was 20°C, and the residual gas pressure in the chamber was about 10^{-4} Torr. The apparatus in which the films were made enabled reflection electron diffraction patterns to be obtained throughout film growth. Evidence that the growth of lead began with the formation of extensive monolayer islands was provided by the profiles of the spots in the electron diffraction patterns. The reflections off the lead could be distinguished from those off the silver substrate because the lead monolayers did not assume the lattice parameter of silver. Their lattice parameter was within 2% of that of unstrained lead. (The misfit between lead and silver is 18%.)

Other specimens which exhibit monolayer-like growth are evaporated deposits of gold on silver (*11*) and deposits of platinum on gold (*12*). In these specimens the condition $\sigma_s \geq \sigma_i + \sigma_0$ is not satisfied. The surface energies of silver, gold, and platinum—at temperatures a little below their melting points —are about 1140 (*12a*), 1400 (*13*), and 1800 (*14*) ergs/cm². Thus, even if we assume that the energies of the gold-silver and platinum-gold interfaces are zero, the contact angles of gold on silver and platinum on gold are greater than zero. This means that continuous deposits of gold on silver and of platinum on gold are unstable and that their energies would decrease if they became three-dimensional islands. Experimental confirmation of the instability of deposits of platinum on gold has been obtained (*12*). A thin continuous deposit of platinum on gold was heated while it was under observation inside an electron microscope. It was found that the platinum film broke up to form three-dimensional islands.

2. Accommodation of Misfit between Overgrowth and Substrate Lattices

a. Theoretical Predictions. In 1949 Frank and van der Merwe (*15*) suggested that an epitaxially aligned single-crystal film would strain to reduce the difference between its normal lattice parameter and that of its substrate. Misfit in excess of that accommodated by elastic strain would be taken up by a grid of interfacial or misfit dislocations. Van der Merwe (*16–18*) has since extended this work,[1] and has shown that the equilibrium strain of an epitaxially aligned film of thickness h is given by

$$\varepsilon_m = -\frac{(1-2\nu)(2-f)(1+f)\mu_0 a}{8\pi^2(1-\nu)(2+f)f\mu_a h} \; \beta \ln[2\beta(1+\beta^2)^{1/2} - 2\beta^2] \qquad (2)$$

where $f = (a - b)/a$, and $\beta = 8\pi\mu_a f/(1 - \nu)(1 + \mu_a/\mu_b)(2 + f)^2 \mu_0$. a and b are the unstrained lattice parameters of the overgrowth and substrate; μ_a, μ_b, and μ_0 are the shear moduli of the overgrowth, substrate, and interface between overgrowth and substrate. The Poisson ratios of the overgrowth and substrate

---

[1] Accommodation of misfit across an interface has also been treated by Brooks (*18a*), Fletcher (*18b*), Fletcher and Adamson (*18c*), and by Jesser and Kuhlmann-Wilsdorf (*18d*).

are assumed equal and are represented by v. Other assumptions made in the derivation of the expression for ε_m are that the lattice parameters of overgrowth and substrate differ along one axis in the interface but are identical along the perpendicular axis; that misfit in excess of that accommodated by strain is taken up by an array of identical edge dislocations whose Burgers vector lies in the interface and is parallel to the direction of misfit; and that the substrate is infinitely thick and unstrained.

The expression for ε_m predicts that if the misfit between the overgrowth and substrate lattices is large (greater than about 10%) then much of the misfit will be accommodated by misfit dislocations. If the misfit is about 0.2% and the interfacial bonding is strong (i.e., μ_0 is comparable with μ_a and μ_b), then all of the misfit will be accommodated by elastic strain until a film thickness of about 400 A is reached. If the interfacial bonding is strong and the misfit is 4%, then all of the misfit will be accommodated by elastic strain until the film thickness reaches about 5 A. When the thickness of this film exceeds 5 A some misfit will be accommodated by dislocations. As the film thickness increases, more and more of the misfit will be accommodated by dislocations. When the thickness is 100 A the overgrowth will have almost acquired its normal lattice parameter.

All of these predictions can be illustrated by means of Bragg and Nye's model of a crystal lattice (*19*). The prediction that large misfits will be accommodated almost entirely by dislocations is illustrated by Fig. 1. Figure 1a shows portions of two large, parallel, bubble rafts which are separated from one another by a barrier. The misfit between the two rafts is about 16%. A horizontal row of the upper crystal contains about four and a half more bubbles than a row of the lower one. Figure 1b shows the rafts after removal of the barrier. It can be seen that the misfit between the two lattices is now accommodated by four misfit dislocations. Notice that the dislocation on the right has absorbed a nearby vacancy and become jogged.

The prediction that a small misfit will be accommodated entirely by elastic strain is illustrated by Fig. 2. Figure 2a shows part of a large raft of bubbles separated from a row of larger bubbles. The misfit between the row and raft is about $7\frac{1}{2}$%. Figure 2b shows the same area after removal of the barrier. It is clear that all of the misfit between the monolayer and its substrate is accommodated by elastic strain.

b. Comparison between Theory and Experiment. If μ_a is assumed equal to μ_0, and if suitable values for h, and for the various constants, are inserted into the expression for ε_m, then the strain predicted for a monolayer of lead on silver is 0.7%. This strain accommodates only 4% of the misfit between the two lattices. Thus, the observation that monolayers of lead on silver have approximately the same lattice parameter as unstrained lead (*8, 9*) is in agreement with the theory.

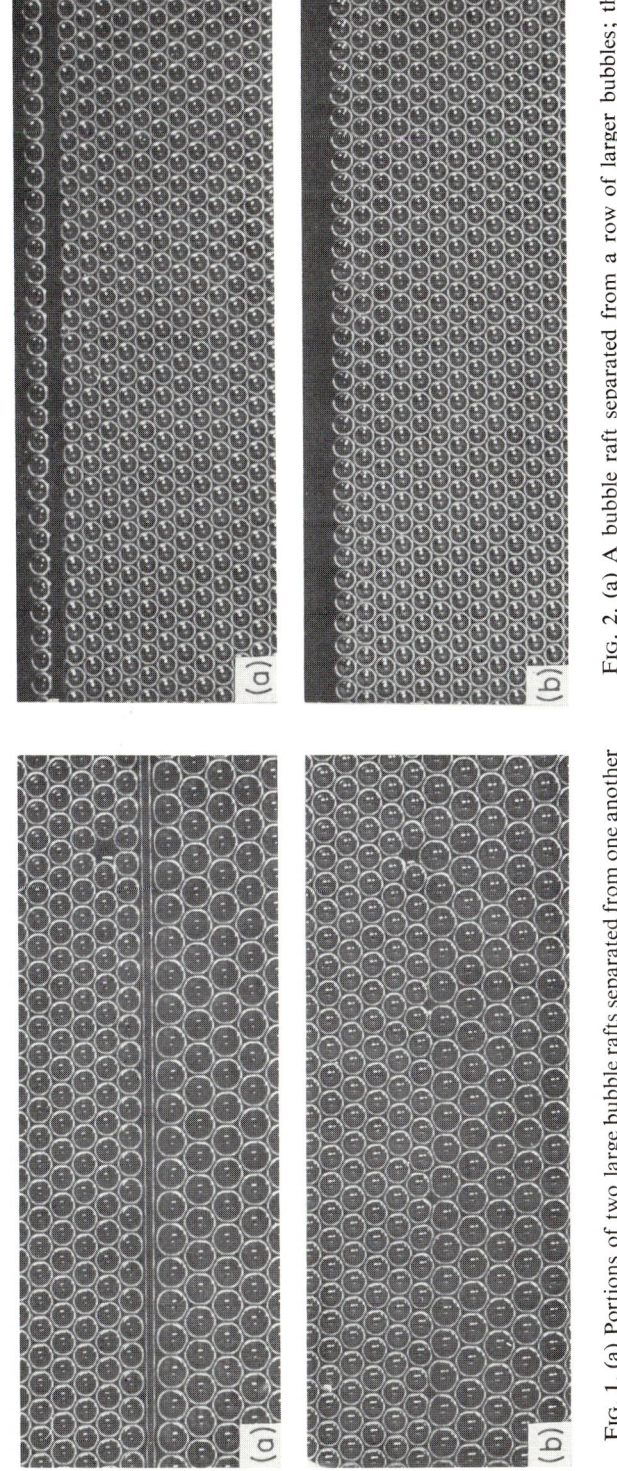

FIG. 1. (a) Portions of two large bubble rafts separated from one another by a barrier; the misfit between the rafts is 16%. (b) Same area after removal of the barrier; four misfit dislocations are available.

FIG. 2. (a) A bubble raft separated from a row of larger bubbles; the misfit is $7\frac{1}{2}$%. (b) Same area after the removal of the barrier; all the misfit is accommodated by elastic strain.

If similar calculations are made for deposits of gold on silver, and for deposits of platinum on gold, it is found that the initial layers will strain to accommodate all the misfit. The thickness at which the accommodation of misfit by dislocations is expected to begin is 460 A for gold on silver, and 5 A for platinum on gold. [Note: The calculations were made assuming that μ_0 was equal to the shear modulus of the softer of the two metals. Allowance was also made for the Burgers vectors of the misfit dislocations (see below).]

Electron micrographs of gold-silver specimens, taken from areas where the gold is less than 250–300 A in thickness, do not reveal gold nuclei, moire fringe patterns, or misfit dislocations. The absence of these features shows, firstly, that gold grows on silver approximately as a monolayer and, secondly, that gold deposits less than 250–300 A in thickness assume the lattice parameter of silver as predicted by van der Merwe (*16–18*).

It should be emphasized that the absence of misfit dislocations from thin deposits of gold on silver could not have been due to complete alloying of the two films. This is because the gold side of the specimen was gold in color and the silver side was silver. The absence of misfit dislocations could also not have been due to partial alloying of the films. This is because conversion of a thin gold overgrowth into a dilute gold-silver alloy increases the misfit. [The misfit between pure gold and silver is smaller than that between gold-silver alloys and silver if the alloys contain between zero and 68 at% silver (*20*).] The absence of misfit dislocations could also not have resulted from differences in the thermal expansion coefficients of gold and silver. The thermal expansions of these metals are such that the misfit between them is larger at the temperature of film growth (360°C) than it is at room temperature.

Areas of the specimen, in which the thickness of the gold deposit exceeded 250–300 A, contained misfit dislocation lines. The dislocation lines were straight and accurately parallel to the [110] directions in the (001) specimen plane. Examples of the dislocations are seen in Figs. 3a and b. These figures are electron micrographs taken of the same specimen area but under different diffraction conditions. The reflections that gave rise to the image contrast were 220 in Fig. 3a and $\bar{2}00$ in Fig. 3b. It can be seen that the straight dislocations labeled *A* are visible in both images, and that the straight dislocations labeled *B* are visible in Fig. 3a but are invisible or almost invisible in Fig. 3b. It can also be seen that two dislocations *A* and *B* combine to form a dislocation *C* which is visible in Fig. 3b but not in Fig. 3a. From these features of the dislocation images (*21*) and the assumption that the Burgers vectors of complete dislocations in fcc lattices are of the type $\frac{1}{2}a \langle 110 \rangle$ or $a \langle 100 \rangle$ (*22*), one can deduce that possible Burgers vectors of the dislocations labeled *A* are $\pm\frac{1}{2}a$ [10$\bar{1}$] and $\pm\frac{1}{2}a$ [$\bar{1}$0$\bar{1}$] and those of the dislocations labeled *B* are $\pm\frac{1}{2}a$ [0$\bar{1}$1] and $\pm\frac{1}{2}a$ (011). The possible Burgers vectors of the dislocation labeled *C* are $\pm\frac{1}{2}a$ [1$\bar{1}$0].

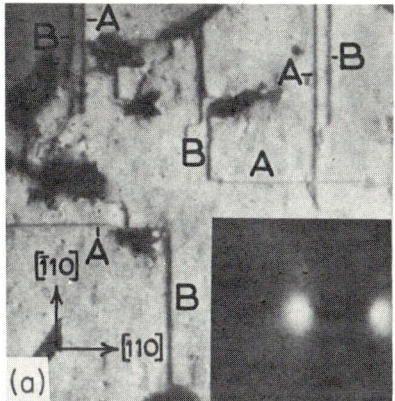
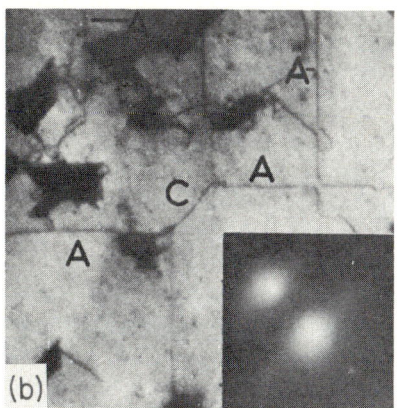

Fig. 3. Electron micrographs and selected area diffraction patterns from the same area of an evaporated gold-silver specimen. The residual gas pressure during the desposition of gold was 5×10^{-8} Torr. The thicknesses of the gold and silver films are approximately 300 and 1500 A. Dislocations labeled A, B, and C are present to accommodate part of the misfit between the two metals. Magnification $\times 69,000$ [from Matthews (11)].

The dislocations labeled A and B are thus mixed dislocations with Burgers vectors inclined at 45° to the (001) gold-silver interface. The misfit that they can accommodate is equal to their edge component projected into the film plane. This is only half the misfit accommodated by dislocations which are in pure edge orientation and have Burgers vectors of the type $\frac{1}{2}a \langle 110 \rangle$ that lie in the interface (see Sections IV,4 and IV,9). Dislocations like A and B are thus rather inefficient misfit dislocations. They are, however, the most efficient dislocations that can glide on {111} planes from the (001) specimen surfaces into the (001) interface between the two crystals (11). Misfit dislocations similar to those described above have been observed in doped silicon by Washburn et al. (23) and in electrodeposits of nickel on copper by Thompson (24).

The fact that misfit dislocations appear in gold-silver specimens before the thickness of the gold reaches 460 A cannot be regarded as significant disagreement between theory and experiment. The early generation of misfit dislocations in these specimens may arise partly from diffusion of silver into the gold, and partly from the larger misfit at the temperature of film growth.

Observations made on deposits of platinum on gold are also in agreement with the predictions of van der Merwe.[2] Electron micrographs of very thin

[2] Observations which appear to contradict one another have been made on deposits of nickel on copper. Haque and Farnsworth (24a) find that thin nickel deposits have the normal lattice parameter of nickel. Gradmann (24b) finds that the thin (<10A) nickel deposits are strained to exactly match the lattice of copper. Gradmann's results agree with the theoretical predictions but Haque and Farnsworth's do not.

(less than about 10 A) deposits of platinum on gold did not reveal nuclei, moire fringe patterns, or misfit dislocations. Platinum deposits greater than 10 A or so in thickness contained long straight misfit dislocations similar to those in deposits of gold on silver. Examples of these dislocations are seen in Fig. 4. The number of these dislocations increases as deposit thickness increases, and moire fringe patterns (25,26) eventually become visible. These fringe patterns are interesting because they show that the dislocations which move into the interface between platinum on gold do indeed cause a local reduction in the misfit accommodated by elastic strain. An electron micrograph in which moire fringes are visible is seen in Fig. 5. The moire fringes are the rather irregular lines roughly parallel to the [100] direction. The straight markings parallel to the [110] and [1$\bar{1}$0] directions are traces left by the dislocations that slipped from an (001) specimen surface into the (001) platinum-gold interface. It can be seen that the separation of moire fringes is smaller at or near the slip traces than it is in regions where little slip took place. This shows that the difference between the lattice parameters of the platinum and gold is greatest in the regions containing many slipped-in dislocations.

The separation of moire fringe patterns becomes smaller as the thickness of the platinum increases, indicating that the fraction of misfit accommodated by elastic strain decreases as deposit thickness increases. This is qualitatively in agreement with the theory. The observed decrease in elastic strain with thickness is, however, significantly smaller than expected. Similar results are obtained for deposits of oxide (Cu_2O) on copper (27), for evaporated deposits of gold on palladium (11), and for electrodeposits of nickel on copper (24). Copper oxide films 450 A in thickness are strained by 2% near the oxide metal interface. This strain accommodates only 12% of the misfit between the two lattices, but it is about 300 times the expected strain. A 100-A film of gold on a 400-A palladium substrate strains 0.6% to accommodate 13% of the misfit between the two metals. The strain predicted by theory is 0.065%. A 200-A nickel film electrodeposited onto an (001) copper surface is strained by 0.86% to accommodate 33% of the misfit between the two lattices. The strain expected from theory is 0.04%.

There are three factors which may have contributed to these disagreements between theory and experiment. The first is partial alloying of overgrowth and substrate (28). This leads—in the majority of systems—to a reduction in the misfit to be accommodated and to an apparent elastic strain. The second factor is the strain of the substrate, and is of negligible importance unless the substrate is itself very thin. It contributed little to the three unexpectedly large strains cited above. The elastic strain of the 400-A palladium substrate, for example, must have been about one sixth of the strain of the gold overgrowth. On van der Merwe's theory this would accommodate only 0.23% of the misfit between the two metals. The third factor which probably contributed

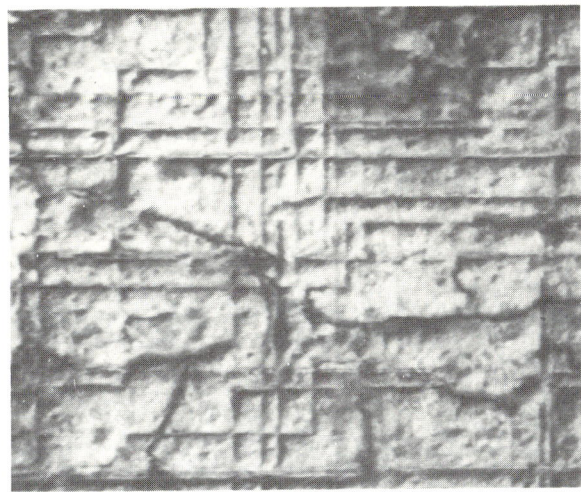

FIG. 4. Electron micrograph of a thin evaporated deposit of platinum on gold. The residual gas pressure during film growth was 3×10^{-9} Torr. The borders of the micrograph are parallel to the [110] and [1$\bar{1}$0] directions. The dark lines parallel to [110] and [1$\bar{1}$0] are images of misfit dislocations. Magnification ×180,000 [from Matthews and Jesser (12)].

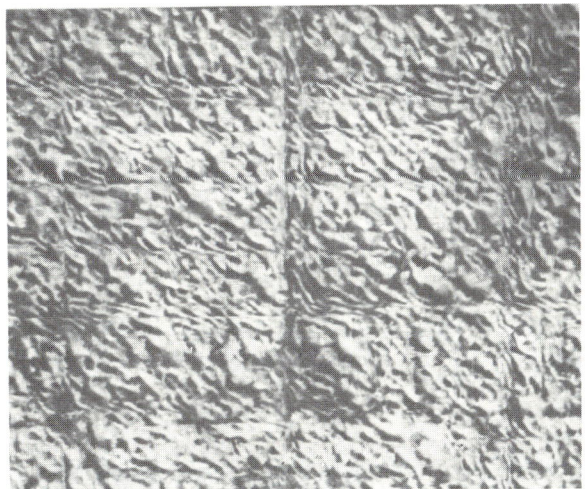

FIG. 5. Electron micrograph of a deposit of platinum on gold. The borders of the figure are parallel to the [110] and [1$\bar{1}$0] directions. The irregular lines roughly parallel to [100] are moire fringes. The markings parallel to [110] and [1$\bar{1}$0] are traces left by misfit dislocations that moved into the interface by glide. Magnification ×180,000 [from Matthews and Jesser (12)].

to the disagreement between theory and experiment was considered by Cabrera (29) and is discussed below.

c. *Generation of Misfit Dislocations.* The generation of dislocations to accommodate the misfit between monolayer islands of lead on silver is almost certainly the same as that described in Section IV,4 for the formation of misfit dislocations between three dimensional islands and their substrates.

The misfit dislocations in gold-silver specimens seem to be generated from dislocations which have suitable Burgers vectors and whose lines extend from the silver substrate through the interface and through the gold overgrowth (11). The conversion of these dislocations into long, straight, misfit dislocations is illustrated in Figs. 6a and 6b. The convention used in Fig. 6 is as

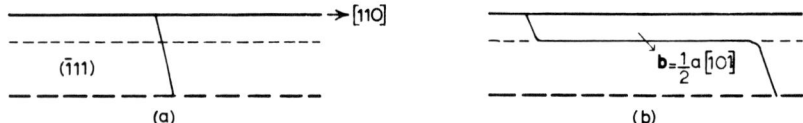

FIG. 6. The generation of a misfit dislocation from a dislocation that initially extended from one surface of the specimen to the other. The convention used is described in the text [from Matthews (11)].

follows: thick continuous and thick broken lines represent the intersections of the ($\bar{1}11$) slip plane with the upper and lower specimen surfaces; the fine broken line is the intersection of the slip plane and the gold silver interface; and the fine continuous line is the dislocation.

Misfit dislocations between platinum and gold may be generated in two ways. The first is the mechanism illustrated in Fig. 6. An example of a length of misfit dislocation line which was made in this way is seen in Fig. 7. The part of the dislocation labeled A extends through the gold substrate. The long part labeled B was drawn out as illustrated in Fig. 6. The image contrast of B is low because the dislocation line is only 10 A or so from the free platinum surface. At C is a length of dislocation line that extends through the platinum layer. The platinum is too thin for this line to be discernible.

The second mechanism for misfit dislocation formation in deposits of platinum on gold begins with the nucleation of a dislocation—either at the

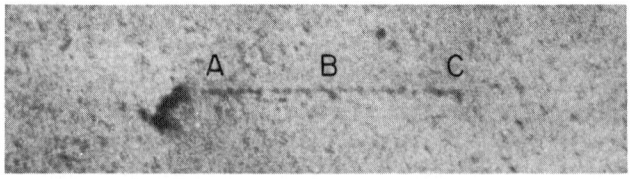

FIG 7. Electron micrograph showing a length of misfit dislocation line generated as described in the text. Magnification × 120,000 [from Matthews and Jesser (12)].

platinum surface or in the interior of the platinum film—and proceeds with the propagation of this dislocation. This mechanism is illustrated in Fig. 8. The reason that the mechanism may operate in films of platinum on gold but not in films of gold on silver is that large strains are needed for dislocation nucleation. The small misfit between gold and silver is unable to provide these strains. An estimate of the strain at which the nucleation of dislocations might occur can be made from the theoretical shear strength of a perfect crystal (30). The result for platinum films oriented with (001) parallel to their plane is 3.3%.

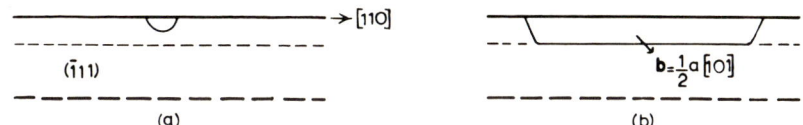

FIG. 8. Nucleation and propagation of a misfit dislocation.

We now come to a description of the third factor which probably contributes to the unexpectedly large strains present in fairly thick films of platinum on gold, oxide on copper, gold on palladium, and nickel on copper (see Section III,2,b above). This factor was first discussed by Cabrera (29). He pointed out that the elastic strain of an overgrowth film will decrease with deposit thickness in a manner close to that predicted by van der Merwe only if misfit dislocations can be generated easily enough to approximately maintain their equilibrium concentration. If they cannot be generated so easily then deposit growth will be accompanied by a smaller decrease in elastic strain than is predicted by the theory. The modes of misfit dislocation formation described above suggest that there will be circumstances under which generation of dislocation lines will be difficult enough to prevent the establishment of an almost equilibrium concentration of misfit dislocations. It is, for example, possible for the stress in an overgrowth film to be too small to nucleate new dislocations, and for there to be obstacles in the film which prevent the lengthening of misfit dislocation lines already present.

d. Cross-Slip of Misfit Dislocations. Near the ends of the dislocation line in Fig. 6, and near the left-hand end of the line in Fig. 8, are lengths of line which are in screw orientation. These lengths are able to cross-slip. If the plane of the interface is (001), and the angle between the two {111} planes involved in cross-slip is obtuse ($180° - 70°32'$), then the misfit accommodated per unit line length is the same on the cross-slip plane as it is on the primary one (*11*). If the angle between the two planes is acute then the dislocation line on the cross-slip plane increases the amount of misfit accommodated by elastic strain. If the plane of the interface is (111), and if the angle between the primary and cross-slip planes is acute, then the misfit accommodated per unit

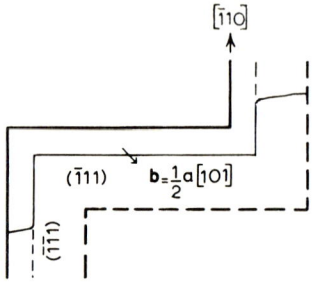

FIG. 9. Cross-slip of a misfit dislocation in a specimen oriented with (001) parallel to the interface [from Matthews (*11*)].

line length is the same on the two slip planes. If the angle between the slip planes is obtuse, then the line on the cross-slip plane increases the misfit accommodated by elastic strain. If the plane of the interface is (110) then the misfit dislocation line on the cross-slip plane accommodates no misfit. Thus, in (001) specimens one would expect the angle between the primary and cross-slip planes to be always obtuse; in (111) specimens one would expect it to be acute; and in (110) specimens one would not expect cross-slip to occur.

The cross-slip of the ends of the dislocation in Fig. 6 onto planes inclined at an obtuse angle to ($\bar{1}$11) is illustrated in Fig. 9. An example of a dislocation that has twice undergone cross-slip is seen in Fig. 10. The specimen from which Fig. 10 was obtained was oriented with (001) parallel to its plane.

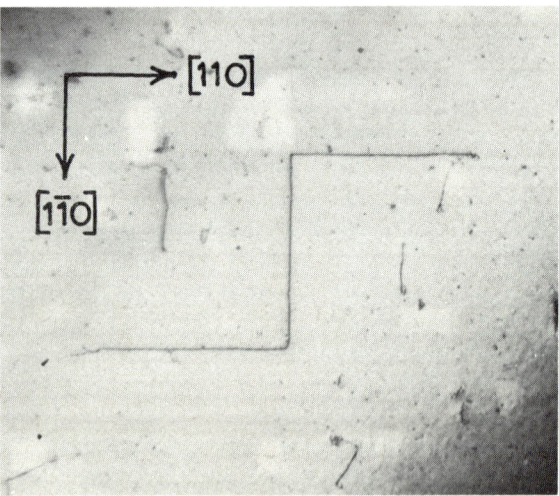

FIG. 10. Electron micrograph of a gold-silver specimen showing a misfit dislocation that has twice undergone cross-slip. Magnification ×46,000 [from Matthews (*11*)].

It is possible for misfit dislocations to cross-slip more than twice, and dislocations which have cross-slipped as many as sixteen times have been observed. In every example of multiple cross-slip a right turn by the dislocation was followed by a turn to the left. It is easily demonstrated that this is expected if the angle between the primary and the cross-slip plane is either always acute or always obtuse.

3. Defects in Films

No study has been made of the defects in deposits of lead on silver, or in systems which resemble lead on silver in both misfit and mode of film growth. Defects in films of gold on silver seem to be simply extensions of defects in the silver surface. The evidence for this is the observation that the perfection of evaporated gold films depends on the perfection of their substrate. If the silver substrate is grown on sodium chloride, then the gold film contains about 10^{10} dislocation lines/cm^2, and large densities of both microtwins and stacking faults. This defect content is similar to that of the silver substrate (*31–34*). If the substrate is an annealed silver sphere then the gold film contains few defects. A micrograph of a gold film grown in ultrahigh vacuum (3×10^{-9} Torr) on a silver sphere at 300°C is seen in Fig. 11. The number

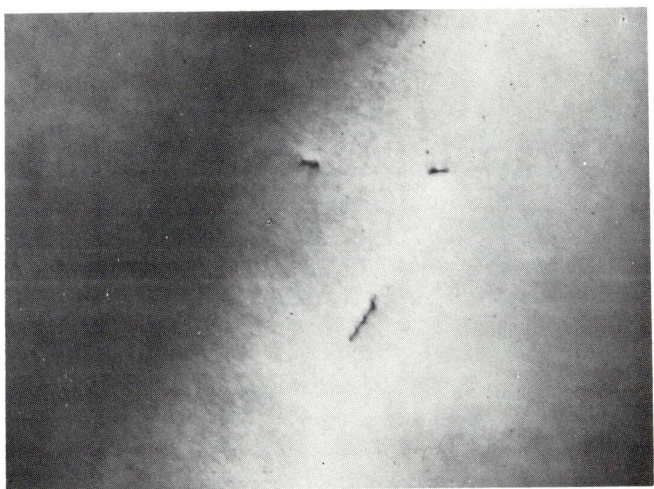

Fig. 11. Electron micrograph of a gold film grown on a silver ball. Magnification ×40,000.

of dislocations per square centimeter of this film was 7×10^7, and the densities of stacking faults and twins were negligibly small.

Stacking faults, twins, and many of the dislocations in deposits of platinum on gold seem also to be extensions of defects in the substrate surface. This may, however, not be the only origin of the dislocations in the platinum films. The nucleation of dislocations to accommodate misfit (see Fig. 8) results in the formation of pairs of dislocation lines that extend through the film.

If the extension of defects in the substrate and the nucleation of dislocations in the overgrowth are the only modes of defect formation in films that are initially pseudomorphic, then it should be possible to grow films which are free of dislocations, stacking faults, and twins. All that one requires—in addition to the formation of an initially pseudomorphic layer—are a perfect substrate and a misfit of less than about 3%.

IV. Film Formation by the Generation, Growth, and Coalescence of Nuclei

1. Nucleation

a. Introduction. Studies of the early stages in the epitaxial growth of one material on another have shown that growth begins, in the majority of systems, with the generation of three-dimensional nuclei (*2*). Examples of overgrowth-substrate combinations in which nuclei have been observed are silver on mica (*35, 36*), alkali halides on mica (*37*), silver and gold on molybdenite (*38–41*), fcc metals and germanium on alkali halides (*4, 41–50*), gold on magnesium oxide (*51*), lead sulfide on sodium chloride (*52*), alkali halides on alkali halides (*53*), oxides on copper (*4, 54*), cadmium (*55*), magnesium (*56*), and nickel (*57, 58*), silicon on silicon (*59, 60*), gold on silver (*4, 61–63*), gold on platinum (*12*), and rhodium on silver (*4*).

Theoretical treatments of the nucleation of an overgrowth on a substrate have been given by Hirth and Pound (*3*), Hirth and Moazed (*63a*), and by Walton (*64*), and Walton and Rhodin (*65*). Hirth and Pound's treatment is an extension of the classical theory of nucleation (*5, 66*). It is assumed that the substrate surface contains a number of mobile adsorbed atoms or molecules and a number of clusters in the form of spherical caps. The contact angle between cap and substrate is related to the surface and interfacial free energies by Eq. (1) in Section II. Derivation of the expression for nucleation rate begins with a calculation of the concentration of nuclei of critical size, assuming the system is in equilibrium. This concentration is then multiplied by the frequency with which a single atom joins a critical nucleus to promote it to a stable one, and by a nonequilibrium factor. The result is thought to be a good description of nucleation in systems where the critical nuclei contain many atoms. It should, as Hirth and Pound have emphasized, be used with caution when the critical nuclei contain few atoms. This is because macroscopic properties, such as surface free energy, are used in the derivation of the expression for nucleation rate, and these properties cannot be defined for clusters containing few atoms (67). It seems that in many examples of epitaxy the critical nuclei are large enough for Hirth and Pound's treatment to be valid (63a). In other examples the critical nuclei contain less than ten atoms and are probably too small. Specimens in which the critical nuclei may be too small are evaporated deposits of fcc metals on sodium chloride (45), and the deposits described in Section III.

Nucleation theory has been extended to systems in which the critical nuclei are very small by Hirth et al. (67a), Walton (64), and Walton and Rhodin (65). Walton and Rhodin find that the nucleation rate for a critical nucleus containing n^* atoms is given by

$$I_{n*} = N_0 R a_0^2 (R/\gamma N_0)^{n*} \exp[((n^* + 1)Q_{ad} + E_{n*} - Q_D)/kT] \tag{3}$$

where R is the rate of incidence from the vapor [cm^{-2}sec^{-1}], N_0 is the number of adsorption sites per square centimeter, γ is the vibration frequency, Q_{ad} is the binding energy of an atom to the surface, E_{n*} is the dissociation energy of the critical nucleus, Q_D is the activation energy for surface diffusion, and a_0 is the distance covered in a single diffusion jump. A difficulty in this theory is that E_{n*} is not known and n^* cannot be determined. It is, however, possible to write down expressions for the nucleation rates of clusters of particular sizes. At high supersaturations the critical nucleus is a single atom, $E_1 = 0$, and the nucleation rate is given by

$$I_1 = N_0 R a_0^2 (R/\gamma N_0) \exp[(2Q_{ad} - Q_D)/kT] \tag{4}$$

This equation gives the rate at which pairs of atoms are formed and holds only if a pair of atoms will not dissociate before being joined by a third atom. If the supersaturation is reduced a stage will be reached where Eq. (4) no longer applies. When this is so configurations in which there are two bonds per atom become the smallest stable clusters. The smallest cluster with two bonds per atom consists of three atoms arranged at the corners of an equilateral triangle. The critical nucleus is a pair, and the expression for nucleation rate is obtained by inserting $n^* = 2$ into Eq. (3). Another cluster in which there are two nearest-neighbor bonds per atom is that in which four atoms are arranged at the corners of a square. The critical nucleus contains three atoms and the nucleation rate is given by

$$I_3 = N_0 R a_0^2 (R/\gamma N_0)^3 \exp[(4Q_{ad} + E_3 - Q_D)/kT] \tag{5}$$

Deposits of fcc metals, grown under conditions where three atoms arranged at the corners of an equilateral triangle form a stable cluster, would be expected to be oriented with the (111) plane parallel to the plane of the deposit. Deposits grown under conditions where atoms arranged at the corners of a square form the first stable cluster would be oriented with (001) parallel to their plane.

Walton *et al.* (*45*) have measured the nucleation rate of silver deposited in ultrahigh vacuum onto vacuum-cleaved sodium chloride over a range of substrate temperatures. The graph of ln I against $1/T$ consisted of two straight portions of different slope. In the high-temperature region the deposit was oriented with (001) parallel to its plane. They considered that in this region the smallest stable cluster was made up of four atoms arranged at the corners of a square. In the low-temperature region the deposit showed no well-defined orientation and they assumed that here the critical nucleus was a single atom. Thus, the nucleation at low temperatures was considered to be described by Eq. (4) and nucleation at high temperatures by Eq. (5). (Evidence in support of this was provided by the experimental results which gave reasonable values for the pre-exponential factors.) The transition temperature is obtained by setting Eqs. (4) and (5) equal to one another and is given by

$$T_t = -(Q_{ad} + E_3/2)/k \ln(R/\gamma N_0) \qquad (6)$$

By inserting the observed transition temperature into Eq. (6), and determining the slopes of the straight portions of the graph of ln I versus $1/T$, they obtained values for Q_{ad}, E_3, and an upper limit for Q_D.

b. Nucleation at Surface Steps. Nuclei of deposit material are often arranged in lines on the substrate surface (*42–46, 68–72*). The change in surface elevation across a number of parallel lines (*42*), and analysis of dislocations that terminate these lines (*46, 70*), has shown that the lines of nuclei lie along surface steps, and that many of the steps are monatomic. A theoretical treatment of nucleation at surface steps has been given by Chakraverty and Pound (*73*) [see also Hirth and Moazed (*63a*)]. They predict that there will be a strong preference for nucleation at surface steps when the contact angle between overgrowth and substrate is less than about 90°.

c. Influence of Substrate Perfection and Purity. Robbins and Rhodin (*51*) have studied the nucleation of gold in ultrahigh vacuum on vacuum-cleaved magnesium oxide substrates. They found that the maximum number of nuclei per unit area did not depend on either deposition rate or substrate temperature in the ranges studied. The maximum number of nuclei per unit area did, however, depend on the crystal from which the substrate was cleaved. They concluded that the generation of gold nuclei was controlled by impurities or point defects in the substrate surface. Results which are probably related to these have been obtained for gold deposits grown on clean and on air-contaminated sodium chloride surfaces (*47, 50*). Gold deposits 1 A in average thickness were condensed onto a pair of sodium chloride crystals cleaved from the same parent crystal. The two crystals were equal distances from the gold source and were clamped together so that they were at the same temperature. The difference between them was that the surface of one had been exposed to air at atmospheric pressure and the other was cleaved inside the ultrahigh vacuum chamber shortly before the deposition of gold began. It was found that the number of nuclei generated per unit area of the contaminated surface was about twice as large as the number generated on the clean surface. This can be seen by comparing the electron micrographs in Figs. 12a and 12b. A further observation which shows that nucleation can be influenced by impurities in the substrate surface was made by Young (74). He has found that the oxidation of copper occurs preferentially at the emergence points of dislocations, but only when the copper is impure.

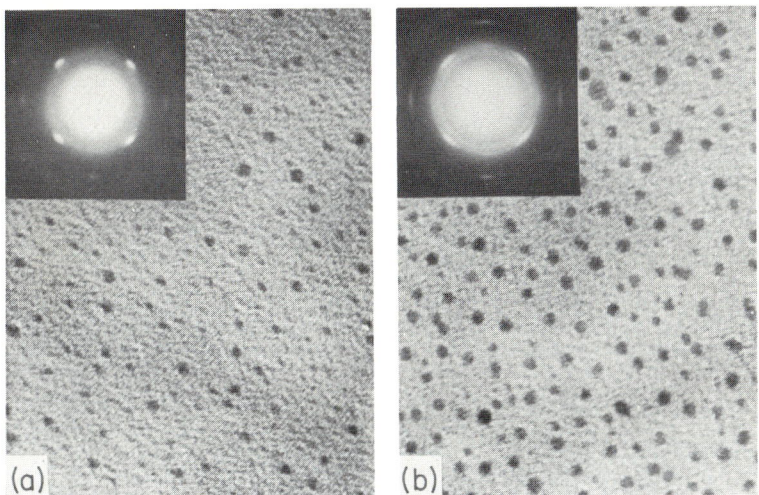

FIG. 12. Electron micrographs and diffraction patterns from 1-Å gold deposits grown side by side in ultrahigh vacuum (a) Grown on clean sodium chloride surface. (b) Grown on air-contaminated sodium chloride surface. Substrate temperature 360°C. Magnification ×570,000 [from Matthews (50)].

Preferential nucleation at points where dislocations end on the substrate surface cannot be an important factor in the nucleation of the majority of evaporated thin films. This is because the number of nuclei formed per unit area is usually much larger than the number of dislocation lines that end on the substrate surface. The dislocation density in well-annealed sodium chloride crystals, for example, is about $10^5/cm^2$, and the number of gold nuclei formed per square centimeter of a sodium chloride substrate is about 10^{12} (47).

Preference for nucleation at the emergence points of dislocations seems to be small. The observations of Faust (75), Young (74), and Lawless and Garmon (58) indicate that dislocations in pure germanium, copper, or nickel have little influence on the nucleation of oxide.

The nucleation of silver sulphide at stacking faults and thin twins in silver films has been studied by Phillips (76). He found that these defects did indeed aid the formation of nuclei. As steps in the silver surface are associated with these defects it seems probable—as Phillips has pointed out—that this is simply another example of preferential nucleation at surface steps.

d. *Influence of Deposition Rate.* Nucleation rate is expected to increase when the deposition rate is increased, and experimental evidence for this has been obtained (*51, 63a*). An increase in deposition rate does, however, not necessarily increase the maximum number of nuclei formed per unit area. Robbins and Rhodin (*51*) found that the maximum number of gold nuclei per unit area of a magnesium oxide substrate is not altered when the deposition rate is increased by a factor of about ten. If deposition rate is varied over a wider range than that tested by Robbins and Rhodin then it is clear that the maximum number of nuclei generated per unit area does depend on deposition rate. Figures 13a and 13b are respectively, electron micrographs of gold

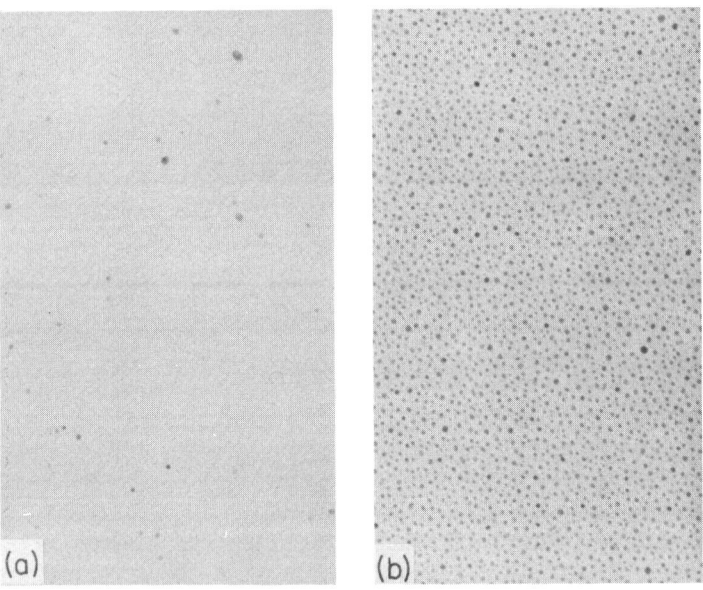

FIG. 13. Electron micrographs of slowly (0.02 A/sec) and rapidly (1000 A/sec) grown gold deposits. The number of nuclei per unit area of the rapidly grown specimen greatly exceeds the number per unit area of the slowly grown one. Magnification × 170,000.

deposits grown slowly (0.02 A/sec) and rapidly (1000 A/sec) in ultrahigh vacuum on sodium chloride surfaces prepared inside the vacuum chamber. The nuclei in Fig. 13a are on the average larger than those in Fig. 13b but are much less numerous.

e. Effect of Substrate Temperature. Nucleation rate increases if the deposition rate is kept constant and the substrate temperature is lowered (*3, 48, 51, 63a, 64, 65*). This increase may result in the increase in the maximum number of nuclei per unit area (*48*), but this is not invariably so. Robbins and Rhodin (*51*) found that the maximum number of gold nuclei formed per unit area of magnesium oxide did not depend on the temperature of the substrate.

f. Perfection of Nuclei. Dislocations in crystals of very small volume can be detected by means of the moire fringe technique of Hashimoto and Uyeda (*77*), and Pashley *et al.* (*78*). This technique has been used to study dislocations in small nuclei by Bassett (*38*) and Matthews (*35*) and more recently by Pashley *et al.* (*41*). These investigations showed that the majority of small nuclei in evaporated deposits of silver on mica, and in deposits of silver and gold on molybdenite, do not contain any dislocations. This is illustrated by Fig. 14 which shows a silver nucleus oriented with the (111) plane parallel to the surface of its mica substrate. The moire fringes in the nucleus were formed as a result of type $2\bar{2}0$ reflections in the silver lattice (*25, 26*). The absence of dislocations in the fringe patterns shows that the nucleus did not contain any dislocations (*25, 28, 78*). The volume of the nucleus in Fig. 14 was about 10^{-18} cm^3.

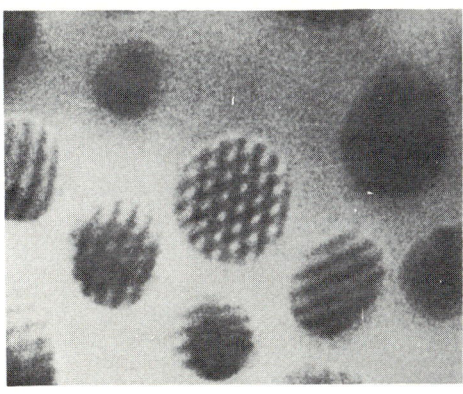

FIG. 14. Electron micrograph of a dislocation-free nucleus of silver on mica. Magnification × 700,000 [from Matthews (*35*)].

Nuclei which are similar to or smaller than the nucleus in Fig. 4, and are grown in ultrahigh vacuum from pure (99.9999%) starting material, contain not only no dislocations but may also contain no point defects or impurity atoms. They are, however, strained a little to match their substrate, and misfit dislocations may be present in the interface between nucleus and substrate.

2. ORIENTATION OF NUCLEI

a. Introduction. Deposits of one material on another sometimes appear to contain only one orientation at all stages in film growth. More often several preferred orientations are present (*79–83a*). Specimens in which two preferred orientations have been observed are deposits of silver on mica (*10, 36*), and of gold on molybdenite (*40*). The two orientations are illustrated in Fig. 15 with the aid of Thompson's standard tetrahedron (*84*). The faces of the tetrahedron are parallel to the {111} planes, and its edges are parallel to the ⟨110⟩ directions. One of the orientations in Fig. 15 is converted into the other by a rotation of π about the normal to the (111) specimen plane. The orientations are thus twins of one another; their twinning plane is (111). The presence of these two orientations is called double-positioning.

FIG. 15. The two orientations present in deposits of silver on mica, and deposits of gold on molybdenite.

Deposits of fcc metals grown in ultrahigh vacuum on vacuum-cleaved sodium chloride may contain as many as ten preferred orientations (*14, 49, 50, 81*). The same ten preferred orientations have been found in nickel oxide grown on the (001) surface of nickel (*75*). (It is perhaps significant that nickel oxide has the sodium chloride structure.) The ten orientations are illustrated in Fig. 16. Orientation (a) is parallel to the substrate lattice and is the normal alignment of continuous fcc metal films grown on (001) sodium chloride surfaces (*1, 85*). (b) has the (001) plane parallel to the (001) substrate surface, and a ⟨110⟩ direction parallel to the ⟨100⟩ direction in the surface of the substrate. (c)–(j) all have the (111) plane parallel to the substrate surface. (c)–(f) have a ⟨110⟩ direction parallel to one of the two ⟨110⟩ directions in the substrate surface. (g)–(j) have a ⟨110⟩ direction parallel to one of the two ⟨100⟩ directions in the surface of the salt. (c) and (d) are in twin relationship (cf. Fig. 15). The same relationship exists between (e) and (f), (g) and (h), and between (i) and (j).

In addition to nuclei in the preferred orientations there are usually nuclei present whose orientations deviate from the preferred ones by a small rotation about the normal to the deposit plane. Evidence for the presence of these nuclei was first obtained by reflection electron diffraction (*81*). More recently small misalignments of individual nuclei have been measured using dark-field electron microscopy (*34*) and moire fringe patterns (*35, 38, 41, 86*). The moire fringe technique has the advantage that small misalignments of individual nuclei can be measured with precision. This is because the rotation of the fringe pattern is large compared with the rotation of the lattice. The relation between the actual lattice rotation α and the rotation of the fringe pattern β is given by

$$\tan \beta = \pm g_2 \sin \alpha / (g_1 - g_2 \cos \alpha) \qquad (7)$$

where g_1 and g_2 are the lengths of reciprocal lattice vectors that define the substrate and overgrowth planes involved in the formation of the fringes. The

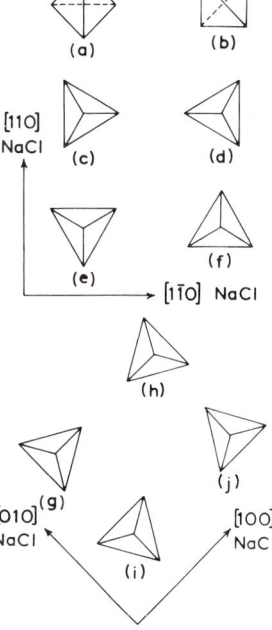

FIG. 16. Ten orientations found in deposits of fcc metals on sodium chloride, and of nickel oxide on nickel [from Matthews (50)].

plus sign is to be used when g_1 is greater than g_2, and the minus sign when g_2 is greater than g_1. An electron micrograph of a thin deposit of silver on mica in which small misalignments of nuclei are revealed by the moiré fringes is seen in Fig. 17.

The presence of various orientations in thin deposits has been discussed by Cabrera (6, 29) who assumed firstly that nucleation is controlled by the surface energy of the nucleus, and secondly that nuclei with the lowest surface energy will be formed the most frequently. He discusses interfacial energy using Frank and van der Merwe's model (15), and concludes that there will be a number of minimum free-energy configurations and that these will correspond to minimum numbers of interfacial or misfit dislocations. These energy minima are cusps of various depths in the interfacial energy versus orientation relationship. Nuclei with orientations corresponding to the minimum free energy cusps will be generated. The most common orientation will be that corresponding to the cusp with the lowest free energy. In addition to the nuclei oriented at the free-energy minima there will be nuclei that are rotated out of the favored alignments about an axis normal to the specimen plane. These nuclei are in unstable positions and may rotate into the nearest minimum free-energy position and reduce the number of interfacial dislocations in the process (see Section IV,4). To do this they must overcome the

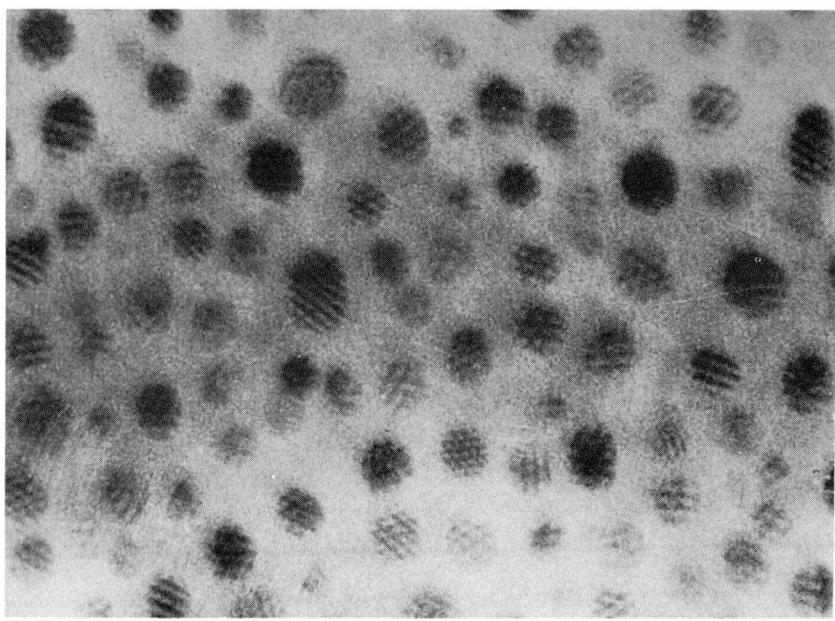

FIG. 17. Electron micrograph of a thin deposit of silver on mica. The moire fringes reveal that many of the nuclei are misaligned by a rotation about the normal to the specimen plane. Magnification ×400,000 [from Matthews (*35*)].

frictional force opposing misfit dislocation motion. In situations where the frictional force is too large for the misfit dislocations to move the nuclei will remain misaligned and grow in size to give a deposit resembling that in Fig. 17. An expression giving the distribution in the alignments of nuclei—in specimens where spontaneous rotations into minimum energy orientations do not occur—has been derived by Cabrera (*29*). This distribution agrees fairly well with that observed by Jesser *et al.* (*86*) in annealed electrodeposits of platinum on gold.

  b. Influence of Substrate Temperature. The orientation of evaporated deposits has been measured as a function of substrate temperature for many overgrowth and substrate materials. In the majority of systems it has been found that the preference for a particular orientation increases as the substrate temperature increases. In many systems there seems to be a critical substrate temperature known as the epitaxial temperature (79, 80, 84): if the substrate is above this temperature a single crystal film is obtained; if it is below this temperature the film is polycrystalline. The epitaxial temperature is found to depend on deposition rate (87), the pressure in the vacuum chamber (88), and on contamination of the substrate surface (81).

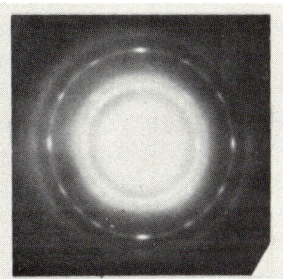

FIG. 18. Electron diffraction pattern from a gold deposit grown on sodium chloride at room temperature [from Matthews and Grunbaum (88a)].

The effect of substrate temperature on the orientation of nuclei of gold on sodium chloride (88a) is seen by comparing Fig. 18 with Fig. 30a. Fig. 18 was obtained from a deposit grown at room temperature, and Fig. 30a from one grown at 360°C. The substrates were cleaved in ultrahigh vacuum (approximately 5×10^{-9} Torr) while the evaporation of metal was in progress to ensure that growth began on a clean surface. The thicknesses of the deposits were less than 10 Å. Thin deposits were chosen because they give a better indication of the orientation of the initial nuclei than do thick ones (88a) (see Section IV,7).

Figs. 18 and 30a reveal that the preference for the orientation parallel to the sodium chloride lattice was much stronger in the specimen grown at 360°C than it was in the one grown at room temperature. [This is in agreement with earlier work performed under poorer vacuum conditions (79, 80, 85).] The deposit grown at room temperature contained nine preferred orientations in addition to that parallel to the substrate. These were orientations (b)–(j) in Fig. 16. The arcing of the spots in Figs. 18 and 30a reveals that both deposits contained nuclei whose orientations deviated from the preferred ones by rotations about the normal to the specimen plane.

The experimental results described above are not ideal for comparison with the theoretical predictions of Hirth and Pound (3) and Moazed and Hirth (89). In experimental studies of the effects of substrate temperature on orientation it is customary to use the same deposition rates for the low temperatures as for the high. This means that not only is the temperature changed from one experiment to the other but also the supersaturation. The distribution in the orientation of nuclei depends both on substrate temperature and on supersaturation (*3, 29, 89*). However if appropriate values for the temperature and supersaturation are inserted into the expression given by Moazed and Hirth (*89*) for the nucleation rate of the favored orientation divided by the nucleation rate of the less favored one, then it is found that the prominence of the favored orientation of gold nuclei is expected to be greater at 360°C than it is at room temperature.

The change from the (001) orientation (Fig. 30a) to the (111) orientation (Fig. 18) as the temperature of the substrate is reduced can be explained using the ideas of Walton (*64, 90*), Rhodin and Walton (*65*), and Walton et al. (*45*) (see Section IV,1,a) if the following assumptions are made. At elevated temperatures the smallest stable cluster consists of four gold atoms arranged at the corners of a square. At low temperatures the smallest stable cluster is made up of three atoms at the corners of an equilateral triangle.

c. Influence of Deposition Rate. Theories of nucleation predict that the alignment of deposits is improved by a lowering of the supersaturation (*3, 29*). Some experimental results seem at first sight to be inconsistent with this prediction. It has, for example, been observed that the growth of single-crystal films of various materials is aided by high deposition rates in the early stages of film growth (*91, 91a*). These results should, however, be interpreted with caution. They do not necessarily mean that the rapidly grown nuclei are more perfectly aligned than the slowly grown ones. An increase in deposition rate changes not only the orientation of nuclei but also their number (see Section IV,2,c), and it is known that the number of nuclei per unit area can have a controlling influence on the orientation of the final film (*9, 47*). There is little doubt that rapid deposition aids epitaxy in certain systems because of the difference in the number of nuclei per unit area rather than the difference in the alignment of the nuclei.

Comparison between the alignment of nuclei in thin, slowly grown, deposits of gold on sodium chloride and their alignment in thin rapidly grown ones shows that the slowly grown nuclei are better aligned. The difference between the orientations of slowly (0.02–10 A/sec) and rapidly (1000 A/sec), grown specimens is, however, not very marked. Both specimens show a strong preference for the orientation parallel to the sodium chloride lattice. The main differences between the slowly and rapidly grown specimens are, firstly, that the rapidly grown ones contain more nuclei oriented with (111) parallel to the deposit plane, and, secondly, that in the rapidly grown deposits the orientations (c)–(f) and (g)–(j) are about equally prominent whereas in the slowly grown specimens orientations (c)–(f) are much more prominent than (g)–(j) (*47, 50, 81*).

d. Orientation of Nuclei at Surface Steps. Bassett et al. (*28*) have found that monatomic steps in (001) sodium chloride surfaces have remarkably little influence on the orientation of nuclei formed along them. This conclusion has been confirmed for gold deposits grown in ultrahigh vacuum on vacuum cleaved sodium chloride surfaces (92). Allpress and Sanders (71) have found that the epitaxy of gold on the heavily stepped regions of a silver substrate was more perfect than it was in regions that contained no steps. The thickness of their specimens was such that much coalescence had occurred on the steps but little on the surrounding flat areas. Thus, it is possible that the orientation differences in the stepped and unstepped areas may have resulted not only from the influence of steps on the alignment of nuclei but also orientation changes that accompany coalescence (see Section IV,7).

e. Effect of Contaminants on the Alignment of Nuclei. Diffraction patterns from thin (1 A) gold deposits grown side by side on clean and contaminated sodium chloride can be seen in Figs. 12a and b. The patterns show that the two deposits contained the same preferred orientation. The arcs indicate that the preference for this orientation was stronger in the deposit grown on the clean surface than it was in that grown on the air contaminated surface. Thus, the exposure of a sodium chloride surface to air does not improve the alignment of gold nuclei formed upon it.

Taylor (93) has found that the epitaxy of copper on tungsten is inhibited by oxidation of the tungsten surface.

3. THE SHAPE OF NUCLEI

Some information about the shape of nuclei is given by their outlines in electron micrographs. Further information can be obtained from the images of stacking faults or thin twins that extend through some of the larger nuclei. These image details show that nuclei greater than 100 A or so in diameter usually have facets parallel to low-energy surfaces. In deposits of fcc metals these facets are parallel to the {111} and {100} planes. The profiles of (001) and (111) nuclei in deposits of gold on (001) sodium chloride surfaces are approximately as shown in Fig. 19.

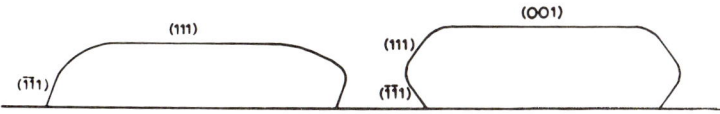

FIG. 19. Profiles of (001) and (111) gold nuclei grown on the (001) surface of sodium chloride [from Matthews (47)].

4. ACCOMMODATION OF MISFIT BETWEEN NUCLEUS AND SUBSTRATE

The accommodation of misfit between a hemispherical nucleus and its substrate has been treated by Cabrera (29). He finds that the nucleus strains elastically to take up part of the misfit. The magnitude of this strain is about

1% for a nucleus 100 A in diameter, and is inversely proportional to the radius of the hemisphere. The theory has been refined by Jesser et al. (86), and an attempt to measure the strain and its variation with radius has been made. The specimens studied were annealed electrodeposits of platinum on gold. The strains were calculated from the direction and spacing of moire fringe patterns visible in electron micrographs of the specimens. The results were in agreement with the theory.

Misfit in excess of that accommodated by elastic strain is taken up by a network of interfacial or misfit dislocations (15–18). Examples of misfit dislocations in a nucleus of an unidentified material on a chromium bromide substrate were observed by Delavignette et al. (94). Grünbaum and Mitchell (95) found misfit dislocations between islands of nickel bromide grown epitaxially on chromic bromide. Dislocations in (001) interfaces between gold nuclei and platinum substrates have been observed by Matthews and Jesser. The dislocations were in edge orientation and their Burgers vectors were $\pm\frac{1}{2}a$ [110] and $\pm\frac{1}{2}a$ [1$\bar{1}$0]. They were thus the same as misfit dislocations observed in (001) interfaces between continuous films of lead sulfide on lead selenide (96), and in (001) interfaces between continuous films of gold on palladium (11) (see Section IV,9). The misfit accommodated by unit line length of these dislocations is twice that accommodated by unit line length of the dislocations found in (001) specimens of gold on silver, platinum on gold, and nickel on copper (see Section III,2,b).

The difference between misfit dislocations found in specimens which grow as pseudomorphic continuous films, and the dislocations found in specimens which grow as three-dimensional islands, results from the different modes of misfit dislocation formation. In deposits which grow as pseudomorphic continuous films the misfit dislocations glide from the upper or lower specimen surface into the interface. To do this they must have Burgers vectors inclined to the interface. In deposits which grow as three-dimensional nuclei this restriction no longer exists. The misfit disclocations can be generated at the junction between the surface of the nucleus and the surface of the substrate as is illustrated in Figs. 20a and 20b. The dislocations in Fig. 20 are in pure edge orientation and have Burgers vectors parallel to the (001) interface.

It should be emphasized that misfit dislocations formed between three-dimensional islands and their substrate will only be in edge orientation and have Burgers vectors in the interface if the interface contains suitable lattice vectors. Suitable lattice vectors are present in (001), (111), and possibly in (110) interfaces between fcc metals, but there are an infinite number of high-index interfaces for which this will not be true.

Dislocations like those in Fig. 20 do not remain motionless as the size of the nucleus increases, but move to reduce the average separation of their lines. This is because, as both theoretical (29) and experimental (86) studies have shown, the misfit accommodated by elastic strain decreases as the size of the nucleus increases.

In Section IV,2,a it was mentioned that the density of misfit dislocations is increased if a nucleus is rotated out of the epitaxial alignment about the normal to the specimen plane. This increase is easily calculated. Suppose, for simplicity, that the network of misfit dislocations is made up of arrays of parallel dislocations, that the dislocations in each array are identical, that

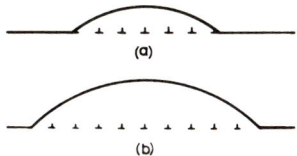

Fig. 20. Diagrams illustrating the generation of misfit dislocations during the growth of nuclei [from Matthews (*11*)].

they are in edge orientation when the nucleus is perfectly aligned, and that they have Burgers vectors which lie in the film plane. Under these conditions the effect of a lattice rotation on the misfit dislocations is similar to its effect on moire fringe patterns. The relation between S, the separation of misfit dislocations, and α, the rotation of the nucleus about the normal to the specimen plane, is given by

$$S = b_1 b_2 / (b_1^2 + b_2^2 - 2 b_1 b_2 \cos \alpha)^{1/2} \tag{8}$$

where b_1 is the magnitude of the Burgers vector of the misfit dislocations measured in the substrate lattice, and b_2 is its magnitude measured in the lattice of the overgrowth.

The rotation α of the nucleus is accompanied by a much larger rotation β of the misfit dislocation lines. During this rotation the dislocation lines acquire a screw component which is proportional to $\sin \beta$. The relationship between β and α is as follows:

$$\tan \beta = \pm b_1 \sin \alpha / (b_2 - b_1 \cos \alpha) \tag{9}$$

5. Growth of Nuclei

The growth of a nucleus takes place partly by the capture of atoms that diffuse across the substrate surface and strike its periphery, and partly by the capture of atoms that land directly upon it. The relative importance of these two processes depends on the fraction of the substrate surface covered by deposit. The rate of growth by the capture of atoms at the periphery of a nucleus is proportional to its perimeter, and its growth rate by the capture of impinging atoms is proportional to the solid angle it subtends at the source of film material. Thus, if we have a pair of nuclei of equal volume but different contact angle, then the one with the smallest contact angle will grow the most rapidly. Consider a deposit in which the nuclei prefer to be parallel to the substrate, but which also contains nuclei whose lattices deviate from the parallel orientation by a rotation about the normal to the deposit plane. The energies of the free surfaces of the parallel and misaligned nuclei will be very nearly equal. The energy of the interface between a well-aligned nucleus and the substrate will, however, be smaller than the energy of the interface between a badly aligned nucleus and its substrate (see Section IV,2,a and IV,4). As a result of this difference in interfacial energy the contact angles of the well-aligned nuclei will be smaller than those of the badly aligned ones. The well-aligned nuclei will therefore grow more rapidly than the badly aligned ones.

Experimental results which are consistent with this prediction have been obtained from evaporated deposits of silver on mica (35). The preferred orientations of the nuclei in deposits of silver on mica have (111) parallel to the (001) mica surface, and have either the [$\bar{1}$10] or the [1$\bar{1}$0] direction parallel to the [010] direction in the surface of the mica (10, 97). In addition, there are nuclei present whose orientations deviate from the preferred ones by small rotations about the normal to the specimen plane. Measurements of the size of individual nuclei, and of their deviation from the preferred orientation (35) showed that the large nuclei were better aligned than the small ones. Thus the nuclei in the preferred orientations grew more rapidly than did their misaligned neighbors.

Experimental results which seem, at first sight, to be inconsistent with the predictions have been obtained from gold deposits grown in ultrahigh vacuum on (001) sodium chloride surfaces prepared inside the vacuum chamber. The most common orientation in very thin (1–10 A) deposits is parallel to the sodium chloride lattice. The largest nuclei in deposits 25 A in average thickness are oriented with (111) parallel to the (001) salt surface and with a $\langle 110 \rangle$ direction parallel to one of the two $\langle 110 \rangle$ directions in the surface of the salt (47, 49, 50). Thus, the gold nuclei which are formed the most easily are not those which grow the most rapidly.

An explanation for this perhaps surprising result is provided by the theory of Hirth and Pound (3). Their theory predicts that nuclei with a contact angle of about 45° will be generated much more rapidly than nuclei whose contact angle is near zero. Thus, if the contact angle for (001) nuclei on sodium chloride is near 45°, and that for {111} nuclei is near zero, then one would expect the (001) nuclei to be the most numerous and the (111) nuclei to grow the most rapidly. The results of Hirth and Pound's theory should, however, be applied to deposits of gold on sodium chloride with caution (see Section IV,2,a).

An alternative explanation is provided by the anisotropy in the surface free energy of gold (47, 50). The anisotropy in the surface free energy of fcc metals has been measured by Sundquist (98) and calculated by MacKenzie et al. (99).

They find that the energies of the {111} and {100} surfaces are less than the energies of surfaces parallel to other planes, and that the energy of {100} surfaces exceeds that of {111}. The way in which this difference between the energies of {001} and {111} surfaces favors the rapid growth of (111) nuclei can be seen from Fig. 19. Both nuclei in this figure have sides approximately parallel to {111}, but the upper surface of the (111) nucleus is parallel to (111), and the upper surface of the (001) nucleus is parallel to (001). Clearly, the difference between the energies of the {001} and {111} surfaces will tend to make the (001) nuclei tall and thin relative to their (111) neighbors. It is conceivable that this tendency is strong enough to cause a faceted (001) nucleus to have a smaller perimeter and to subtend a smaller angle at the gold source than a (111) nucleus of equal volume. If this is indeed so then a (111) nucleus, with well-developed facets, will grow more rapidly than an (001) nucleus of equal volume.

A third explanation for the relatively rapid growth of (111) nuclei has been suggested by Ino (*49*). He observed that (001) nuclei grown in ultrahigh vacuum on vacuum-cleaved sodium chloride often have twins attached to their surfaces and has suggested that these twins cause the (001) nuclei to grow more slowly than their untwinned (111) neighbors.

6. Coalescence of Nuclei and the Formation of Defects

a. Studies of Coalescence. Three-dimensional islands or nuclei grow in size with the addition of more material and eventually coalesce. This coalescence process has been studied by Bassett (*38*), Pashley and Stowell (*39*), Pashley *et al.* (*41*), Poppa (*100, 101*), and Jacobs *et al.* (*102*). These authors grew evaporated deposits inside the electron microscope and were able to observe the coalescence of nuclei directly. The most striking feature of their observations is the liquid-like behavior of the coalescing nuclei. This behavior is particularly noticeable when the nuclei are very small. If a pair of small (about 200 A in diameter) rounded gold or silver nuclei coalesce at 350°C then the pair of rounded nuclei change into one larger rounded nucleus in less than 0.1 sec. Large nuclei take longer to approach the equilibrium configuration. If a small and a large nucleus join one another then the small nucleus seems to flow into the large.

The liquid-like behavior of coalescing nuclei is not because the nuclei are actually liquid (*41*); it results from diffusion of atoms over the surfaces of nuclei. Pashley *et al.* (*41*) have pointed out that it resembles the sintering of crystals in contact with one another.

The stage at which nuclei coalesce to form a continuous film depends on the shape of nuclei and on the number of nuclei generated per unit area. It is therefore dependent on contact angle, deposition rate, substrate temperature, contamination, and on the presence of steps in the substrate surface.

Most evaporated films are continuous before the average deposit thickness reaches 1000 A. Chopra (103) has found that the thickness at which deposits of silver on sodium chloride become continuous is reduced if an electric field of about 100 volts/cm is applied parallel to the substrate surface during film growth.

b. Stacking Fault Formation. A feature of evaporated thin films of fcc metals is the presence of stacking faults that extend from one surface of the film to the other (4, 28, 31, 103). A mechanism for the formation of these faults was suggested to the author (31) by F. C. Frank and independently by Bassett et al (4). A factor on which the mechanism depends is the misfit between the lattices of the deposit and the substrate. As a result of this misfit the lattice of one nucleus may be translated relative to that of another by a nonlattice vector. If these nuclei coalesce then much of the displacement between their lattices may be taken up by a stacking fault. The fault may be either intrinsic or extrinsic. Consider a pair of growing nuclei separated from one another by a single {111} plane of vacancies. Three possible configurations are shown in Fig. 21. The full lines in this figure are the {111} planes seen from the side,

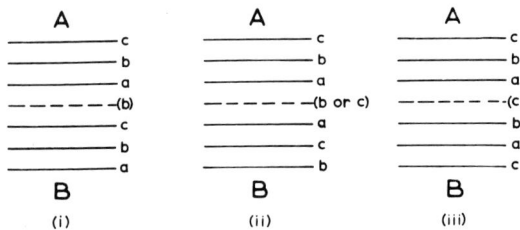

FIG. 21. Coalescence of nuclei A and B to form (i) an extrinsic stacking fault, (ii) an intrinsic stacking fault, and (iii) an unfaulted sequence [from Matthews (31)].

and the dotted line is the plane of vacancies. Adjacent planes cannot have the same letter, so the letters in parentheses give the only ways in which the vacant planes can be filled. The stacking sequences when growth is complete are as follows:

$$a_\Delta b_\Delta c_\nabla b_\nabla a_\Delta b_\Delta c \qquad b_\Delta c_\Delta a_\Delta b_\nabla a_\Delta b_\Delta c \qquad c_\Delta a_\Delta b_\Delta c_\Delta a_\Delta b_\Delta c$$
$$b_\Delta c_\Delta a_\nabla c_\Delta a_\Delta b_\Delta c$$

$$\text{(i)} \qquad\qquad \text{(ii)} \qquad\qquad \text{(iii)}$$

The Δ and ∇ convention is due to Frank (104). The successions a to b, b to c, and c to a are indicated by Δ, and b to a, c to b, and a to c by ∇. There is an extrinsic stacking fault in sequence (i); both sequences in (ii) contain an extrinsic fault; (iii) is an unfaulted sequence. Figure 21 is a little misleading because (i), (ii), and (iii) are special cases. Before nuclei coalesce they can be displaced from one another by a quite arbitrary amount. The sequence of planes on either side of the gap between nuclei may, for example, be somewhere between sequences (ii) and (iii). It is, however, unlikely to be midway between these sequences and there will be a tendency for the planes to go into the sequence to which they approximate most closely. There will also be a tendency for them to take up the unfaulted sequence, and as a result of this a perfect joint will sometimes be formed when the sequence before coalescence is nearer to (ii) than to (iii). This will result in a perfect joint being formed more often than one which contains an intrinsic stacking fault. Similarly, if the surface energy of an extrinsic fault is greater than that of the intrinsic variety (*104a*) it will be formed less often in the films.

It is possible for nuclei in the situations considered above to join so that the stacking sequence over a portion of the joint surface differs from that over the remainder. The probability of this is increased if the nuclei concerned are not in exactly parallel orientation. The misalignment necessary is roughly 0.1°, and nuclei misaligned by this amount are common in many evaporated deposits (see Section IV,2,*a*).

Evaporated thin films frequently contain stacking faults on {111} planes which intersect faults on other nonparallel {111} planes. There are also faults which bend from one {111} plane to another (*31, 36*). These intersecting and bent faults can result from the coalescence of three nuclei. Suppose, for example, that three nuclei *A*, *B*, and *C* coalesce as in Fig. 22. If stacking faults

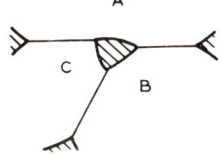

FIG. 22. Coalescence of three nuclei oriented with (111) parallel to the deposit plane [from Matthews (*36*)].

are made between *A* and *C* and between *B* and *C* but not between *B* and *A*, then a bent fault will be formed. The angle between the faulted planes will be acute (70°32′). If faults are made between *A* and *B*, and between *B* and *C*, then a bent stacking fault with an obtuse angle (180° − 70°32′) between the faulted planes will be formed. The formation of other stacking fault configurations during coalescence is described elsewhere (*31, 36*).

Direct observations of the formation of stacking faults during the coalescence of nuclei have recently been made by Jacobs *et al.* (*102*). A sequence of electron micrographs that they have taken showing the formation of stacking faults is seen in Fig. 23. Figure 23a shows three nuclei of gold on molybdenite that are about to coalesce. Fig. 23b shows the nuclei shortly after coalescence has taken place. Stacking faults in the compound nucleus are labeled F_1 and F_2. Notice that F_1 is a bent stacking fault; the angle between the two faulted planes is obtuse. Figure 23c shows an interesting and perhaps unexpected

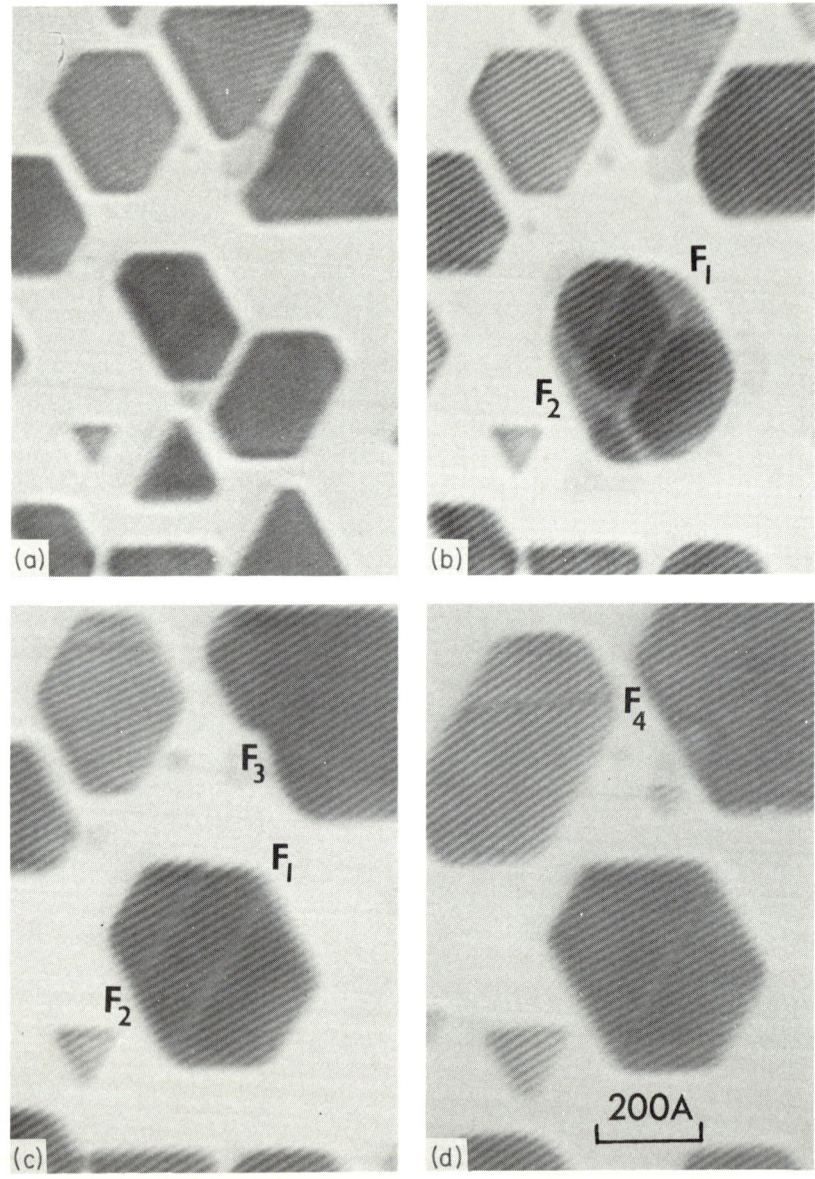

Fig. 23. Successive electron micrographs showing the generation and elimination of stacking faults during the coalescence of gold nuclei [from Jacobs et al. (102)].

feature; this is the straightening of the bent fault F_1. A feature shown by Fig. 23d is the elimination of the faults F_2 and F_3. All the stacking faults in deposits of gold on molybdenite were eliminated by the time the deposit covered the substrate surface.

Sloope and Tiller (105) have recently concluded that the concentration of stacking faults present in germanium films grown by evaporation onto calcium fluoride can be explained by the above mechanism for stacking fault formation.

Deposits of silicon on silicon also contain stacking faults on {111} planes inclined to the film plane (*106–114*). In deposits oriented with (111) parallel to their plane the stacking faults are frequently arranged in defects consisting of three faults. The faults lie on the three {111} planes inclined at 70°32' to the film plane, and form three faces of a regular tetrahedron. The fourth face coincides with the deposit surface. The apex of the tetrahedron which is common to the three faults lies in the initial substrate surface. Sometimes one or two of the faults are missing from the defect, so that only one or two of the faces of the tetrahedron are faulted. The stacking faults are usually of the intrinsic variety, but defects consisting of overlapping intrinsic and extrinsic faults have been observed (*111*). Extrinsic faults are also present if the silicon is heated in wet oxygen (*115*).

Stacking fault formation during the growth of silicon on silicon requires that the lattice in one part of the deposit be displaced from that in another by a non-lattice vector. In deposits like fcc metals on sodium chloride this displacement can arise from the misfit between overgrowth and substrate. This is not possible in silicon on silicon since the misfit is zero. It has been suggested that the displacements in deposits of silicon on silicon may result from the fortuitous wrong stacking of silicon atoms (*106, 108*), from the condensation of vacancies (*106*), from defects in the substrate surface (*106, 107, 112, 113*), and from contaminants on the substrate surface (*106, 112–114*). Evidence that surface damage (*107, 112, 113*) and contamination of the substrate surface by oxygen (*111*) do increase the concentration of faults has been obtained. It has also been found that comparatively perfect films can be made by evaporating the silicon in ultrahigh vacuum (10^{-10} Torr) onto carefully cleaned silicon surfaces (*116*).

c. *Dislocation Formation.* There seem to be four rather closely related ways in which the coalescence of nuclei can lead to dislocation formation. All the mechanisms depend on the fact that the lattices of adjacent nuclei are often rotated and displaced relative to one another. One of the mechanisms was discovered by Bassett (*38*). He observed large nuclei—whose lattices were rotated relative to one another about the normal to the specimen plane—to coalesce and form a tilt boundary between them. A second mechanism was suggested by Matthews (*31*). Suppose three nuclei in parallel orientation coalesce as shown in Fig. 22. As a result of displacements between these nuclei it is possible for one, two, or three stacking faults to form during coalescence. It is also possible for no stacking faults to be made and for the compound nucleus to be perfect. A third possibility is for no stacking faults to be formed but for a dislocation to be made inside the hole. A series of electron micrographs which show the operation of this mechanism have been obtained by Jacobs *et al.* (*102*), and are seen in Fig. 24. Figure 24a shows three gold nuclei shortly before their coalescence. Figure 24b shows the same area after the coalescence of the nuclei to form a single island. A dislocation formed during the coalescence is visible near the center of the island. Figures 24c and d are later micrographs. They show an important feature which is the escape of the dislocation to the surface of the island.

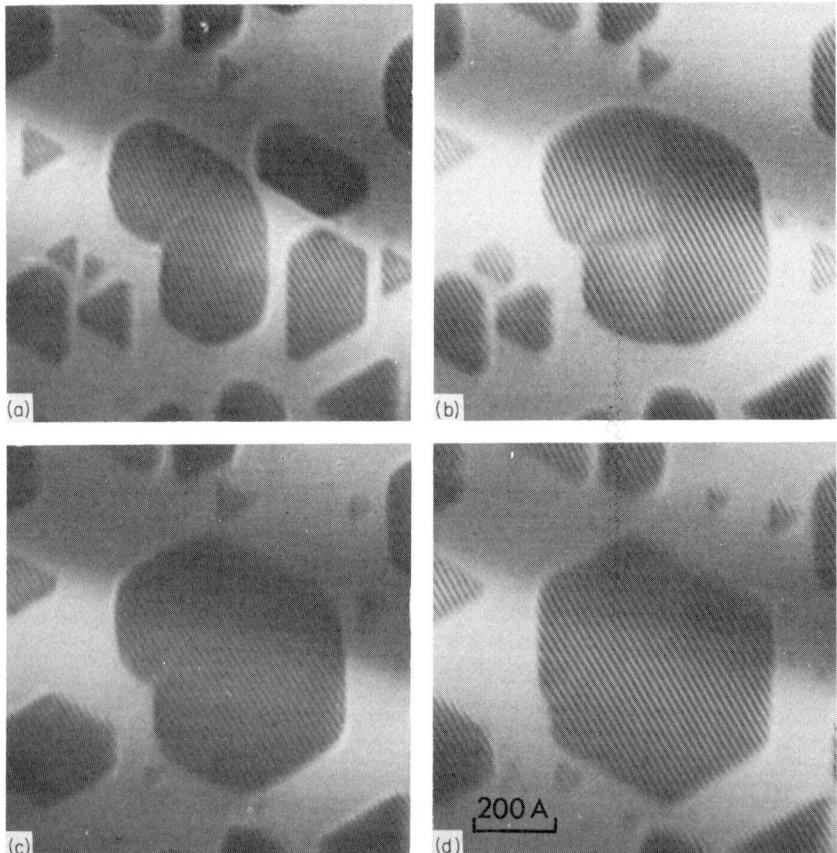

FIG. 24. Successive electron micrographs showing the formation and elimination of a dislocation during the coalescence and growth of gold nuclei [from Jacobs *et al.* (*102*)].

The third mechanism for the creation of dislocations is similar to the one described above in that it also involves the formation of dislocations in holes. It differs in that both displacements and rotations between neighboring nuclei contribute to the dislocation content of the holes. It begins with the coalescence of rather large nuclei to form large snake-like islands in which strains are readily detectable (see Section IV,6,g). The deposition of more material causes the long islands to join together and make a film in which there are large holes. These holes generally contain at least one dislocation. This can be shown using a method for detecting dislocations in holes that was first described by Kamiya and Uyeda (*117*). The method depends on the presence of moire fringe patterns formed either between the deposit and its substrate, or between the deposit superposed on a suitable single-crystal film (*52*). The number of moire fringes ending on one side of a hole and the number emerging on the other are counted. If the number entering the hole differs from the number emerging from it then there is a dislocation either in the hole or in the area of substrate covered by the hole. If the density of dislocations in the substrate is known then the probability of dislocations lying in the area covered by the hole can be determined. This probability is usually small enough to be neglected. This method for detecting dislocations in holes has been applied to deposits of silver on molybdenite (*117*), silver on mica (*36*), lead sulfide on sodium chloride (*52*), and gold on molybdenite (*102*). In all these specimens it was found that a large fraction of the dislocations were inside the holes.

The fourth mechanism for dislocation formation depends on the presence of stacking faults or thin twins (see Section IV,6,*d* below) in some of the nuclei. When the nuclei containing these defects join their neighbors then partial or twinning dislocations to bound the defects must be formed. The sum of the Burgers vectors of these imperfect dislocations plus the Burgers vectors of any dislocations inside the fault (e.g., "stair-rod" dislocations) must be either zero or a complete lattice vector. If the sum is a complete lattice vector then at least one perfect dislocation has been made in the film.

d. Twin Formation. Fcc metal films grown epitaxially on sodium chloride usually contain a high density of microtwins on the four {111} planes inclined at 54°44′ to the (001) deposit plane (*32–34, 118–121*). Twins are also found in deposits of fcc metals on mica (*10*), or molybdenite (*122*), and in deposits of germanium on calcium fluoride (*105, 123*). A number of mechanisms have been proposed to explain the presence of these twins. Menzer (*118*) suggested that the deposits were initially in the twin orientation, and that the final orientation resulted from twinning of the initial ones. The shortcomings of this hypothesis have been discussed by Pashley (*1*). Burbank and Heidenreich (*120*) suggested that twins were formed to accommodate the displacement between coalescing nuclei. The formation of twins by a process which is certainly closely related to this one has been observed by Pashley and Stowell (*123a*). Hall and Thompson have suggested that twins result from the accidental wrong stacking of atoms on the (111) faces of growing nuclei. This mechanism is consistent with much of the experimental evidence but direct evidence for its operation has not been obtained. A fourth mechanism suggested by Matthews and Allinson (*34*) seems to be responsible for many of the twins in deposits of fcc metals on alkali halides (*2*). It begins with the coalescence of two nuclei. This is followed by the conversion of one nucleus into a twin of the other. The way in which this conversion takes place is still not clear. If the nuclei happen to be very near to twin relationship before coalescence then it is probable that one of the nuclei rotates to become a twin of the other. If the nuclei are far from twin relationship before coalescence then it is probable that a grain boundary is formed during coalescence and that this boundary migrates through one of the nuclei leaving it precisely a twin of the other. It is not known how near to twin relationship the nuclei need to be before conversion into precisely twin relationship is probable. In thin deposits of gold on air-contaminated sodium chloride there are many nuclei which are nearer to twin relationship than they are to parallel alignment. These are the nuclei in orientations (c)–(f) in Fig. 16. Each of these nuclei is inclined at 15°48′ to a twin orientation but at 54°44′ to the parallel one. The high density of twins in gold and other fcc metals grown on sodium chloride suggests that nuclei 15°48′ from twin orientation have a fairly high probability of becoming twins.

A feature of twins in thin deposits of fcc metals on sodium chloride which supports the coalescence mechanism for twin formation is shown by Fig. 25. This figure is a dark-field electron image formed by a 111 reflection off one of the four twin orientations. The twins appear white, the nuclei parallel to the salt lattice appear black, and the carbon supporting film is gray. It can be seen that the twins are often attached to the surfaces of the nuclei as one would expect from the coalescence mechanism. Other features of twins in evaporated deposits which are explained by the mechanism are the stage in film growth at which twins appear, the size and shape of twins, the formation of twins at surface steps, and the relative concentration of the two defects which are made up of a pair of twins that lie on different twinning planes and share a lateral twin boundary (*34, 122*).

It has for many years been considered that twins of twins—which are not in the orientation of the matrix—are absent from evaporated thin films (*1*). Recently, however, Ino (*49*) has obtained evidence for multiple twinning in deposits of gold grown in ultrahigh vacuum on sodium chloride surfaces prepared inside the vacuum chamber. The evidence was obtained from dark-field electron microscopy and from transmission electron diffraction patterns.

Complicated defects made up of twins with twinning planes inclined to the specimen plane have been observed in deposits of silicon on silicon by Mendelson (*113*) and by Booker (*125*). They appear as star-like hillocks on the deposit surface.

  e. *Formation of Boundaries between Doubly Positioned Nuclei.* Fcc metal films prepared by evaporation onto the cleavage faces of either molybdenite or muscovite mica usually contain the two orientations illustrated in Fig. 15. These orientations are in twin relationship and their (111) twinning plane is parallel to the film plane. They are present from the earliest stages of film growth showing that nuclei in both orientations are generated. The presence

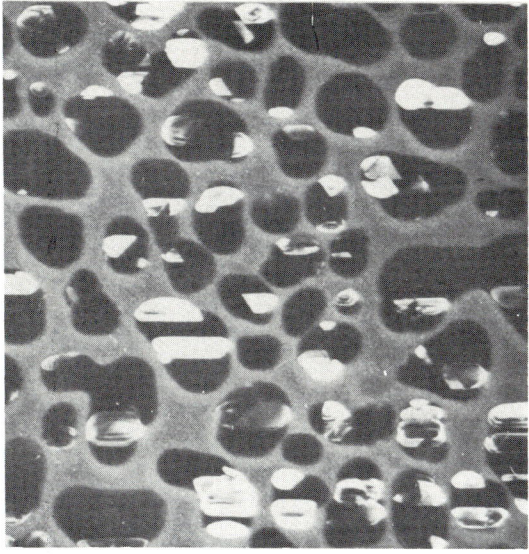

Fig. 25. Dark-field electron micrograph of twins in a deposit of silver on air-contaminated sodium chloride. The twins are white, the silver nuclei in the orientation of the substrate are black, and the carbon supporting film is gray. Magnification × 58,000 [from Matthews and Allinson (*34*)].

of the two orientations results from the fact that the substrates can control the stacking of the layer of atoms in contact with their surface but cannot control the stacking of the second layer.

  Lateral twin boundaries are formed when nuclei in the two orientations grow and coalesce. The geometry of these boundaries has been described by Matthews (*36*) and independently by Dickson and Pashley (*40*). The boundaries appear in electron micrographs as fine lines which are accurately parallel to the $\langle 110 \rangle$ directions in the film plane. This shows that the boundaries are parallel to the $\{\bar{2}11\}$ planes perpendicular to the film plane. These planes are common to the two lattices. The fact that the boundaries are parallel to $\{\bar{2}11\}$ planes shows that $\{211\}$ lateral twin boundaries have lower energies than lateral twin boundaries parallel to other planes in the same zone (*36*). The low energy of $\{211\}$ lateral twin boundaries was predicted by Ellis and Treuting (*126*).

The boundaries between the two orientations are not always everywhere parallel to $\{\bar{2}11\}$ planes. Sometimes a part of a boundary is parallel to $\{\bar{2}11\}$ and the remainder is parallel to the (111) film plane. That this is so is shown by the geometry of lateral twin boundaries in bright-field electron micrographs (*36*), and very elegantly by the dark-field electron micrographs of Jacobs and Stowell (*127*). A diagram of a twin boundary which is partly parallel to ($\bar{2}$11) and partly parallel to (111) is shown in Fig. 26. This type of twin boun-

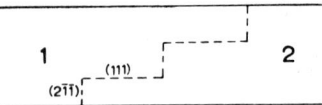

FIG. 26. Diagram showing twin boundaries parallel to the ($\bar{2}$11) and (111) planes. Plane of paper is (0$\bar{1}$1) [from Matthews (*36*)].

dary seems to result from the coalescence of nuclei of different height (*36, 102, 127*).

f. Formation of Grain Boundaries. Deposits of one material on another often contain a variety of orientations (see Section IV,2*a*). Coalescence between nuclei in different orientations may result in the formation of twins or lateral twin boundaries as described above. They may also result in the formation of grain boundaries. An example of a grain boundary formed by the coalescence of a pair of gold nuclei is seen in Fig. 27. The nuclei were

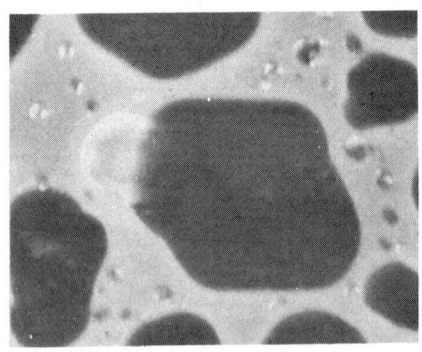

FIG. 27. Dark-field electron micrograph showing a grain boundary formed between (111) and (001) nuclei in a deposit of gold on clean sodium chloride. The (001) grain is white, and the (111) grain is dark. Magnification ×135,000 [from Matthews (*50*)].

grown in ultrahigh vacuum (5×10^{-9} Torr) on a sodium chloride surface prepared inside the vacuum chamber. The white grain in Fig. 27 is in the orientation of the salt. The dark areas are nuclei oriented with (111) parallel to the (001) salt surface. The gray background is the carbon supporting film.

g. Generation of Strains. Cabrera (*29*), and Frank and van der Merwe

(*15–18*) have discussed the strain of overgrowths to accommodate misfit between the overgrowth and substrate lattices. This is, however, not the only origin of strains in evaporated thin films. Nuclei in evaporated thin films are often displaced and rotated relative to one another. These displacements and rotations may be accommodated by stacking faults or dislocations. They may also be eliminated by glide of a nucleus over the substrate surface as discussed in Section IV,7. In addition, it is possible for displacements and rotations to be accommodated by elastic strain. It has been found that particularly large strains result when big (~ 1000 A in diameter) nuclei join to form long snake-like islands. An example of a long, strained, silver island on a mica substrate is seen in Fig. 28. The strains in the island are revealed by changes in the direction and spacing of moire fringes and are particularly noticeable in the arrowed region.

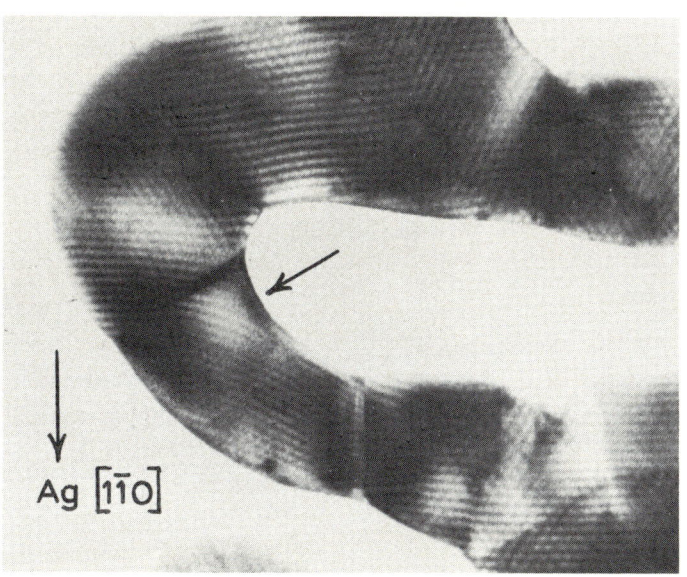

FIG. 28. Electron micrograph showing an elastically strained island of silver on mica. The strains are revealed by changes in the direction and spacing of the moire fringes. Magnification ×450,000 (from D. L. Allinson, Physics Dept., Univ. of the Witwatersrand, Johannesburg, South Africa).

7. Changes in Orientation

It has been found that the alignment of deposits may improve as their thickness increases (*10, 34, 35*). Two processes which are responsible for this improvement have been observed inside an electron microscope by Bassett (*38*). One of these is the spontaneous rotation of a nucleus about an axis perpendicular to the specimen plane (see Section IV,2,a), and the other is the coalescence of a pair of almost parallel nuclei followed by the rotation of one into the orientation of the other. The latter process will improve the alignment of the deposit for two reasons. Firstly, there is a tendency for the smaller of the two nuclei to rotate into the orientation of the larger, and large nuclei are on the average better aligned than small ones. Secondly, there is a tendency for the rotation to be towards the epitaxial orientation rather than away from it. This is because the interfacial energy is lowered if the rotation is into the orientation of the better aligned of the two nuclei.

Not all the improvements in the alignment of evaporated deposits can be explained by these two processes. Deposits of silver on mica, for example, are doubly positioned early in film growth but may—under carefully controlled growth conditions—be singly positioned when the deposit thickness reaches 1000 A (10). A process which plays an important part in the elimination of one of the orientations of silver on mica has been studied by Jacobs *et al.* (102), Pashley and Stowell (123a), and Stowell and Law (128). They have observed that the coalescence of doubly positioned nuclei of gold on molybdenite is often followed by the migration of the lateral twin boundary through the smaller of the two grains. The driving force for the migration comes from the decrease in boundary area that accompanies motion through the small grain (102, 128, 128a). A series of electron micrographs showing the formation of a lateral twin boundary and its migration through the small grain are seen in Fig. 29.

In deposits of gold on molybdenite the migration of twin boundaries leads to the formation of large singly positioned grains. It does not result in the elimination of one of the two orientations as has been found for deposits of silver on mica (10). The orientation change in deposits of silver on mica has not been investigated inside the electron microscope. The observations of Jacobs *et al.* (102) and of Pashley and Stowell (123a) do, however, enable one to speculate on the mechanism for the orientation change. The contact angle between the favored of the two orientations of silver on mica is almost certainly smaller than the contact angle of the less-favored one. As a result, the nuclei of the favored orientation become larger than the nuclei of the less-favored one. Coalescence between large nuclei in the favored orientation and small nuclei in the less-favored one is followed by the migration of the lateral twin boundaries through the small grains (Fig. 29).

Similar processes are responsible for the orientation changes that accompany the growth of gold and other fcc metals on sodium chloride substrates (47, 49, 50, 79, 80,88a). The orientation changes that occur during the growth of gold in ultrahigh vacuum (1×10^{-9} to 6×10^{-9} Torr) on hot (360°C), vacuum-cleaved, sodium chloride are shown by Figs. 30a, b, and c. The diffraction patterns in these figures were obtained from different parts of the same

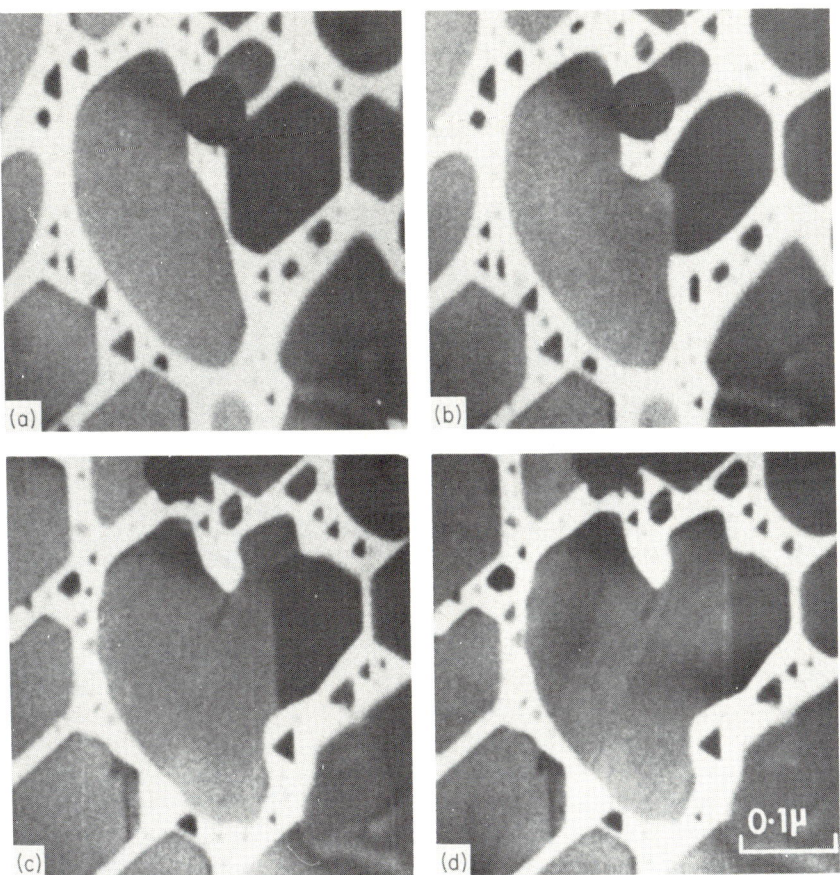

Fig. 29. Successive electron micrographs of a growing deposit of gold on molybdenite. The temperature of the substrate was 400°C. The micrographs were exposed at the following times relative to (a) as the arbitrary zero: (b) 3.6 sec; (c) 62.4 sec; (d) 64.8 sec. The micrographs show the coalescence of a pair of islands to form a lateral twin boundary which migrates part of the way through the smaller of the two grains (from Pashley and Stowell (*123a*)].

gold deposit. (A shutter was moved between source and substrate during metal deposition so that a specimen in which there was a thickness gradient was obtained.) The arced spots in Fig. 30a show, firstly, that many orientations are present early in film growth and, secondly, that the only prominent preferred orientation is (a) in Fig. 16. There are also a number of nuclei oriented with (111) parallel to the salt surface; the reflections off these nuclei are obscured by electrons scattered off the carbon supporting film (*47*).

Figure 30b shows that the ten orientations illustrated in Fig. 16 are all detectable when the deposit thickness reaches 60 A. Orientations (a) and (c)–(f) are prominent, but the preference for the orientations (b) and (g)–(j) is weak. Figure 30c shows that the thick continuous areas of the specimen contain much of orientations (c)–(f), no preference for (g)–(j), and too little of (a) and (b) for the diffraction pattern to contain visible reflections off them.

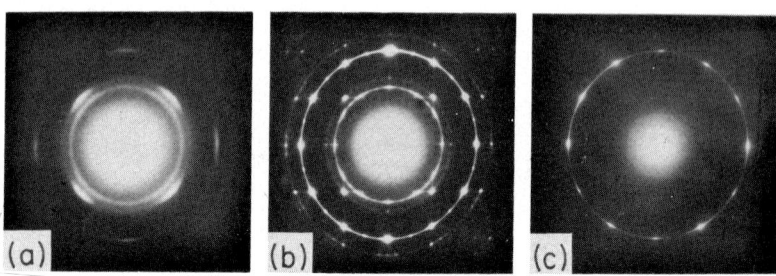

FIG. 30. Transmission electron diffraction patterns from different areas of a gold deposit grown in ultrahigh vacuum on sodium chloride cleaved inside the vacuum chamber. The average thicknesses of the areas were about 10, 60, and 1500 A (from Matthews and Grunbaum (*88a*)].

The elimination of orientation (a) from gold deposits grown on clean salt surfaces takes place partly by the rapid growth of (111) nuclei (*47, 49, 50*, Section IV,5). Two additional mechanisms are suggested by micrographs of deposits between 25 and 1000 A in thickness. Both mechanisms involve the coalescence of large (111) nuclei with their small neighbors in orientation (a). In the first mechanism the nuclei coalesce and form a polycrystalline island. An example of one of these islands is seen in Fig. 27. The formation of an island like that in Fig. 27 is followed by the elimination of the (001) grain. This is thought to proceed partly by diffusion of gold atoms across the surface of the nucleus from the (001) to the (111) grain, and partly by migration of the grain boundary through the (001) grain (*47, 50*). In the second mechanism for orientation change the small (001) nucleus becomes a twin of the large (111) nucleus shortly after coalescence occurs (see Section IV,6,*d*). The twinning plane is one of the three {111} planes inclined at 70°32′ to the film plane. The lattice rotation—about an axis in the film plane—that is involved in twin formation is only 15°48′. The conversion of small (001) nuclei into twins of their (111) neighbors is consistent with the large density of microtwins present in thick gold films grown on clean salt surfaces (*47, 88a, 128a*).

The orientation changes that accompany the growth of gold on vacuum-cleaved sodium chloride are very different from those that take place on sodium chloride contaminated by an exposure to air (*47, 50, 88a*). This is shown by the transmission electron diffraction patterns in Figs. 31a, b, and c.

The patterns were obtained from different parts of the same gold film. Comparison of Fig. 31a with Fig. 30a shows that the orientation of thin gold deposits grown on air-contaminated salt is similar to that of deposits grown on clean salt surfaces (cf. Section IV,2,*e*). Figure 31b shows that the most prominent orientation in the 60-A region is (a), but that some of (c) to (f) and small amounts of (b) and (g) to (j) are also present. Figure 31c shows that the change from 60 to 600 A in thickness is accompanied by the disappearance of all orientations except (a) and its twins.

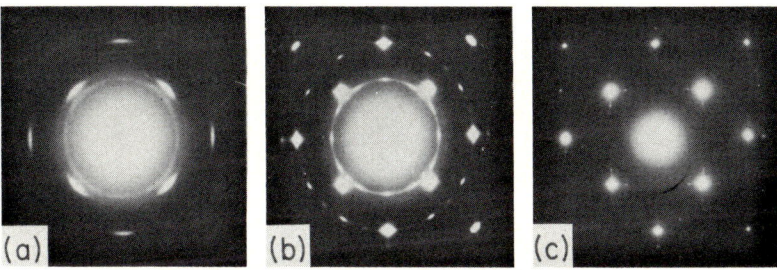

FIG. 31. Transmission electron diffraction patterns from areas of a gold deposit grown in ultrahigh vacuum on air-contaminated sodium chloride. The average thicknesses of the areas were about 10, 60, and 600 A [from Matthews and Grunbaum (*88a*)].

Although the orientation changes of gold on air-contaminated sodium chloride differ from those on clean surfaces, the mechanisms for the changes seem to be similar. The difference between the two changes results largely from the difference in the number of nuclei generated early in film growth (*47, 50, 92*). The number of nuclei generated per unit area of contaminated salt surfaces exceeds the number formed on clean salt by a factor of about two (see Section IV,2,*c*). As a result the coalescence of nuclei begins on contaminated salt surfaces at an earlier stage of film growth than it does on clean surfaces. Early coalescence does not allow the (111) nuclei present to outgrow their (001) neighbors.

Coalescence between a (111) nucleus and its equally large but more numerous (001) neighbors begins with the formation of a grain boundary. This is followed by the elimination of the (111) grain. This seems to take place partly by diffusion of gold atoms from the (111) to the (001) grains and partly by migration of the boundary through the (111) grain. For this migration to be energetically favorable the (111) grain must be smaller than a certain critical size. This size can be estimated if a simple model is assumed. Consider a (111) nucleus that has joined its (001) neighbors to form a disk-shaped (111) grain in an (001) matrix. The flat upper and lower surfaces of the disk coincide with the upper and lower film surfaces, and the cylindrical surface is the boundary between the (001) and (111) orientations. It is easily shown that the (111) grain will tend to shrink if its radius is smaller than

$$h\sigma_b/[(\sigma_o' + \sigma_i') - (\sigma_o'' + \sigma_i'')] \tag{10}$$

where h is the film thickness, σ_b is the surface free energy of the grain boundary, σ_0' and σ_0'' are the free energies of the {001} and {111} surfaces, and σ_0' and σ_i'' are free energies of the interfaces between the substrate and the (001) and (111) grains.

Coalescence between large (001) and small (111) nuclei in gold deposits grown on contaminated sodium chloride surfaces seems to result in the conversion of the (111) nucleus into a twin of the (001). This is consistent with the high concentration of twins in gold films grown on contaminated sodium chloride, and is discussed in Section IV,6d.

The difference between the orientation changes that take place on clean and on air-contaminated sodium chloride suggests that any process which increases the number of nuclei formed per unit area, without much influencing their orientation, will aid the growth of single-crystal films of gold on (001) sodium chloride surfaces. One way of increasing the number of nuclei per unit area without seriously affecting their orientation (see Sections IV,1,d and IV, 2,c) is to greatly increase the rate of metal deposition in the early stages of film growth. This has been done (*91*), and it has been found that rapid deposition in the initial stages of film growth does enable single-crystal films of gold to be grown in ultrahigh vacuum on sodium chloride surfaces prepared inside the vacuum chamber.

An alternative way of increasing the number of nuclei formed per unit area is to increase the number of surface steps. Evidence that the orientation of continuous deposits grown on heavily stepped surfaces are more perfectly aligned than those grown on flat surfaces has been obtained (*50, 71, 72*). Since heavily stepped areas are high-index surfaces, these results indicate that epitaxy is sometimes more easily achieved on high-index substrate surfaces than on low-index ones.

8. Defects in Complete Films

Many of the defects in continuous films are formed during the coalescence of nuclei (Section IV, 6) but this is not true of all defects present. Pashley (*129*) has found that gold films grown on silver substrates contain stacking faults whose width is much greater than the diameter of the largest nucleus. These faults are formed by the separation of Shockley partial dislocations after film growth is complete.

Gold, silver, and nickel films that have not been handled with care may contain large, lenticular, twins (*130*). A study of the generation of these twins during the deformation of (001) gold films has been made by Catlin et al. (131). An electron micrograph of a large deformation twin in an evaporated gold film is seen in Fig. 32. The film was prepared by evaporation in ultrahigh vacuum onto air-contaminated sodium chloride, and was deformed in tension along [110] by attaching it to a strip of adhesive tape and stretching the tape at room temperature. The presence of deformation twins in (001) films stretched along the [110] direction is not surprising. This is because the shear stress in the twinning plane and along the twinning direction is almost the largest possible fraction of the total stress. It is larger than the resolved shear stress on any glide system.

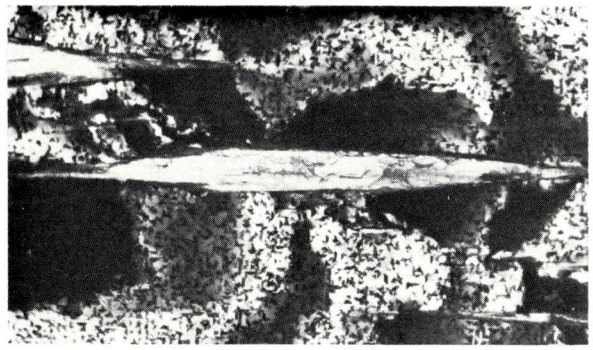

FIG. 32. Large lenticular twin in an (001) gold film. The film was deformed in tension along the [110] direction. The small dark patches are microtwins formed during film growth. Magnification ×4,000.

Some of the dislocations in continuous films may not be generated during coalescence. Dislocations whose lines end on the substrate surface may continue to grow in the overgrowth film. This process is important when growth begins with the formation of a pseudomorphic layer (see Section III,3). It may also be important in films formed by the coalescence of three-dimensional islands, but only if the density of dislocations in the substrate is comparable with that in the overgrowth layer. This is not so in many overgrowth substrate combinations. Well-annealed single crystals of sodium chloride for example contain about 10^5 dislocations/cm^2. The number of dislocations that extend through 1 cm^2 of fcc metals grown on sodium chloride is about 10^{10}. Systems in which the dislocation densities in the substrate are comparable with those in the overgrowth are those in which the substrate is itself an epitaxially grown film.

A further mechanism for dislocation formation that does not involve the coalescence of nuclei was suggested by Phillips (132). He observed that dislocation lines appeared at the edges of holes in silver films while the films were examined by transmission electron microscopy. As a result of these observations he suggested that dislocations in thin films are generated at holes. This is entirely plausible: it would be much easier to generate dislocations in holes and to move them from there to the matrix than it would be to generate the dislocations inside the matrix itself (*133*). It should, however, be pointed out that the dislocations observed by Phillips may not have been generated in the hole. It is possible that they were made inside the hole when the hole itself was formed, and that they were simply escaping from the hole as a result, possibly, of forces between them and other dislocations inside the hole. It is possible to distinguish experimentally between dislocations that are generated in holes and those that are escaping from holes. When a dislocation escapes from a hole the number of dislocations in the hole is decreased by one. If a dislocation is nucleated in a hole, and a dislocation line emerges at the edge of this hole, the number of dislocations in the hole is increased by one. Thus, to distinguish between the two processes one requires specimens in which the dislocations in both matrix and holes can be detected. This is possible in deposits of silver on mica, and in deposits of silver or gold on molybdenite (see Section IV,6,*c*).

9. Misfit Dislocations

The geometry of the misfit dislocations in interfaces between substrates and films which grow by the generation and coalescence of three-dimensional islands has been studied using transmission electron microscopy. The specimens examined were single-crystal films of lead selenide on lead sulfide (*96*), gold on palladium (*11*), and gold on platinum (*12*). In all of these specimens the overgrowth and substrate were in parallel orientation, and the interfaces were parallel to (001). The separation of the misfit dislocations changed from one specimen to another but the geometry of the dislocations did not. Misfit dislocations in a deposit of gold on palladium can be seen in Fig. 33. The dislocations make up a square network in which the dislocation lines are parallel to the [110] and [1$\bar{1}$0] directions. The reflections responsible for the image contrast in Fig. 33 were 200 and 220. In areas of the specimen where the contrast resulted from 220 and $\bar{2}\bar{2}$0 reflections only one set of misfit dislocation lines is visible. This is shown by Fig. 34. The moire fringes near *A* in Fig. 34 were formed by interference between the undeviated beam and a beam which had experienced 220 and $\bar{2}\bar{2}$0 reflections in the gold and palladium lattices (*25, 26*). The lines near *B* are misfit dislocation lines. The set of dislocations with lines perpendicular to those at *B* are not visible. The invisibility of these dislocations shows that they have Burgers vectors whose component in the film plane is parallel to $\pm$[1$\bar{1}$0] (*21*). The magnitude of this component along $\pm$[1$\bar{1}$0] can be determined by comparing the separation of indexed

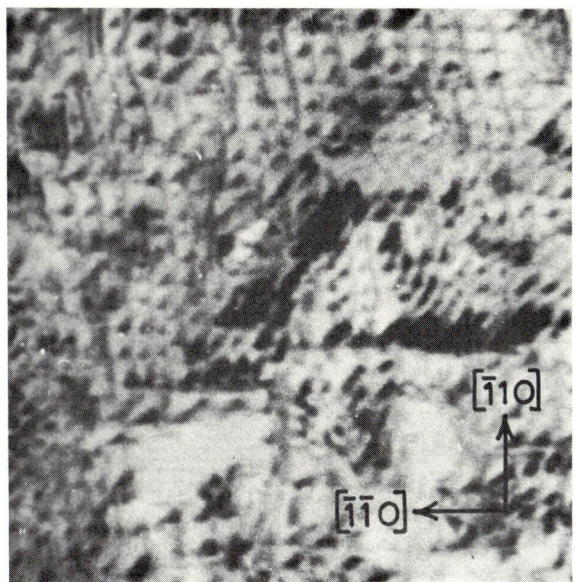

FIG. 33. Electron micrograph of misfit dislocations in a deposit of gold on palladium. The dislocation lines form a square network parallel to the [110] and [1̄10] directions. Magnification ×370,000 [from Matthews (*11*)].

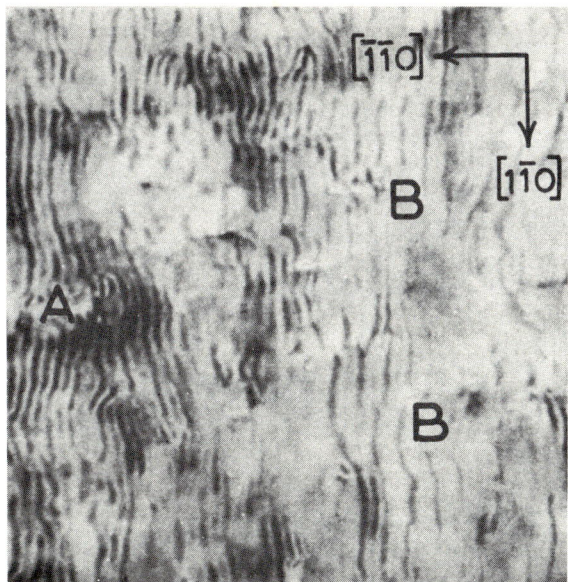

FIG. 34. Electron micrograph showing type 220 moire fringes (at *A*) and misfit dislocations (at *B*) in a deposit of gold on palladium. The image contrast resulted from type 220 reflections. Magnification ×370,000 [from Matthews (*11*)].

moire fringes with the separation of the misfit dislocations (*96*). The most convenient set of fringes to use for this purpose are the type 220 fringes labeled *A* in Fig. 34. These fringes are parallel to the visible set of misfit dislocations and have half their spacing. This indicates that the component of the Burgers vector in the film plane has magnitude equal to twice the separation of the 220 planes. Thus, this component is $\pm\frac{1}{2}a$ [110]. This is a lattice vector equal in length to the Burgers vectors of the stable dislocations in fcc metals (*22*). This, taken together with the fact that a component of the Burgers vector out of the interface increases the energy of the misfit dislocation line but accommodates no misfit, suggests very strongly that the Burgers vectors of the dislocations near *B* in Fig. 34 are $\pm\frac{1}{2}a$ [110]. Symmetry considerations suggest that the Burgers vectors of the invisible set of dislocations are $\pm\frac{1}{2}a$ [1$\bar{1}$0].

It should be emphasized that the misfit dislocations in Figs. 33 and 34, and those observed between lead selenide and lead sulfide films, cannot be interpreted as moire fringes. Fringes with twice the spacing of those near *A* in Fig. 34 could only be formed by interference between the undeviated beam, and a beam which had experienced type 110 reflections in the overgrowth and substrate lattices. Type 110 reflections do not occur either in fcc metals or in lead sulfide and lead selenide.

Misfit dislocation networks between lead sulfide and lead selenide, and between gold and palladium or platinum, are often "dislocated" themselves. This can be seen in Fig. 35 which is an electron micrograph of misfit dislocations between lead sulfide and lead selenide. These dislocations in the networks of misfit dislocations are the result of dislocation lines that extend through one of the two films. They are analogous to dislocations in moire fringe patterns (*25, 26*). The Burgers vector of the dislocation that passes through one of the films can be determined using Frank's theorem for dislocation nodes (*134*). This theorem states that the sum of the Burgers vectors of the dislocations meeting at a node must vanish if each dislocation is considered to go into the node. Thus, the dislocations responsible for the network "dislocations" at *A* in Fig. 35 must have Burgers vectors which are of the type $\frac{1}{2}a\langle 110\rangle$ and lie in the film plane. The dislocation responsible for the "dislocation" at *B* must have a type $a\langle 100\rangle$ Burgers vector that lies in the film plane.

The behavior of misfit dislocations during diffusion across the interface between two crystals, and during the diffusion of foreign atoms from the surface of a crystal into its interior, has been studied experimentally by many authors (*23, 135–140*), and theoretically by Tiller (*141*), Hirth (*142*), and by Vermaak and van der Merwe (*143*). Diffusion between miscible pairs of crystals, such as lead sulfide and lead selenide (*138*) or gold and palladium

(*139*), replaces the interface between the crystals by an alloyed region containing alloys of all compositions. The misfit dislocations move during this diffusion and become distributed throughout the alloyed volume. Some of the dislocations move upwards while others move down. If the Burgers vectors of the misfit dislocations are inclined to the original interface then this motion can take place by glide and by climb (*11, 23*). If the Burgers vectors are parallel to the original interface then the motion out of the interface is by climb alone (*138*). If the initial separation of misfit dislocations is much smaller

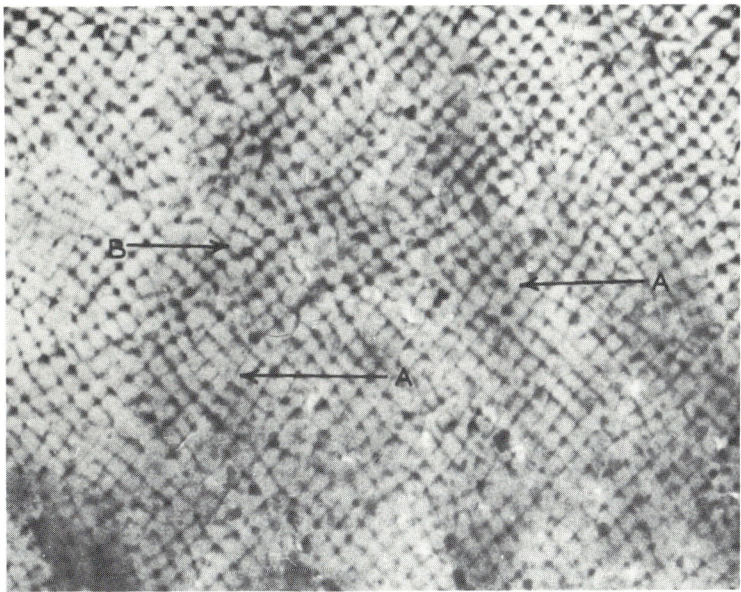

FIG. 35. Misfit dislocation network between lead sulfide and lead selenide films. Magnification × 170,000.

than the thickness of the crystals, then diffusion can be accompanied by the arrangement of the misfit dislocations into tilt boundaries perpendicular to the original interface (*143, 144*). The gradient in lattice parameter in the regions between these boundaries is accommodated by lattice curvature. An electron micrograph showing curved grains formed during diffusion between single-crystal films of gold and palladium is seen in Fig. 36. The matrix in the figure is labeled *A* and the curved grains are labeled *B*. The curvature of the grains can be determined from the bend extinction contours inside the grains (*144, 145*).

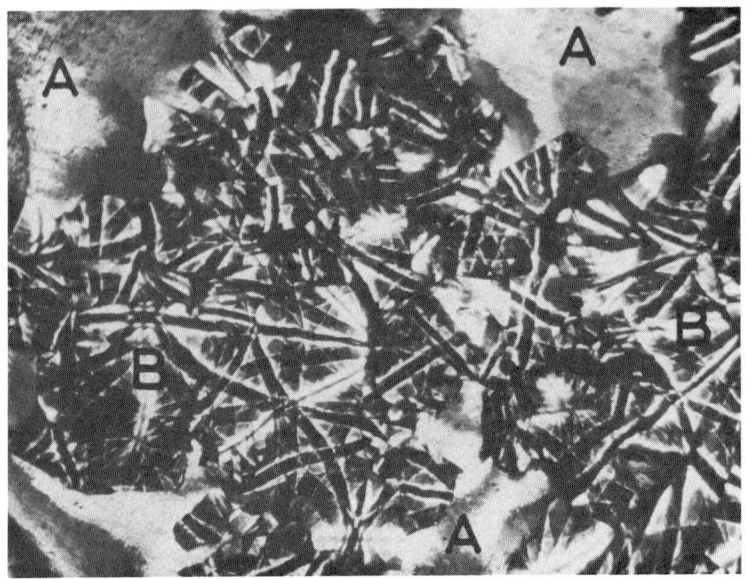

FIG. 36. Electron micrograph of curved grains formed during diffusion between single-crystal films of gold and palladium. Magnification ×5,750 [from Matthews and Crawford (*144*)].

V. Annealing of Thin Films

The perfection of evaporated thin films can be improved by annealing treatments. The anneal can be done while the film is attached to its substrate or after the substrate has been dissolved away. Schoening and Baltz (*121*) have used annealing treatments to convert polycrystalline permalloy films—in which there was a preferred orientation—into single-crystal films. Schlotterer (*146*) has annealed gold films to remove 95% of the microtwins that they contained. Mendelson (*113*) and Booker and Valdre (*147*) have removed stacking faults from evaporated silicon films by means of heat treatments. Pashley (*129*) found that the annealing of gold films is accompanied by the arrangement of some of the dislocations into low-angle grain boundaries. Many other dislocations are eliminated by mutual annihilation. The number of dislocation lines extending through unit area of gold foils can easily be reduced from 10^{10} per cm^2 to less than 5×10^8 per cm^2 by this process.

Acknowledgments

I would like to thank Mr. J. L. Crawford, Dr. W. A. Jesser, Professor Doris Kuhlmann-Wilsdorf, Dr. K. A. Lawless, Professor F. R. N. Nabarro, and Dr. D. W. Pashley for helpful discussions and correspondence. I am also indebted to Mr. D. L. Allinson and to Dr. D. W. Pashley for supplying some of the electron micrographs.

References

1. D. W. Pashley, *Advan. Phys.* **5**, 173 (1956).
2. D. W. Pashley, *Advan. Phys.* **14**, 327 (1965).
3. J. P. Hirth and G. M. Pound, "Progress in Materials Science," Vol. 11. Macmillan, New York, 1963.
4. G. A. Bassett, J. W. Menter, and D. W. Pashley, *in* "Structure and Properties of Thin Films" (C. A. Neugebauer, J. B. Newkirk, D. A. Vermilyea, eds.), p. 11. Wiley, New York, 1959.
5. J. W. Gibbs, "Collected Works," Vol. 1, p. 326. Yale Univ. Press, New Haven, Connecticut, 1948.
6. N. Cabrera, *in* "Structure and Properties of Thin Films" (C. A. Neugebauer, J. B. Newkirk, D. A. Vermilyea, eds.), p. 528. Wiley, New York, 1959.
7. S. Mader, *J. Vacuum Sci. Technol.* **2**, 35 (1965).
8. R. C. Newman, *Phil. Mag.* **2**, 750 (1957).
9. E. Grunbaum, *Proc. Phys. Soc. (London)* **72**, 459 (1958).
10. D. W. Pashley, *Phil. Mag.* **4**, 316 (1959).
11. J. W. Matthews, *Phil. Mag.*, **13**, 1207 (1966).
12. J. W. Matthews and W. A. Jesser, *Acta Met.* **15**, 595 (1967).
12a. E. R. Funk, H. Udin, and J. Wulff, *J. Metals, J. Petrol. Technol. Mining Eng.* **191**, 1206 (1951).
13. F. H. Buttner, H. Udin, and J. Wulff, *J. Metals, J. Petrol. Technol. Mining Eng.* **191**, 1209 (1951).
14. L. L. Kunin, *Dokl. Akad. Nauk SSSR* **79**, 93 (1951).
15. F. C. Frank and J. H. van der Merwe, *Proc. Roy. Soc.* **A198**, 216 (1949).
16. J. H. van der Merwe, *Phil. Mag.* **7**, 1433 (1962).
17. J. H. van der Merwe, *J. Appl. Phys.* **34**, 117 (1963).
18. J. H. van der Merwe, *in* "Single Crystal Films" (M. Francombe and H. Sato eds.), p. 139. Pergamon Press, Oxford, 1964.
18a. H. Brooks, *in* "Metal Interfaces," p. 20. Am. Soc. Metals, 1952.
18b. N. H. Fletcher, *J. Appl. Phys.* **35**, 234 (1964).
18c. N. H. Fletcher and Peggy L. Adamson, *Phil. Mag.* **14**, 99 (1966).
18d. W. A. Jesser and D. Kuhlmann-Wilsdorf, *Phys. Status Solidi* **19**, 95 (1967).
19. W. L. Bragg and J. F. Nye, *Proc. Roy. Soc.* **A190**, 474 (1947).
20. C. S. Barrett, *in* "Structure of Metals," p. 222. McGraw-Hill, New York, 1953.
21. P. B. Hirsch, A. Howie, and M. J. Whelan, *Phil. Trans. Roy. Soc. London* **A252**, 499 (1960).
22. F. C. Frank and J. F. Nicholas, *Phil. Mag.* **44**, 1213 (1953).
23. J. Washburn, G. Thomas, and H. J. Queisser, *J. Appl. Phys.* **35**, 1909 (1964).
24. E. R. Thompson, Dissertation, Univ. of Virginia, p. 55 (1966).
24a. C. A. Haque and H. E. Farnsworth, *Surface Sci.* **4**, 195 (1966).
24b. U. Gradmann, *Ann. Phys. (Leipzig)* **17**, 91 (1965).
25. J. W. Menter, *Advan. Phys.* **7**, 299 (1958).
26. S. Amelinckx, "The Direct Observation of Dislocations," p. 414. Academic Press, New York, 1964.
27. B. Borie, C. J. Sparks, and J. V. Cathcrart, *Acta Met.* **10**, 691 (1962).
28. G. A. Bassett, J. W. Menter, and D. W. Pashley, *Proc. Roy. Soc* **A246**, 345 (1958).
29. N. Cabrera, *Mem. Sci. Rev. Met.* **62**, 205 (1965).
30. A. H. Cottrell, "Dislocations and Plastic Flow in Crystals," p. 8. Oxford Univ. Press, London and New York, 1953.
31. J. W. Matthews, *Phil. Mag.* **4**, 1017 (1959).

32. A. Nagasawa and S. Ogawa, *J. Phys. Soc. Japan* **15**, 1421 (1960).
33. H. Schlotterer, *in* "Electron Microscopy: Fifth International Congress for Electron Microscopy, Philadelphia, 1962" (S. S. Breese ed.), Vol. 1, paper DD-5. Academic Press, New York, 1962.
34. J. W. Matthews and D. L. Allinson, *Phil. Mag.* **8**, 1283 (1963).
35. J. W. Matthews, *in* "Proceedings of the European Regional Conference on Electron Microscopy Delft, 1960" (A. L. Houwink and B. J. Spits, ed.), Vol. 1, p. 276. De Nederlandse Vereniging voor Electronenmikroscopie, Delft, 1960.
36. J. W. Matthews, *Phil. Mag.* **7**, 915 (1962).
37. L. G. Schultz, *Acta Cryst.* **4**, 483 (1951).
38. G. A. Bassett, *in* "Proceedings of the European Regional Conference on Electron Microscopy, Delft, 1960" (A. L. Houwink and B. J. Spits, eds.), Vol. 1, p. 270. De Nederlandse Vereniging voor Electronenmikroscopie, Delft, 1960.
39. D. W. Pashley and M. J. Stowell, *in* "Electron Microscopy: Fifth International Congress for Electron Microscopy, Philadelphia, 1962" (S. S. Breese, ed.), Vol. 1, paper GG-1. Academic Press, New York, 1962.
40. E. W. Dickson and D. W. Pashley, *Phil. Mag.* **7**, 1315 (1962).
41. D. W. Pashley, M. J. Stowell, M. H. Jacobs, and T. J. Law, *Phil. Mag.* **10**, 127 (1964).
42. G. A. Bassett, *Phil. Mag.* **3**, 1042 (1958).
43. C. Sella, P. Conjeand and J. J. Trillat, *in* "Fourth International Conference on Electron Microscopy, Berlin, 1958" (W. Bargmann *et al.*, eds.), Vol. 1, p. 508. Springer, Berlin, 1960.
44. C. Sella and J. J. Trillat, *in* "Single Crystal Films" (M. Francombe and S. H. Sato, eds.) p. 201. Pergamon Press, Oxford, 1964.
45. D. Walton, T. N. Rhodin, and R. W. Rollins, *J. Chem. Phys.* **38**, 2698 (1963).
46. H. Bethge, *Phys. Status Solidi* **2**, 3, 775 (1962).
47. J. W. Matthews, *Phil. Mag.* **12**, 1143 (1965).
48. G. G. Sumner, *Phil. Mag.* **12**, 767 (1965).
49. S. Ino, *J. Phys. Soc. Japan* **21**, 346 (1966).
50. J. W. Matthews, *J. Vacuum. Sci. Technol.*, **3**, 133 (1966).
51. J. L. Robbins and T. N. Rhodin, *Surface Sci.* **2**, 346 (1964).
52. J. W. Matthews and K. Isebeck, *Phil. Mag.* **8**, 469 (1963).
53. L. G. Schultz, *Acta Cryst.* **5**, 130 (1952).
54. K. R. Lawless and D. F. Mitchell, *Mem. Sci. Rev. Met.* **62**, 27 (1965).
55. F. Bouillon and M. Jardinier-Offergeld, *Acta Met.* **11**, 287 (1963).
56. T. N. Rhodin, *in* "Structure and Properties of Thin Films" (C. A. Neugebauer, J. B. Newkirk, D. A. Vermilyea, eds.), p. 87. Wiley, New York, 1959.
57. A. U. MacRae, *Appl. Phys. Letters* **2**, 88 (1963).
58. K. R. Lawless and L. B. Garmon, Private communication, 1965.
59. J. M. Charig, B. A. Joyce, D. J. Stirland, and R. W. Bicknell, *Phil. Mag.* **7**, 1847 (1962).
60. G. R. Booker and B. A. Stickler, *Phil. Mag.* **11**, 11 (1965).
61. G. A. Bassett and D. W. Pashley, *J. Inst. Metals* **87**, 449 (1958–1959).
62. M. H. Jacobs and D. W. Pashley, *in* "Electron Microscopy: Fifth International Congress for Electron Microscopy, Phildelphia, 1962" (S. S. Breese, ed.) Vol. 1, paper DD-4. Academic Press, New York, 1962.
63. E. W. Dickson, M. H. Jacobs, and D. W. Pashley, *Phil. Mag.* **11**, 575 (1965).
63a. J. P. Hirth and K. L. Moazed, this volume.
64. D. Walton, *J. Chem. Phys.* **37**, 2182 (1962).
65. T. N. Rhodin and D. Walton, *in* "Single Crystal Films" (M. Francombe and H. Sato, eds.), p. 31. Pergamon Press, Oxford, 1964.

66. M. Volmer, "Kinetic der Phasenbildung," Steinkopff, Darmstadt, 1939.
67. H. Reiss, *J. Chem. Phys.* **20**, 1216 (1952).
67a. J. P. Hirth, S. J. Hruska, and G. M. Pound, *in* "Single Crystal Films" (M. Francombe and H. Sato, eds.), p. 9. Pergamon Press, Oxford, 1964.
68. E. N. da C. Andrade and J. G. Martindale, *Phil. Trans. Roy. Soc. London* **A235**, 69 (1935).
69. A. J. Forty and F. C. Frank, *Proc. Roy. Soc.* **A217**, 262 (1953).
70. J. T. Barlett and J. W. Mitchell, *Phil. Mag.* **5**, 445 (1960).
71. J. G. Allpress and J. V. Sanders, *Phil. Mag.* **9**, 645 (1964).
72. J. G. Allpress and J. V. Sanders, *Phil. Mag.* **10**, 827 (1964).
73. B. K. Chakraverty and G. M. Pound, *Acta Met.* **12**, 851 (1964).
74. F. Young, *Acta Met.* **2**, 117 (1960).
75. J. W. Faust, *Acta Met.* **11**, 1077 (1963).
76. V. A. Phillips, *J. Appl. Phys.* **33**, 712 (1962).
77. H. Hashimoto and R. Uyeda, *Acta Cryst.* **10**, 143 (1957).
78. D. W. Pashley, J. W. Menter, and G. A. Bassett, *Nature* **179**, 752 (1957).
79. H. Gottsche, *Z. Naturforsch.* **11a**, 55 (1956).
80. R. B. Kehoe, *Phil. Mag.* **2**, 445 (1957).
81. S. Ino, D. Watanabe, and S. Ogawa, *J. Phys. Soc. Japan* **19**, 881 (1964).
82. T. E. Hutchinson, *J. Appl. Phys.* **36**, 270 (1965).
83. H. Schlotterer, *Phys. Status Solidi* **11**, 219 (1965).
83a. S. Shinozaki and H. Sato, *J. Appl. Phys.* **35**, 2320 (1965).
84. N. Thompson, *Proc. Phys. Soc. (London)* **B66**, 481 (1953).
85. L. Bruck, *Ann. Phys. (Leipzig)* **26**, 233 (1936).
86. W. A. Jesser, J. W. Matthews, and D. Kuhlmann-Wilsdorf, *J. Vacuum Sci. Technol.* **2**, 276 (1965); *Appl. Phys. Letters* **9**, 176 (1966).
87. B. W. Sloope and C. O. Tiller, *J. Appl. Phys.* **32**, 1331 (1961).
88. A. Baltz, *J. Appl. Phys.* **34**, 1575 (1963).
88a. J. W. Matthews and E. Grunbaum, *Phil. Mag.* **11**, 1233 (1965).
89. K. L. Moazed and J. P. Hirth, *Surface Sci.* **3**, 49 (1965).
90. D. Walton, *Phil. Mag.* **7**, 1671 (1962).
91. J. W. Matthews, *Appl. Phys. Letters* **7**, 131 (1965).
91a. L. E. Murr and M. C. Inman, *Phil. Mag.* **14**, 135 (1966).
92. E. Grunbaum and J. W. Matthews, *Phys. Status Solidi* **9**, 731 (1965).
93. N. J. Taylor, *Surface Sci.* **4**, 161 (1966).
94. P. Delavignette, J. Tournier, and S. Amelinckx, *Phil. Mag.* **6**, 1419 (1961).
95. E. Grünbaum and J. W. Mitchell, *in* "Single Crystal Films" (M. Francombe and H. Sato, eds.), p. 221. Pergamon Press, Oxford, 1964.
96. J. W. Matthews, *Phil. Mag.* **6**, 1347 (1961).
97. O. Rudiger, *Ann. Phys. (Leipzig)* **30**, 505 (1937).
98. B. E. Sundquist, *Acta Met.* **12**, 67 (1964).
99. J. K. MacKenzie, A. J. W. Moore, and J. F. Nicholas, *Phys. Chem. Solids* **23**, 185 (1962).
100. H. Poppa, *Z. Naturforsch.* **19a**, 835 (1964); *in* "Electron Microscopy: Fifth International Congress on Electron Microscopy, Philadelphia, 1962" (S. S. Breese, ed.), Vol. 1, paper GG-14. Academic Press, New York, 1962.
101. H. Poppa, *J. Vacuum, Sci. Technol,* **2**, 42 (1965).
102. M. H. Jacobs, D. W. Pashley, and M. J. Stowell, *Phil. Mag.* **13**, 121 (1966).
103. K. L. Chopra, *Appl. Phys. Letters* **7**, 140 (1965).
104. F. C. Frank, *Phil. Mag.* **42**, 1014 (1965).

104a. P. C. J. Gallagher, *Phys. Status Solidi* **16**, 95 (1966).
105. B. W. Sloope and C. O. Tiller, *J. Appl. Phys.* **37**, 887 (1966).
106. H. J. Queisser, R. H. Finch, and J. Washburn, *J. Appl. Phys.* **33**, 1536 (1962).
107. W. C. Dash, *J. Appl. Phys.* **33**, 2395 (1962).
108. G. R. Booker and R. Stickler, *J. Appl. Phys.* **33**, 3281 (1962).
109. D. P. Miller, S. B. Watelski, and C. R. Moore, *J. Appl. Phys.* **34**, 2813 (1963).
110. G. R. Booker and A. Howie, *Appl. Phys. Letters* **3**, 156 (1963).
111. B. A. Unvala and G. R. Booker, *Phil. Mag.* **9**, 691 (1964).
112. S. Mendelson, *J. Appl. Phys.* **35**, 1570 (1964).
113. S. Mendelson, *in* "Single Crystal Films" (M. Francombe and H. Sato, eds.), p. 251. Pergamon Press, Oxford, 1964.
114. D. J. D. Thomas, *Phys. Status Solidi* **13**, 359 (1966).
115. R. J. Jaccodine and C. M. Drum, *Appl. Phys. Letters* **8**, 29 (1966).
116. H. Widmer, *Appl. Phys. Letters* **5**, 108 (1964).
117. Y. Kamiya and R. Uyeda, *Acta Cryst.* **14**, 70 (1961).
118. G. Menzer, *Z. Krist.* **99**, 398, 410 (1938).
119. F. Kirchner and O. Rudiger, *Ann. Phys. (Leipzig)* **30**, 609 (1937).
120. R. D. Burbank and R. D. Heidenreich, *Phil. Mag.* **5**, 373 (1960).
121. F. R. L. Schoening and A. Baltz, *J. Appl. Phys.* **33**, 1442 (1962).
122. J. W. Matthews and D. L. Allinson, *Phil. Mag.* **10**, 9 (1964).
123. A. Catlin, private communication, 1964.
123a. D. W. Pashley and M. J. Stowell, *J. Vacuum Sci. Technol.*, **3**, 156 (1966).
124. M. J. Hall and M. W. Thompson, *Brit. J. Appl. Phys.* **12**, 495 (1961).
125. G. R. Booker, *Phil. Mag.* **11**, 1007 (1965).
126. W. C. Ellis and R. G. Treuting, *J. Metals, J. Petrol. Technol. Mining Eng.* **189**, 53 (1951).
127. M. H. Jacobs and S. M. J. Stowell, *Phil. Mag.* **11**, 591 (1965).
128. M. J. Stowell and T. J. Law, *Phys. Status Solidi* **16**, 117 (1966).
128a. J. W. Matthews and E. Grunbaum, *Appl. Phys. Letters* **5**, 106 (1964).
129. D. W. Pashley, *Phil. Mag.* **4**, 324 (1959).
130. K. R. Lawless, *J. Vacuum Sci. Technol.* **2**, 24 (1965).
131. A. Catlin, W. P. Walker, and K. R. Lawless, *Acta Met.* **8**, 734 (1960).
132. V. A. Phillips, *Phil Mag.* **5**, 571 (1960).
133. M. J. Whelan, *Proc. Roy. Soc.* **A249**, 114 (1958).
134. F. C. Frank, *Phil. Mag.* **42**, 809 (1951).
135. H. J. Queisser, *J. Appl. Phys.* **32**, 1776 (1961).
136. S. Prussin, *J. Appl. Phys.* **32**, 1876 (1961).
137. G. H. Schwuttke and H. J. Queisser, *J. Appl. Phys.* **33**, 1540 (1962).
138. J. W. Matthews, *Phil. Mag.* **8**, 711 (1963).
139. J. W. Matthews, *in* "Single Crystal Films" (M. Francombe and H. Sato, eds.), p. 165. Pergamon Press, Oxford, 1964.
140. J. Washburn, G. Thomas, and H. J. Queisser, *J. Appl. Phys.* **35**, 1909 (1964).
141. W. A. Tiller, *J. Appl. Phys.* **29**, 611 (1958).
142. J. P. Hirth, *in* "Single Crystal Films" (M. Francombe and H. Sato, eds.), p. 173. Pergamon Press, Oxford, 1964.
143. J. S. Vermaak and J. H. van der Merwe, *Phil. Mag.* **12**, 453 (1965).
144. J. W. Matthews and J. L. Crawford, *Phil. Mag.* **11**, 977 (1965).
145. O. Rang, *Optik* **10**, 90 (1953).
146. H. Schlotterer, *Z. Naturforsch.* **20a**, 1201 (1965).
147. G. R. Booker and U. Valdre, *Phil. Mag.* **13**, 421 (1966).

The Growth and Structure of Electrodeposits

KENNETH R. LAWLESS

Department of Materials Science
School of Engineering and Applied Science
University of Virginia
Charlottesville, Virginia

I. Introduction 191
II. The Nucleation and Growth of Electrodeposits 192
   1. Deposition from the Vapor 192
   2. Differences between Vapor Deposition and Electrodeposition 195
   3. Mechanism of Monolayer Growth 196
   4. Morphology of Electrodeposits 199
III. The Structure of Electrodeposits 217
   1. Experimental Methods 217
   2. Results of Structure Studies 226
References 251

I. Introduction

Electrodeposits play an important role in science and industry today. The fundamental laws of electrolysis, which provide the foundation for the science of electrodeposition, were first formulated by Faraday in 1833. The first application of the principles of electrolysis to the deposition of metals is the subject of some controversy (1), but probably took place around 1838. Despite this early beginning, little progress in understanding the mechanism of electrodeposition was made until fairly recently. This is probably the result of the concentration on empirical studies aimed at preparing specific types of deposits. In the past 15 years, however, there has been a great increase in the amount of research aimed at understanding the process of crystal growth. Although this work has been mostly in the area of crystal growth from the vapor phase, a significant contribution in the area of the growth of electrodeposits has also been made. Recent studies of electrochemical kinetics have made a major contribution to the current knowledge of the fundamental processes involved in electrodeposition.

This review has been intentionally limited in its scope to a discussion mainly of the growth and structure of single crystal electrodeposit films. For more details on other aspects of the mechanism of electrodeposition, the reader is referred to the recent outstanding review articles by Bockris and Damjanovic (2) and by Fleischmann and Thirsk (3). The electrochemical kinetics of the deposition process and their importance in the growth process are discussed thoroughly in these references. A somewhat older, but still excellent and extremely thorough account of the field of electrodeposition up to 1954 has been given by Fischer (4).

It is not the purpose of this review to discuss the experimental techniques involved in the formation of electrodeposits. Procedures and techniques have been discussed in great detail in books by Brenner (5), Blum and Hogaboom (6), and Lowenheim (7). The necessity for extremely careful control of solution impurity levels and for the use of well-characterized single crystal surfaces in studies of electrodeposition should be emphasized. Much of the significance of earlier studies has been obscured by the use of poor techniques. The importance of very careful techniques has been particularly emphasized by Bockris and Damjanovic (2), and details of solution preparation and cell construction have been given.

II. The Nucleation and Growth of Electrodeposits

1. Deposition from the Vapor

It seems advisable to start the discussion of the nucleation and growth of electrodeposits by first reviewing briefly the growth of crystals from the vapor. Many of the concepts are directly transferable to the case of electrodeposition. The special features which make the growth of electrodeposits differ in certain ways from growth from the vapor will be considered in the next section.

The surfaces of perfect crystals may be classified as either close-packed (low-index) surfaces or vicinal (high-index) surfaces. In this classification a high-index plane is always stepped on an atomic scale whereas a low-index plane is generally considered as smooth. The steps on the high-index surfaces are segments of close-packed planes. As pointed out by Frenkel (8) and later by Burton and Cabrera (9), these steps will always have a high concentration of kink sites.

If atoms are added to a vicinal surface from a supersaturated vapor, three major steps are involved in its growth: (a) adsorption of atoms on the surface, (b) surface diffusion of the atom to a step, and (c) diffusion along the step to a kink site. The remarkable ease of diffusion of an atom on a crystal surface was pointed out by Volmer (10, 11). The steps on the surface will then advance by the addition of atoms at the kink sites until the steps grow out of the crystal, leaving only low-index surfaces. The rate of advance of the steps will be proportional to the amount of supersaturation.

If atoms are added to a low-index surface, growth of the perfect crystal is controlled by two-dimensional nucleation. This fact was first appreciated by Gibbs (12). In this case then the rate of growth is limited by the difficulty in nucleating a new monolayer on the surface and not by the rate of advance of a step which is proportional to the supersaturation. The growth rate will remain zero until a certain critical supersaturation is reached at which point the growth rate will rapidly go from zero to the ideal rate if the spacing between monatomic steps is small compared to the mean-free path of the atom on the surface. This has been discussed by Burton and Cabrera (9), and by Becker and Döring (13). It is not appropriate to go into details of the two-dimensional nucleation here, but such details may be found in recent works by Hirth (14), Hirth and Pound (15), and Burton et al. (16).

In practice, it is found that crystal growth already occurs at observable rates at supersaturations which are quite low (1 % or lower) compared to the critical supersaturation. At supersaturations this low, the probability of the formation of nuclei is essentially negligible. It is clear that a new concept is needed to explain the continued growth of a crystal at these low supersaturations. It was first shown by Frank (17) that this growth may be attributed to the presence of steps associated with dislocations having a screw component normal to the surface.

Burton et al. (16) have given a detailed treatment of the rate of growth of a crystal surface by advancement of steps associated with a screw dislocation. A schematic diagram of such a surface with one dislocation is shown in Fig. 1.

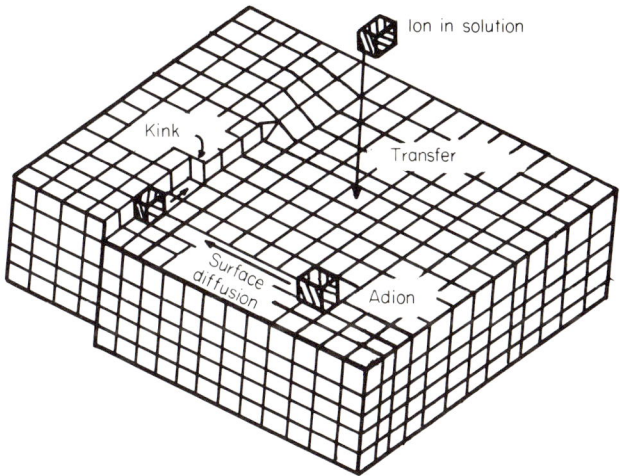

FIG. 1. Model of a suface with a screw dislocation. Transfer of an ion or atom from solution or vapor to the surface and subsequent diffusion to a kink site are shown schematically.

As atoms are added to the surface from a supersaturated environment, they diffuse to the step and are incorporated in the lattice at kink sites. As the step advances, it winds itself in a spiral, thus developing a growth cone or pyramid on the surface. A pair of dislocations of opposite sign will send out closed loops if their separation is greater than the diameter of the critical nucleus, and will likewise lead to the development of a cone or pyramid on the surface. Both of these situations are illustrated in Fig. 2.

The development of low cones on the surface occurs if the rate of advance of a step is essentially independent of its orientation. On the other hand, if this rate depends on orientation, the steps will be along crystallographic directions, and the growth will have a pyramidal form. The spacing between successive turns of the spiral, y_0 is given approximately by $y_0 = 4\pi r_c$ where r_c is the critical radius of curvature which depends on the supersaturation. For very low values of supersaturation, r_c will be quite large and the resulting cones or pyramids will be very shallow. For high supersaturations, r_c will be small and the sides of the cones or pyramids will be steep.

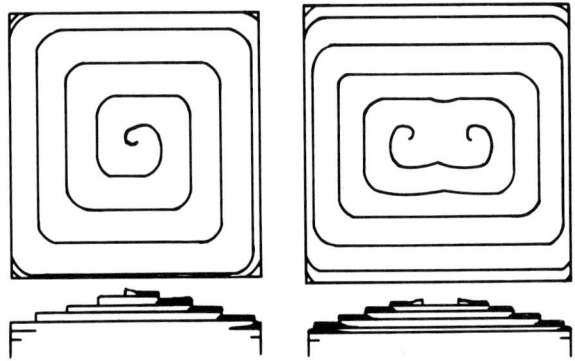

FIG. 2. Pyramidal growth due to a simple screw dislocation and to a pair of screw dislocations of opposite sign [after Burton et al. (16)].

In the usual case, many dislocations intersect the surface and the growth phenomena will be complex, depending on the distance separating the dislocations, their relative signs, and on the amount of supersaturation. If a pair of opposite sign are closer together than $2r_c$, no growth occurs. If they are farther apart, then closed loops of steps go out from the pair. Two similar pairs of dislocations of opposite sign behave essentially as one pair, if the distance between pairs is not too large, and form a single cone or pyramid on the surface. A pair of dislocations of the same sign gives a more complicated case than that of opposite signs, but the rate of growth normal to the surface turns out to be essentially the same as for a single dislocation if the distance between dislocations, l, is large, i.e., if $l > 2\pi r_c$. If $l < 2\pi r_c$, then the rate of growth normal to the surface is greater than that for a single dislocation. A group of dislocations of the same sign, each separated by a distance $l < 2\pi r_c$ from its nearest neighbor, gives a multiple-branched spiral system, and the rate of growth normal to the surface can be many times greater than the growth for a single dislocation. This is an oversimplification and the reader is referred to the original discussions by Frank (*17*), Burton *et al.* (*16*), and the monograph by Verma (*18*) for more complete discussions.

There is now a considerable amount of experimental data available showing spirals on crystals grown from the vapor as well as from solution (*18–21*). In many cases the agreement with theory is only qualitative and not quantitative, since microscopic growth spirals with step heights as large as 1000 A are observed. Definite evidence that growth spirals can originate at screw dislocation-surface intersections was found by Frank and Forty (*22*) in a study of silver growth.

2. Differences between Vapor Deposition and Electrodeposition

It is obvious that certain major differences exist between the growth of crystals on a surface by vapor deposition and the growth by electrodeposition (*2*). One expects that the major differences would arise from the presence of an environment about the crystal surface consisting of a water solution containing various anions and cations. (In this review we will not consider deposits from nonaqueous solutions or fused salts.) The presence of an electric field and the fact that deposits are usually made at temperatures which are relatively low compared to those for epitaxial growth from the vapor are also of considerable importance. In practice, many vapor depositions are carried out in relatively poor vacuums ($p > 10^{-6}$ Torr), and the true state of the surface may not differ as much from that of a surface in an aqueous solution as is often assumed.

A metal surface in an aqueous solution will have an adsorbed layer or layers on its surface. Under "clean" conditions (i.e., a true metal surface, oxygen-free solution, ultrahigh-purity water and chemicals), the surface will have water molecules as well as both cations and anions from the solution adsorbed on its surface. Under practical deposition conditions various addition agents or impurities may be present and also adsorbed on the surface. An oxide film, oxide inclusions, or adsorbed oxygen may frequently be present. These adsorbed substances will generally decrease the surface energy of the metal.

The above situation, however, may not be drastically different from the usual case of vacuum deposition at pressures of the order of 10^{-7} Torr or greater. Under these conditions, the metal may have adsorbed molecules of water, carbon monoxide or dioxide, hydrogen, oxygen, or nitrogen on its surface, all of these being common residual gases in a vacuum system. Other perhaps more serious contaminants such as oil vapors and their cracking products are also commonly present. It is quite clear from the work of Matthews (*23*) that epitaxial growth can be markedly affected by these adsorbed gases on the substrate. It is of course possible to obtain really clean surfaces for vapor deposition by the use of modern ultrahigh-vacuum techniques.

The presence of adsorbed layers on a metal surface in solution is expected to influence the mobility of the deposit ions or atoms on the surface. In particular, the large adsorbed water molecules should make the surface diffusion of these ions or atoms considerably more difficult. On the other hand, if the adsorbed cations are hydrated, their bonding to the surface would be weakened and the activation energy needed for surface diffusion would be expected to be less than that for unhydrated atoms on the surface.

The particles arriving at the surface double layer are thought to be hydrated ions. These must diffuse across the double layer at the surface and then be adsorbed as partially hydrated ions. This compares with the arrival of atoms at the metal surface in the case of vapor deposition and their adsorption as atoms. The arrival of metal atoms from the vapor is not restricted by a surrounding atmosphere as in the case where the ions are transported through a solution.

Finally the electric field present in the case of electrodeposition can be very high, e.g., of the order of 10^7 volts/cm, between the metal surface and ions in the double layer. A high field may also exist at the surface of a metal in a vacuum system if chemisorbed oxygen or a thin oxide is present, but the direction of the field will be opposite to that of the electrodeposition case.

3. Mechanism of Monolayer Growth

Bockris and co-workers (*2, 24–39*) have made an extensive electrochemical study of the mechanism by which a metal ion in the bulk of solution arrives at a growth site on the metal surface and is finally incorporated into a crystal lattice. This process is termed "monolayer deposition," and will be considered briefly in this section.

It is well known that a cation in aqueous solution is closely bound by a sheath of water molecules, i.e., it is a hydrated ion. Before such an ion can be made a part of the crystal lattice, it must first cross the double layer and then lose its sheath of water molecules. A schematic modern representation of this double layer at a metal surface immersed in an aqueous solution of cations and anions is shown in Fig. 3 (*40*). The loss of solvent molecules of hydration will probably take place in steps, as indicated by Conway and Bockris (*24, 25*).

In the first step the solvated cation crosses the double layer, loses part of its water of hydration, and the cation becomes adsorbed on the metal surface as an adion. Theoretical considerations (*24, 25*) indicate that the ion transfer takes place at planar portions of the metal surface, rather than at edges or kink sites. Calculations show that an unfavorably high activation energy would be required at the latter sites because of the extra energy needed to remove most or all of the water of hydration about an ion in one step [60 kcal/mole for copper (24)]. Adsorption on kink sites is also unlikely on purely statistical grounds, since the area of the surface exposed as edges or kink sites is apt to be small compared to the area of smooth planes (41).

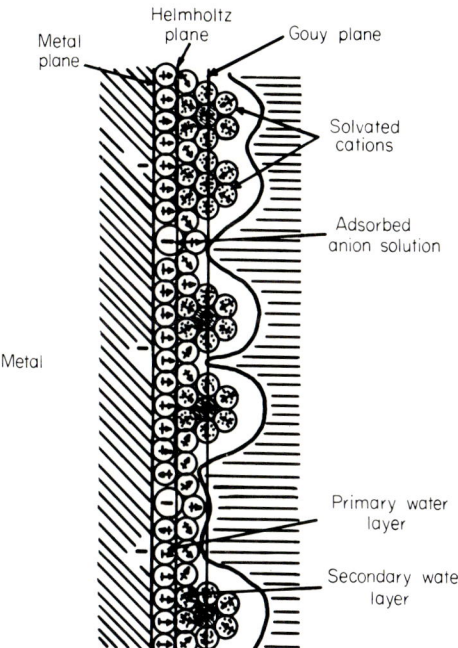

FIG. 3. Schematic representation of electrical double layer at a metal surface in an aqueous solution [after Devanathan et al. (40)].

The second step involves the surface diffusion of the partially hydrated adion until it reaches a step on the crystal surface, at which site it loses additional water of hydration. The ion is still not incorporated into the crystal lattice and further diffusion along the step until a kink site is reached is necessary. The adion finally loses the last of its water of hydration and becomes incorporated as an ion into the metal lattice. This process of transfer of an ion from solution to a kink site is shown schematically in Fig. 1.

Either of the above steps may be rate determining in the over-all reaction process. Theory (24, 25) indicates that the ion-transfer step is the most probable rate-determining process at overvoltages much above the reversible potential for the deposition. At low overvoltages, the surface diffusion of adions is the rate controlling process.

The theory presented so far is not in agreement with the assumption of Mott and Watts-Tobin (42) that all sites on the surface are equally probable for transfer. It is also not consistent with the idea of direct incorporation of an ion at a step or kink site as proposed earlier by Volmer (43). Brandes (44), and Lorenz (45), on the other hand, have suggested that transfer takes place at planes followed by surface diffusion. Because of these differences of opinion, it is desirable that experimental evidence be obtained in support of either the direct transfer of ions to growth sites, or the charge transfer process at any site followed by surface diffusion to a growth site. Such experimental evidence has been obtained by Bockris and co-workers (26, 29, 32, 33).

Two experimental techniques have been used: (1) a study of dc charging transients, and (2) a study of the kinetics of deposition onto both liquid and solid gallium surfaces. The details of these experiments will not be considered here; it suffices to say that the results give support to the theoretical concepts of Conway and Bockris and are inconsistent with the direct transfer picture.

The above concepts all require the presence of edges or steps on a surface. Most surfaces are not smooth on an atomic basis but consist of a multitude of steps or edges which may be more than one atomic unit in height. During deposition such steps could grow laterally, completing the atomic planes and leaving a smooth surface. It would be necessary to create new steps on the surface if growth were to continue. Two-dimensional nucleation by aggregation of adions provides a possible means for the creation of these new steps.

The process of two-dimensional surface nucleation of electrodeposits has been considered in detail by Bockris and Damjanovic (2). In this treatment it is shown that the rate of nucleation is given by

$$R = 2\pi r_c n^2 \left(\frac{kT}{2\pi m}\right)^{1/2} \exp\left[-\frac{\Delta F_c + E}{kT}\right] \quad (1)$$

Here r_c is the radius of the critical nucleus, n is the number of adions/cm^2, ΔF_c is the free-energy change for formation of the critical nucleus, and E is the activation energy for surface migration.

The radius of the critical nucleus, r_c, is given by

$$r_c = \frac{\sqrt{3}}{2} \frac{d^2 \gamma}{kT \ln c/c_0} \quad (2)$$

where γ is the edge energy of the nucleus, d is the interatomic distance in the embryo, and c and c_0 are the adion concentrations at a given overvoltage and at zero potential, respectively.

Since the values of both r_c and ΔF_c depend on the adion concentration, the rate of nucleation is critically dependent on the overvoltage. Calculations for silver reveal that significant two-dimensional nucleation may occur if the overvoltage is of the order of 80 to 100 mV (2). Vermilyea (46) carried out an important experiment in which he deposited copper on small (75-μ) wire and whiskers of copper varying in size down to 3 μ. It was found that overvoltages greater than 100 mV were necessary to obtain deposition on the smallest whiskers. The increased overvoltage required for the smaller whiskers was suggested as indicating a higher relative perfection (presumably surface perfection) for the smaller whiskers. These results seem to be in good agreement with the above predictions. On most copper surfaces, which do not show the atomic perfection of whisker surfaces, copper can be electrodeposited at far lower values of overvoltage indicating that two-dimensional nucleation is not necessary on such surfaces for deposition.

4. Morphology of Electrodeposits

a. Types of Morphology. The types of morphology exhibited by electrodeposits are generally more varied than those shown by vapor deposits. For the deposition of a given metal, the morphology may depend on:

(1) The current density,
(2) the presence of addition agents or impurities,
(3) the nature of the anions in the solution,
(4) the nature of the cations being deposited or in solution,
(5) whether the current is continuous or pulsed,
(6) the orientation of the crystallographic face used as a substrate,
(7) solution concentration,
(8) temperature.

It is clear that in the general case the growth of the deposit will be influenced by several of the above factors, although one factor may be sufficiently influential that it controls the growth form. In particular, the current density and solution purity seem to be especially important.

Experimentally a number of different growth forms have been observed. A layer-type growth has been most frequently observed (*36, 38, 39, 47–68*). Simple and complex pyramidal structures have been seen by many workers (*36, 38, 39, 52, 55, 56, 59, 60, 63–71*). Block-like structures (*36, 38, 39, 55, 57, 60, 64–68, 70*) and ridge structures (*36, 38, 39, 57, 60, 64, 65, 67, 68, 71*) also occur under certain conditions. Polycrystalline deposits are a common occurrence, particularly if care is not taken to use high-purity crystals as substrates and if impurities are present in the solution. The use of high current densities for the deposition almost invariably leads to fine-grained polycrystalline growth. Figure 4 from Seiter *et al.* (*55*) shows a plot of current density versus overvoltage for the deposition of copper from $nCuSO_4 + nH_2SO_4$. Regions in which the authors observed the different growth forms are indicated on the graph. Figure 5 shows examples for four of the commonly observed deposit types.

Whisker and dendritic-type growths have been studied by a number of

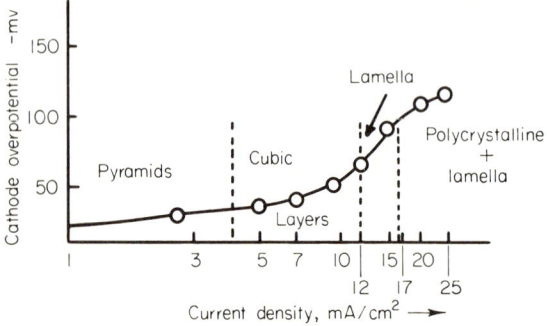

FIG. 4. Graph of current density versus overvoltage for deposition of copper showing current density regions in which specific surface structures were observed [after Seiter et al. (55)].

workers (59, 72–76), but the discussion of these interesting phenomena is beyond the scope of this article.

The different types of growth forms observed will be considered in more detail in the following sections.

b. Pyramidal Growth Forms. Pyramidal growth forms have been observed on copper (36, 38, 39, 52, 55, 56, 60, 61, 66, 68, 70, 71), lead (59, 65, 68), silver (59), and cadmium (59, 67, 68) deposits. A typical micrograph of copper

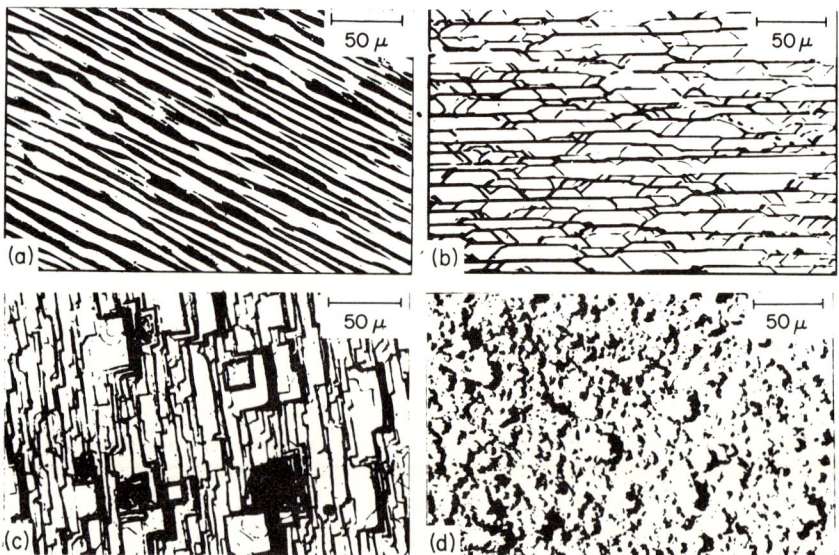

FIG. 5. Four basic deposit-type structures on copper: (a) ridge, (b) platelet, (c) block, (d) polycrystalline [from Barnes et al. (58)].

pyramidal growth on a (100) substrate is shown in Fig. 6. In general, this type of growth takes place at low current densities. For example, pyramids have been observed with copper deposits (from acidified $CuSO_4$ solution) at current densities up to 15 mA/cm^2, but at higher current densities another growth form appears (38).

FIG. 6. Pyramidal growths on copper deposit on (100) substrate [from Seiter et al. (55)].

There is some discrepancy in the literature as to the upper limit of current density for the formation of pyramids. Upper limits of 5 to 8 mA/cm^2 have been reported (55), but it seems that this limit is extremely sensitive to impurities in the solution which would tend to truncate the pyramids. Damjanovic et al. (36) have shown that in the presence of only 10^{-8} to 10^{-9} mole/liter of n-decylamine, truncation occurs at a very early stage of the deposition of copper on the (100) surface of copper.

The formation of growth pyramids seems to depend on the crystallographic orientation, having been observed primarily on planes in the vicinity of the (100) plane of copper, the (111) plane of copper, silver, and lead, and the (0001) plane of cadmium. These are the planes with the highest or second-highest packing density. Such growths have not been observed on high-index planes, probably because of the presence of highly stepped surfaces and the predominance of layer growth. The pyramids are usually four-sided with a square or rectangular base when grown on (100)-oriented substrates, and three-sided (triangular base) or six-sided (hexagonal base) on (111) substrates.

In general the side faces of the pyramids do not correspond to low-index planes but rather are vicinal faces. These faces are stepped and the pyramids have the appearance of being built up by stacking thin rectangular or triangular platelets on top of one another. The angle of inclination of the side faces of the pyramids to the substrate surface is a function of current density and generally decreases with decreasing current density (55).

Seiter et al. (55) have made a study of the dependency of the angle of inclination (α) on current density (i) and have derived the equation

$$\tan \alpha = K \log i \qquad (3)$$

assuming that the adion concentration is proportional to the current density. K is a constant. They have confirmed this equation experimentally by measurements on copper deposits from acidified normal $CuSO_4$ solution. This type of relationship would be expected if the pyramids are growing by a spiral-growth mechanism, assuming a step height of one atomic layer and a distance between two successive turns of the spiral of $y_0 = 4\pi r_c$. The angle of inclination α is then given by

$$\tan \alpha = a/y_0 = a/4\pi r_c \qquad (4)$$

As has been pointed out, however, by Bockris and Damjanovic (2), values of $\tan \alpha \geq 0.2$ as actually observed correspond to critical nuclei with a radius less than atomic dimensions. It is possible that this apparent failure of the theory is due to the presence of step heights considerably greater than one atomic unit resulting from multiple screw dislocations or other faults leading to large Burgers vectors.

Evidence of growth spirals with microscopic steps large enough for observation by optical microscopy has been found by Pick and Wilcock (54), Pick (77), and Seiter et al. (55, 78) on copper deposits, by Kaischew et al. (79) on silver deposits, and by Wranglen (59, 73) on lead deposits. A typical growth spiral on copper is shown in Fig. 7. The occurrence of these spiral growths is rare under normal deposition conditions. It has been observed that the use of high-purity solutions and of a square pulse current tends to increase the frequency of their formation. The spirals are almost always observed on low-index planes. Characteristically the step heights of the spirals may vary from 100 to 1000 A and their widths from 1 to 10 μ. Although there is currently no completely satisfactory explanation of the occurrence of such large step heights, it has been suggested (80) that a group of cooperating screw dislocations can give the large Burgers vectors required.

It is generally considered that the growth pyramids and the macrospirals both grow by the screw-dislocation mechanism (2). It is not, however, clear at the present time whether these growths originate on screw dislocations in the substrate surface, or on dislocations which are generated in the growth process, possibly by the growing together of nuclei. Kaishew et al. (79) have demonstrated the formation of a growth spiral originating at the same site on the substrate, regardless of the amount of substrate dissolved away prior to deposition, thus providing the only direct evidence of the influence of substrate imperfections. However, essentially all observations of spiral growths on electrodeposits have been made on thick deposits. This could indicate the development of the spirals at a later time in the deposition.

FIG. 7. Growth spiral on copper electrodeposit [from Seiter et al. (55)].

Several mechanisms have been suggested by which impurities could generate screw dislocations in a growing crystal. It has been postulated by Frank (19) that if a material is growing as a thin platelet and takes up impurities nonuniformly as it grows, a situation which is very likely in electrodeposition, the impurity gradient would set up shear stresses which would cause the platelet to shear and to generate a line of screw dislocations. Another proposal (81) was that two crystals growing together with a small misorientation could lead to a line of screw dislocations at their juncture. It is also possible that the incorporation of a large impurity particle could lead to a screw dislocation as a result of the growing crystal not joining perfectly after passing around the impurity. Grain boundaries can be a source of dislocations for growth processes if the boundaries are twist boundaries or consist of a crossed grid of screw dislocations (*82*).

Although the screw-dislocation mechanism of growth for electrodeposits seems to have been generally accepted, and is indeed a very attractive mechanism, there is essentially no direct evidence relating the observed spirals to known screw dislocations in the substrate. The rarity of occurrence of the growth spirals suggests that this is not the major growth mechanism for electrodeposition. It would seem that more studies in this area are badly needed.

c. Layer Growth. A layer- or platelet-type growth has been observed more frequently than any other type growth in metal electrodeposits (*36, 38, 39, 47–68*). Such features have been observed in certain cases from the very early stages of growth up to very large deposit thicknesses. A typical example of layer growth is shown in Fig. 5(b).

Observations with both electron microscope and optical microscope techniques reveal a great diversity in the appearance of layer growths and this is primarily the result of the orientation of the substrate. On low-index planes, broad flat areas are frequently observed, whereas on high-index planes, terraces or steps inclined to the substrate surface are found. Thus a deposit on a (111) or (100) surface of copper might be quite smooth, whereas that on a (311) or (321) surface usually appears very rough. The edges of the growth layers may be straight lines along specific crystallographic directions in many cases, but irregular or circular edges have also been observed (*55, 57*).

It seems clear that layer growth occurs, at least on certain surfaces, at low current densities. Very careful studies by Damjanovic *et al.* (*36, 38, 39, 64*) of copper deposits on single crystal copper substrates have shown that macrosteps occur on the (111) and (100) substrate planes along with pyramids at current densities from 2 to 5 mA/cm^2. The steps all propagate in the same direction as a result of a slight misorientation of the substrate from the exact low-index plane. Bicelli and Poli (*68*) also observed square-based pyramids and cubic growth layers formed on the (100) copper surface at 1 mA/cm^2, whereas at 5 and 10 mA/cm^2 the cubic growth layers prevailed. On the (111) surface they found a microscopically rough deposit at 1 and 10 mA/cm^2. These studies were primarily concerned with deposits of the order of 1 μ thickness and the macrosteps were visible in the optical microscope so that they were certainly not of atomic dimensions.

On the other hand, Vaughan and Pick (*83*) made an electron microscope study of a series of copper deposits prepared at 10 mA/cm^2 on cube-textured copper sheet. The deposition time was short and ranged from 15 to 90 sec. At 15 sec the study shows the formation of nuclei which were about 200 A high and about 0.5μ in diameter. Even at this stage many of the nuclei were growing together to give a step-like deposit, and at 90 sec the steps covered the surface and the individual nuclei had essentially disappeared. Figure 8 shows an example of this type growth.

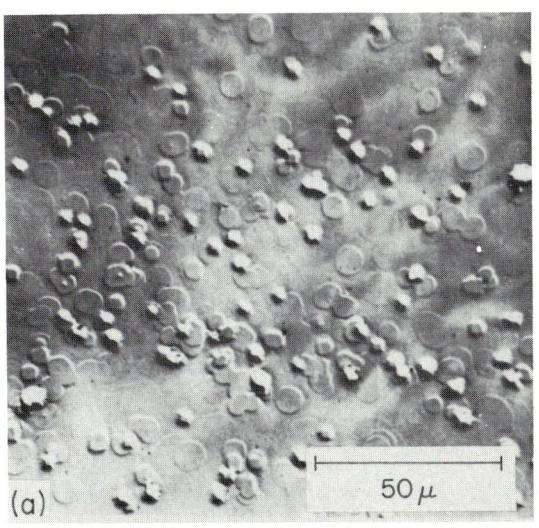

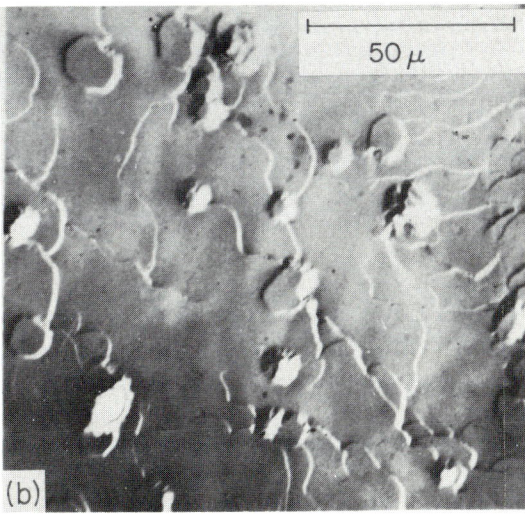

FIG. 8. Micrographs of copper deposit after 15 sec and 60 sec plating time showing two types of nuclei and a layer-type structure: (a) 15-sec deposit, (b) 60-sec deposit [from Pick et al. (57)].

(110) and higher-index planes were found in most cases to show a ridge-type structure (*36, 38, 39, 54, 57, 60, 61, 64*) at low current density or overvoltage. Bicelli and Poli (*68*), however, report the (110) deposits as being microscopically rough, becoming a ridge structure at a thickness of about 15 μ. Barnes *et al.* (*58*) found that with increasing current density the ridge structure changed to the platelet or layer structure. At current densities above about 15 mA/cm^2 a so-called block structure was obtained.

Fischer and his co-workers (*55, 56*) did not report finding layer growth on the (100) surface at low-impulse current densities (<8 mA/cm^2) but between 8 and 40 mA/cm^2 they report a cubic layer structure. Experiments on the deposition of copper onto spherical single crystals by Economou and Trivich (*61*) showed that the layer growth occurred in such a manner that in the vicinity of the [100] pole the main faces of the layers were parallel to the (100) face. The extent of the area covered by this (100) layer structure was dependent on current density between 1 and 20 mA/cm^2, being greater at the higher current densities in this range. Layer growth was not reported for the (100) or (111) faces under the same conditions. This work seems to be in good agreement with the work of Pick *et al.* (*54, 57, 58, 83*).

The so-called block or cubic layer structure (*36, 38, 39, 55, 57, 60, 70*) as shown in Fig. 5(c) on surfaces near the (100) seems to be a special case of layer formation, and the occurrence of this growth form is sensitive to the purity of the solution. Barnes (*84*) found that the incidence of blocks is greater the higher the current density. The occurrence of these blocks was explained on the basis of two-dimensional nucleation and the fact that they were found only at overpotentials around 100 mV was taken to be confirmation of this mechanism, on the basis of Vermilyea's (*46, 85*) work. Blocks, however, have been observed on the (100) surface at deposition current densities around 20 mA/cm^2 (*36, 38*). Hexagonal blocks have been observed by Damjanovic *et al.* (*64*) on (111) surfaces of copper at 2 to 15 mA/cm^2. These appear to form by truncation of pyramids, the truncation being more complete at the higher current density. The truncation could result from the blocking of an emerging screw dislocation by adsorbed impurities. The side faces of the block could then continue to grow. This is more likely to occur at higher current densities where local solution exhaustion might occur, making it easier for impurities to compete for adsorption sites in the growth surface.

Layer- and block-type structures have also been observed for lead deposits on the (100) and (111) faces of lead single crystals in the current density range of 10 to 50 mA/cm^2 (*65, 68*). Deposition on the (100) surface at increased current density of 30 to 50 mA/cm^2 caused the growths to assume a more regular cubic shape. On (111) substrates, an increase in current density brought about an increase in the number of triangular growths. Layer- and block-type structures were not observed on the (110) substrate.

Similar growth structures have also been observed by Bicelli and Poli (67, 68) on Cd (10$\bar{1}$0), and (0001) surfaces with 2 to 8 μ deposits in the range of 5 to 50 mA/cm^2 current density.

The types of deposit observed in all cases seem to be characteristic of the particular substrate surface used, with detailed modifications depending on such factors as current density, impurities, and temperature.

In all studies cited, it is apparent that the growth features observed are much greater than atomic dimensions. Growth layers as observed are made up of macrosteps which may vary, in individual cases, from several hundred to several thousand angstroms in height, the step height increasing with time (38). The density of the macrosteps is usually high at early stages of the deposition and decreases with increasing time of deposition.

A mechanism for the formation of macrosteps on electrodeposits was first proposed by Pick et al. (57). In the proposed model, atomic steps on a high-index surface advance by the addition of deposit atoms to kink sites. Such a surface is shown schematically in two dimensions in Fig. 9. The surface is

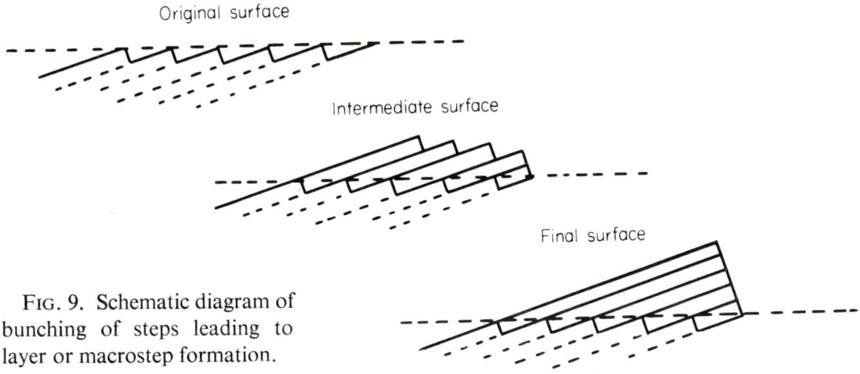

FIG. 9. Schematic diagram of bunching of steps leading to layer or macrostep formation.

made up of a series of low-index facets, and the monatomic steps advance across these planes. It was then proposed that a bunching or clustering process occurs in which some steps advance sufficiently fast to catch up with others, thus forming higher steps which are assumed to grow more slowly. The motion of the atomic steps in the bunching process would of course not be visible, but the motion of the macrosteps resulting from the microsteps advance would be visible after the steps reached a certain size.

On a less ideal surface, the spacing between the steps will not be uniform. According to the kinematic theory developed for crystal growth by Frank (86) and by Cabrera and Vermilyea (87) following a treatment by Lighthill and Whitham (88) for traffic flow, these unequally spaced steps will travel across the surface at different velocities. The steps which are closer together will travel at a slower speed than those which are far apart, i.e., at a particular point on the surface the velocity of a step depends on the density of steps in that vicinity. Following Frank's nomenclature, if k is the density of steps near a point x, and q is the flux of steps, then, on the basis of the above assumption,

$$q = q(k) \qquad (5)$$

From the conservation of steps, we then have the continuity equation:

$$\partial q/\partial x + \partial k/\partial t = 0 \qquad (6)$$

Since q is a function of k only, Eq. (6) is equivalent to

$$\frac{dq}{dk}\frac{\partial k}{\partial x} + \frac{\partial k}{\partial t} = 0 \qquad (7)$$

or

$$c(k)\frac{\partial k}{\partial x} + \frac{\partial k}{\partial t} = 0 \qquad (8)$$

where

$$c(k) = dq/dk = dx/dt \qquad (9)$$

is called the "kinematic wave velocity." The meaning of Eq. (9) is that there are certain regions of constant step density on the surface of the crystal which move with a constant velocity, $dx/dt = c(k)$. For a given value of k, and hence for q, dq/dk and therefore dx/dt is determined, and there will be a straight line in the (x, t) plane along which k is constant. This line is called the "characteristic."

It was shown (86) that the step-density profile will change with time. Suppose a surface has a low density of steps except for a symmetrical cluster of high density in one region and the steps propagate in one direction. At the leading edge of the cluster, the characteristics diverge and behind the cluster they converge, and at some time t_1 later than t_0 they will meet. Where the characteristics meet, a discontinuity in the density of steps develops which follows a trajectory in the (x, t) plane of a slope given by the equation

$$\frac{dx}{dt} = \frac{q_2 - q_1}{k_2 - k_1} \qquad (10)$$

q_1, q_2 and k_1, k_2 are fluxes and densities adjacent to the discontinuity. This is mathematically equivalent to a shock wave.

A bunch of steps will then move across the surface, but it will gain steps from one side and lose them from the other side. The bunch will not increase but will actually fade out and disappear as a result of the assumption that q at a point x is a function only of k at that point. The discontinuity in the step density occurs at the rear of the advancing cluster if $d^2q/dk^2 < 0$, and the profile of the bunch becomes less defined. On the other hand, if dq/dk increases with increasing k, then $d^2q/dk^2 > 0$, and the discontinuity occurs at the front of the advancing cluster. This is necessary if bunching is to occur with the production of a visible macrostep.

It is necessary at this point to consider the effect of impurities adsorbed on the steps. Suppose that a low concentration of impurity which adsorbs strongly on the surface is present in the solution. The impurity will reduce the velocity $v = q/k$ with which a step travels across the surface. It is assumed that as the step advances, the impurity is buried in the crystal and not simply desorbed, leaving behind a clean surface on which further adsorption can occur. A step following closely behind the first step will move faster than the first step which was hindered by impurities and may catch up with the first step. It will also move faster than a step which is further apart and thereby meets a surface with a higher density of impurities adsorbed on it, since the amount of impurities on the surface is assumed to increase with time. Thus for low values of the step density k, the flux q will be decreased more than for larger values of k. Thus for low values of k, dq/dk increases with increasing k and d^2q/dk^2 becomes positive, causing the discontinuity to develop at the front of the advancing cluster.

The phenomenon of bunching is, therefore, dependent on the presence of a low concentration of impurities in the solution which are adsorbed on the steps in a time-dependent fashion. A higher concentration of impurity may lead to adsorption equilibrium which can eliminate the bunching. The general picture of the bunching process is as follows: Assume a regular array of steps except for one in the middle which lags behind the ones ahead of it. As the steps advance this one moves more slowly since it is encountering more adsorbed impurity. The next step behind this one will move faster as it meets a cleaner surface and will eventually catch up with the preceding step forming a pair which will move even more slowly. Other steps behind these may catch up also, increasing the height of the step and decreasing the possibility of its fading away. This then gives rise to a flat area, followed by a bunch, which as it moves away from the source may become high enough to be visible in the optical microscope.

d. Ridge-Type Deposits. Deposits in the form of ridges on the surface such as those shown in Fig. 5(a) have been observed by a number of workers (*36, 38, 39, 57, 60, 64, 65, 67, 68, 71*). Pick *et al.* (*57*) found symmetrical ridges developed on copper deposits on (110) planes, but also ridges developed on other orientations. Economou and Trivich (*61*) using single crystal spheres of copper as substrates found that at low current densities this ridge structure defined by the $\langle 110 \rangle$ poles extended over almost the whole area of the sphere. At higher current densities the area covered by these ridges was smaller. On a substrate 8° off the (001), Barnes *et al.* (*58*) found for the [110] zone that the ridge structure formed at low overvoltages was aligned perpendicular to the close-packed direction in the surface, i.e., in the [$\bar{1}$10] direction. It was also found that the sides of the ridges did not correspond to low-index planes. Barnes (84) states that at overvoltages less than 10–20 mV, the ridges were generally aligned in a ⟨110⟩ direction.

Damjanovic et al. (64) also found ridges developed on the (110) surface of copper at current densities from 2 to 30 mA/cm^2. In some cases the surface was not completely covered by ridges, and smooth areas, occasionally showing macrosteps, were also present. These workers observed the particularly interesting fact that at 2 to 5 mA/cm^2 current density the ridges were aligned parallel to the [001] direction, whereas at higher current densities they were aligned parallel to the close-packed [$\bar{1}$10] direction in agreement with Barnes (84). No significant changes were reported in the ridge structure when n-decylamine was added to the pure solution.

Bicelli and Poli (68), however, found only a microscopically rough surface for deposits of copper 1 μ thick formed at 1 mA/cm^2 on the (110) copper substrate, and attribute this discrepancy from the above results to thickness differences. These authors found lead deposits on the (110) surface of lead formed at 10 to 30 mA/cm^2 to be in the form of ridges aligned along the [001] direction. Cadmium deposits on the (10$\bar{1}$0) surface were found to be ridged for a 4-μ deposit formed at 15 mA/cm^2, with the ridges in the [$\bar{1}$2$\bar{1}$0] direction, but growth steps were present between the ridges. At 5 mA/cm^2 the ridges were not seen. On the (11$\bar{2}$0) plane, 4-μ deposits formed at 15 mA/cm^2 were also ridged with the ridges aligned parallel to the [1$\bar{1}$00] direction. Ridges were not reported on the (0001) plane.

Barnes (84) has proposed an explanation for the formation of ridges on copper aligned in the close-packed ⟨110⟩ directions which is based on the observation (89) that these are the directions of easiest surface self-diffusion. This proposed mechanism does not seem to have been widely accepted and no other explanation for the ridge formation have been proposed.

e. Impurity, Thickness, and Temperature Effects. The preceding discussion of the morphology of electrodeposits has been primarily concerned with: (1) deposits of several metals onto themselves, (2) the types of growth observed on the major crystallographic planes, (3) the effect of current density on the nature of the growth, and (4) the possible mechanisms involved in the various types of growth. Other important factors in the development of particular growth structures on the surface, such as impurities, specific anions, thickness of deposit, and temperature, have only been mentioned. It is not possible to consider all of these additional factors in detail and only a few further comments will be included here.

The effect of impurities on the types of growth observed and on the mechanisms involved is obviously of great practical importance as well as fundamental interest. Many studies have been made of the effect of addition agents of different kinds on the crystal morphology and a good presentation of much of this work has been given by Fischer (4). Usually these intentional impurities (addition agents) are added to the solution because they produce a smoother and brighter deposit. This leveling effect is generally considered to be due to the adsorption of the impurities on growth peaks, possibly at screw dislocations, so that deposition is hindered at these higher points but may continue in the valleys. Damjanovic et al. (38, 64) have shown, as indicated above, that the addition of a concentration of 10^{-5} moles/liter of n-decylamine causes truncation of hexagonal pyramids on (111) copper to occur readily at 5 mA/cm^2, and 10^{-4} moles/liter causes hexagonal pyramids to form in preference to triangular ones, all truncating quickly. Similarly the pyramid growth on the (100) surface may be caused to truncate. On the other hand, it has also been shown that surface active agents may cause the development of ridges on a previously developed layer structure (36). The greater the concentration of the addition agent, the smaller the thickness at which ridges develop.

As shown above, the presence of impurity adsorption on steps is essential to the concept of bunching in layer growth. It was assumed there that the impurities were buried in the deposit and there is considerable evidence in support of this idea (90). This fact may have an important bearing on the creation of dislocations in the deposit and hence on the properties of the material. It is probable that the anions of the solution are one of the principal "impurities" adsorbed on the surface and eventually buried. Thus the particular anion present in the solution may have a marked effect on the type of growth obtained and may likewise influence the properties of the deposit. Impurities on the surface may also influence the orientation of the deposit.

It is quite clear that the surface structures observed depend to a great extent on the average thickness of the deposit at the time of observation. A coarsening of the structure of the deposit is generally seen with increasing thickness. The bunching process does not necessarily lead to a change in the geometry of the deposits, but brings about a change in the scale of surface features (57). The average distance between macrosteps has been shown to increase with increasing thickness (38). Growth spirals are usually not observed in the early stages of deposition but only at large average thicknesses. This could possibly result in some cases from grown-in dislocations formed as a result of the incorporation of impurities in the deposit. The formation of twins occurs frequently in some deposits as the thickness is increased (68, 91). This subject will be considered in more detail in a later section.

Barnes et al. (58) have considered the effect of temperature on the growth habit of copper deposits at temperatures between 20 and 45°C. The normal types of structures were observed for the substrate oriented near (100), i.e., depending on current density, a ridged, platelet, block, or polycrystalline deposit was formed (Fig. 5). The effect of increasing the temperature was simply to increase the current density at which a particular structure formed. This was interpreted as follows: If the temperature was increased, the cathodic polarization at a certain current density decreased and therefore to obtain the same overvoltage, and in the view of the authors the same crystal form, it was necessary to increase the current density.

f. Influence of Substrate Metal. The discussion of morphology up to this point has been concerned with deposits of various metals onto themselves. This has been primarily a result of the fact that far more fundamental research has been carried out on these systems than for the case of deposition of one metal onto a different metal substrate. Most studies of the bimetal systems have been carried out under ill-defined conditions with solutions of doubtful purity. Despite these facts, many of the growth features observed are identical to those seen, for example, in the heavily studied copper system. In this section a few observations on the morphology of several different metals, each deposited on a substrate different from the deposited material, will be considered.

The surface structure of nickel deposited on copper substrates has been studied rather extensively, particularly by means of electron-microscope replica methods. Weil and Cook (*92*) examined surfaces of nickel deposits grown on copper substrates which were prepared by vapor deposition and electroforming in an attempt to minimize the effect of the substrate. Replicas revealed a fine microscopic roughness, which became coarser for longer plating times. Growth layers inclined to the surface were detected at an early stage of the deposition and tended to increase in size with time. There was an increase in size of certain preferentially oriented grains.

Studies of nickel deposits were also made by Hashimoto (*93*) who found it difficult to obtain reproducible results on chemically polished copper surfaces. The 5 to 15 μ deposits made at 31 or 47 mA/cm^2 onto mechanically polished copper disks all showed preferred orientations which depended on the pH and current density. Electron micrographs of the surfaces showed microscopic roughness in the form of growth hillocks with some flat planes inclined to the surface, and in some cases small pyramidal growths. Many of the features observed were explained in terms of the formation of twins. Banerjee and Walker (*94*) also studied the surface structure of nickel deposited on etched copper foil and on copper foil plated with copper in a preferred orientation. One-minute deposits on the etched foil at a pH of 2.1 or 5.1 and a current density of 10 mA/cm^2 reproduced the particle size and texture of the substrate, but deposits made at a pH of 3.2 showed an elongated substructure within each grain. The growth on the oriented copper substrate showed dendritic areas as well as steps and striations.

Garmon (*95*) and Lawless (*63*) have examined the surface structure of nickel deposited onto carefully prepared smooth single crystal substrates, using both one- and two-stage replica techniques. The nickel was deposited from a Watts bath at a pH of 4.0 and a temperature of 60°C with current densities of 1 or 10 mA/cm^2. Garmon's (95) micrographs showed clearly that on the (100) and (111) faces of copper the nickel deposit roughened and developed small facets even at thicknesses less than 100 A. There was no evidence of definite layer-type growth on these surfaces at any thickness up to 1000 A. Figure 10 shows the typical appearance of a 100-A deposit on a (100) surface.

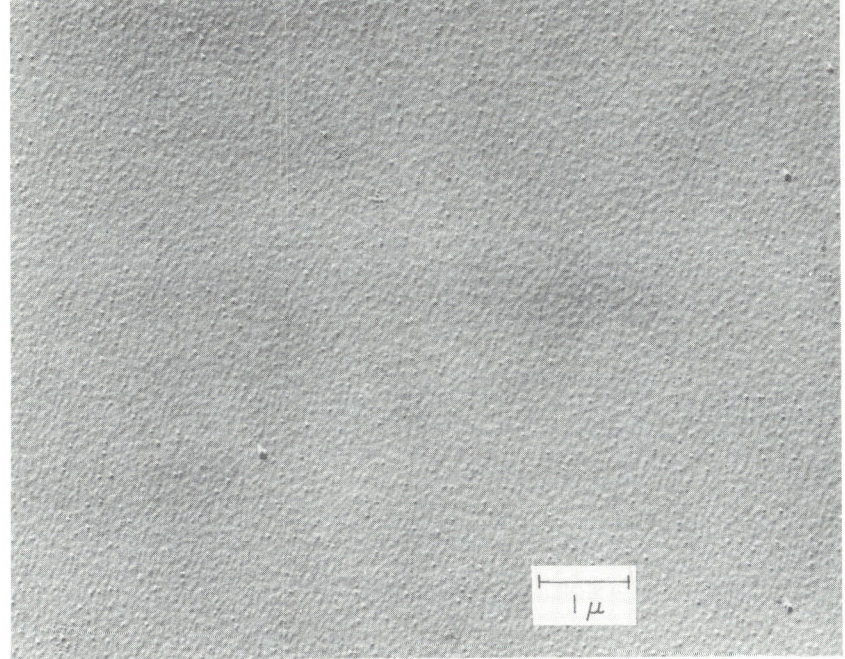

FIG. 10. Electron micrograph of 100-A nickel deposit on (100) copper substrate.

Pyramidal growths on both (100) and (111) surfaces were visible at thicknesses of 500 to 1000 A in a series of experiments in which the plating was interrupted to make Faxfilm replicas of the surface at regular thickness intervals, but such growths were not observed at 1000 A after continuous plating to that thickness. This seems to indicate that surface impurities introduced by the replication process may have caused pyramidal growth to occur at a smaller average thickness. Truncated pyramidal growths have been observed by Thompson (96) and a typical example is shown in Fig. 11.

As the deposits thickened the facets on the deposit became larger and more regular. This is shown in Figs. 12(a) and 12(b) for a 60,000-A nickel deposit on the (100) face and on a high-index face near (110), respectively. It is quite clear that the size and form of the facets depended on the orientation of the substrate. It was frequently observed on thick growths that very irregular structures developed, as shown in Fig. 13. These irregular growths may have been the result of trapped impurities, or, as indicated later, they may have been associated with impurities decorating dislocation configurations in the base metal.

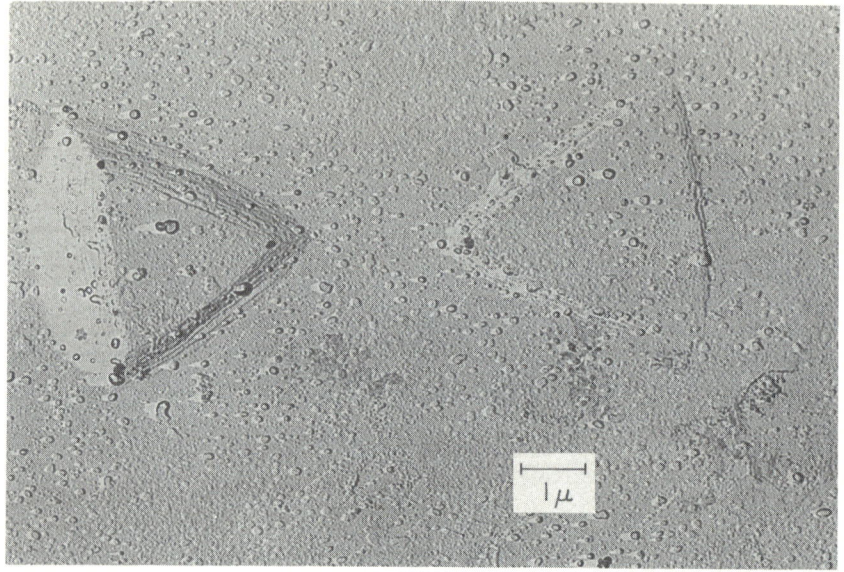

FIG. 11. Electron micrograph of truncated doubly positioned pyramids of nickel grown on a (111) plane of copper.

Thompson (96) has examined gold deposits on the (111) and (100) planes of copper. At a thickness of 5000 A, these surfaces showed a fine-scale roughness with very small facets. This is shown in Fig. 14. At a lower thickness of 1000 A, small pyramidal structures were observed for growths on the (111) surface. Figure 15 shows the general appearance of these pyramids, many of which are truncated.

Most of these studies, which were made by electron-microscope replica techniques, were concerned with the surface structure of relatively thin deposits, i.e., under 1 μ, and it might be expected that the results would differ somewhat from those obtained by optical microscope techniques on thicker deposits. In fact, however, the results are remarkably similar to those discussed previously, although there is no clear evidence of layer growth on the (111) or (100) faces in these studies.

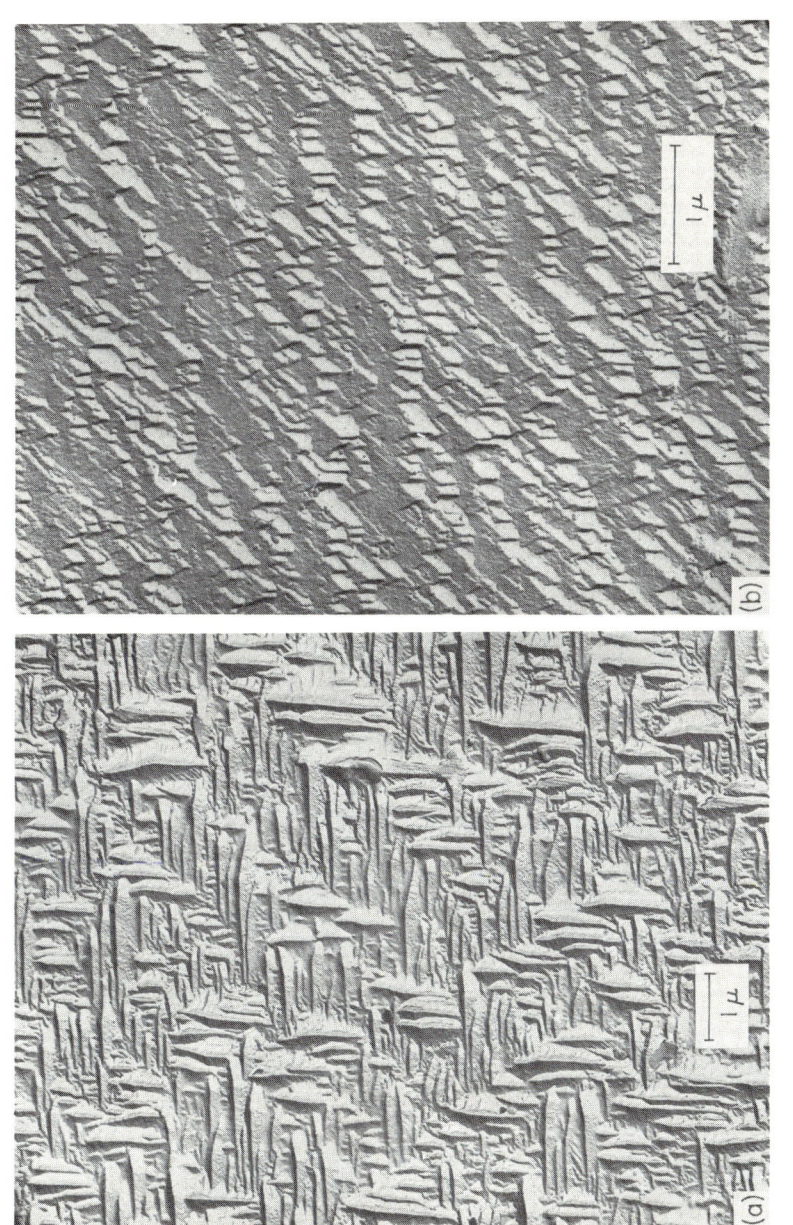

Fig. 12. Electron micrograph of 60,000-A copper deposits on (a) a (100) surface, and (b) a high-index surface near (110).

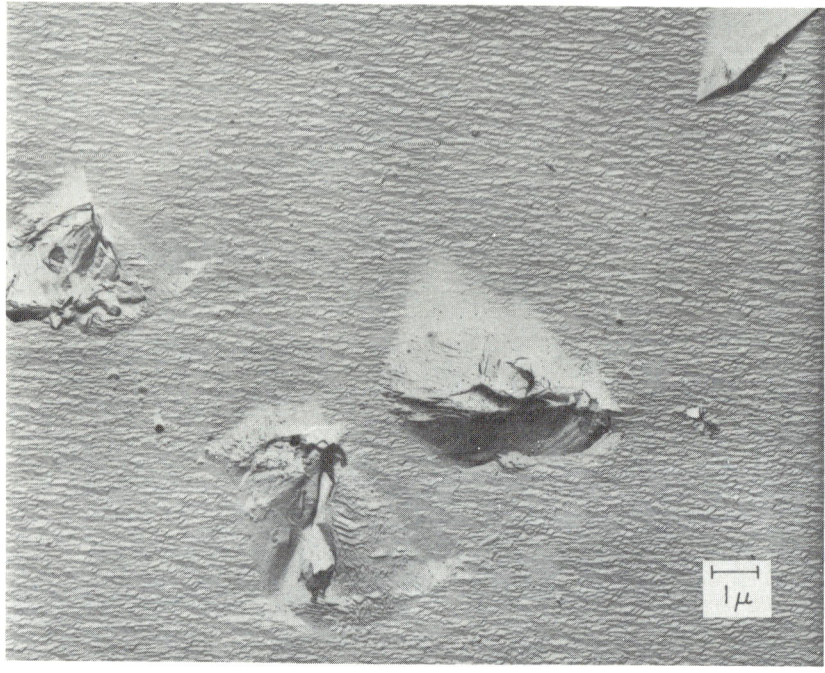

Fig. 13. Electron micrograph showing irregular growths on 60,000-A copper deposit near (110) orientation.

Fig. 14. Electron micrographs of 5000-A gold deposits on copper substrate: (a) (111) copper substrate, (b) (100) copper substrate.

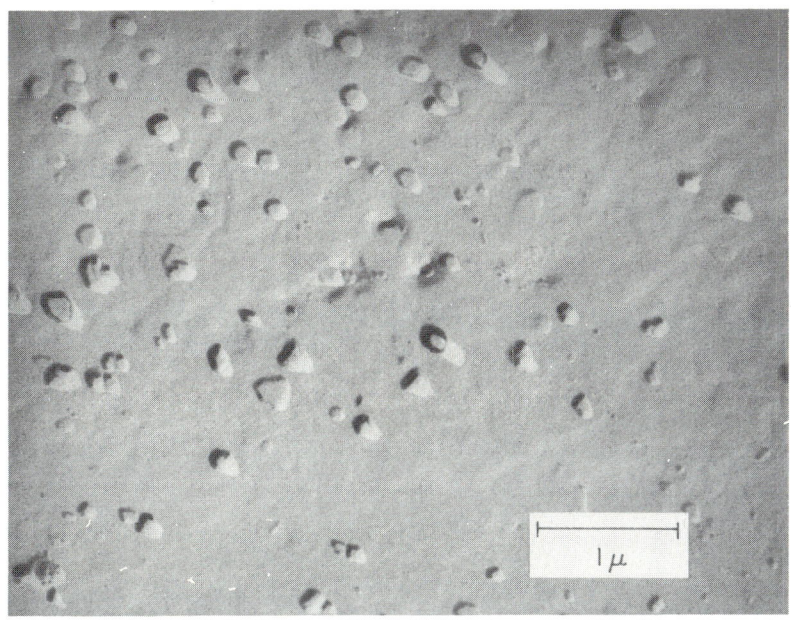

FIG. 15. Electron micrograph of 1000-A gold deposit on (111) Cu.

III. The Structure of Electrodeposits

1. EXPERIMENTAL METHODS

The detailed structures of electrodeposited films of metals have been studied primarily by three different techniques: (1) X-ray diffraction, (2) electron diffraction, and (3) electron microscopy. All these techniques are complimentary to one another and all are needed in any attempt to determine the detailed structure of an electrodeposit. X-ray techniques are useful only for relatively thick deposits (>500 A) except under very special conditions and the early stages of the growth can be studied only by means of electron diffraction and electron microscopy. The majority of structural studies have unfortunately been made on polycrystalline deposits on polycrystalline substrates. Since this review is primarily concerned with single crystal deposits, only those studies on polycrystalline deposits which seem particularly pertinent will be discussed in the following sections.

The electron diffraction technique is particularly useful for the study of thin deposited films, or the surface layers of thicker deposits. Used in combination with electron microscopy, this can be the most powerful method for studying the surface structure of electrodeposits. It is only recently that modern high resolution transmission electron microscope techniques have been applied to the study of thin-deposit films, although, as shown in the previous section, surface replica techniques have been used to great advantage in studies of surface morphology.

a. X-Ray Diffraction Methods. Standard X-ray diffraction techniques, i.e., Laue or Debye–Scherrer methods, have been used in the study of electrodeposits since about 1924. More recently diffractometer techniques have been widely employed. These standard instrumental methods have been thoroughly described in the literature (*97, 98*) and will not be discussed here. In 1963, Lighty *et al.* (*99*) used back-reflection divergent-beam X-ray diffraction in the study of epitaxial copper deposits. Since this technique shows considerable promise as a powerful tool for such studies it will be described in some detail.

A divergent beam of X-rays can be generated by using electron optical lenses to focus a narrow beam of high-energy electrons onto a thin metal foil as target. If the accelerating voltage of the electrons is sufficiently high, characteristic X radiation emerges from the opposite side of the foil with a divergence of nearly 180°. If a bulk specimen is placed about 1 to 5 mm in front of the X-ray source, characteristic back-reflection patterns, which are closely analogous to Kossel line patterns, are obtained. If a thin foil is used as a sample, both forward-and back-reflection patterns are obtained. Imura *et al.* (*100–102*) have termed these patterns pseudo-Kossel patterns. Figure 16 shows a schematic representation of the generation of these patterns.

The back-reflection patterns are of most interest for the study of electrodeposits. These patterns will normally consist of sets of curves which approximate ellipses, each of these curves corresponding to a reflection from a particular (hkl) set of planes. A typical pattern from an electrodeposit 15 μ thick is shown in Fig. 17. The reflections can be readily indexed, the d_{hkl} values can be calculated, and the lattice parameters determined with high precision. It is possible to determine any anisotropic distortions of the lattice due to strain distributions in the specimen quite readily since many individual hkl reflections can be measured on the same film. In using this technique, the measurements of a, the distance from the X-ray source to the film, and b, the distance from the X-ray source to the specimen, were found to be the principal source of error. Ellis *et al.* (*103*) have introduced measuring techniques to overcome this difficulty. The method involves the determination of the slopes of the diffraction rays, given by

$$m_1 = p/c = \tan(\alpha + \beta) \tag{11}$$

$$m_2 = q/c = \tan(\alpha - \beta) \tag{12}$$

The distances p, q, and c are as shown in Fig. 16. A series of consecutive

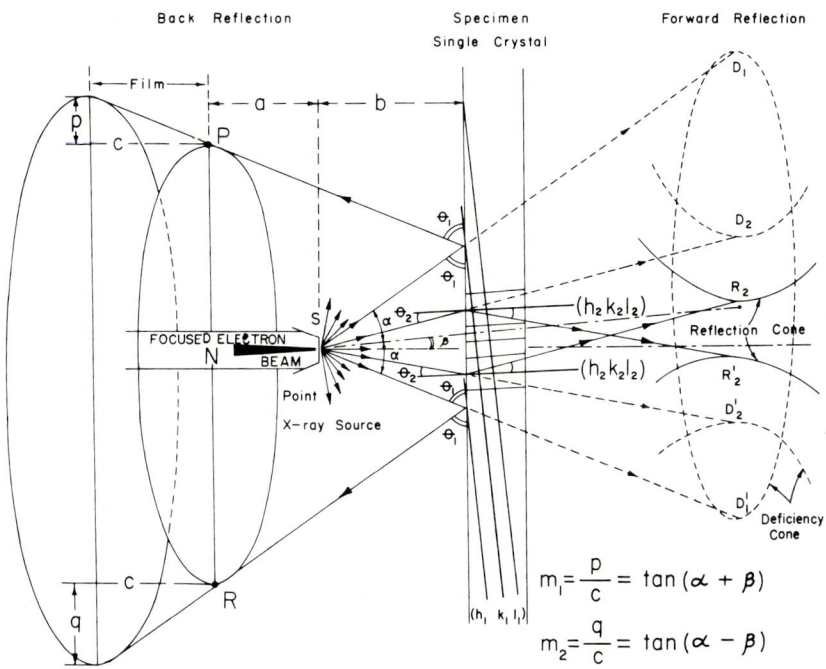

FIG. 16. Schematic diagram of the generation of pseudo-Kossel patterns by the divergent-beam method [from Ellis et al. (*103*)].

photographs are taken, with the exact distance c between successive film positions being determined by the use of precision spacers. α is the semiapex angle of the incident X-ray cone and is equal to $\pi/2 - \theta$, where θ is the Bragg angle. β is the angle between the normal to the reflecting (hkl) plane and the axis of the X-ray tube. A precision determination of the slopes is made using a method of least squares. Knowing λ, the wavelength of the characteristic X-rays, the lattice spacings d_{hkl} can be calculated for each reflection.

In addition to lattice distortions, it is also possible to determine other information relating to the perfection of the crystal. Polygonization boundaries show up as a displacement of certain segments of the elliptical pattern, and misorientations of the order of 5 to 10' of arc can be detected. Local lattice inhomogeneities due to dislocations lead to a local broadening of the diffraction lines.

The technique of X-ray line profile analysis has been applied in studies of the structure of electrodeposited films (*96, 104–107*). If a crystalline material contains only small amounts of nonuniform distortion, and if the grain size (or better, the size of the coherent diffracting domains) is greater than about

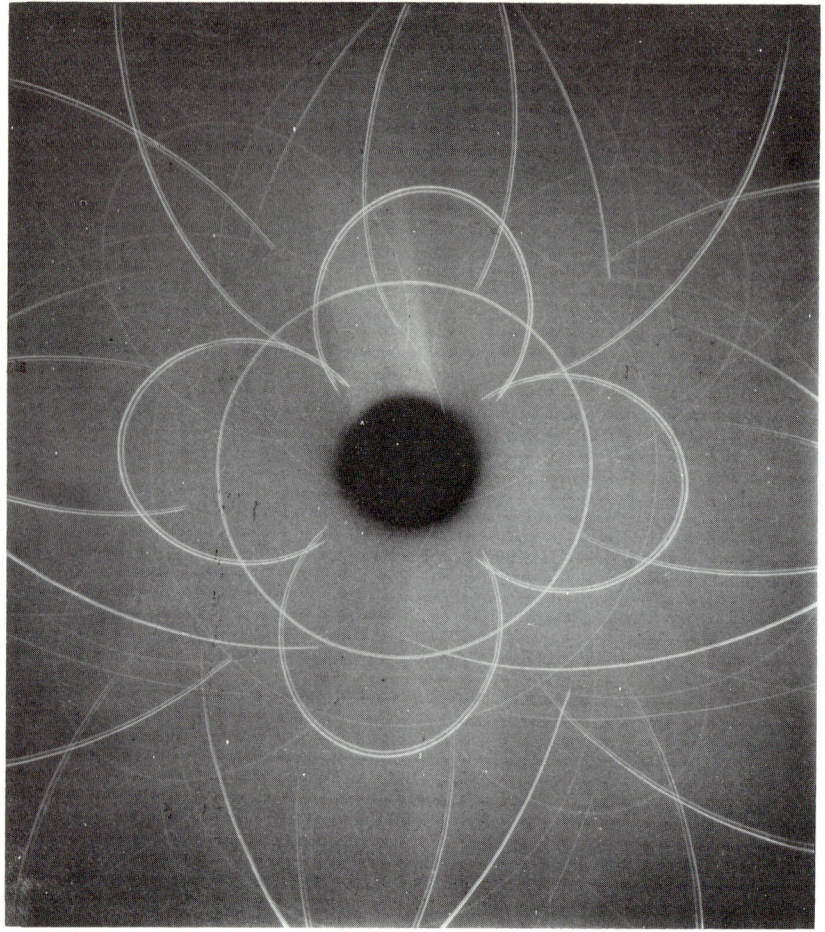

FIG. 17. Back-reflection divergent-beam X-ray photograph of a 15-μ copper (100) electrodeposit [from Lighty et al. (99)].

1000 to 1500 Å (97, 108), the X-ray diffraction peaks are sharp and narrow. If the spacing of a particular set of diffracting planes (hkl) is changed from d_{hkl} to some other value d'_{hkl}, a shift is noted in the angular position of the maxima. On the other hand, if the spacing of the (hkl) planes is changed so that a range of spacings $d_{hkl} - \delta d$ to $d_{hkl} + \delta d$ is included, the breadth of the diffraction peak is extended. This is called inhomogeneous strain broadening or microstrain whereas the effect causing a shift in the maximum is called homogeneous strain or macrostrain. If the size of the crystallites in the specimen is less than about 1000 to 1500 A, a broadening of the diffraction peak will also occur.

The theory of line profile analysis has been very thoroughly treated by Warren (*109*) and by Warren and Averbach (*110*) and a method for the determination of the inhomogeneous strain and coherent domain size from the broadened profiles has been developed. These authors have shown that the distribution of diffracted power with diffraction angle for the pure diffraction profile of a 00*l* reflection (using an orthorhombic system of axes) can be described by a Fourier series:

$$P(2\theta) = K(\theta) N \sum_n \{C_n \exp(2\pi i n h_3)\} \tag{13}$$

where N is the number of unit cells in the coherently diffracting domain; h_3 is given by $2a_3 \sin\theta/\lambda$ where a_3 is the magnitude of the lattice vector normal to the diffracting plane, θ is the Bragg angle, and λ is the wavelength of the X-rays; $K(\theta)$ is a slowly varying function of θ. If the diffraction peak is symmetrical, this series can be simplified to

$$P(2\theta) = K(\theta) N \sum_n \{A_n \cos(2\pi n h_3)\} \tag{14}$$

where

$$A_n = \frac{N_n}{N_3} \langle \cos 2\pi l Z_n \rangle \tag{15}$$

The terms in the coefficient of the cosine function, A_n, have the following meanings: N_3 is the average number of cells in the columns of unit cells parallel to a_3; N_n is the number of cells having nth neighbors in the same column; l is the order of reflection; Z_n is a lattice displacement in the column direction which is related to the strain ε_n by $\varepsilon_n = Z_n/n$. The term $\langle \cos 2\pi l Z_n \rangle$ is an average which is taken over pairs of nth neighbors in all columns of the sample.

It can be shown that the cosine coefficients A_n may be represented as the product of a particle-size coefficient and a distortion coefficient:

$$A_n = A_n^{PS} \cdot A_n^{D} \tag{16}$$

where

$$A_n^{PS} = \frac{N_n}{N_3} = \frac{1}{N_3} \sum_{i=n}^{\infty} (i-n) p_i \tag{17}$$

and

$$A_n^{D} = \langle \cos 2\pi l Z_n \rangle \tag{18}$$

p_i is the fraction of columns of length i cells. For small l and n the distortion coefficient can be written as

$$A_n^D = (1 - 2\pi^2 l^2 \langle Z_n^2 \rangle) \tag{19}$$

Bertaut (*111*) has shown that the average column length N_3 normal to the diffraction plane is given by

$$-\left(\frac{dA_n^{PS}}{dn}\right)_{n \to 0} = \frac{1}{N_3} \tag{20}$$

so that the negative initial slope of a graph of particle-size coefficient against n gives N_3 directly.

From Eqs. (17) and (18), it is clear that the distortion coefficient is dependent upon the order of reflection, while the particle-size coefficient is not. This makes it possible to separate these two effects when the Fourier coefficients for more than one order or reflection are known. If the natural logarithm of Eq. (16) is formed, it is found that

$$\ln A_n(l) = \ln A_n^{PS} + \ln A_n^D(l) \tag{21}$$

and, for small l and n,

$$\ln A_n(l) = \ln A_n^{PS} - 2\pi^2 l^2 \langle Z_n^2 \rangle \tag{22}$$

If $\ln A_n(l)$ is plotted against l^2 for various values of n, a straight line should be obtained, and the intercept at $l = 0$ gives the value of $\ln A_n^{PS}$. The initial slope of this line gives $2\pi^2 \langle Z_n^2 \rangle$ from which a mean-square strain $\langle \varepsilon_n^2 \rangle$ can be derived. For the cubic system, it is convenient to replace the index n by the length $L = na_3$. Equation (22) then becomes

$$\ln A_L(h_0) = \ln A_L^{PS} - 2\pi^2 h_0^2 (L/a)^2 \langle \varepsilon_L^2 \rangle \tag{23}$$

where

$$h_0 = (h^2 + k^2 + l^2)^{1/2}, \quad \varepsilon_L = \Delta L/L = a_3 Z_n / a_3 n$$

and

$$d_{hkl} = a_3/l = a/h_0$$

The term a is the edge length of the unit cell.

Practically, it is necessary to have extremely accurate measurements of the line profiles. The experimental procedures for line profile analysis have been described by a number of workers (*97, 109, 112*) and need not be discussed here. It should be pointed out that it is not possible to make inhomogeneous strain measurements using this technique if there is an adjacent diffraction peak sufficiently close that the tails of the peaks overlap. Such is the case, for example, for thin deposits of nickel on copper, or copper on nickel.

b. Electron Diffraction Methods. The technique of high-energy electron diffraction has been used in the study of electrodeposits since about 1931 (*113*), and it still provides one of the most useful tools available for determining the structure of such deposits. The technique, in contrast to X-ray methods, is sensistive to less than a monolayer of deposit material (*114–116*) and is, therefore, particularly useful for the study of very thin films or of surface structure and topography. Extensive treatments of the theory and technique of electron diffraction have been given by Thomson and Cochrane (*117*), Pinsker (*118*), Bauer (*119*), and Raether (*120*), and so will not be considered here in detail.

Both glancing-angle diffraction from bulk specimens and transmission diffraction through thin films have been used advantageously in studies of electrodeposits. The latter technique has been used primarily in conjunction with transmission electron-microscope studies. The glancing-angle method has been more widely used since the deposit can be studied directly on its substrate without the necessity of thinning the substrate or of stripping the deposit film. Thick deposits which could not normally be studied by transmission are easily examined at a glancing angle. It should be noted that the electron beam does not penetrate very deeply, and on a smooth substrate a deposit of only 10 to 20 A covering the surface will block out any substrate pattern. It is clear then that this technique is most useful where it is desired to know the surface structure. For certain deposit materials on specific substrates (e.g., Ni on Cu) it is possible to chemically strip the deposit film for examination by transmission diffraction studies. As is pointed out later, this process of stripping a deposit film may introduce a structure into the film which is not characteristic of the deposit as grown on its substrate.

Electron diffraction provides an especially convenient method for the determination of the epitaxy of a deposit film. The diffraction pattern from a single crystal deposit is essentially a direct projection of a plane through the reciprocal lattice perpendicular to the beam. This comes about because of the small wavelength of the electrons and the resulting large radius of the Ewald sphere of reflection. This direct relationship makes the indexing of diffraction patterns and subsequent orientation determination relatively simple. Epitaxial studies of electrodeposited films will be considered in detail in Section III,2*b*.

The electron-diffraction method is also extremely useful for the determination of twinning, or the formation of stacking faults in electrodeposits. In some cases, however, it is not possible to distinguish between true twinning and double positioning (*121*) from the diffraction pattern alone, and it is necessary to use electron-microscope observation of thin films to supplement the diffraction data. The expression "double positioning" is used to describe the situation when there are two possible deposit orientations which are exactly equivalent as regards the atomic fitting at the interface between deposit and substrate. As an example, two possible orientations in which the (*111*) plane of gold is parallel to the (*111*) plane of silver can occur, one orientation having all planes parallel to the equivalent plane of the substrate, the other orientation being rotated 180° about the [111] axis. These two orientations bear crystallographically a twin relationship to each other, but are not growing as true twins; in fact, they may grow as entirely separated nuclei. Because of this relationship, the diffraction pattern is the same for a doubly positioned structure as for a twinned structure. It is likely that many diffraction results interpreted as due to twinning were in fact due to double positioning.

Both growth twins and deformation twins give rise to additional points in the reciprocal lattice, and hence in the diffraction pattern, which have irrational indices. The reciprocal lattice points due to a twin in a face-centered cubic crystal will either coincide with the basic lattice points or will be displaced from these points by vectors of $\pm \frac{1}{3}\langle 111 \rangle$. Therefore, all lines in the $\langle 111 \rangle$ directions joining the matrix points of the reciprocal lattice are divided into thirds, but in general not all of these one-third positions are occupied. Pashley and Stowell (*122*) have shown that the occupied points can be determined by use of the selection rule:

$$hu + kv + lw = \pm(3N + 1) \qquad (24)$$

where N is an integer. The twin points resulting from twinning on planes of the type $\{hkl\}$ are then of the form $(u'v'w') = (u \pm \frac{1}{3}h, v \pm \frac{1}{3}k, w \pm \frac{1}{3}l)$, where uvw is a reciprocal lattice matrix point.

Planar defects, such as stacking faults, give rise to streaks or rods in the reciprocal lattice which are normal to the fault plane. Since the fault plane in face-centered cubic lattices is $\{111\}$, stacking faults lead to rods in the $\langle 111 \rangle$ directions joining the reciprocal lattice matrix points. Either streaks or spots may be observed in the diffraction pattern, depending on the manner in which the Ewald reflecting sphere intersects these rods, i.e., on the direction of the electron beam with respect to the fault plane.

c. Electron Microscopy. The basic techniques of electron microscopy are well known (*123, 126*) and need not be described in detail here. Two methods have been used in the study of electrodeposits, one involving the preparation of replicas of the surface, and the other utilizing thin films. Replicas of a surface may be prepared by either a one- or a two-stage technique. The single-stage replica is most commonly prepared by first preshadowing the surface at a low angle with platinum, palladium, chromium or another suitable heavy metal, then evaporating either carbon or silicon monoxide at normal incidence onto the surface, and finally removing the replica by means of a chemical etchant. The primary disadvantages of this technique are (1) the destruction of the surface replicated and (2) the difficulty of finding a suitable etchant for the electrodeposit material which does not attack the preshadowing metal. A postshadowing technique may be used but with some loss of resolution.

In the two-stage technique, a first-stage replica of the surface is usually made using a plastic material such as formvar, collodion, Faxfilm, or polymerized methyl methacrylate. This is mechanically removed from the surface after it has hardened, the replica side is shadowed, and then carbon or silicon monoxide is evaporated for the second-stage replica. Finally the plastic first-stage replica must be dissolved. The main difficulties in this technique arise during the last stage since swelling of the plastic tends to break up the replica, and very careful procedures must be used to minimize this problem.

The replica techniques are most useful for studies of the morphology of the deposit surface, particularly during the early stages of deposition when features of the surface are too small to be resolved by light optical means. The replica techniques, however, give no direct evidence of the detailed structure of the deposit. It is in this area that transmission electron microscopy techniques are particularly valuable

Transmission electron microscopy of thin crystalline materials has been the subject of several books in the past few years (*127–130*). The specialized techniques of specimen preparation and the complexities of contrast theory essential for the interpretation of the images are thoroughly covered in these references. The transmission technique has the advantage of making possible the direct observation and the easy identification of such structural features as dislocations, stacking faults, point defect aggregates, twins, and inclusions. In some cases information on topographical features may also be obtained as shown later. Reimer (*131*) has discussed the application of electron-microscope techniques to the study of electrodeposits.

Three different techniques of specimen preparation have been used in the study of electrodeposits by transmission electron microscopy. The simplest technique, which is only applicable for specific substrate-deposit pairs of metals, involves stripping the deposit from the substrate by means of a suitable chemical etchant. If the deposit so stripped is sufficiently thin (<2–3000 A) it may then be studied in the electron microscope. This method must be used with caution, however, since the stresses exerted on the film in the stripping and handling process may introduce defects, and the structure observed may not be a true representation of the as-grown deposit (see Section III,2c).

A second technique involves the thinning down of the substrate by chemical or electrochemical means until the substrate-deposit combined thickness is small enough for transmission microscopy. The etching of the substrate must be carefully controlled to obtain reasonably large areas of the sample thin enough for examination. Thinning techniques have been described in detail by Kelly and Nutting (*132*) and more recently by Hirsch *et al.* (*130*).

A third technique utilizes a specially prepared thin film as a substrate on which the electrodeposit is formed. The thin metal film may be prepared by vapor deposition onto a suitable substrate, and may be grown either polycrystalline or monocrystalline by a proper choice of conditions. Suitable substrate thin films may also be prepared by electrodeposition, the deposited film being stripped from its substrate and then used as a base material to be deposited onto. The vapor deposition method is preferable in that there is less chance for the introduction of defects since the stripping technique is milder. It has the disadvantage, however, that it is more difficult to obtain good single crystal thin films of orientations other than the major ones.

The latter two methods have the advantage that structural relationships between the substrate and the deposit can be determined. The possible influence of dislocations or other faults in the substrate on the nucleation, growth, and structure of the deposit can be readily assessed in this manner.

Strains present in the deposit film may in many cases be determined from the spacings of moiré fringes, and very slight misorientations can be determined readily from the rotation of these fringes. Moiré fringes result from the superposition of two crystal lattices of different lattice spacing and/or orientation. The theory of the formation and the application of these patterns is beyond the scope of this paper but many accounts of these images are available in the literature (*130, 133*). The spacings of the moiré patterns can be determined from the formula

$$D = \frac{1}{|\mathbf{g}_1(hkl) + \mathbf{g}_2(h'k'l')|} \quad (25)$$

where $\mathbf{g}_1(hkl)$ and $\mathbf{g}_2(h'k'l')$ are the reciprocal lattice vectors corresponding to the particular reflections hkl and $h'k'l'$ which are active in producing the pattern. The rotation ϕ of one lattice with respect to the other about the normal to the film can be determined from the relationship

$$\tan \psi = \frac{|\mathbf{g}_2| \sin \phi}{|\mathbf{g}_1| - |\mathbf{g}_2| \cos \phi} \quad (26)$$

where ψ is the angle of rotation of the moiré fringes. It is apparent from Eq. (26) that a small rotation ϕ produces a large rotation ψ so that the method is extremely sensitive to small misalignments of the two superimposed lattices. Some recent results on the structure of electrodeposited films obtained by use of the moiré images are discussed below in Section III,2c.

2. Results of Structure Studies

a. Results from X-Ray Diffraction Studies. The orientation or the texture of electrodeposited metals has been the object of many X-ray diffraction investigations because of its great technical importance. Back-reflection Laue and glancing-angle techniques have been used most commonly. One of the first such studies was made as long ago as 1924 by Glocker and Kaupp (*134*) who determined fiber textures for thick deposits of Ni, Cu, Ag, Fe, and Cr. A summary of texture studies of electrodeposits up to 1939 is given by Barrett (*108*) and more recently by Fischer (*4*). These fiber textures occur generally for very thick deposits where the substrate influence is negligible, although they have been observed in thin deposits also. Characteristic textures are observed for each metal but depend on the plating conditions. Since this review is primarily concerned with single crystal deposits, this complex subject will not be considered further.

Wood (*135*) was the first to make the important observation from X-ray data that, under certain deposition conditions, the electrodeposit assumed the orientation of the substrate. He found that at low current densities on cleaned polycrystalline copper electrodes, a copper deposit copied the orientation of the grains of the substrate, but at 12 mA/cm^2 the orientation began to disappear, and at 15 mA/cm^2 the deposit was completely random. Wood also observed strange results on nickel deposits where a fiber texture was found for current densities below 7.5 mA/cm^2; a completely random deposit was found at 7.5 mA/cm^2, and a completely parallel oriented deposit was found at higher current densities up to 40 mA/cm^2; finally a random deposit was found at 60 mA/cm^2. The results on nickel seem to be highly questionable in view of many recent studies on this metal. Many other workers primarily using optical microscopy of cross sections arrived at the same conclusion as Wood concerning the continuation of the substrate orientation by a deposit metal (*136, 137*).

Studies of deposits on single crystal substrates have been more revealing than those on polycrystalline bases. Leidheiser and Gwathmey (*138*) used a glancing-angle Laue technique to study Ni deposited over a wide range of conditions on (111) and (100) copper substrates. The deposit on the (100) face was monocrystalline in nature and parallel oriented to great thicknesses, whereas the deposit on the (111) became polycrystalline at a very low thickness.

Orem (*139*) has used the back-reflection Laue technique to study the epitaxy of copper electrodeposited at 30 mA/cm^2 on electropolished (100), (110), and (111) copper substrates. The general conclusions from this work were (1) that the deposit on the (110) face was monocrystalline in nature with the same orientation as the substrate; (2) that the deposit on the (100) face consisted of crystallites having the same orientation as the substrate and its four twin orientations; and (3) that the deposit on the (111) face consisted of crystallites having the same orientation as the substrate and an orientation which was twin related to the substrate (111) plane.

Giron and Ogburn (*62*) in studies on copper deposits made at a current density of 10 mA/cm^2 reported no evidence of twinning on (100), (110), or (111) substrates of copper, although for thick deposits some polycrystallinity was present. This is in agreement with the work of Barnes (*140*) who reported no twinning on Cu deposits on the (111) surface for current densities up to 15 mA/cm^2, or on the (100) face for current densities up to 25 mA/cm^2. At higher current densities twinning parallel to the substrate (111) plane was reported, and also twinning on inclined {111} planes for a (100) substrate.

Bicelli and Poli (*68*) made Laue back-reflection studies of lead and cadmium deposits onto single crystal substrates over a range of current densities, for several different compositions of solutions, and for a range of thicknesses. Lead deposits on (100) and (110) showed parallel epitaxy at thicknesses of 1 to 8 μ and current densities from 5 to 50 mA/cm^2. Lead on the (111) surface exhibited twinning for 5-μ films formed at current densities of 30 mA/cm^2 or more, the amount of twinning increasing with thickness of deposit. The apparent twinning occurred only on the (111) plane parallel to the surface.

Cadmium deposits on the (11$\bar{2}$0) planes copied the substrate orientation for all conditions studied, whereas deposits on the (10$\bar{1}$0) surface were parallel oriented only for low thicknesses (1 μ) and low current densities (2 mA/cm^2), becoming twinned on the (10$\bar{1}$2) plane at 4 μ thickness and 5 mA/cm^2. Deposits on the (0001) planes showed a tendency to disorient about the [0001] axis, apparently as a result of twinning on the {10$\bar{1}$2} planes.

It is clear from these X-ray studies, despite some discrepancies as to the magnitude of the current density at which twinning is detected, that there is a general tendency for the deposit material to copy the orientation of the substrate at low current densities and thicknesses. It should be noted, however, that, with the exception of the deposits of nickel on copper, most of the data presented are for deposition of a given metal onto a substrate of the same metal. Additional data for deposits on different substrates will be given later. With increasing current density or thickness so-called twinning develops, particularly on the (111) plane of the face-centered cubic materials, and a continued increase of current density or thickness eventually leads to a polycrystalline deposit. Twinning does not occur nearly as easily on the (100) or (110) planes of the fcc crystals.

The use of techniques other than the Laue technique has increased tremendously the amount of structural data which can be determined from X-ray studies of electrodeposits. Refined techniques have been used by a number of workers (*96, 104–107, 141*) to obtain data on grain size and stresses in electrodeposits as well as orientation. Most of this work has been carried out on deposits of fine-grained substrates in order to minimize the influence of the substrate on the structure of the film. The reader is referred to the literature for detailed discussions of the results of these studies.

A detailed X-ray diffractometer investigation of thin (<1500 A) electrodeposits of gold and nickel onto (100) and (111) copper substrates was carried out by Thompson (96). The deposits were all made at low current densities (0.5 mA/cm^2) from purified solutions onto highly perfect electropolished single crystal surfaces. The depositions were all carried out at room temperature in a controlled atmosphere. Under these conditions the nickel deposits were parallel monocrystalline except for a small amount of the antiparallel double-positioning orientation on the (111) surface. The gold deposits showed a greater diffraction volume of antiparallel-oriented portions than parallel-oriented on the (111) surface, and the (100) showed a quadruple-positioned (111) orientation with polycrystalline patches developing as the thickness increased above about 400 A. Intensity data from the doubly positioned, parallel and antiparallel orientations were used to determine the relative amounts of the two orientations present.

The homogeneous strain in the deposits was determined from the angular displacements of the diffraction peaks, with the copper substrate reflection serving as an internal standard. The results of a series of these measurements on Ni and Au deposits of different thickness on (111) Cu are shown in Table I. ε_{33} is the strain normal to the substrate plane, ε is the strain in the plane of the film, and d_3 is the lattice spacing of the (111) planes parallel to the surface as calculated from the 2θ values.

TABLE I

HOMOGENEOUS STRAIN RESULT FOR (111) GOLD AND NICKEL DEPOSITS

Deposit	Thickness (A)	2θ (deg)	d_3 (A)	Per cent strain (ε_{33})	Per cent strain (ε)
Gold	120	38.15 ± 0.02	2.359	0.17	−0.07
	180	38.16 ± 0.02	2.358	0.13	−0.05
	300	38.18 ± 0.02	2.357	0.08	−0.03
	350	38.15 ± 0.02	2.359	0.17	−0.07
	475[a]	38.20 ± 0.01	2.356	0.04	−0.02
	700[b]	38.27 ± 0.01	2.352	−0.13	+0.05
	1250	38.18 ± 0.01	2.357	0.08	−0.03
Nickel	100[c]	—	—	—	—
	190	44.88 ± 0.06	2.028	−0.29	0.45
	250	44.66 ± 0.06	2.029	−0.25	0.39
	380	44.63 ± 0.04	2.030	−0.20	0.31
	1000	44.57 ± 0.02	2.033	−0.05	0.08

[a] Electron diffraction shows faulting on inclined {111} planes.
[b] Electron diffraction indicates regions of polycrystalline deposit.
[c] Line too broad for measurement.

For the gold (111) deposit, it is clear that there is a consistent shift of the diffraction peak to a lower Bragg angle, which implies a planar compressional stress. The 700-A gold film was an exception to this, since the peak shifted to a higher Bragg angle indicating a dilatational stress in the film plane. It should be noted that this was the only deposit studied which showed any polycrystallinity and this suggests that grain boundary interactions were responsible for the stress reversal in this film (*142*). The position of the diffraction peak from the 475-A film was probably shifted additionally as a result of faults in the film (*143*).

For the nickel (111) deposit, the diffraction peaks are shifted to a higher Bragg angle, indicating a high dilatational stress in the film plane which decreased with increased film thickness. This was in contrast to the gold deposit which showed no clear dependence of angular displacement on deposit thickness.

The Warren and Averbach (*110*) method of line profile analysis was used to determine the microstrain for the gold deposits. It could not be used for the nickel because of the overlap of the peaks for nickel and the substrate copper. The thicknesses of the gold deposits were also determined from integrated intensity measurements as described by Borie and Sparks (*144*).

The microstrain, as determined by the Fourier analysis, decreases with the distance L in the crystal over which the strain is averaged. Figure 18 shows

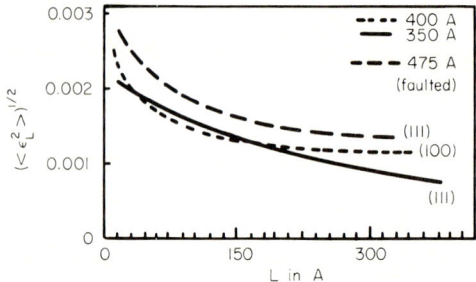

FIG. 18. Microstrain determinations for three gold electrodeposit films.

curves of root-mean-square strain plotted against L for two different deposits on the (111) face and one deposit film on the (100) face. The curves for the 350-A deposit on the (111) and the 400-A deposit on the (100) are generally similar, but the curve for the 475-A (111) deposit which contained faults on the inclined {111} planes shows a consistently higher microstrain. The curve for the 700-A film which showed some polycrystallinity was similar to the 475-A film and gave a higher initial value of the root-mean-square strain than any other film.

Although no other measurements have been made on similar electrodeposits, it might be instructive to compare the above results with some data from polycrystalline deposits. Hofer and Javet (*105*) examined 30-μ copper deposits from an alkaline bath and from an acid bath containing an inhibitor. The deposits were separated from their base for examination. The microstrain generally decreased with increasing L as above. A coherent domain size of 800 A and an rms strain $(\langle \varepsilon_L{}^2 \rangle)^{1/2}$ of 0.300 and 0.205% resulted for L values of 20 and 50 A, respectively. The acid bath with an inhibitor gave a coherent domain size of 250 A and a microstrain $(\langle \varepsilon_L{}^2 \rangle)^{1/2}$ of 0.310% for an L of 50 A. The increased microstrain in this case was attributed to inclusions.

Eichkorn and Fischer (107) made similar measurements on 30-μ copper deposits from an acid bath containing an inhibitor. Their data gave a microstrain, $(\langle \varepsilon_{50}^2 \rangle)^{1/2}$, of 0.4% with a coherent domain size of 70 A. The large value of the microstress was attributed to occlusion of the organic addition agent in the grain boundaries and inclusions within the grains.

The origin of the residual stress in the monocrystalline gold and nickel electrodeposited films seems definitely to be related to the misfit between the lattices. The bulk lattice parameters for gold and copper are 4.078 and 3.615 A, respectively, giving a misfit of 12.7%. It would be expected that the epitaxial forces would tend to compress the gold lattice to reduce the difference in lattice parameters, so that the compressional strain observed in the gold film would be expected. The bulk lattice parameter for nickel is 3.524 A which is less than that for copper, giving a misfit of −2.5%, and so it would be expected that a tensile strain would be present in the nickel, as observed.

It is probable that the observed residual stress behavior depends on the manner in which the first continuous film develops. According to Cabrera (145, 146), the equilibration of the interfacial dislocation density and the epitaxial strain is possible only when isolated nuclei exist on the surface. As the nuclei coalesce to form a continuous film, interfacial dislocations can no longer form in the usual manner to decrease the strain and the film continues to grow under strain until the stress builds up to the level that dislocations are nucleated at the upper surface of the film. Cabrera concludes that the smaller the thickness at which coalescence of the nuclei occurs, the higher the strain in the continuous film.

Thompson (96) has calculated, using the theory of van der Merwe (147), that in the gold-copper system a homogeneous strain of 0.07% corresponds to that expected in a deposit with a thickness of 90 A, and in the nickel-copper system a homogeneous strain of 1% corresponds to a deposit thickness of 20 A. As indicated later, these values correspond approximately to the thickness of nuclei coalescence for these systems.

Lighty et al. (99) have used the technique of back-reflection divergent-beam X-ray diffraction to study fairly thick (3–15 μ) copper electrodeposits on electropolished (100) copper substrates. The crystal perfection of both the substrate and the deposit was studied in detail. Highly purified solutions were used and it was found that pre-electrolysis improved the perfection of the electrodeposits.

Deposits 15 μ thick on a highly perfect substrate crystal (less than 2' misorientation between subgrains and a dislocation etch-pit count of $2 \times 10^4/$ cm^2) were oriented the same as the substrate and actually showed a higher degree of perfection than the base crystal (see Fig. 17). It was apparent that local lattice inhomogeneities in the substrate surface did not influence the perfection of the deposit, and no coarse misorientations or appreciable strains were found.

Deposits on a less perfect substrate showing 5–10' misorientation across polygonization boundaries were markedly different from those on the more perfect substrate. 3-μ deposits showed divergent-beam patterns with characteristic broadening of the diffraction doublets in areas associated with the polygonization boundaries of the substrate. At a thickness of 15 μ there was a marked decrease in intensity, especially of the broadened areas of the diffraction lines, as a result of the presence of polycrystalline regions which were preferentially nucleated in areas associated with the polygonization boundaries. The nucleation sites were established by means of Berg–Barrett X-ray reflection micrographs (*148*). The formation of the polycrystalline regions was attributed not to the misorientations associated with a polygonization boundary but to the presence of impurity atoms associated with the dislocations.

Deposits onto crystals which were mechanically deformed to introduce lattice inhomogeneities and distortions showed a distorted single crystal structure but no evidence of polycrystalline material. If this deformed substrate crystal was annealed in air at 700°C and then etched and electropolished to remove the surface layers, a subsequent electrodeposit was clearly polycrystalline, presumably as a result of the oxygen impurities associated with the dislocations.

It seems evident, as the authors concluded, that the nucleation process is strongly influenced by the interaction between impurities and adatoms, and not between the dislocations and adatoms. The divergent-beam technique has not at this time been used for the analysis of strains in electrodeposits, but the method provides a very powerful tool for such analyses (*103*) and will undoubtedly be used for this purpose.

b. Results from Electron Diffraction Studies. The earliest reported electron-diffraction examination of an electrodeposit was that of Thomson (*113*) in 1931. It was found that silver deposited on copper had the same orientation as the copper substrate. In 1936, Cochrane (*149*) made a more detailed diffraction study in which he examined electrodeposits of copper, nickel, silver, cobalt, chromium, zinc, and cadmium on etched (110) and (111) copper substrates. Copper was found to continue the orientation of the substrate metal to a thickness of at least 4 μ if the current density was no greater than a few milliamperes per square centimeter. Larger current densities gave a polycrystalline deposit.

Somewhat unusual results were obtained by Cochrane (*149*) for nickel deposited on copper. It was claimed that, at current densities of 0.3 mA/cm^2 or greater, diffraction rings due to polycrystalline nickel passed through the spots from the substrate copper, indicating that the nickel lattice spacing was increased to conform to that of copper. This experiment was repeated by Newman (*150*) who found no change in the spacing of nickel from its normal lattice parameter. Pashley (*151*) has interpreted Cochrane's results as being in fact due to the presence of both oriented and disoriented nickel so that diffraction rings from nickel passed through nickel spots, not copper spots. Such patterns have been commonly observed by Lawless (*63*) for nickel deposits on (111) copper (see Fig. 19(a)].

At very low current densities (0.025 mA/cm^2), deposits of nickel and cobalt of about 60 A thickness, when studied by electron diffraction, revealed only spots in the copper substrate positions. This was also interpreted in terms of pseudomorphic growth but this interpretation has been seriously put in doubt by Newman's (*150*) studies.

All other studies of electrodeposited structures made with electron diffraction have shown the lattice parameters of the deposit materials to be very close to those of the same bulk materials and not changed to match the substrate.

For most metals studied, the deposit material continues the orientation of the substrate (*3, 63, 96, 149, 152–155*). This is illustrated in Table II which lists the orientations observed for a number of metals on various substrates. It was noted by Cochrane (*149*) that there seemed to be an upper limit of current density for the formation of an oriented deposit. For face-centered cubic metals, this upper limit increased with increasing match of the lattice parameters of film and substrate. Many other workers (*38, 55, 58, 84, 95*) have observed this relationship between the current density and the orientation of the deposit.

In most of the epitaxial results reported, the misfits are relatively small, i.e., less than 15%. In a few cases, such as Au and Ag on Fe, the misfit is large in one direction (42%), but very small (1%) perpendicular to it. It should be noted that parallel growth was not observed in these two cases.

The only epitaxial study in which deposits on faces other than the three low-index faces were examined was that of Lawless and Garmon (*156*). In this study nickel was plated from a Watts-type bath at 60°C onto electropolished surfaces of large spherical single crystals at current densities from 1 to 10 mA/cm^2. It was determined that the nickel deposit grew accurately parallel to the substrate copper surface for all orientations. The parallel single crystal orientation extended to 10 μ thickness or more on all faces except the (111) which showed double positioning for extremely thin (100 A) deposits and developed some polycrystallinity at about 1000 A thickness. At 10,000 A the

TABLE II
Orientation Relationships

Deposit	Substrate	Type of surface	Parallel planes	Parallel axes	Remarks	Refs.
Ni	Cu	Electropolished sphere; all possible orientations	Completely parallel	Completely parallel	Double positioning; some twinning on {111} planes	63, 156
β-Co	Cu	Etched (110)	(110)Co//(110)Cu	[1̄10]Co//[11̄0]Cu	Twinning and faulting on {111}-type planes	149
Ag	Cu	Etched(100)	(100)Co//(100)Cu	[001]Co//[001]Cu		152
		Etched (110)	(110)Ag//(110)Cu	[001]Ag//[001]Cu		149, 152
		Etched (100)	(100)Ag//(100)cu	[001]Ag//[001]Cu		152
		Etched (111)	(111)Ag//(111)Cu	[11̄0]Ag//[11̄0]Cu		149
Au	Cu	Etched (111)	(111)Au//(111)Cu	[11̄0]Au//[11̄0]Cu		152
		Electropolished (111)	(111)Au//(111)Cu	[11̄0]Au//[11̄0]Cu	Double positioning	96
				[11̄0]Au//[11̄0]Cu	No twinning observed	
		Electropolished (100)	(111)Au//(100)Cu	[01̄1]Au//[01̄1]Cu	Quadruple positioning	
				[011̄]Au//[011̄]Cu	Patches of polycrystalline deposit developed at thickness <1000 Å	
				[11̄0]Au//[011̄]Cu		
				[110]Au//[011̄]Cu		

Deposit	Substrate	Substrate preparation	Orientation relationship		Notes	Ref.
Cr	Cu	Etched (111)	(110)Cr//(111)Cu	[001]Cr//[1̄10]Cu		149
Cu	Pt	Beaten foil (110)	(110)Cu//(110)Pt	[1̄10]Cu//[1̄10]Pt		153
Ni			(110)Ni//(110)Pt	[1̄10]Ni//[1̄10]Pt		
Co			(110)Co//(110)Pt	[1̄10]Co//[1̄10]Pt		
Cu	Pd	Beaten foil (100)	(100)Cu//(100)Pd	[001]Cu//[001]Pd		
Fe			(100)Fe//(100)Pd	[001]Fe//[001]Pd		
Fe	Au	Beaten foil (100)	(100)Fe//(100)Au	[001]Fe//[011]Au		
Co			(100)Co//(100)Au	[001]Co//[001]Au		
Ni			(100)Ni//(100)Au	[001]Ni//[011]Au		
Pt		Evaporated film (100)	(100)Pt//(100)Au	[001]Pt//[001]Au		154
Au	Fe	(110)	(001)Au//(110)Fe	[010]Au//[001]Fe	Preparation of surface not specified	3
Ag		Evaporated film (111)	(001)Ag//(110)Fe	[010]Ag//[001]Fe		155
Au	Ag		(111)Au//(111)Ag	[1̄10]Au//[1̄10]Ag [1̄10]Au//[1̄10]Ag	Double positioning	
Cu	Ni	Evaporated (100)	(100)Cu//(100)Ni	[001]Cu//[001]Ni		96

(111) deposit still showed double positioning and some polycrystalline material, apparently present in patches, and at 60,000 A the surface of the deposit gave a diffraction pattern of polycrystalline rings only. A typical diffraction pattern for a 1000-A deposit on the (111) surface is shown in Fig. 19(a). The sharpness of the spots and the absence of spot elongations indicated that the surface was microscopically rough. The presence of both the strong spot pattern and the ring pattern suggested that the deposit had become polycrystalline in patches. This was confirmed by electron microscopy.

The diffraction spots from both the (100) and (110) showed considerable elongation towards the shadow edge for deposits under 10,000 A thickness, indicating a relatively smooth, slightly wavy surface, i.e., no well-defined ridge or pyramidal structures were indicated. Electron micrographs indicated that even at 100 A thickness the surfaces were very slightly faceted, although the facets are not sufficiently regular or large enough to give refraction effects. For thicknesses greater than 10,000 A, refraction effects in the diffraction pattern, such as those shown in Fig. 19(b), were very pronounced on all faces, showing very clearly the presence of well-developed facets on the surface.

Several electron-diffraction studies of the deposition of a metal onto itself have been made (*66, 113, 149*), but probably the most complete was that of Setty and Wilman (*91, 157*) who examined deposits of silver made onto electropolished (100), (110) and (111) faces of a silver single crystal. On all three faces it was found that the deposit continued the substrate orientation to a thickness > 10,000 A if the current density did not exceed certain values. The deposit on the (110) face became polycrystalline at a current density of 5 mA/cm^2, for a thickness of 200 A, but under the same conditions showed an oriented deposit with some twins at 1000 A. At 10 mA/cm^2 similar results were obtained with some twinning at 500 A and a polycrystalline deposit at 1000 A.

On the (111) face, parallel growth was observed for current densities below 10 mA/cm^2. With increasing current density above this, additional diffraction spots described as being due to twinning on the (111) plane parallel to the substrate surface were found along with some other spots which were related to twinning on other {111} planes. The general relationship between the current density, the deposit thickness, and the nature of the surface of the deposit for the (111) face is shown in Fig. 20. Deposits on the (100) face of silver made at 1 to 10 mA/cm^2 showed a parallel orientation for thicknesses up to 10,000 A, but at 15 mA/cm^2 twinning on {111} planes was reported, and at 20 mA/cm^2 the surface of the deposit was polycrystalline.

The use of the shapes of the diffraction spots to characterize the topography of the surface is also well illustrated in this work. It is interesting to note that when facets developed other than those parallel to the substrate surface, they were of relatively high indices. The ridge structure observed on the (110)

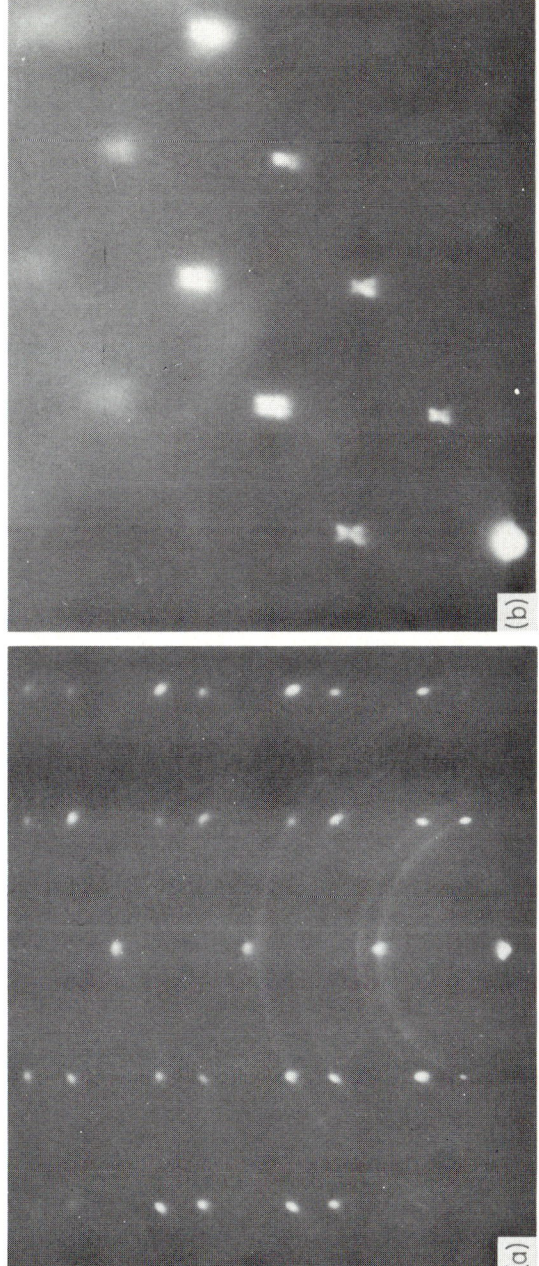

FIG. 19. Electron diffraction pattern of nickel deposit on single crystal copper substrates: (a) 1000-A deposit on (111), (b) 10,000-A deposit on (100).

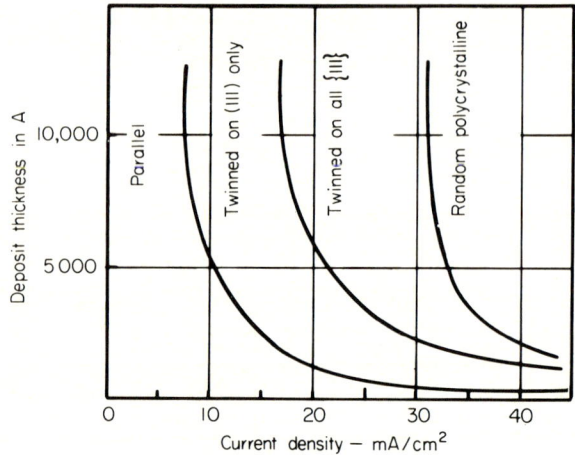

FIG. 20. Orientation at surface of silver deposits on electropolished (111) plane of silver as a function of current density and deposit thickness [after Setty and Wilman (*91*)].

deposits, for example, was bounded by {120}-type facets as determined from the refraction effects on the electron beam.

c. Results from Electron Microscopy. Although electron microscopy offers tremendous possibilities for the study of the detailed structure and topography of electrodeposits, relatively few applications have been made so far. Replica techniques have been used to the greatest extent for characterization of the detailed topography of the deposit surface at various stages in the growth process. Many of the results from these studies have been mentioned previously in this article.

The technique of transmission electron microscopy of the electrodeposit or the deposit plus substrate is relatively new. The first reported work using this method was that of Weil and Read (*158*) in 1950, who stripped thin nickel deposits from copper and zinc substrates and looked at them with the electron microscope. Reimer (*159, 160*) later examined nickel films stripped from polycrystalline copper, but Ogawa *et al.* (*161*) were the first to study nickel films stripped from single crystal substrates. Further studies on nickel stripped from single crystal copper substrates were made by Lawless *et al.* (*63, 162, 163*) and will be discussed in more detail below. Recently studies of cobalt deposits on polycrystalline substrates have been made (*164*).

Steinemann and Hintermann (*165*) have made a detailed examination of the effects of substrate structure and concentration of an inhibitor on the structure of copper electrodeposits. The deposits were made on rolled and annealed, or mechanically polished foils of copper, or on evaporated copper substrates at 20 mA/cm^2 from an acid bath. The samples were thinned chemically from the bottom side so that the region examined in transmission was about 30 μ from the deposit-substrate interface. They reported that in the absence of inhibitors, the grain structure and dislocations in the substrate were reproduced in the deposit. Internal stresses in the deposit were attributed to interactions with dislocations. Additives which were cathodically active were trapped or enclosed in cavities of various sizes in the deposit. Twins, dislocations, and other faults were readily observed in the deposits.

A somewhat similar study of copper deposits was carried out more recently by Stoebe *et al.* (*166*). Deposits were made on an aluminum substrate to make reproduction of the substrate in the deposit unlikely. Several different solutions including an acid sulfate, a cyanide, and a pyrophosphate bath were used and current densities were varied from 11 to 54 mA/cm^2. The samples were thinned from both sides by electropolishing and the position examined was about 40 μ from the substrate. The deposits were characterized by the presence of many stacking faults and twins, and since the aluminum substrate contained neither of these faults, they were assumed to be a product of the deposition process.

Deposits from the acid bath showed a high density of twins at 11 mA/cm^2 with very few dislocations or stacking faults, and with increasing current the density of twins decreased while the density of stacking faults increased. Increasing the current density also caused a decrease in the grain size. Deposits from the cyanide and pyrophosphate baths generally showed a smaller grain size and some stacking faults but no twins. The annealing behavior of these deposits was also investigated.

Ogawa *et al.* (*161*) studied the twin structure of nickel films electrodeposited on single crystal copper substrates. The films were stripped from the substrate using the method of Weil and Read (*158*) and examined by transmission microscopy and diffraction. Deposits made on electropolished surfaces, showed many twins randomly located and varying in width from less than 100 A to several thousand angstroms. Their length often extended 10 μ. These deposits were made at current densities varying from 22 to 31 μA/cm^2. The films were badly broken up in the stripping process, the largest films obtained being about 1 mm^2 in area. The authors concluded from surface replica studies that these twins were true growth twins and were not generated by deformation. Suitable reflection electron diffraction data to support this belief was not given. On etched substrate surfaces many fine twins were formed, and reflection diffraction of a deposit on an etched (110) surface showed extra reflections in twin positions. This, however, is not conclusive since growth on (111) and (11$\bar{1}$) facets would give the same diffraction patterns as a twinned structure.

Lawless *et al.* (*63, 156, 162, 163*) have also made an extensive study of stripped nickel deposits from electropolished single crystal copper substrates. The deposits were all made from a Watts bath at 60°C using a current density of 1–10 mA/cm^2, and the films were stripped by the method of Weil and Read (*158*). The initial microscope studies (*162*) indicated agreement with Ogawa's (*161*) work, but later more detailed experiments in which reflection electron diffraction examinations were made on all deposits before stripping indicated that the majority of the twins formed were actually deformation twins. In fact, under the deposition conditions used, no twins were present for deposits on any substrate orientations except the (111). This was true for all thicknesses from 100 A up to 120,000 A. Figure 21 shows a typical electron micrograph

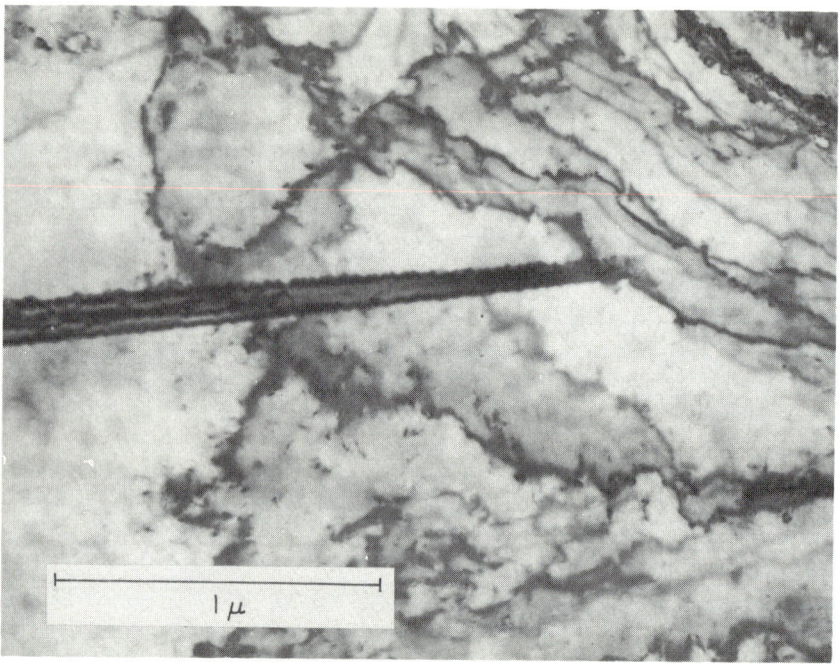

FIG. 21. Electron micrograph of a deformation twin in a nickel deposit film stripped from a copper substrate.

of a deformation twin in a nickel film grown on a high-index plane of copper. The many wavy lines crossing the picture are Bragg extinction contours and the small black spots are dislocations, most of which are nearly normal to the film surface. Higher magnifications reveal more of the details of the structure. Dislocations at the tip of a deformation twin, for example, are clearly visible in the micrograph in Fig. 22. Dark-field electron microscopy provides a very powerful tool for the study of faults in electrodeposits. Figure 23 shows an example of a large number of deformation twins formed in a 200-A (100) nickel deposit and photographed in dark field using a principal 200

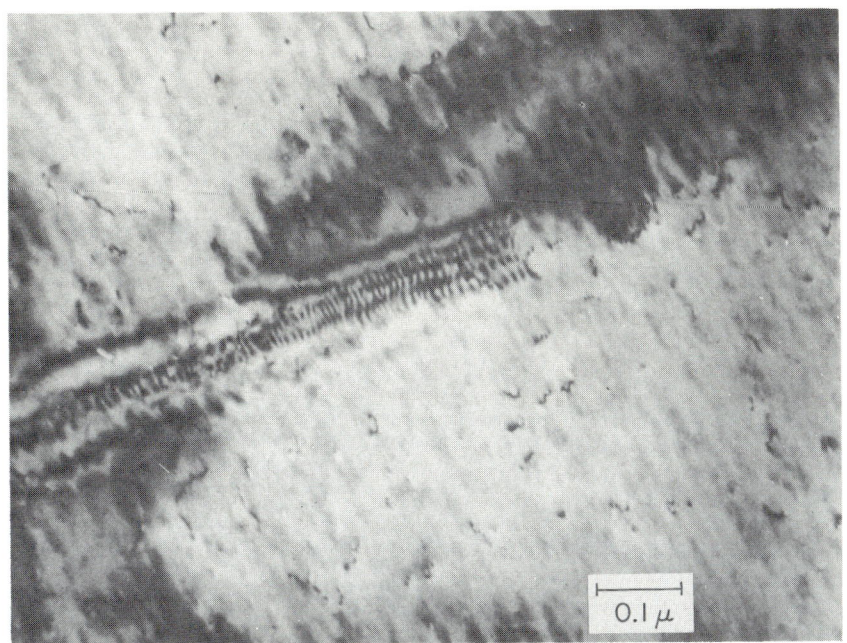

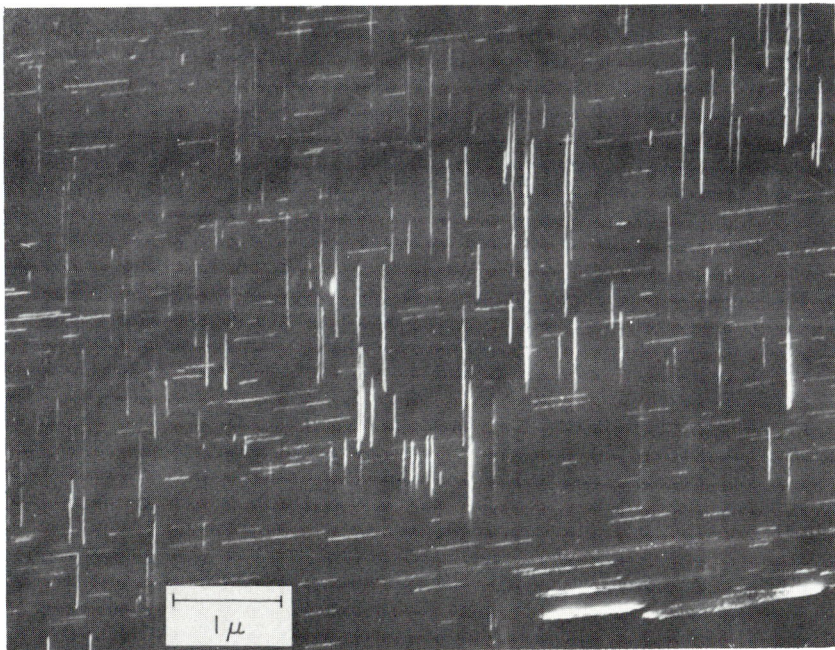

FIG. 22 (top). Electron micrograph of the tip of a deformation twin showing active dislocations. FIG. 23 (bottom). Dark-field electron micrograph of deformation twins in a Ni film stripped from a (100) Cu surface.

reflection and two adjacent twin spots to form the image. Thompson (96) has confirmed these results of stripping nickel films. It is quite clear from these results that extreme caution must be uesd in the interpretation of electron micrographs of stripped deposit films.

It was possible to strip nickel films which were less than 100 A thick, and in most cases these films were continuous. An apparent exception to this is shown in Fig. 24 which is a micrograph of a deposit on a (111) face. The

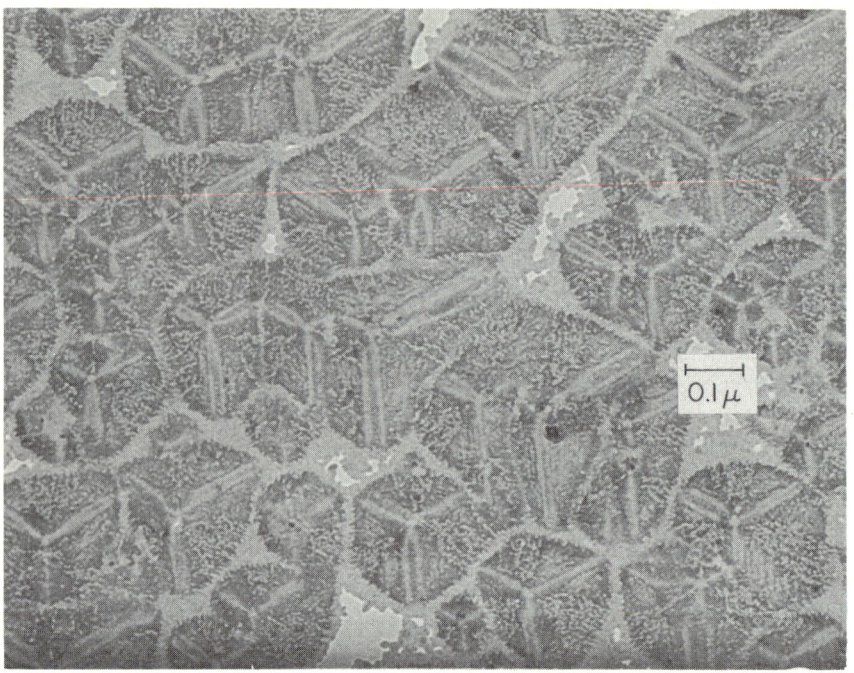

FIG. 24. Electron micrograph of a (111) nickel deposit < 100 A thick. Deposit supported by carbon film.

nickel here is present in the form of pyramidal islands which have mostly grown together leaving some channels between them. The calculated thickness for this deposit was 100 A, but it was probably much thinner, since the thickness of deposits on the (111) was always much less, for a given current density and time, than on any other crystal face (61, 95).

The reflection diffraction patterns from the (111) deposits always showed so-called twin spots at all thicknesses from 100 to 60,000 A. Using transmission microscopy and diffraction techniques (122) it was possible to show that in fact true twins were not present, but that double positioning occurred in the films at least up to a thickness of 500 A or more. For this orientation, true twinning apparently developed on inclined {111} planes at greater thicknesses.

Thompson (96) has used transmission electron microscopy to examine gold deposits stripped from (100) and (111) surfaces of copper. Films of gold on copper were extremely difficult to strip, which suggests the formation of a thin alloy layer at the interface. This is in agreement with some observations of Glossop and Pashley (167) on copper and gold. 1000-A films grown on the (100) face showed many boundaries which were apparently the result of the quadruple positioning of the (111)-oriented gold. (111) deposits showed double-positioning boundaries and many dislocations. In no cases were twins observed in deposits up to 1000 A thickness. Deposits greater than 100 A thickness were continuous, but at thicknesses of 50 to 90 A isolated gold nuclei were present on the copper substrate.

The use of stripped films for the study of the structure of electrodeposits has one major disadvantage, aside from the introduction of artifacts in the stripping process. This disadvantage is that it is not possible to determine the relationships between features in the deposit and those in the substrate. It is possible, however, to maintain the advantages of transmission microscopy and also to observe the relationships between substrate and deposit if the deposits are grown on thin metal films, preferably single crystal films. Studies of this type have been made by Dickson *et al.* (155), Thompson (96), Jesser (154), and Lawless *et al.* (63, 156, 163).

The nucleation and growth of gold electrodeposits on (111) surfaces of silver films was studied by Dickson *et al.* (155). A sequence of micrographs for various calculated average thicknesses of deposit is shown in Fig. 25. The gold was initially in the form of thin isolated plate-like islands. For an average thickness of 20 A, the surface coverage by these islands was only about 22%. Further deposition led to the gradual coalescence of these islands until an almost continuous film was formed at about 80 to 100 A. This growth sequence is very similar to that observed for gold evaporated onto similar substrates (168). The gold electrodeposits were double positioned as has also been observed for evaporated films. Overlapping double-positioning boundaries such as shown in Fig. 26 were apparently more common in the electrodeposits than in evaporated films. These authors concluded that the mode of nucleation and growth was largely independent of the mode of deposition, and depended mainly upon surface migration of gold over the silver substrate and the gold islands.

Thompson (96) studied the early stages of the deposition of gold and nickel onto single crystal copper thin films of (110) and (111) orientations. The results for gold deposits were similar to those of Dickson *et al.* (155) in that isolated nuclei were observed for small amounts of deposit (<50 A) and the films became continuous at about 100 A. It was also found that isolated

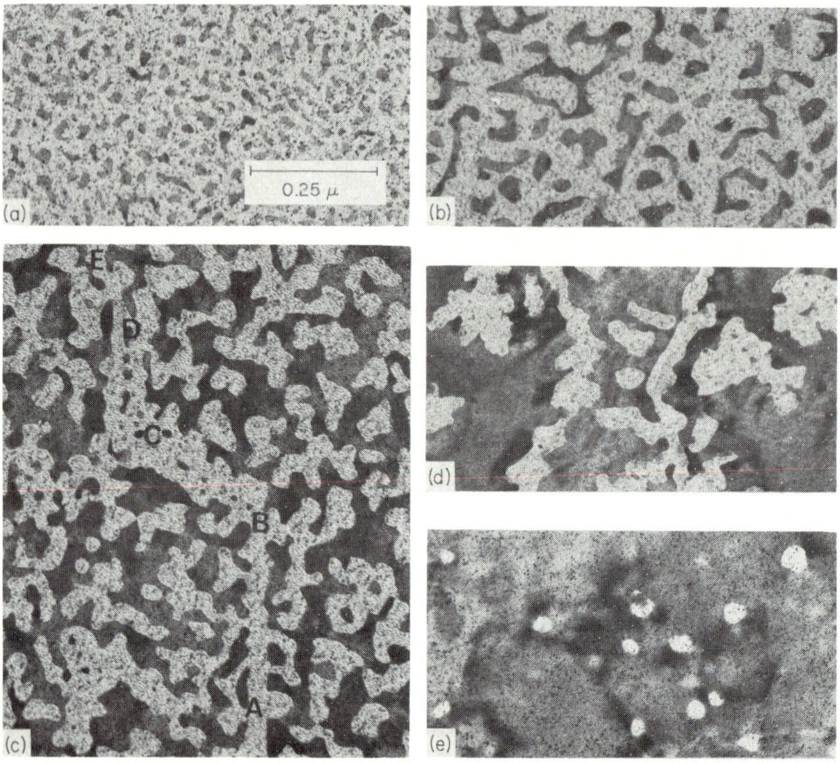

FIG. 25. Sequence of electron micrographs for various thicknesses of gold deposited on (111) silver. The gold was supported by evaporating a thin platinum layer onto the surface and then dissolving away the substrate: (a) 20 A, (b) 25 A, (c) 40 A, (d) 50 A, (e) 80 A [from Dickson et al. (155)].

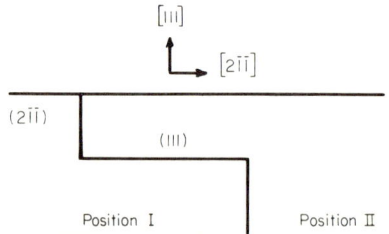

FIG. 26. Schematic diagram of an overlapping double-positioning boundary [after Dickson et al. (155)].

nuclei of gold were present at the early stages of deposition onto thin films of nickel. Nickel on copper, however, showed a somewhat different behavior: the deposits were continuous for the thinnest films observable (<20 A). Isolated nickel nuclei were observed in only one deposit and for a thickness of <50 A.

The nucleation stage of the deposition of platinum onto (111) gold films has been examined by Jesser (*154*) using transmission electron microscopy. The early stages of deposition were characterized by the formation of many small isolated platinum nuclei which showed no obvious relationship to the dislocations present in the substrate. Figure 27 shows a typical example of these initial nuclei. The (111) gold substrates used in this study were prepared by evaporation and contained both double-positioning boundaries and twins. It was found that platinum nuclei formed preferentially on both of these types of faults as is shown in Fig. 28. The average thickness of these deposits was not known definitely but undoubtedly was less than 50 A.

With increasing thickness of the platinum deposits, the films were essentially continuous and showed well-defined, although somewhat irregular moiré fringes. These films nearly always showed small somewhat circular areas which did not show moiré fringes and, therefore, apparently had no platinum on them. It is likely that these areas were regions in which impurities were trapped at the surface of the substrate and for relatively thin deposits prevented the complete coverage of the surface with platinum. As shown below, similar areas have been observed by Lawless (*63*) in nickel deposits. If these gold substrates with a platinum deposit were annealed to about 700°C, it was found that the platinum improved its orientation and became isolated on the gold surface in the form of triangular nuclei. Figure 29 shows a micrograph of a sample after annealing. It was thought that contamination at the interface, as observed by Atkinson (*169*), was removed in the annealing process.

Lawless et al. (*63, 156, 163*) made a fairly extensive electron-microscope study of copper deposits on single crystal films of nickel which had been previously prepared by electrodeposition onto bulk copper single crystals. An acid sulfate bath was used and the deposits of copper were made at room temperature at a current density of 1 mA/cm^2. The substrate films were characterized by the presence of numerous deformation twins and a density of dislocations somewhat less than that normal for evaporated films.

The copper deposits, as shown by the moiré fringes, were essentially continuous over the nickel substrate, even for deposits of a calculated thickness of less than 20 A. The moiré fringes were in general quite complex, wavy, and irregular as shown in Fig. 30. The fringes were not clearly broken up into small clusters such as might be expected if the film were formed by individual, well-developed nuclei growing together as has been observed in evaporated deposits. Since the nickel substrate surfaces were finely faceted, many kink sites and ledges were available so that nuclei of copper could have been initiated simultaneously at many different points on the surface. The coalescence of this high density of nuclei on kink sites present on small facets could then lead to the very thin continuous film observed with the irregularities in the moiré pattern. Figure 31 shows this coalescence model. In some cases

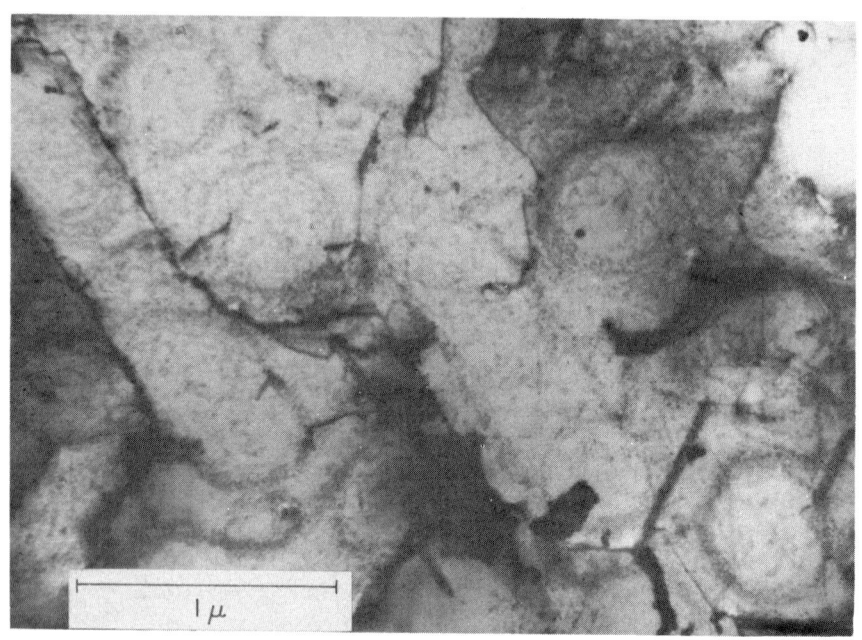

FIG. 27. Electron micrograph of platinum nuclei on a (111) gold substrate.

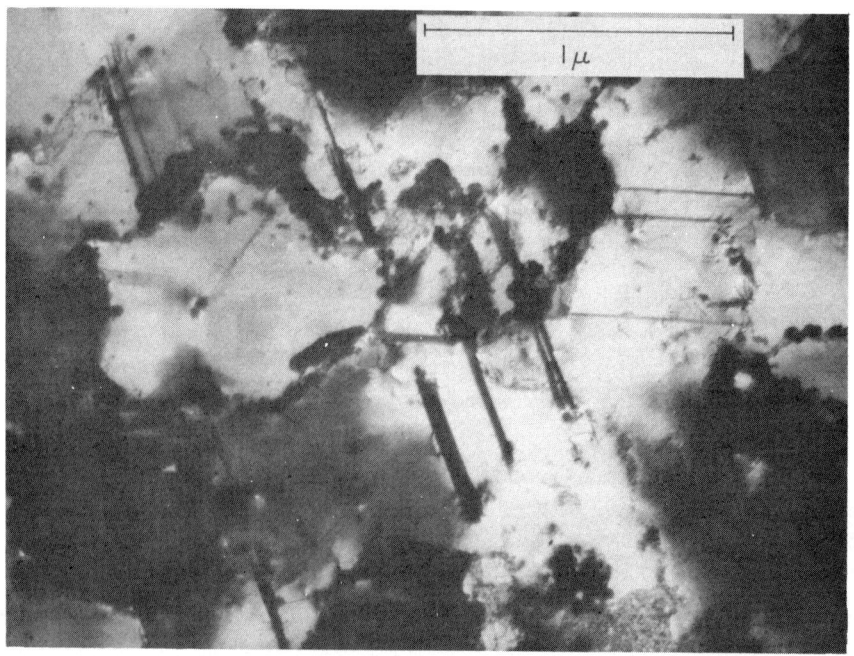

FIG. 28. Electron micrograph showing nucleation of platinum deposit on faults in (111) gold substrate.

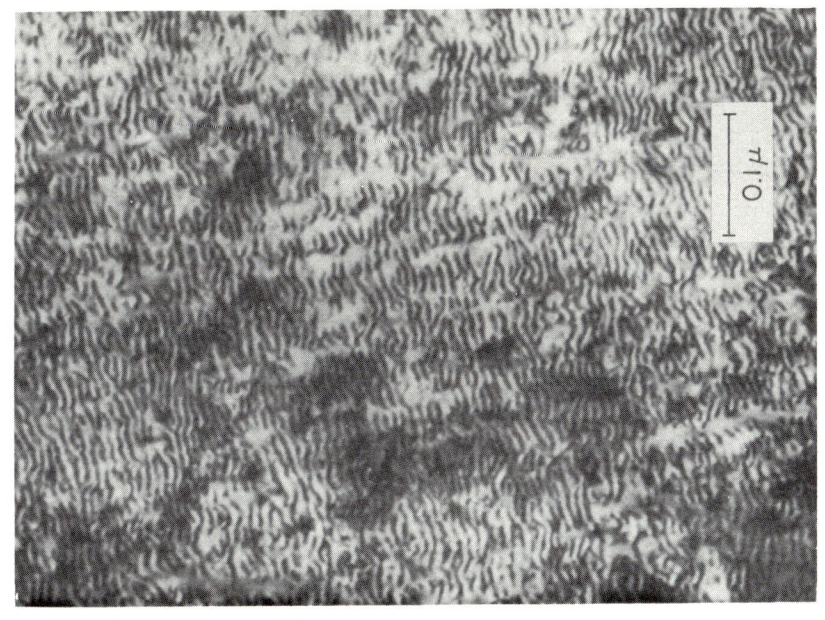

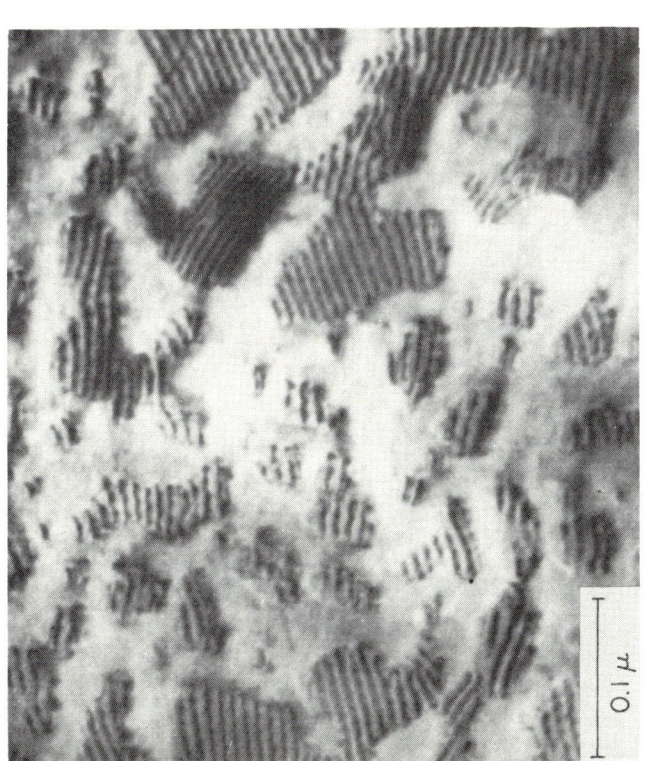

FIG. 29 (above). Electron micrograph of platinum deposit on (111) gold after annealing.

FIG. 30 (right). Electron micrograph of copper deposit on single crystal nickel film showing moiré patterns.

clear, sharp breaks in the moiré patterns were visible which were apparently the result of multiatomic steps on the substrate surface.

Many of the micrographs of very thin deposits contained irregular areas which showed no moiré pattern and seemed to be featureless as shown in Fig. 32. These small regions apparently were devoid of nickel and were probably the result of adsorbed impurities on the surface of the substrate. These regions were similar to those observed by Jesser (*154*) for platinum deposits. Many dislocations were apparent in the moiré fringe patterns, but it is not possible to determine definitely whether the actual dislocations were present in the deposit or in the substrate. The appearance of some of the dislocations suggested that they were caused by trapped impurity atoms.

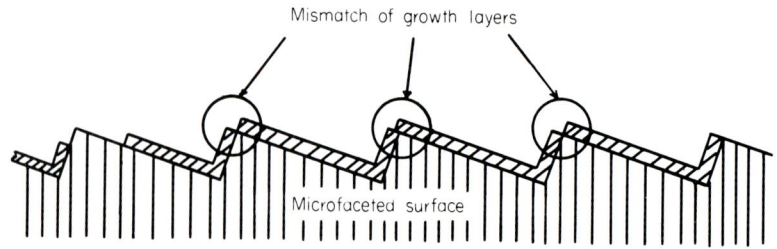

FIG. 31. Schematic diagram of the coalescence of a deposit on a finely faceted surface.

The extreme sensitivity of the rotation of the moiré fringes to misorientations of the deposit lattice make possible the extremely accurate determination of misalignments. The moiré patterns for these deposits showed clearly that the degree of misalignment of the copper with the substrate nickel lattice was much less than 1°.

The spacing of the moiré fringes may also be used to determine whether strains are present in the deposit. Such measurements indicated that the copper lattice was compressed slightly from its normal lattice parameter. This was to be expected since the copper lattice is 2.5% larger than the nickel lattice. No evidence of pseudomorphism was obtained for any thickness of deposit.

There was no clear evidence of dislocations in the substrate influencing the growth or nucleation of the deposit, at least for thin deposits (<200 A). There was, however, evidence of preferential nucleation and growth on the deformation twins in the substrate. Figure 33 shows an example of enhanced growth of a copper deposit on a twin. The entire surface was covered with a thin nickel deposit, but larger crystallites grow along the twin. This phenomenon was also observed by Jesser (*154*) as mentioned previously. It was not obvious whether this enhanced growth resulted from the change in the topography of the surface due to the formation of the twin, or to lattice strain at the twin boundaries.

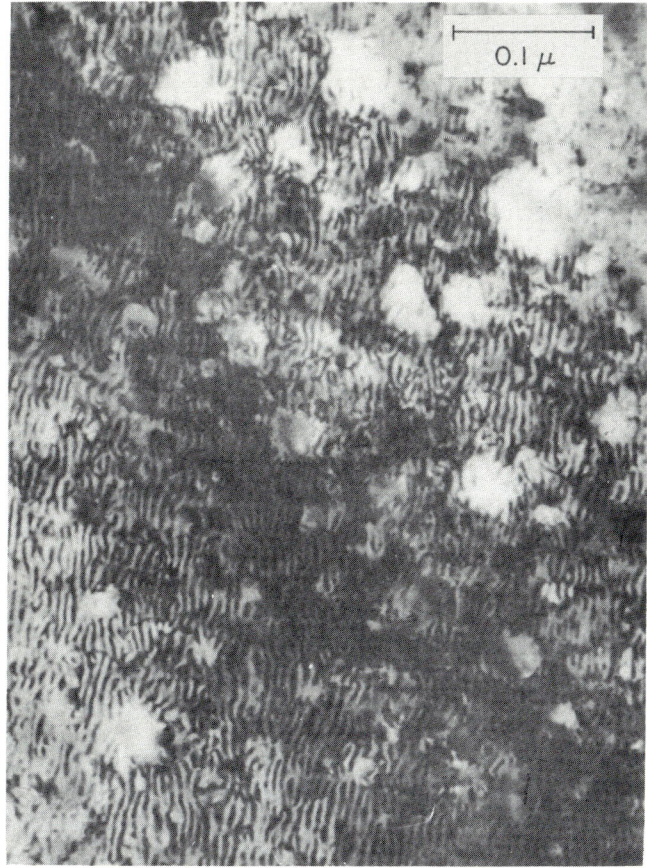

Fig. 32. Electron micrograph of copper deposit on nickel film oriented near (111) showing areas with apparently no deposit.

Evidence for the formation of interfacial dislocations between a 200-A nickel deposit and a copper substrate has recently been obtained by Thompson and Lawless (170). Indications were that some of these dislocations were pulled-in dislocations which helped to relieve the misfit strain between the two crystals. A similar network of dislocations has been observed in a micrograph of a nickel-copper bicrystal prepared by evaporation (171).

The investigation of the important interfacial region of bicrystals prepared by electrodeposition has just begun. This holds promise of being a productive area for future research, both on electrodeposit films and evaporated films. There are many structural similarities between these two types of films, as well as major differences. The situation is not clear, however, as only a very few detailed electron-microscope studies have been made at this time. The

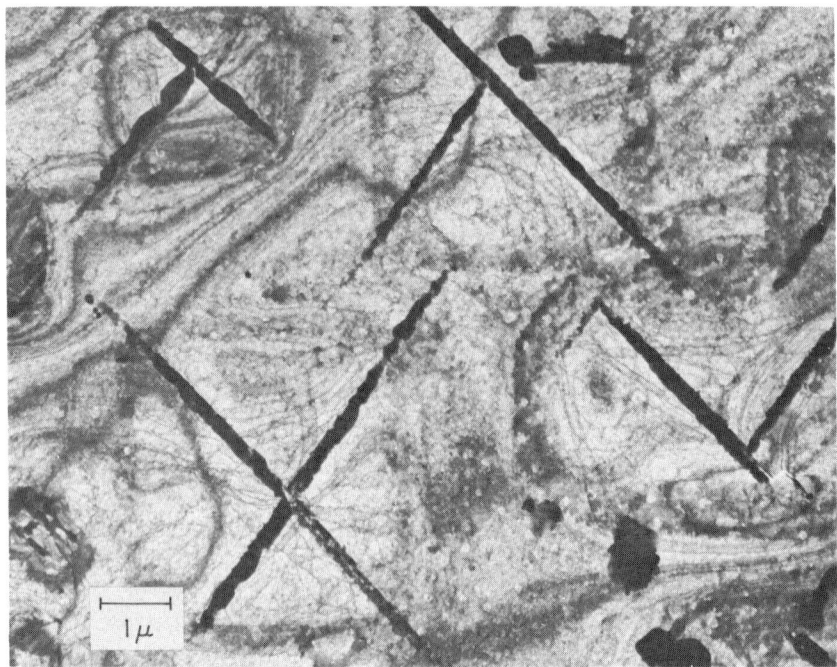

Fig. 33. Electron micrograph of enhanced copper deposition on deformation twins in the nickel substrate.

role of impurities in determining the structure of electrodeposit films is not understood and bears serious investigation by modern techniques. Likewise, the role of substrate defects in determining the mechanism of growth as well as the defect nature of the deposit must be investigated in detail. Spiral-growth mechanisms on screw dislocations are very attractive but have not been confirmed, and in fact have not been observed during the early stages of growth. The understanding of the growth and structure of electrodeposits has taken a giant stride forward in the last 10 years, largely as a result of the application of both modern electrochemical theory and techniques, and refined techniques for the determinations of structure. There is still much to be done.

Acknowledgments

The author is indebted to Drs. D. W. Pashley, H. Fischer, S. Weissmann, and J. P. G. Farr for furnishing illustrations, and to Drs. E. R. Thompson, L. B. Garmon, and W. A. Jesser for permission to report some of their results prior to publication. Acknowledgment is gratefully made of the support provided by the National Science Foundation for Dr. Thompson's work, and to the Office of Naval Research for support of the studies carried out by Dr. Garmon and the author.

References

1. G. Gore, "The Art of Electro-Metallurgy," 3rd ed. Longmans, Green, New York, 1877 (9th printing, 1910).
2. J. O'M. Bockris and A. Damjanovic, *in* "Modern Aspects of Electrochemistry" (J. O'M. Bockris and B. E. Conway, eds.), Vol. 3, p. 224. Butterworths, London and Washington, 1964.
3. M. Fleischmann and H. R. Thirsk, *Advan. Electrochem. Electrochem. Eng.* **3**, 123 (1963).
4. H. Fischer, "Elektrolytische Abscheidung und Elektrokristallisation von Metallen," Springer, Berlin, 1954.
5. A. Brenner, "Electrodeposition of Alloys," Vols. 1 and 2. Academic Press, New York, 1963.
6. W. Blum and G. B. Hogaboom, "Principles of Electroplating and Electroforming." McGraw-Hill, New York, 1949.
7. F. A. Lowenheim, ed., "Modern Electoplating," Wiley, New York, 1963.
8. J. Frenkel, *J. Phys. U.S.S.R.* **9**, 392 (1945).
9. W. K. Burton and N. Cabrera, *Discussions Faraday Soc.* No. 5, 33 (1949).
10. M. Volmer, "Kinetik der Phasenbildung." Steinkopff, Dresden and Leipzig, 1939.
11. M. Volmer, *Z. Physik. Chem. (Leipzig)* **102**, 267 (1922).
12. J. W. Gibbs, "The Scientific Papers of J. Willard Gibbs," Vol. 1, p. 325, footnote. Republication of 1906 edition by Dover, New York, 1961.
13. R. Becker and W. Döring, *Ann. Phys.* **24**, 719 (1935).
14. J. P. Hirth, *Ann. N. Y. Acad. Sci.* **101**, 805 (1963).
15. J. P. Hirth and G. M. Pound, "Condensation and Evaporation, Nucleation and Growth Kinetics." Pergamon Press, Oxford, 1963.
16. W. K. Burton, N. Cabrera, and F. C. Frank, *Phil. Trans. Roy. Soc. London* **A243**, 299 (1951).
17. F. C. Frank, *Discussions Faraday Soc.* No. 5, 48, 67 (1949).
18. A. R. Verma, "Crystal Growth and Dislocations." Butterworths, London, 1953.
19. F. C. Frank, *Advan. Phys.* **1**, 91 (1952).
20. A. J. Forty, *Advan. Phys.* **3**, 1 (1954).
21. W. Dekeyser and S. Amelinckx, "Les Dislocations et al Croissance des Cristaux." Masson, Paris, 1956.
22. F. C. Frank and A. J. Forty, *Proc. Roy. Soc.* **A217**, 262 (1953).
23. J. W. Matthews, *Phil. Mag.* **12**, 1143 (1965).
24. B. E. Conway and J. O'M. Bockris, *Proc. Roy. Soc.* **A248**, 394 (1958).
25. B. E. Conway and J. O'M. Bockris, *Electrochim. Acta* **3**, 340 (1960).
26. W. Mehl and J. O'M. Bockris, *J. Chem. Phys.* **27**, 817 (1957).
27. W. Mehl and J. O'M. Bockris, *Can. J. Chem.* **37**, 190 (1959).
28. E. Mattson and J. O'M. Bockris, *Trans. Faraday Soc.* **55**, 1586 (1959).
29. J. O'M. Bockris and M. Enyo, *J. Electrochem. Soc.* **109**, 48 (1962).
30. H. Kita, M. Enyo, and J. O'M. Bockris, *Can. J. Chem.* **39**, 1670 (1961).
31. J. O'M. Bockris, *Z. Physik. Chem. (Leipzig)* **215**, 1 (1960).
32. J. O'M. Bockris and H. Kita, *J. Electrochem. Soc.* **109**, 928 (1962).
33. A. R. Despic and J. O'M. Bockris, *J. Chem. Phys.* **32**, 389 (1960).
34. A. Damjanovic and J. O'M. Bockris, *J. Electrochem. Soc.* **110**, 1035 (1963).
35. A. Damjanovic, T. H. V. Setty, and J. O'M. Bockris, *J. Electroanal. Chem.* **9** (1965).
36. A. Damjanovic, M. Paunovic, and J. O'M. Bockris, *J. Electroanal. Chem.* **9**, 93 (1965).
37. A. Damjanovic, M. Paunovic, and J. O'M. Bockris, *Plating* **50**, 735 (1963).

38. A. Damjanovic, *Plating* **52** (1965).
39. A. Damjanovic, M. Paunovic, and J. O'M. Bockris, *Electrochim. Acta.* **10**, 111 (1965).
40. M. A. V. Devanathan, J. O'M. Bockris, and K. Müller, *Proc. Roy. Soc.* **A274**, 55 (1963).
41. B. E. Conway, "Theory and Principles of Electrode Processes." Ronald Press, New York, 1965.
42. N. F. Mott and R. J. Watts-Tobin, *Electrochim. Acta*, **4**, 79 (1961).
43. M. Volmer, "Das Elektrolytische Kristallwachstum." Hermann, Paris, 1934.
44. H. Brandes, *Z. Physik. Chem.* (*Leipzig*) **A142**, 97 (1929).
45. W. Lorenz, *Z. Naturforsch.* **9a**, 716 (1954).
46. D. A. Vermilyea, *J. Chem. Phys.* **27**, 814 (1957).
47. M. Volmer, *Z. Physik. Chem.* (*Leipzig*) **A102**, 267 (1922).
48. V. Kohlschütter and F. Ubersax, *Z. Elektrochem.* **30**, 72 (1924).
49. T. Erdey-Gruz and M. Volmer, *Z. Physik. Chem.* (*Leipzig*) **A157**, 165 (1931).
50. V. Kohlschütter and A. Torricelli, *Z. Electrochem.* **38**, 21 (1932).
51. A. T. Wakramian and K. Gorbunova, *Acta Physicochim. U.R.S.S.* **1**, 683 (1937).
52. R. Sroka and H. Fischer, *Z. Elektrochem.* **60**, 109 (1956).
53. J. Wilcock, *Trans. Inst. Metal Finishing* **34**, 483 (1956–1957).
54. H. J. Pick and J. Wilcock, *Trans. Inst. Metal Finishing* **35**, 298 (1958).
55. H. Seiter, H. Fischer, and L. Albert, *Electrochim. Acta* **2**, 97 (1960).
56. N. A. Economou, H. Fischer, and D. Trivich, *Electrochim. Acta* **2**, 207 (1960).
57. H. J. Pick, G. G. Storey, and T. B. Vaughan, *Electrochim. Acta* **2**, 167 (1960).
58. S. C. Barnes, G. G. Storey, and H. J. Pick, *Electrochim. Acta* **2**, 196 (1960).
59. G. Wranglen, *Electrochim. Acta* **2**, 130 (1960).
60. G. G. Storey and S. C. Barnes, *Trans. Inst. Metal Finishing* **37**, 11 (1960).
61. N. A. Economou and D. Trivich, *Electrochim. Acta* **3**, 292 (1961).
62. I. Giron and F. Ogburn, *J. Electrochem. Soc.* **108**, 842 (1961).
63. K. R. Lawless, *J. Vacuum Sci. and Technol.* **2**, 24 (1965).
64. A. Damjanovic, T. H. V. Setty, and J. O'M. Bockris, *J. Electrochem. Soc.* **113**, 429 (1966).
65. G. Poli and L. P. Bicelli, *Met. Ital.* **51**, 399 (1959).
66. G. Poli and L. P. Bicelli, *Met. Ital.* **51**, 548 (1959).
67. G. Poli and L. P. Bicelli, *Met. Ital.* **54**, 497 (1962).
68. L. P. Bicelli and G. Poli, *Electrochim. Acta* **11**, 289 (1966).
69. S. Amelinckx, *Nature* **170**, 760 (1952).
70. D. R. Turner and G. R. Johnson, *J. Electrochem. Soc.* **109**, 798 (1962).
71. D. Shanefield and P. E. Lighty, *J. Electrochem. Soc.* **110**, 973 (1963).
72. V. Kohlschütter and A. Good, *Z. Elektrochem.* **33**, 277 (1927).
73. G. Wranglen, *Trans. Roy. Inst. Technol. Stockholm*, **94** (1955).
74. P. B. Price, D. A. Vermilyea, and M. B. Webb, *Acta Met.* **6**, 524 (1958).
75. H. I. Matthews, T. de S. Mutucumarana, and H. Wilman, *Acta Cryst.* **14**, 636 (1961).
76. J. L. Barton and J. O'M. Bockris, *Proc. Roy. Soc.* **A268** 485 (1962).
77. H. J. Pick, *Nature* **176**, 693 (1955).
78. H. Seiter, H. Fischer, and L. Albert, *Naturwissenschaften* **45**, 127 (1958).
79. R. Kaischew, E. Budewski, and S. Malinowski, *Z. Physik. Chem.* (*Leipzig*) **204**, 348 (1955).
80. N. Cabrera, *J. Chem Phys.* **21**, 1111 (1953).
81. J. C. Fisher, R. L. Fullman, and G. W. Sears, *Acta Met.* **3**, 110 (1955).
82. G. W. Sears, *J. Chem. Phys.* **29**, 979 (1958).
83. T. B. Vaughan and H. J. Pick, *Electrochim. Acta* **2**, 179 (1960).

84. S. C. Barnes, *Electrochim. Acta* **5**, 79 (1961).
85. D. A. Vermilyea, *J. Chem. Phys.* **25**, 1254 (1956).
86. F. C. Frank, *in* "Growth and Perfection of Crystals" (R. H. Doremus, B. W. Roberts, and D. Turnbull, eds.), p. 411. Wiley, New York, 1958.
87. N. Cabrera and D. A. Vermilyea, *in* "Growth and Perfection of Crystals" (R. H. Doremus, B. W. Roberts, and D. Turnbull, eds.), p. 393. Wiley, New York, 1958.
88. M. J. Lighthill and G. B. Whitham, *Proc. Roy. Soc.* **A229**, 281, 317 (1955).
89. N. Hackerman and N. H. Simpson, *Trans. Faraday Soc.* **52**, 628 (1956).
90. R. D. Srivastava and H. Gesser, *Electrochim. Acta* **9**, 1405 (1964).
91. T. H. V. Setty and H. Wilman, *Trans. Faraday Soc.* **51**, 984 (1955).
92. R. Weil and H. C. Cook, *J. Electrochem. Soc.* **109**, 295 (1962).
93. K. Hashimoto, *Trans. Japan Inst. Metals* **6**, 166 (1965).
94. B. C. Banerjee and P. L. Walker, Jr., *J. Electrochem. Soc.* **109**, 436 (1962).
95. L. B. Garmon, M.S. Thesis, Univ. of Richmond, 1960.
96. E. R. Thompson, Ph.D. Dissertation, Univ. of Virginia, 1966.
97. H. P. Klug and L. E. Alexander, "X-Ray Diffraction Procedures." Wiley, New York, 1954.
98. B. D. Cullity, "Elements of X-Ray Diffraction." Addison-Wesley, Reading, Massachusetts, 1956.
99. P. E. Lighty, D. Shanefield, S. Weissmann, and A. Shrier, *J. Appl. Phys.* **34**, 2233 (1963).
100. T. Imura, *J. Japan Inst. Metals* **16**, 10 (1952).
101. T. Imura, *Naniwa Univ. Ser. A* **2**, 51 (1954).
102. T. Imura, S. Weissmann, and J. J. Slade, *Acta Cryst.* **15**, 788 (1962).
103. T. Ellis, L. F. Nanni, A. Shrier, S. Weissmann, G. E. Padawer, and N. Hosokawa, *J. Appl. Phys.* **35**, 3364 (1964).
104. R. S. Smith, *IBM J. Res. Develop.* **4**, 205 (1960).
105. E. Hofer and P. Javet, *Helv. Phys. Acta* **35**, 369 (1962).
106. E. Hofer and P. Javet, *Microtecnic (Lausanne)* **17**, 104 (1963).
107. G. Eichkorn and H. Fischer, *Z. Metallk.* **55**, 582 (1964).
108. C. S. Barrett, "Structure of Metals." McGraw-Hill, New York, 1952.
109. B. E. Warren, *Progr. Metal Phys.* **8**, 147 (1959).
110. B. E. Warren and B. L. Averback, *J. Appl. Phys.* **21**, 595 (1950).
111. F. Bertaut, *Compt. Rend.* **228**, 492 (1949).
112. J. B. Cohen, "Diffraction Methods in Materials Science." Macmillan, New York, 1966.
113. G. P. Thomson, *Proc. Roy. Soc.* **A133**, 1 (1931).
114. R. C. Newman and D. W. Pashley, *Phil. Mag.* **46**, 927 (1955).
115. D. F. Mitchell, G. W. Simmons, and K. R. Lawless, *Appl. Phys. Letters*, **7**, 173 (1965).
116. P. B. Sewell and M. Cohen, *Appl. Phys. Letters*, **7**, 32 (1965).
117. G. P. Thomson and W. Cochrane, "Theory and Practice of Electron Diffraction." Macmillan, New York, 1939.
118. Z. G. Pinsker, "Electron Diffraction." Butterworths, London, 1953.
119. E. Bauer, "Elektronenbeugung." Verlag Moderne Industrie, Munchen, 1958.
120. H. Raether, *in* "Handbuch der Physik" (S. Flugge, ed.), Vol. 32, p. 443. Springer, Berlin, 1957.
121. E. W. Dickson and D. W. Pashley, *Phil. Mag.* **7**, 1315 (1962).
122. D. W. Pashley and M. J. Stowell, *Phil. Mag.* **8**, 1605 (1963).
123. V. E. Cosslett, "Practical Electron Microscopy." Butterworths, London, 1951.
124. C. E. Hall, "Introduction to Electron Microscopy." McGraw-Hill, New York, 1953.
125. D. H. Kay, "Techniques for Electron Microscopy." Blackwell, Oxford, 1965.

126. L. Reimer, "Elektronenmikroskopische Untersuchungs- und Praparationsmethoden." Berlin, 1959.
127. G. Thomas, "Transmission Electron Microscopy of Metals." Wiley, New York, 1962.
128. R. D. Heidenreich, "Fundamentals of Transmission Electron Microscopy." Wiley (Interscience), New York, 1964.
129. S. Amelinckx, "The Direct Observation of Dislocations." Academic Press, New York, 1964.
130. P. B. Hirsch, A. Howie, R. B. Nicholson, D. W. Pashley, and M. J. Whelan, "Electron Microscopy of Thin Crystals." Butterworths, London and Washington, 1965.
131. L. Reimer, *Electrochim. Acta* **2**, 215 (1960).
132. P. M. Kelly and J. Nutting, *J. Inst. Metals* **87**, 385 (1958–1959).
133. G. A. Bassett, J. W. Menter, and D. W. Pashley, *Proc. Roy. Soc.* **A246**, 345 (1958).
134. R. Glocker and E. Kaupp, *Z. Physik* **24**, 121 (1924).
135. W. A. Wood, *Proc. Phys. Soc. (London)* **43**, 138 (1931).
136. A. W. Hothersall, *Trans. Faraday Soc.* **31**, 1242 (1935).
137. W. Blum and H. S. Rawdon, *Trans. Am. Electrochem. Soc.* **44**, 305 (1923).
138. H. Leidheiser, Jr. and A. T. Gwathmey, *J. Electrochem. Soc.* **98**, 225 (1951).
139. T. H. Orem, *J. Res. Natl. Bur. Std.* **60**, 597 (1958).
140. S. C. Barnes, *Acta Met.* **7**, 700 (1959).
141. R. W. Hinton, L. H. Schwartz and J. B. Cohen, *J. Electrochem. Soc.* **110**, 103 (1963).
142. J. D. Finegan and R. W. Hoffman, *U.S. At. Energy Comm. Tech. Rept. No. 18* (1961).
143. M. S. Paterson, *J. Appl. Phys.* **23**, 805 (1952).
144. B. Borie and C. J. Sparks, *Acta Cryst.* **14**, 569 (1961).
145. N. Cabrera, *in* "Structure and Properties of Thin Films" (C. A. Neugebauer, J. B. Newkirk, and D. A. Vermilyea, eds.). Wiley, New York, 1959.
146. N. Cabrera, *Surface Sci.* **2**, 320 (1964).
147. J. H. van der Merwe, *in* "Single-Crystal Films" (M. H. Francombe and H. Sato, eds.), p. 139. Macmillan, New York, 1964.
148. S. Weissmann, *J. Appl. Phys.* **27**, 389 (1956).
149. W. Cochrane, *Proc. Phys. Soc. (London)* **48**, 723 (1936).
150. R. C. Newman, *Proc. Phys. Soc. (London)* **69**, 432 (1956).
151. D. W. Pashley, *Advan. Phys.* **5**, 173 (1956).
152. G. I. Finch, H. Wilman and L. Yang, *Discussions Faraday Soc.* **1**, 144 (1947).
153. G. I. Finch and C. H. Sun, *Trans. Faraday Soc.* **32**, 852 (1936).
154. W. A. Jesser, Ph.D. Dissertation, Univ. of Virginia, 1966.
155. E. W. Dickson, M. H. Jacobs, and D. W. Pashley, *Phil. Mag.* **11**, 575 (1965).
156. K. R. Lawless and L. B. Garmon, Univ. of Virginia, unpublished results, 1963.
157. T. H. V. Setty and H. Wilman, *Electrochim. Acta* **11**, 297 (1966).
158. R. Weil and H. J. Read, *J. Appl. Phys.* **21**, 1068 (1950).
159. L. Reimer, *Z. Metallk.* **47**, 631 (1956).
160. L. Reimer and J. Ficker, *Proc. European Regional Conf. Electron Microscopy, Delft, 1960*, p. 387. De Nederlandse Vereniging voot Electronenmicroscopie, Amsterdam (1961).
161. S. Ogawa, J. Mitzumo, D. Watanabe and F. E. Fujita, *J. Phys. Soc. Japan* **12**, 999 (1957).
162. K. R. Lawless, L. B. Garmon, and H. Leidheiser, Jr., *Proc. European Regional Conf. Electron Microscopy, Delft, 1960*, p. 398. De Nederlandse Vereniging voor Electronenmicroscopie, Amsterdam (1961).
163. K. R. Lawless and L. B. Garmon, *5th Intern. Congr. Electron Microscopy, Philadelphia, 1962*, p. DD-7. (S. S. Breese, Jr. ed.). Academic Press, New York (1962).

164. R. Sard, C. D. Schwartz, and R. Weil, *J. Electrochem. Soc.* **113**, 424 (1966).
165. S. Steinemann and H. E. Hintermann, *Schweiz. Arch. Angew. Wiss. Tech.* **26**, 202 (1960).
166. T. G. Stoebe, F. H. Hammad, and M. L. Rudee, *Electrochim. Acta* **9**, 925 (1964).
167. A. B. Glossop and D. W. Pashley, *Proc. Roy. Soc.* **A250**, 132 (1959).
168. D. W. Pashley, M. J. Stowell, M. H. Jacobs, and T. J. Law, *Phil. Mag.* **10**, 127 (1964).
169. R. H. Atkinson, *Trans. Inst. Metal Finishing* **36**, 7 (1958).
170. E. R. Thompson and K. R. Lawless, *Appl. Phys. Letters* **9**, 138 (1966).
171. V. Gradmann, *Ann. Physik* **13**, 213 (1964).

Thin Glass Films

W. A. Pliskin, D. R. Kerr, and J. A. Perri

*Components Division, International Business Machines Corporation
East Fishkill Facility, Hopewell Junction, New York*

I. Introduction	257
II. Preparation	259
1. Thermal Oxides	260
2. Vacuum Evaporation	263
3. Pyrolytic Decomposition and Pyrolytic Reaction	263
4. Fused Glasses from Sedimented Glass Powders	266
5. Reactive Sputtering	267
6. Radio-Frequency Sputtering	268
7. Pyrolytic and Sputtered Silicon Nitride	269
III. Evaluation of Physical and Chemical Properties	270
1. General Use of Infrared Spectroscopy	270
2. Optical Techniques	271
3. Etching Techniques	272
4. Application of Techniques	273
IV. Electrical Properties of Glass Films	289
1. Electrical Requirements for Passivation	289
2. Methods of Measuring Ionic Polarization	293
3. Films of Major Interest	300
4. Thermal SiO_2	300
5. Glasses Formed during Diffusion	305
6. Deposited Glasses	309
V. Applications of Glass Films to Semiconductor Devices	316
1. General Advantages	316
2. Special Considerations for Each Method of Application	316
3. Illustrations of Applications	319
References	320

I. Introduction

Due to the importance of thin-film insulators for diffusion masking, for crossover insulation, and for surface passivation of semiconductor devices, a great deal of interest in oxide and glass films has been generated (*1–4*). In this article we shall cover techniques of thin-film glass formation and deposition which have received the most attention in recent years. We shall also cover techniques for determining and characterizing physical, chemical, and electrical properties of glass films. Some typical glasses and glass types will be characterized in detail together with a comparison of similar glasses formed by different techniques. Finally, the practical application of glass films in the development and manufacture of semiconductor devices will be discussed.

Due to space and time limitations we cannot cover all the details with regard to preparation and properties of various types of glass films. We shall review the general preparation procedures together with the advantages and disadvantages of the various techniques of film preparation. For general evaporation and sputtering procedures one can always refer to Holland (5). More recent reviews which the reader should find helpful include those written by Schwartz and Berry (6), Gregor (7), Maissel (8), and Glang (9). Because of the present greater emphasis on silicon technology, we shall emphasize glasses used with silicon device technology. However, many of the deposited films can also be applied to other substrates. The main criterion is compatibility of the glass film with the substrate. This includes expansion matching, temperature limitations to prevent junction movement or overalloying of any predeposited metals, and possible reaction of the glass with the substrate, depending on the deposition conditions.

Since the glasses are generally applied at temperatures greater than device operating temperature, it is desirable to have a glass whose coefficient of expansion is close to that of the substrate to eliminate stresses and, in the extreme case, to eliminate the possibility of glass cracking. The greater the application temperature of the glass, the greater is the need for good expansion matching of the glass to the substrate. It is better for the glass to have an expansion coefficient lower than that for the substrate than it is to have a higher expansion coefficient. A glass film with expansion coefficient less than that of the substrate will be under compression on cooling, whereas a higher expansion coefficient glass will be under tension. Glass films under compression are much stronger and have a greater resistance to cracking than glasses under tension. Glasses with expansion coefficients higher than that of the substrate can be used providing the glass film thickness is decreased as the expansion mismatch increases.

For effective passivation the glass films should be pinhole-free and should have long-term chemical and water stability. However, the water and chemical stability decreases as the softening point of the glass decreases. At the same time, the expansion coefficient generally increases as the softening point decreases. Thus, both of these factors limit the usefulness of those application techniques which require softening the glasses on structures which have an upper temperature limit. In other words, an upper temperature limit exists for those transistor structures which are metalized prior to the final glassing (10). Since aluminum is commonly used, this puts an upper limit of 577°C (the aluminum-silicon eutectic) for the glass application temperature in this system. Such limitations are the reasons for the great interest in producing the equivalent of high-temperature softening-point glasses on relatively low-temperature substrates by various external means. The techniques for producing such films and the properties of these films will be discussed in later sections.

The glass films should also have good thickness and compositional uniformity to simplify etching or hole opening for making contact with the underlying substrate. No general conclusion can be made with regard to thickness and compositional uniformity for all of the various glassing techniques. However, thickness and compositional control is more difficult for those processes which are strongly temperature dependent and reactant concentration dependent. In such cases reactor design, methods of heating and cooling, flow rates, mixing, etc., are variables which strongly influence the product. Thus, of the various techniques described in the next section, pyrolytic decomposition and pyrolytic reaction are more difficult to control than the fused-powder or sputtering processes.

For effective surface passivation, glass films should have long-term stability to moisture attack. Since it is difficult to evaluate glasses under moderate moisture conditions which might be encountered in device operation, accelerated tests have been used for these evaluations. The most drastic and rapid simple test for fused glass was found to be exposure of a glassed silicon wafer to boiling water for times ranging from a few minutes to a few hours (*11*). The results were more severe than those experienced by milder, long-term tests, but the results could be correlated. With some low-temperature-deposited glass films, the one-hour boiling-water test was found to be less severe than a few days exposure to high humidity (85%) and temperature (85°C) (*12*). Because of the importance of moisture stability, it has been covered in detail in the section on the evaluation of physical and chemical properties of glass films.

The electrical properties of glass films of most importance in passivation are dielectric constant, dielectric strength, resistivity, and the glass-silicon interface potential. Stability of the glass-silicon interface potential over the device operating lifetime requires extremely low ionic conductivity in the glass. In multilevel passivation layers the most stringent electrical requirements are placed on the glass contacting the semiconductor surface. These factors will be discussed in Section IV.

II. Preparation

It is probably most simple to group the glasses by their techniques for formation. These include: (1) thermal oxidation and glasses formed by subsequent diffusion processes, (2) vacuum evaporation, (3) pyrolytic decomposition and pyrolytic reaction, (4) fusing sedimented glass powders, (5) reactive sputtering, and (6) radio-frequency (rf) sputtering.

1. Thermal Oxides

Under thermal oxides we include oxides formed by the oxidation of silicon and the glasses formed on and with such silicon dioxide by subsequent diffusion. The latter type glasses include phosphosilicates and borosilicates. A great deal has been written on the thermal oxidation of silicon both in steam and in dry oxygen. The oxidation kinetics has been covered quite thoroughly in the last two years and will not be covered in any detail here (13–17). Fairly complete references to earlier papers can be found in the work of Deal and Grove (13), Pliskin (14), and Burkhardt and Gregor (15). The steam oxidation follows a linear-parabolic law very closely; its parabolic nature becomes dominant with increased temperature and with increased film thickness as shown by Eq. (1):

$$X = [-k_1 + (k_1^2 + 4k_2 t)^{1/2}]/2 \qquad (1)$$

where X is the film thickness; k_1 a surface-sensitive parameter whose value is dependent on temperature, crystal orientation, and other surface-sensitive factors; k_2 is a parabolic constant arising from the diffusion of the oxidizing species through the oxide film and is dependent on temperature, pressure of the oxidizing gas, oxide composition, and oxide structure; and t is the time of oxidation (14). As the temperature increases k_2 increases and k_1 decreases, giving rise to a more parabolic oxidation rate. Similarly, as t increases the effect of k_1 on the thickness X decreases and the rate also approaches a parabolic representation. In the nonparabolic region crystal orientation plays a large role through the k_1 term (14). The oxidation rate is fastest along the $\langle 111 \rangle$ direction, and this is the crystal plane which has been used most in the making of silicon semiconductor devices. However, recent studies on surface state densities indicate that the $\langle 100 \rangle$ surface is more favorable in that the surface state density is significantly less along this orientation (18–25).

The dry-oxygen oxidation appears to be slightly more complicated because of an initial rapid rate of oxidation for thicknesses less than 300 A (13). According to Deal and Grove (13) a linear-parabolic relation similar to Eq. (1) describes the dry-oxygen oxidation providing the time t is increased by a factor τ whose value is temperature dependent. However, Burkhardt and Gregor (15) find that their data fit the equation $X = At^n$ (with $n > 0.5$) better than the parabolic-linear relation.

For most practical purposes, steam oxidation is used followed by a dry-oxygen cycle to remove silanol groups. The reason for the oxidation being carried out in steam is that the steam oxidation is much more rapid that the dry-oxygen oxidation as shown in Table I, and thus the desired film thicknesses are obtained in a shorter time. A shorter time is desirable so that the amount of junction movement during oxidation will be held to a minimum. Since the oxides formed by steam oxidation do contain some water in the

TABLE I

Rate Constants for Oxidation of Silicon in Dry Oxygen[a] and in Steam[b] at Atmospheric Pressure (Nonhighly Doped ⟨111⟩ Surface)

Temperature (°C)	Dry oxidation			Steam oxidation	
	k_1 (A)	k_2 (A²/min)	τ (min)	k_1 (A)	k_2 (A²/min)
1200	400	7.5×10^4	1.6	180	1.40×10^6
1100	900	4.5×10^4	4.6	760	0.941×10^6
1000	1650	1.95×10^4	22.2	2620	0.594×10^6
920	2350	0.817×10^4	84.0	6380	0.389×10^6

[a] See Deal and Grove (13).
[b] See Pliskin (14).

form of silanol groups, the oxidations are generally followed by a drying cycle in dry oxygen or dry nitrogen to remove the absorbed water. In some cases when thick films are not desired, the oxidations are carried out in dry oxygen.

Thermal oxides grown in this manner have been found to be very similar in chemical and physical properties to those of fused quartz. The thermal oxide has a very slightly higher refractive index which tends to approach the refractive index of fused quartz as the film thickness increases (26, 27). This has been attributed to a very thin silicon-enriched layer at the silicon-silicon dioxide interface, the effect of which decreases as the film thickness increases (27). However, Archer (28) reports a refractive index for dry oxygen which is very slightly less than that for fused quartz. Because of the chemical and water stability and inert nature of films of thermal oxides, they have often been used as comparison standards in evaluating silica films formed by other techniques (28–40).

An unusual type of low-temperature silicon oxidation was observed by Ligenza (40). The oxidation is claimed to be caused by negatively charged oxygen ions penetrating the oxide film. The ions are produced in an oxygen plasma excited by a 2450-MHz microwave power generator. The oxidation rate appears to be parabolic with time and is both pressure and temperature dependent. Films as thick as 6000 A can be grown in one hour at temperatures below 300°C. The films were not evaluated in detail but appear to be relatively good silicon dioxide.

Accelerated oxidation of silicon at relatively low temperatures (~600–800°C) by exposure of the silicon to air or oxygen in the presence of PbO has been reported (41, 42). Evaluation (29) of similar films using infrared spectroscopy, refractive index, and etch rates indicate the film to be lead silicate with 60 wt % PbO, the high concentration of which would be unsatisfactory with regard to water stability and expansion coefficient matching. Tokuyama (*43*, *44*) carried out the catalytic oxidation of silicon after having evaporated lead films on bare silicon or on a thin layer of silicon dioxide. The refractive indices of these films also indicated lead silicate with a high PbO content.

In semiconductor device processing a phosphosilicate glass is often formed on top of the thermal oxide layer during phosphorus diffusion. This phosphosilicate glass will form when either $POCl_3$, P_2O_5, or other phosphorus compounds in an oxidizing atmosphere are used as diffusion sources. During the diffusion P_2O_5 reacts with the top layer of silicon dioxide to form a phosphosilicate layer over the remaining silicon dioxide (*45*, *46*). This phosphosilicate layer has very desirable electrical properties as will be discussed later.

When the diffusion source is B_2O_3 or a compound which will form B_2O_3 during diffusion, then a borosilicate glass is formed on the silicon dioxide (*45*). This borosilicate glass is similar to other type borosilicate glasses formed by rf sputtering or by fusing borosilicate powders. On the other hand, if a source is used which does not give the B_2O_3 but is only elemental boron then a borosilicate glass does not form on the SiO_2 (*47*).

Although under proper care the silica films formed from oxidation of silicon can be very pure and stable, there is a great interest in lower-temperature methods of formation. In many cases to obtain reasonable film thicknesses the oxidation must be carried out at temperatures and times which would result in significant junction movement and thus lower-temperature methods of formation are desired. Furthermore, external insulator deposition techniques are desired to deposit diffusion barriers on semiconductors other than silicon. In addition, external deposition techniques are desired for passivation and insulation after metalization. Since SiO_2 is the simplest of various stable inorganic glasses, films of SiO_2 formed by various deposition techniques, such as evaporation, pyrolytic decomposition, and sputtering, have been emphasized. Due to its very high softening point, about 1600°C, it is not practical to apply it by fusing a deposited powder. However, due to its simplicity, it is the easiest glass to form and to study in evaluating various low-temperature deposition techniques. Generally, if a poor-quality silica film is obtained by a particular low-temperature deposition process, then it is rather doubtful that with a more complicated mixed glass system a good quality film can be obtained by the same deposition process. With this philosophy in mind, we have limited the number of glasses and deposition techniques evaluated in detail. Thus, in evaluating mixed glasses, such as aluminosilicates, borosilicates, and boroaluminosilicates, we have emphasized fused glass films and rf-sputtered films.

2. Vacuum Evaporation

Vacuum evaporation techniques can be classified according to the means used to supply the energy necessary to evaporate the source material. In the following discussion we use the subdivisions of thermal evaporation, electron gun evaporation, and flash evaporation.

Straight thermal evaporation should be limited to the simplest of glasses, such as silicon monoxide, due to the tendency of glass decomposition and nonuniform volatility of the glass components (*48*). Even a simple glass such as SiO_2 will decompose to form a film of silicon monoxide if evaporated thermally as will be discussed later.

In electron gun evaporation the target is bombarded by high-energy electrons which supply the energy necessary to evaporate the target material. The amount of decomposition or nonuniform evaporation of the original source is less in this case than with thermal evaporation and films can be deposited at rates as high as 6000 A/min (*49*). However, even the simplest glasses (such as SiO_2) deposited by this technique at deposition rates of 1300 to 2000 A/min on 400°C substrates are of poor quality, showing significant porosity, strain, and absorbed water (*29, 35, 50a*). It is thus doubtful that other stable glasses will produce high-quality films unless they are deposited at substrate temperatures approaching the annealing point of the mixed glass system.

Flash evaporation should be more favorable than straight thermal evaporation with regard to inhomogeneity; however, the fast evaporation rate should produce a poor-quality film. Generally speaking, the porosity and strain in a deposited film will increase with increased deposition rate, decreased arrival energy, and decreased substrate temperature. Flash evaporation could include evaporation produced by laser bombardment. Recently, Schwarz and Tourtellotte reported the deposition of $SrTiO_3$ and $BaTiO_3$ in a vacuum of 10^{-6} to 10^{-7} Torr at rates of 10^5 to 10^6 A/sec made possible by a high-intensity laser beam (*50b*). They claimed that under certain conditions they obtained films of the same chemical composition as the source material. We are unaware of any detailed evaluations available on the quality of glass films formed by this technique.

3. Pyrolytic Decomposition and Pyrolytic Reaction

The decomposition of alkoxysilanes or the reaction of various silanes to form SiO_2 films has been studied in detail in recent years (*29, 31–34, 36, 38, 39, 51–58*). The most common technique has involved the decomposition of tetraethoxysilane or ethyltriethoxysilane at 600 to 800°C. At the higher temperatures (750–800°C) Jordan (*51*) had observed the films to be black presumably due to incorporation of carbon. Klerer (*31*) obtained good-quality silica films at temperatures as high as 900°C with better insurance of surface decomposition by impinging the alkoxysilane vapor (with its carrier gas) on a heated silicon wafer. In his detailed study on actual furnace decomposition (where the wafer and vapor are essentially at the same temperature as opposed to the surface decomposition process) he had shown that with ethyltriethoxysilane no films form from 250 to 600°C. The films formed at temperatures less than 250°C were very porous and contained a significant quantity of organic matter.

Tetraethoxysilane (TEOS) can be used to form silica films at temperatures below 600°C by using oxygen either as a carrier gas (*38*) or from an rf-induced oxygen plasma (*56–58*). Alt *et al.* (*56*) claim that oxygen is necessary in the plasma process only when the oxygen to silicon ratio is low. Secrist and Mackenzie (*58*), in their investigation of the films formed by the decomposition of TEOS with oxygen from an rf plasma, found silicic acid as a major constituent of those films formed at lower temperatures (below 290°C under certain operating conditions).

Silica films have also been formed by the hydrolysis of $SiCl_4$ to form SiO_2 by the reaction $SiCl + 2H_2O \rightarrow SiO_2 + 4HCl$. This reaction can take place at fairly low temperatures, but give then a poor quality film. Steinmaier and Bloem (*53*) have overcome this difficulty by utilizing the water-gas reaction

$$CO_2 + H_2 \rightleftharpoons H_2O + CO$$

which occurs at elevated temperatures only and, therefore, can be confined in an epitaxial reactor to the vicinity of the substrate which is heated inductively to a temperature in the 1000–1300°C range. Since epitaxial silicon is normally formed from mixtures of $SiCl_4$ and H_2, one can deposit an SiO_2 film on the substrate in the same reactor simply by injecting a small quantity of CO_2 with the $SiCl_4$-H_2 mixture. This process is generally referred to as the "CO_2 process" or "Philips' process." Steinmaier and Bloem reported deposition rates of 60 to 3300 A/min at temperatures of 1050 and 1250°C, respectively; whereas, Tung and Caffrey (*32*), with somewhat different process parameters, reported deposition rates of 100 to 1400 A/min for the same temperature ranges. MacKenna *et al.* (*55*) showed the deposition rates to be affected significantly by the flow rate, $SiCl_4$ concentration, and deposition time.

Rand (*36*) has lowered the reaction temperature of this type process by using NO instead of CO_2 as shown by Fig. 1. Lehman *et al.* (*54*) have lowered it even further by the use of NO_2. Both NO and NO_2 react with hydrogen to form water at lower temperatures than does CO_2. Furthermore, with the nitric oxides there are regions where the reaction is not as temperature sensitive (see Fig. 1) thus resulting in more uniform films on the substrate surface. Substitution of $SiBr_4$ for $SiCl_4$ also lowers the reaction temperature (*33, 36*).

Mixed glasses such as borosilicate, aluminosilicate, and boroaluminosilicate

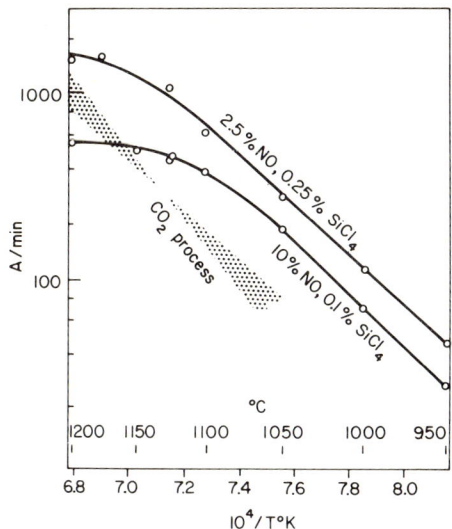

FIG. 1. Deposition rates of silica from the H_2-NO-$SiCl_4$ system [Rand (36)].

have also been formed by pyrolytic decomposition and/or pyrolytic reaction of alkoxy silanes, alkyl silanes, or other silanes with alkyl borates or other boron compounds and with alkyl aluminates or alkyl aluminum compounds with and without the presence of oxygen (59–64). Peterson et al. (60) deposited aluminosilicates and boroaluminosilicates at 200 to 400°C with rates up to 300 A/min. Accelerated power aging tests showed the beneficial effects of such films on planar transistors (61) and capacitors (59, 62). In the most detailed published paper on the preparation and properties of such films, Eversteijn reported the reaction of TEOS and triisobutyl aluminum (TIBAL) to form aluminosilicate films at 250 to 500°C (64). He found that the TIBAL had a catalytic effect on the decomposition of TEOS as shown in Table II.

Pyrolytic techniques have also been used for the deposition of phosphosilicate films by the reaction of wet oxygen with a mixture of $SiCl_4$ and $POCl_3$ at temperatures above 900°C (65). The presence of phosphosilicate was verified by the absorption band near 1330 cm^{-1} (66).

In pyrolytic decomposition and reaction processes water is a frequent reaction product, and the films themselves will thus often contain some silanol groups and possibly water. The amount present will increase with decreased deposition temperatures. It will also depend on the mechanics of film formation. The more the reaction in the gas phase is prevalent over surface decomposition, the more porous will be the film. The porosity and strain in the film will also tend to increase with increased deposition rate or decreased deposition temperature, for then the bonds between the atoms

TABLE II

THE GROWING RATE OF SILICA, ALUMINA, AND ALUMINA-SILICA FILMS
AT DIFFERENT TEMPERATURES[a,b]

Substrate temperature (°C)	Pyrolysis of TEOS (μ/hr)	Pyrolysis of TIBAL (μ/hr)	Pyrolysis of TEOS and TIBAL (μ/hr)
250	< 0.05	0.07	0.07
300	< 0.05	0.13	0.15
325	< 0.05	—	0.18
350	< 0.05	0.11	0.30
375	< 0.05	—	0.46
400	< 0.05	0.09	0.51
425	< 0.05	—	0.55
450	< 0.05	0.07	0.60
475	< 0.05	—	0.64
500	< 0.05	0.05	0.72

[a] From Eversteijn (64).
[b] Conditions: nitrogen with/without TEOS 270 ml/min,
argon with/without TIBAL 970 ml/min,
oxygen 1160 ml/min.

will not reach their best equilibrium position or lowest energy state. Since the presence of water can have deleterious effects on junction properties, these films should be examined closely for their water content and stress tested under high humidity conditions if they are not to be sealed from room ambient. In the infrared examination of films for silanol (67) or water content, precautions should be taken not to overlook weak absorption bands. This is accomplished by amplifying the spectrum of the sample in the 2.5–3.5-μ range while maintaining in the reference beam a dry film of the same thickness as the sample film to compensate for interference fringes caused by the sample film.

4. FUSED GLASSES FROM SEDIMENTED GLASS POWDERS

One of the simplest techniques for forming a glass film is by fusing sedimented colloidal (~ 0.1 μ particle size) glass applied by centrifugation from a suspension (68). We sometimes refer to it as the fused-frit or frit-firing method. With this technique, it is possible to obtain pinhole-free films of controlled composition and uniform thickness. The compacted powdered glass remaining after decanting the suspending fluid forms a continuous glass film on firing for five minutes at a temperature close to the glass softening point. This technique is well suited for mass production; however, there are several suspension properties which must be adequately controlled. They are the dielectric constant, viscosity, and volatility of the suspending medium and the particle size of the glass. Particular attention must be paid to the dielectric constant of the suspending medium. Suspensions are generally made with mixtures of ethyl acetate and isopropyl alcohol, the relative amounts of which depend on the type of glass and the glass particle size. Mixtures of other fluids can also be used to give similar dielectric constants. By use of a double-medium system in which the glass suspension is sedimented through a second more dense, relatively low dielectric constant medium, maximum film thickness uniformity can be obtained (68).

Using this technique glass films have been formed on oxidized silicon wafers at temperatures less than 500°C and as high as 1200°C, depending on the glass. If the films are fired in a dry ambient at the minimum temperature necessary to give a good glazed film, then the film composition will not be altered from that of the original glass. On fusing, the glass forms an excellent bond to the oxidized wafer surface by limited penetration of the glass into the oxide (69).

5. Reactive Sputtering

The sputtering process in which atoms or particles are ejected from a metal target due to high-energy ion bombardment can be used for the deposition of oxide glass films by sputtering in the presence of oxygen. Since the oxygen reacts with the sputtered metal to form metal oxides, this process is one example of reactive sputtering. The reactive sputtering process was reviewed as of 1953 by Holland and Siddall (70). More recently various sputtering processes have been reviewed by Maissel (8).

The reactive sputtering of silicon to form SiO_2 has been investigated quite thoroughly in recent years (30, 71–74). Sinclair and Peters (71) usually sputtered at pressures of 2.5×10^{-3} Torr at ~1800 volts. They showed increased deposition rates by diluting their oxygen with argon. A more thorough study on this effect and the effects of other sputtering parameters was done by Valletta et al. (30). These authors examined the physical and chemical properties of the sputtered SiO_2 films in detail as a function of the deposition rate, substrate temperature, and oxygen pressure. They found that the porosity and the water content of the films increased with increased deposition rate, decreased deposition temperature, and high oxygen pressure. Increased deposition rates were obtained by use of a magnetic field which presumably increased the electron and ion density of the plasma. The effect of oxygen concentration on the deposition rates with and without a magnetic field is shown in Figs. 2 and 3.

Alumina and mixed oxide glass films have also been obtained by reactive sputtering (71, 75–77). Sinclair and Peters (71, 76) deposited aluminosilicate

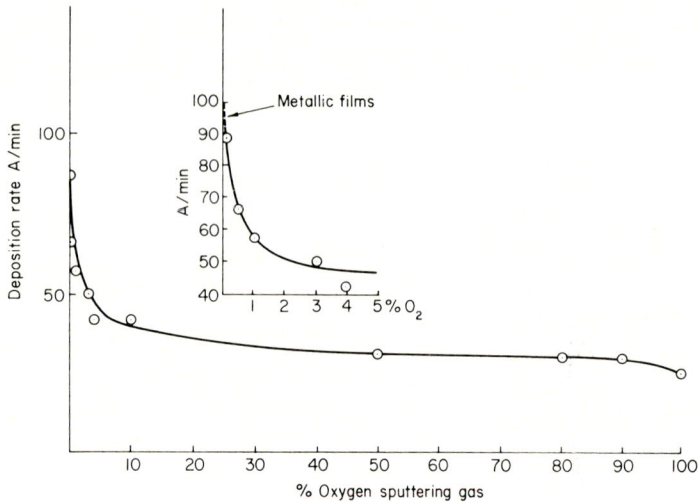

FIG. 2. Deposition rate versus percent oxygen in sputtering gas [Valletta (30)].

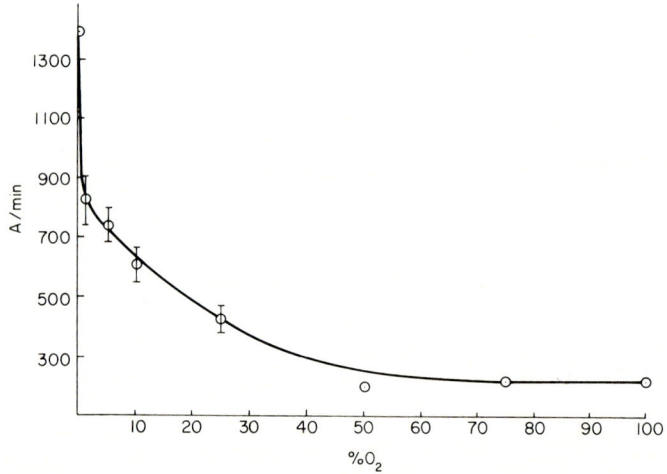

FIG. 3. Deposition rate versus percent oxygen in sputtering gas with magnetic field [Valletta (30)].

films by reactively sputtering from aluminum-silicon alloy cathodes and lead silicate films by reactively sputtering from a silicon cathode partially covered with lead foil.

6. RADIO-FREQUENCY SPUTTERING

Lodge and Stewart (78) showed that the deposits formed on the walls of high-frequency discharge tubes were caused by a sputtering-type process;

however, the importance of this discovery was not then realized. In a review article, Wehner (79) proposed the possibility of rf sputtering and later with his co-workers (80, 81) demonstrated its feasibility. Davidse and Maissel (8, 82–85) further developed the technique into a practical method for the deposition of insulating films. With an insulating target one cannot support a dc glow and, therefore, one cannot apply dc-sputtering methods to insulators. The extinction of the glow is caused by the accumulation of positive charges on the target surface which cannot be dissipated. However, with the application of a high-frequency field, the surface of such a target remains in effect negatively charged because the positive ions in the plasma cannot follow the high-frequency field due to their slow mobilities, whereas the electrons can. By rf sputtering, Davidse and Maissel (84) were able to deposit films from a fused quartz target at a deposition rate of 30 A/sec. The deposition rate is dependent upon the electrode potential, rf input power, temperature, and the composition of the glass target. Fig. 4 shows the effect of substrate

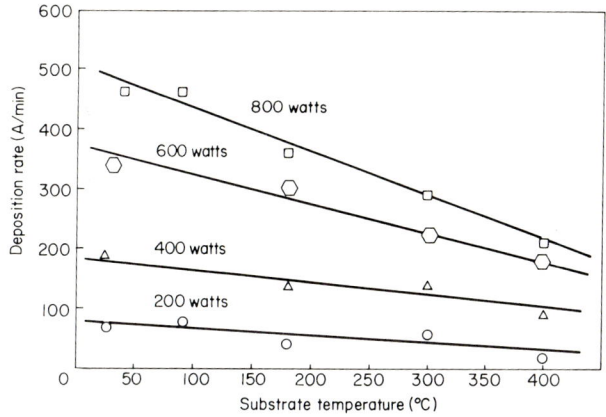

FIG. 4. Deposition rate versus substrate temperature for various rf input power levels (permanent magnets, axial field intensity at center of target—100 gauss) [Davidse and Maissel (82)].

temperature and rf input power on the deposition rate of fused quartz (82). Various types of glasses have been rf sputtered successfully by Davidse and Maissel (82–85), and the properties of these films were examined in detail by Pliskin et al. (37).

7. Pyrolytic and Sputtered Silicon Nitride

Very recently there has been a great deal of interest in silicon nitride films because of their desirable physical and chemical properties. Since the field is still new, there are very few published papers and therefore this subject will be covered only briefly. However, many detailed papers should appear in the near future as evidenced by the many related presentations at the 1966 Philadelphia meeting of the Electrochemical Society.

The first reported formation of actual silicon nitride films was by the reaction of SiH_4 and NH_3 in an rf discharge (86). Silicon nitride films can also be prepared by the pyrolytic reaction of SiH_4 with NH_3 in the temperature range of 750 to 1100°C (87). At lower temperatures films are obtained by rf and dc reactive sputtering of a silicon cathode in pure nitrogen (88, 89). Silicon nitride appears to be a promising insulating glass which will get more emphasis in the future.

III. Evaluation of Physical and Chemical Properties

1. General Use of Infrared Spectroscopy

Compositional and structural evaluation of glass films can be made most easily by use of infrared spectroscopy (39). By comparing the intensities of various infrared absorption bands one can determine relative amounts of various components in the glasses.

Common glass components which give rise to strong absorption bands in the infrared are B_2O_3 and SiO_2. Since many of the glasses of interest are borosilicate glasses, it is desirable to know the relative amounts of B_2O_3 and SiO_2 in the glass. In general, chemical analysis is not useful for such films. An example of the results obtainable by infrared spectroscopy is shown in Fig. 5, where Spectrum A is that of an alumino borosilicate film rf sputtered from a fire-polished alumino borosilicate glass plate (General Electric GSC-1 glass), and Spectrum B is of a film sputtered from a target of GSC-1 whose outer layer had been ground away. It is quite obvious from a comparison of the intensity of the B-O band at 1390 cm^{-1} that the film corresponding to Spectrum A is boron deficient. It thus can be presumed that the outer layer of the GSC-1 target was boron deficient. The target as a whole was not, however, since the spectrum of a sedimented and fused film formed from a ground portion of the target was similar to the spectra of other fused GSC-1 glass films. That the boron composition is low near the surface of fired glass objects has been demonstrated on fused glass films (68) which were fired for extended periods at high temperatures and then analyzed by P-etch[1] rate techniques (45). The analysis showed that at elevated temperatures the boron can out-diffuse leaving a boron-deficient layer near the surface. This will be discussed in more detail later.

Other common components such as lead oxide and alkali cannot be determined easily by infrared spectroscopy, although they do have an influence

---

[1] P-etch consists of 15 parts by volume hydrofluoric acid (49%), 10 parts by volume nitric acid (70%), and 300 parts water (45).

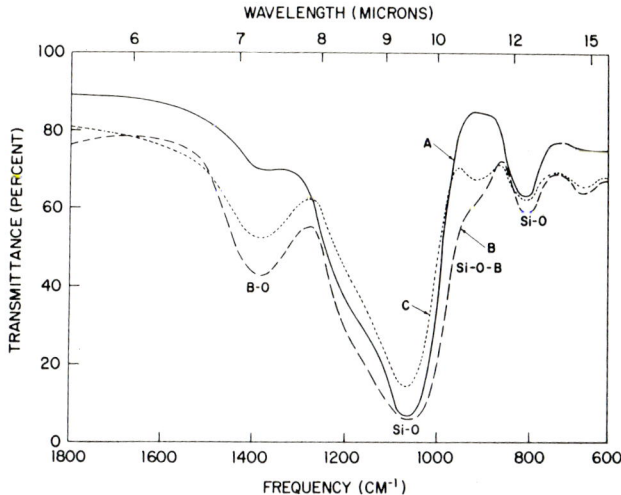

FIG. 5. Infrared spectra of: A, film of General Electric GSC-1 glass rf sputtered from a fire-polished GSC-1 plate; B, film sputtered from same plate after removal of the outer layer of the plate by grinding; C, film sputtered from same plate after grinding and run-in period [Pliskin et al. (37)].

on the relative shapes and intensities of various absorption bands. An increase in lead oxide content shifts the Si-O stretching band to longer wavelengths and makes the band broader, resulting in an increased absolute (or integrated) band intensity (39). This shift has been observed on fused glasses of varied lead to silicon ratio. The technique is not very sensitive but can be used for screening glasses as to their relative lead oxide content.

A shift, broadening, and intensity increase of the Si-O absorption band similar to the one due to the addition of lead oxide was also seen when other metal oxides were introduced into the glass (39). In some borosilicates a small addition of cations will shift the Si-O band to higher frequency, which is indicative of increased polymerization of SiO_4 tetrahedra (90–94). On the other hand, the specific intensity of the B-O band near 1380 cm^{-1} decreases with the addition of monovalent and divalent metal oxides. In addition to the shift and broadening of the 9-μ Si-O absorption band, the absorption near 11 μ appears to be weakened very markedly by the addition of cations.

2. Optical Techniques

Refractive indices and film thicknesses can be measured accurately and simply by the use of Vamfo (26, 27, 95, 96), which is a specially constructed interference microscope. When properly used, this nondestructive technique is the simplest, fastest, and most accurate method of pin-pointing and measuring film thickness changes of transparent films on silicon. The refractive index is an important physical property which is useful for determining the composition and density of glass films (29). For example, the per cent composition of lead oxide in the film has a strong influence on the refractive index. Other compounds such as aluminum oxide also influence the refractive index, but to a more limited extent. The refractive index changes also with the oxygen stoichiometry in the glass film (29). For example, glass films which are oxygen deficient will show higher refractive indices than corresponding films which are completely oxidized. A decrease in density due to porosity will also result in a decreased refractive index. Thus, the refractive index can give leads as to composition, oxygen deficiency and density.

Accurate measurements of thicknesses are important for determining subsequent densification on heating of the glass films, for determining the stability of the glass film when subjected to various ambient atmospheres, and for determining its etch stability and etching characteristics.

3. Etching Techniques

As Pliskin and Lehman (29) have shown, selective etching is useful for determining the strain and density in deposited silicon dioxide films. The same can be said for various types of glass films. In addition to affecting strain and porosity, the composition of the glass film also influences its etch rate (39). For example, glasses which are rich in either lead or boron have faster P-etch rates than glasses with no lead or boron oxide. Also, as far as other common compositional components of glasses are concerned, the P-etch rate of a glass can be decreased by increased alumina or silica content, and, in the case of some active deposition techniques, by increased oxygen deficiency. The decrease in P-etch rate with oxygen deficiency has been shown by comparing the etch rates of various rf-sputtered glass films (37).

Similarly, the use of P-etch for determining composition has yielded interesting results for phosphosilicate glass formed at the surface of SiO_2 films which had been either exposed to an elevated post heating cycle for a "drive-in" diffusion of the phosphosilicate or had been reoxidized following the phosphorus diffusion. The etch rate was slow at the outer surface of the phosphosilicate, then faster within the interior of the phosphosilicate layer, and finally reached the low value characteristic of pure SiO_2 (45). The slow etch rate near the surface is due to the out-diffusion of the phosphorus from the phosphosilicate during the post heating cycle. At the same time, the phosphorus concentration within the bulk phosphosilicate layer decreases, and with it its P-etch rate. In these studies P-etch was found to be a better etch for delineating phosphosilicate layers than conventional buffered etches (45).

The same can be said for borosilicate glass fired at a high temperature. Since during firing the boron near the surface of the borosilicate out-diffuses, the etch rate near the surface is again lowered as shown in the P-etch rate plot of Fig. 6. The sample material was General Electric GSC-1 borosilicate

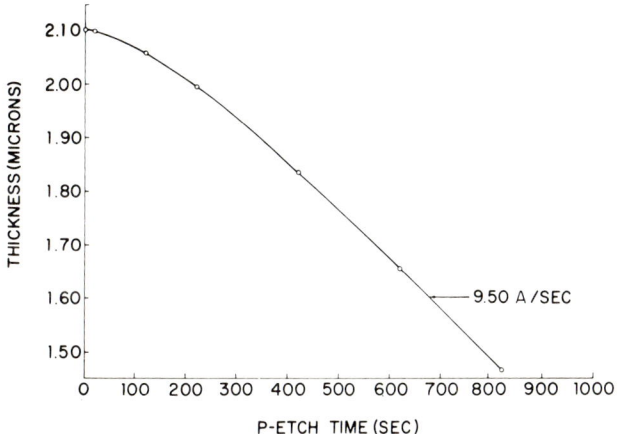

FIG. 6. P-etch rate plot of fused GSC-1 glass fired 5 min in dry O_2 (~1195°C) [Pliskin (39)].

glass made by fusing sedimented powder through a five-minute firing in oxygen at 1195°C (39). The slower etch rate near the surface (less than 5 A/sec for the first 500 A) is due to the out-diffusion of some of the boron. It was necessary to remove about 4000 A of glass before reaching a steady etch rate of 9.5 A/sec. This glass was fired in dry oxygen; had it been fired in a moist ambient, there would have been much more out-diffusion and leaching of the boron, and the etch rate would have been even slower at the surface. In the case of Pyrex, where a good glazed film can be formed by firing the sedimented powder at about 820–840°C, no significant boron out-diffusion was detected when fired in a dry ambient (39). However, if the powder is fired in a moist ambient, there is some loss in boron content, depending on the firing temperature.

4. APPLICATION OF TECHNIQUES

a. Infrared Transmission and Reflection Spectra. The spectra shown in Fig. 5 were the spectra of glass films formed on infrared transparent (high resistivity), thick, silicon substrates (12, 27, 29, 39). Transmission spectra of glasses are simpler than reflection spectra, but require thin samples because of the very strong absorption bands exhibited by glasses. With the advent of good techniques for depositing and forming thin glass films on silicon substrates, such films are now much more easily obtainable than in the past. Reflection spectra are more complicated due to reflections at more than one interface and due to the strong variation of the real part of the refractive index in the vicinity of the absorption band. Because of these effects weak bands are often less pronounced (39). For the study of actual device wafers, however, where the doping levels make the wafers opaque to infrared radiation, reflection spectroscopy must be employed. Using the latter, Murray and Goldsmith (34) have seen the same types of variation on heating deposited SiO_2 films as Pliskin and Lehman (29) have observed using transmission spectroscopy. Corl et al. (97) have made use of reflection spectroscopy for detecting phosphosilicate in actual device wafers as shown in Fig. 7.

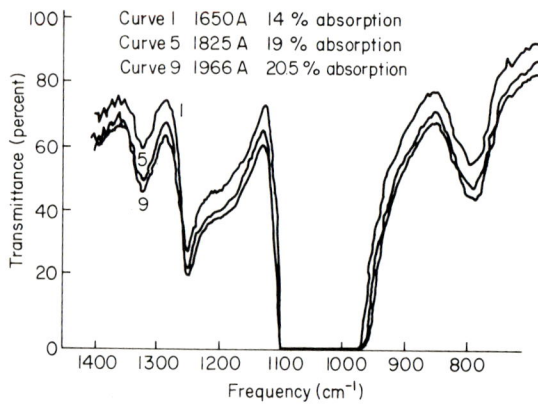

FIG. 7. 5X-amplified reflection spectra showing absorptions with small $P = 0$ differences [Corl et al. (97)].

Phosphosilicate is important for device passivation as will be discussed later in the section on the electrical properties of glass films. From transmission infrared spectra of phosphosilicate films, Pliskin (66) had concluded that there was greater polymerization of the SiO_4 tetrahedra in phosphosilicate than in silica thus leading to a tighter and more dense structure which would hinder the diffusion of impurity ions through the film. However, this suggestion was offered as a possible explanation for the mechanism of phosphosilicate stabilization only for those cases where the device degradation was caused by ion migration through the oxide.

b. *Structural Differences between Fused and rf Sputtered Glasses*
(*1*) *General Electric GSC-1 glass and effect of annealing.* A detailed study

was made of rf-sputtered glass films and how they compare with sedimented and fused glass films with regard to composition and structure (*37, 49*). In making these comparisons, the effect of substrate temperature and annealing on the structure of the sputtered films was considered. Figure 8 shows the

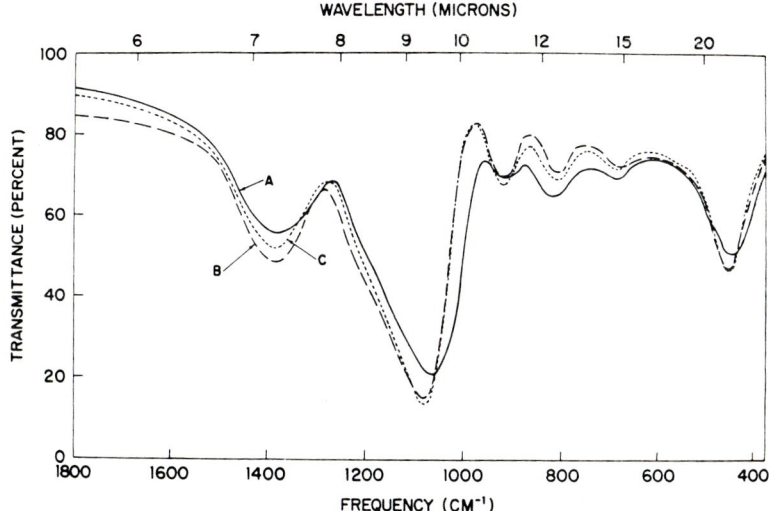

FIG. 8. Infrared spectra of: A, rf-sputtered GSC-1 film on ~100°C silicon substrate (0.809 μ thick); B, GSC-1 film formed by fusing sedimented powder (0.788 μ thick); C, GSC-1 film from "A" after heating in dry N_2 for 5 min at 965°C (0.786 μ thick) [Pliskin et al. (*37*)].

spectrum of a 0.809-μ-thick GSC-1 film rf sputtered onto a 100°C silicon substrate. Spectrum B is that of a fused sedimented powder of nearly the same thickness (0.778 μ). In the rf-sputtered film the Si-O-B band at 920 cm^{-1} is significantly weaker than that of the fused glass film. This relation is similar to the difference found between the infrared spectra of powdered borosilicates and those of fused glass films (*39*). However, the absorption band in the sputtered film, due to Si-O stretching, is at a lower frequency than the fused glass film absorption band, whereas that of the powdered film was at a higher frequency. This difference is attributed to the fact that the sputtered film is not quite as dense as that of either the powdered or the fused film. The shift to lower frequency and broadening of the 1100 cm^{-1} band is probably caused by a slight oxygen deficiency in addition to some bond strain and some slight decrease in film density (*29*). After heating the sputtered film at 965°C for five minutes, Spectrum C was obtained. This spectrum is practically the same as that of the fused glass film. It was, therefore, concluded that the sputtered film had practically the same composition as the fused glass film. This is confirmed by the observation that both films had the same *P*-etch rate and the same refractive index after annealing.

(2) *Corning 191 CP glass and effect of annealing.*[2] Similar results as with the borosilicate films of GSC-1 glass have been obtained with a calcium aluminosilicate glass (Fig. 9). Spectrum A is that of a 0.889-μ film of Corning

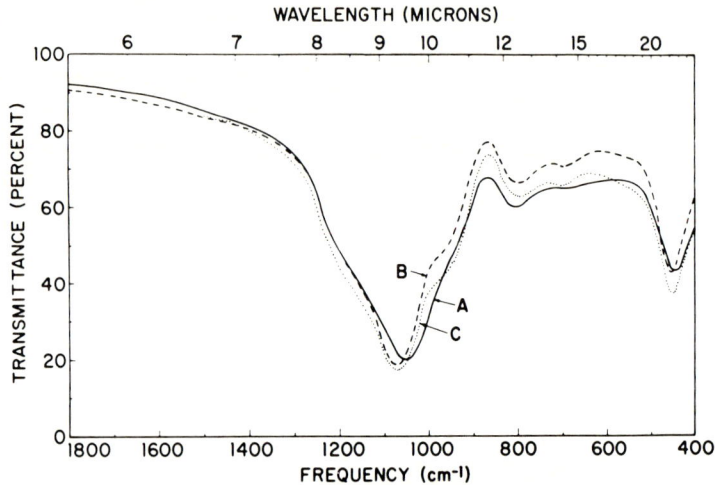

FIG. 9. Infrared spectra of: A, Corning 191 CP glass rf sputtered on ~100°C silicon substrate (0.889 μ thick); B, film of 191 CP glass formed by fusing sedimented powder (0.75 μ thick); C, film of 191 CP from "A" after heating in dry N_2 for 10 min at 780°C (0.887 μ thick) [Pliskin (*39*)].

191 CP glass deposited at ~100°C. Spectrum B was obtained from a fused 191 CP glass film formed by heating sedimented glass powder. In addition to the pronounced difference between the Si-O stretching bands near 1070 cm^{-1}, the sputtered film shows practically no absorption at 950 cm^{-1}, whereas there is a distinct shoulder in Spectrum B of the fused film. This absorption is attributed to the stretching vibration of Si-O$^-$, the presence of which is due to calcium cations in the glass structure. After heating the sputtered 191 CP film in nitrogen for ten minutes at 780°C, Spectrum C was obtained. For all practical purposes, the spectrum of the heated rf-sputtered glass is the same as that of the fused glass, and thus it is concluded that the glass films are the same. In this case, the rf-sputtered glass was heated at a temperature significantly below the glass annealing temperature of 884°C to form the identical structure.

[2] See Pliskin (*39*).

(3) *Rf-sputtered SiO₂ films and effect of substrate temperature.* Rf-sputtered SiO_2 films deposited at a substrate temperature of 450°C resemble thermally grown SiO_2 films more closely than do films deposited at 100°C. This is shown in Table III where two rf-sputtered SiO_2 films are compared to

TABLE III

Comparison of rf-Sputtered SiO_2 Films with a Thermally Grown SiO_2 Film
(~ 5700 A)[a]

Sample	Substrate temp. (°C)	Optical density OH at 3600 cm^{-1}	Si-O stretching absorption bands			R.I. at 5461 A
			Position ν_a	Half-Width ν_a	Position ν_s	
rf SiO_2	100	0.0026	1057	107	816	1.476
rf SiO_2	450	0.0004	1072	98	813	1.473
Thermal (DWD)	980	—	1087	81	805	1.461$_8$

[a] From Pliskin et al. (37).

thermally grown SiO_2 films of the same thickness (37). Note that the Si-O band position and half-width for the higher-temperature film is more similar to that of the thermally grown SiO_2. It was also found that the P-etch rate of the higher-temperature film was closer to that of thermally grown SiO_2, its P-etch rate being approximately 4.6 A/sec, whereas the 100°C temperature film had a P-etch rate of 10.2 A/sec. The P-etch rate of thermally grown SiO_2 is 2.0_2 A/sec at 25°C (29). Similarly, rf-sputtered films of other glasses become more similar to the fused glass films as the substrate temperature increases.

The slightly higher refractive index than that observed with thermal SiO_2 can be attributed to a slight oxygen deficiency (see Section III,4f) combined with the entrapment or occlusion of gases or volatile impurities in the sputtered films (37).

c. *Boiling Water and Humidity Tests on Fused Glass Films.* The evaluation procedures can best be shown by selecting a few specific glasses for a detailed discussion. The fused glasses first to be discussed are Corning 7050 and Pemco S1117.

(1) *Corning 7050.* This borosilicate glass was selected to show that thickness measurements and weight determinations have limited usefulness for evaluating the water stability of glasses (11). Three 7050 glazed wafers were subjected to boiling water for one hour. In each case there was no decrease in the glass film thickness. In fact, the thickness of one film (0.76 μ thick)

increased 60 A and two other films (1.53 μ and 1.61 μ) increased about 100 A. If these were the only measurements made, it would be concluded that there was a slight amount of water pickup. This would be a gross understatement as shown by the spectra in Fig. 10. The intensity decrease of the

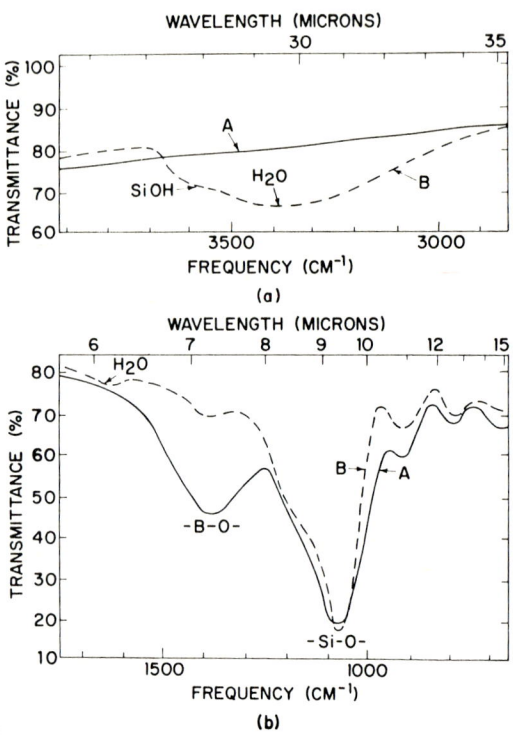

FIG. 10. Effect of boiling water on the spectrum of a 0.76-μ film of Corning 7050 glass: (a) short-wavelength region; (b) long-wavelength region; A, before boiling; B, after boiling for 1 hr. [Pliskin (*11*)].

1390 cm^{-1} B-O absorption band shows that 85% of the boron was leached out of the glass. The absorption bands at 3400 and 1630 cm^{-1} show the presence of a considerable amount of water in the glass film. The 3630 cm^{-1} band is due to hydrogen-bonded silanol groups (SiOH) on the surface of the newly made porous glass. Thicker films (1.6 μ and 3.2 μ) subjected to one-hour boiling water were also examined by infrared spectroscopy with the same catastrophic results. Even heating at 770°C for five minutes was insufficient for removal of all the surface hydroxyl groups. The heating generally caused crazing of the thicker films. These results show that such a glass film would probably be unsatisfactory for silicon transistor and diode passivation.

(2) *Pemco S1117.* Pemco S1117 is a zinc borosilicate glass. It was chosen as an example of a glass which, according to its infrared spectrum, shows no preferential leaching of its components and shows no water pickup, but does lose about 900 A on boiling in water for one hour (*11*). The infrared spectrum of a 0.71-μ film before and after boiling in water is shown in Fig. 11. Although it does show a significant decrease in film thickness due to

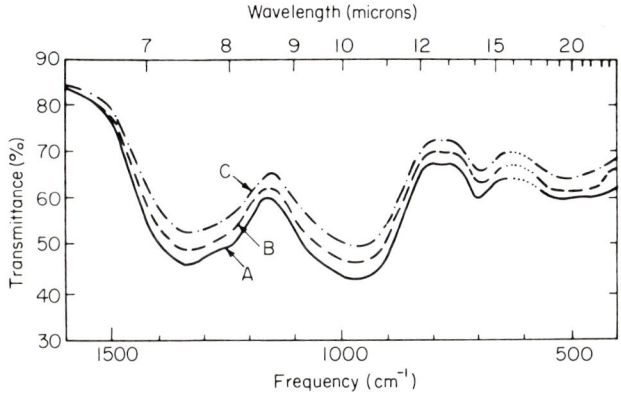

FIG. 11. Effect of boiling water on a 0.71-μ film of Pemco S1117 glass: A, before boiling; B, after 1 hr boiling; C, after 2 hr boiling [Pliskin (*11*)].

water attack, the lack of preferential leaching or water retention makes it a more desirable glass than one which either retains water or shows considerable leaching of glass components.

(3) *Other glasses.* Many other glasses such as Corning 3320, 7740, 1715, and 191 CP; General Electric GSC-1; and other high-softening-point glasses, have been evaluated (*11*). These glasses, when properly fired, are generally much more stable than the glasses previously discussed, showing no significant water retention, component leaching, or thickness losses (less than 100 A) on boiling in water. In some cases, the water stability of the glass films is dependent on the firing conditions. An example of this phenomenon is Corning 7720, which when fired for five minutes at 770°C showed a thickness loss on boiling in water of 200 A. A similar sample fired for ten minutes at 770°C nearly completely disintegrated on boiling in water.

d. Effect of Moisture on rf-Sputtered Glass Films. Generally, the glasses which resist water dissolution and component leaching in fused films will show similar stability in rf-sputtered films of the same glass. Some differences in the glass film properties occur, depending on the thermal history of the deposited films (37). Similarly, there are some differences in the water stability of rf-sputtered films, depending on the deposition temperature of the film. The results obtained with rf-sputtered SiO_2 films is a good example of this. Pliskin (12) examined the water stability of rf-sputtered SiO_2 films by use of infrared spectroscopy. The results show that films which have been deposited at low substrate temperatures ($\leq 100°C$) picked up several times as much water as films which have been deposited at higher temperatures ($\geq 300°C$). These results are consistent with other data which show that the low-temperature films are somewhat less dense, have more bond straining, have initially more hydrogen-bonded silanol groups, and are more dissimilar from thermal oxide than the high-temperature films (37). All these features are demonstrated in Figs. 12 and 13. In Fig. 12, Spectrum A is that of an rf-sputtered SiO_2 film which was deposited at 100°C. The spectrum shows a very weak absorption band at 3650 cm^{-1} which is attributed to strongly hydrogen-bonded SiOH groups in the sputtered film. Spectrum B was obtained after exposure of the sample to 85°C and 85% relative humidity for five days. This spectrum shows a large increase in the amount of absorbed water and

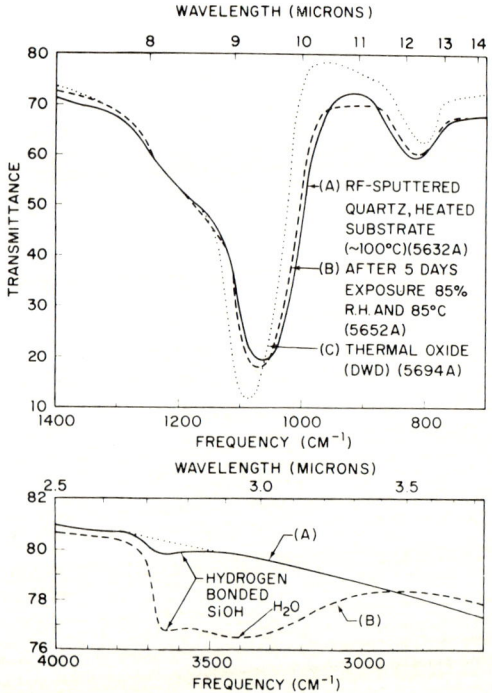

FIG. 12. The effect of moisture on a rf-sputtered SiO_2 film deposited at 100°C [Pliskin (12)].

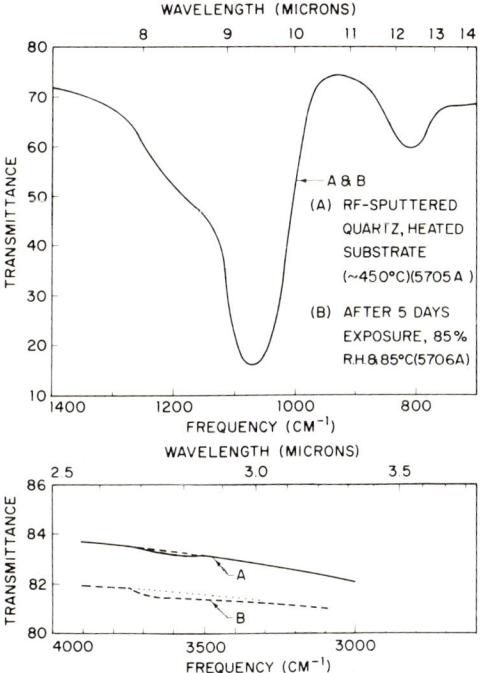

Fig. 13. The effect of moisture on a rf-sputtered SiO_2 film deposited at 450°C [Pliskin (12)].

hydrogen-bonded silanol groups. (The actual presence of water was proven by the observation of the absorption band at 1618 cm^{-1} due to the scissors (deformation) vibration of H_2O. This wavelength region is not covered in Fig. 12.) It should be noted that the region of the OH stretching bands near 3 μ is amplified fivefold from the remaining spectrum. The amount of absorbed water, therefore, is not as great as one would at first conclude. For comparison, a thermal oxide grown at 975°C in a sequence of dry oxygen, steam, and dry oxygen (DWD) is shown. In comparing Fig. 12 with Fig. 13 it is seen that the amount of water absorbed in the 450°C substrate sample after exposure for five days in the high humidity chamber is much less than that in the low-temperature sputtered film. The spectra also show the greater stability of the higher-temperature films in that the humidity exposure causes no change in the Si-O absorption band near 1070 cm^{-1}. The shift of the 1060 cm^{-1} Si-O absorption band for the low-temperature film can be attributed to some strain relief in the Si-O bonding [see section III,e(3)].

It was also found that exposure to 85% relative humidity and 85°C for five days had a greater effect on the amount of moisture pickup than did boiling water for one hour (*12*). Boiling, in fact, resulted only in one third the water content of the long-term 85°C exposure. In fused glasses, on the other hand, the short boiling water test had been found to be more severe.

Sputtered glasses such as 191 CP, GSC-1, and other relatively high-temperature glasses show very little water pickup on exposure to high humidity and high temperature or to boiling water. When glasses in the fused state are normally stable to such chemical agents as concentrated nitric acid or sodium hydroxide, they have also been found to be stable when properly sputtered.

e. Evaporated SiO and SiO_2 Films

(*1*) *SiO evaporation.* A significant amount of work on the optical properties of evaporated SiO films and on films of higher oxidation states obtained by evaporating under oxidizing "vacuum" conditions has been done by Hass and Ritter and their co-workers (*98–104*). Because of interest as a possible insulating coating for thin-film circuitry and component devices, others have also examined the optical, electrical, and mechanical properties of evaporated SiO films (*29, 105–107*). The essentials have been reviewed by Drummeter and Hass (*104*) and by Schwartz and Berry (*6*) in a previous volume of this series and will not be covered in detail here. An important point is that the stoichiometry of evaporated silicon oxide films is a strong function of the evaporating parameters and can be followed by observation of the Si-O stretching band frequency. Parameters which determine the type of film formed are temperature, rate of evaporation, and residual gas pressure. With good vacuum conditions and relatively fast evaporations, SiO films are formed for which the Si-O stretching band occurs near 1000 cm^{-1} as opposed to the main Si-O stretching band near 1085 cm^{-1} and a weaker band near 800 cm^{-1} for SiO_2 films. With slower deposition rates and poor vacuum conditions films of higher oxidation states can be formed including an intermediate type of oxide which gives rise to a strong absorption band near 1040 cm^{-1} and a weaker intensity band near 870 cm^{-1} (*29, 102*). This oxide is believed to be Si_2O_3, and it has a refractive index intermediate between those for SiO_2 and SiO (*102*).

In the case of deposition on heated substrates, decomposition of the SiO to form Si and Si_2O_3 can occur (*29*). The measured refractive index of one such film was found to be 2.02 at 5460 A, a value higher than the 1.99 of pure SiO, and this despite the fact that its infrared spectrum indicated the presence of the two higher oxides. This indicates the presence of Si, probably because the substrate temperature of 400°C resulted in the thermal decomposition of SiO into a mixture of SiO, Si_2O_3, SiO_2, and Si.

It should be noted that no evidence has been obtained for oxygen deficiency in the pyrolytic SiO_2 films studied (*29*). After densification, the refractive indices of the pyrolytic films were comparable to those obtained for thermally grown oxides (1.463 compared to 1.462) and the spectra showed no evidence of Si_2O_3.

(2) *Thermal evaporation of SiO_2.* In the straight thermal evaporation of SiO_2 under good vacuum conditions (29) one obtains films of SiO rather than SiO_2 as shown in Fig. 14. This result is not surprising in view of the fact

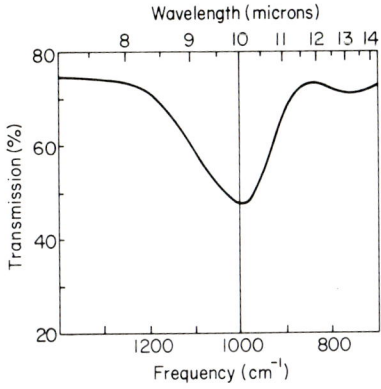

FIG. 14. SiO formed by the thermal evaporation of SiO_2 [Pliskin and Lehman (29)].

that the SiO_2-SiO equilibrium highly favors SiO at the elevated temperatures necessary for thermal evaporation of SiO_2 (105, 108a,b).

(3) *Electron gun evaporation of SiO_2 and Al_2O_3.* In the evaluation of various low-temperature-deposited SiO_2 films, very interesting results with regard to electron gun evaporated films were obtained (35). It has been found that these films are more reactive with water than most other low-temperature SiO_2 films. This reactivity was easily seen by infrared spectroscopy and by etching techniques.

The reactivity of electron gun evaporated films is shown quite clearly in the spectral regions given by Fig. 15. Spectrum A is the spectrum of the electron gun evaporated film within one day after deposition. The film was deposited on a silicon substrate held at 400°C. Spectrum B is of the same film after it was exposed for 24 days to a temperature of 85°C and to 85% relative humidity. Spectrum C finally was observed after densification of this film at 983°C. In the OH stretching region of the spectrum, a significant pickup of water is shown by the increase in the absorption of Spectrum B over that of Spectrum A in the 3-μ region. In addition, the absorption band due to Si-O stretching at 1055 cm^{-1} has shifted significantly to higher frequency, and it has undergone a pronounced decrease in bandwidth. In previous studies of pyrolytic oxide films deposited at temperatures greater than 650°C, it had been found that this absorption band would decrease in bandwidth and shift to higher frequencies whenever the porosity in the film

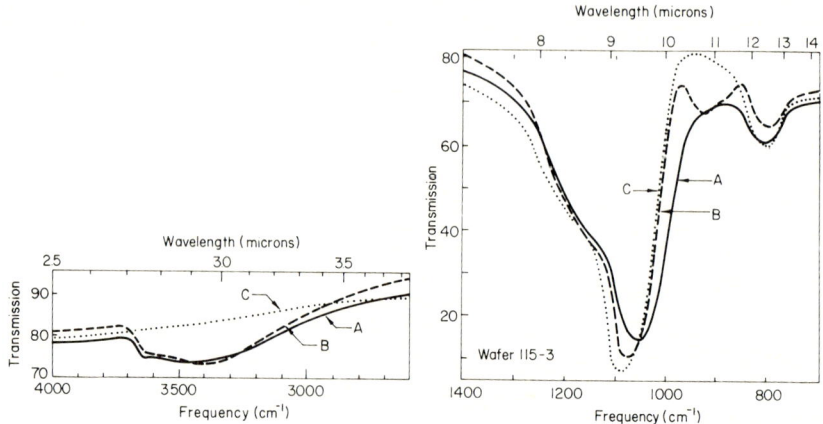

FIG. 15. Infrared spectra showing the effect of humidity at moderate temperature on an electron gun evaporated SiO_2 film (8070 A initially) on a 400°C substrate; A, initial spectrum; B, 24 days exposure of 85% R.H. and 85°C; C, densified 10 min in N_2 at 983°C [Pliskin and Castrucci (35)].

decreased (29). In this case, however, the porosity of the film must have increased on exposure to high humidity since additional water was absorbed and the film thickness had increased. In addition, Spectrum B shows the presence of a new band at 935 cm^{-1}. This band is attributed to the presence of silanol (SiOH) groups, thus showing that water had reacted with the SiO_2 to form SiOH. In addition, P-etch rate data showed that the etch rate of an initially deposited film was much faster than a film which had been exposed to high humidity and temperature. Pyrolytic oxides deposited at temperatures of 650°C and higher did not form silanol groups as readily on exposure to high humidity. Furthermore, the P-etch rate of the pyrolytic oxides decreased with a decrease in porosity (29). Yet with electron gun evaporated SiO_2 films the etch rate decreased with the increase in porosity as reflected in a film thickness increase. These results were explained on the basis of a high degree of bond strain in addition to porosity in the electron gun evaporated films (29, 35). The initial broadness of the Si-O band was interpreted to be due to a great deal of strain and variation in bond energies in addition to the porosity of the film. This strain makes the oxides more reactive, and the greater surface due to pores provides a larger reaction area. On reaction of the water with the oxide to form silanol groups, strain in the bonds is relieved and the absorption band due to the Si-O stretching becomes sharper and shifts to higher frequencies. With the relief of the strain, the etch rate of the oxide decreases.

Because of the greater reactivity of electron gun evaporated films, the differences in the severity of various treatments are more amenable to investigation and can serve as an indication as to the type of treatment to be used on the evaluation of films deposited at low temperatures. Surprisingly, an electron gun film of SiO_2 which had been deposited on a 400°C substrate showed significant densification after exposure for one-half hour to steam at 450°C (35). The densification and oxide improvement was indicated by a thickness decrease of 3.8%, P-etch rate decrease from 30 to 8 A/sec, significant decrease in water content, a 20 cm^{-1} shift of the Si-O stretching band to higher frequency, and a 23 cm^{-1} decrease in bandwidth. Thus, what is normally considered to be a severe moisture test (450°C steam for one-half hour) actually improves poor-quality SiO_2 films such as those obtained by electron gun evaporation.

Amorphous alumina films have also been formed by electron gun bombardment (49, 101). According to Lewis (49) these films had higher resistivities and were more stable than the electron gun evaporated SiO_2 films.

f. Oxygen Deficiency. Except for evaporated films, no significant oxygen deficiency is normally seen in deposited SiO_2 films. When it occurs, oxygen can be added to aid the reaction. In reactive sputtering, unfortunately, an increase in oxygen concentration reduces the deposition rate as was shown in Figs. 2 and 3 of Section II,5. Valletta *et al.* (30) found that this rate decrease was most pronounced between 0.1 and 1% oxygen in argon. At the lowest oxygen levels they obtained oxygen-deficient films as would be expected in the reactive sputtering of silicon. In rf-sputtering, Davidse and Maissel (84) also found a decrease in deposition rate with increased oxygen content. However, in this case the sputtering source provides oxygen independently of the externally supplied sputtering atmosphere, and Pliskin *et al.* (37) indeed found usually no significant oxygen deficiency in SiO_2 films rf-sputtered in argon.

In general, oxygen deficiency can be indicated by[3]:

(1) the shift of the 1100 cm^{-1} band to lower frequencies (longer wavelengths);
(2) the presence of a band near 870 cm^{-1} due to Si_2O_3;
(3) slow P-etch rate;
(4) high refractive index;
(5) growth of the film during a subsequent oxidation treatment.

As previously mentioned, the Si-O stretching band in the spectrum of silicon monoxide is near 1000 cm^{-1}, in Si_2O_3 near 1040 cm^{-1}, and in thermally grown silicon dioxide near 1085 cm^{-1}, depending on the film thickness. The use of this band position for determining oxygen deficiency is not, in itself, satisfactory because of the effects of density and bond strain. In addition

---

[3] See Pliskin *et al.* (37).

to the shift of the main Si-O stretching absorption band with the state of oxidation, a band near 870 cm^{-1} is observed in the spectra of Si_2O_3 films (29, 99, 102). In the case of electron gun evaporated SiO_2 films a band at this position was observed after slowly heating the films up to 600°C (35), but the band intensity was relatively weak, indicating only a slight oxygen deficiency. This band had not been observed in the spectra of rf-sputtered SiO_2 films and, therefore, it was concluded that the oxygen deficiency of the sputtered films was even less. The actual oxygen content of some rf-sputtered SiO_2 films was determined by measuring the film thickness changes produced by thermal oxidation. A correction factor was applied, accounting for the densification of the film on heating (37). These measurements showed that the composition of most rf-sputtered films was approximately $SiO_{1.95}$, indicating that rf-sputtering does not usually cause any appreciable oxygen deficiency. However, occasionally oxygen deficiency had been observed in rf-sputtered SiO_2 films, resulting in a higher refractive index ($\gtrsim 1.50$) and slower P-etch rate.

g. Refractive Index and Etch Rate Summary for SiO_2 Films. Pliskin and Lehman (29) showed the importance of the combined use of refractive index, exact infrared Si-O absorption band position and half-width, close scrutiny on hydroxyl content, and densification effects in the evaluation of various low-temperature-deposited SiO_2 films. As an example, if there is no oxygen deficiency, porous or less-dense structures will have low refractive indices,

TABLE IV

Densification Produced by Various Treatments[a]

Relative quan. ads. water	Densification treatment			Refrac. index		Density (g/cc)		% Densification	
	Ambient	Temp. (°C)	Time (min)	Before dens.	After dens.	Before dens.	After dens.	By R.I.	By film shrinkage
High	Argon	800	15	1.45$_0$	1.45$_5$	2.15[b] (1.99)[c]	2.18	1.1[b] (9.2)[c]	9.0
Low	Steam	850	15	1.43$_7$	1.46$_3$	2.09	2.22	6.0	6.4
Med.	Nitrogen	975	5	1.44$_4$	1.45$_6$	2.12[b] (2.07)[c]	2.18	2.7[b] (5.2)[c]	6.3
Low	Steam	975	15	1.44$_4$	1.46$_5$	2.12	2.23	4.7	5.4

[a] From Pliskin and Lehman (29).
[b] The water content was not considered in determining these values.
[c] Before densification, these samples contained a significant amount of water as shown by the infrared absorption spectra. The relative quantity of absorbed water was considered in calculating their densities.

TABLE V

Refractive Indices and Etch Rates of Various T.F. Pyrolytic Oxides[a]

Deposition temp. (°C)	Deposition time (min)	Densification ambient	Densification temp. (°C)	Densification time (min)	Thickness (μ)	Refractive index (5460 Å)	P-etch rate A/sec	P-etch rate Temp. (°C)
675	75	—	—	—	0.78	1.44_7	13.2	25.1
675	120	Argon	800	15	1.42	1.45_2	2.9_1	25.1
675	120	Steam	800	15	1.27	1.46_0	2.1_7	25.1
675	120	Steam	975	15	1.09	1.46_5	2.0_3	25.1
835	10	—	—	—	1.56	1.45_3	6.7_5	26.0
~835	10	—	—	—	1.21	1.45_0	10.6_5	26.0
Thermal oxide					0.59	1.46_2	2.07	25.4

[a] From Pliskin and Lehman (29).

faster etch rates, Si-O band displaced to lower frequency and broadened, greater water susceptibility as shown in the 3-μ region of the infrared spectra, and densification or film thickness decreases on thermal treatment. The effects of various thermal densification treatments on refractive index and film shrinkage are shown in Table IV. The influence of similar treatments on the refractive index and P-etch rate of pyrolytic SiO_2 films is given in Table V. These results show that heating in a moist ambient at temperatures greater than 800°C was more effective for densification than heating in a dry ambient. As a spectroscopic indication of the densification of pyrolytic SiO_2 films, the Si-O absorption band in the vicinity of 1050 to 1100 cm^{-1} shifted to higher frequency and decreased in half-width, while the 800 cm^{-1} band shifted to lower frequency. The spectra of films densified in steam at temperatures greater than 800°C were virtually indistinguishable from those of thermally grown SiO_2 films of comparable thicknesses.

A summary of the refractive indices and P-etch rates of various silicon dioxides is given in Table VI.

TABLE VI

SUMMARY: REFRACTIVE INDICES AND P-ETCH RATES OF SILICON DIOXIDES[a]

Oxide type and description	Refractive index at 5461 A	P-etch rates at 25°C (A/sec)
T.F. pyrolytic	1.44–1.45	6–20
T.F. pyrolytic, densified	1.463	2.0
CO_2 process	1.465	2.4–4.2
Reactive sputtering, deposition rate < 300 A/min	1.46	3.5–21
Reactive sputtering, depositioh rate ≥ 700 A/min	—	≥ 100
Anodized	1.30–1.49	18–228
PbO catalyzed oxidation (lead silicate)	1.72	600
Electron-gun evaporated SiO_2	1.464–1.487	20–70
rf sputtered	1.467–1.479	4–12
Thermal	1.462	2.0

[a] From Pliskin and Esch (26), Pliskin and Lehman (29), Valletta et al. (30), Pliskin (35), Pliskin et al. (37), and Pliskin and Gnall (45).

The variability in refractive index and P-etch rate can be attributed to changes in substrate temperature and deposition rate. Generally, lower substrate temperature will result in less dense and more strained films which are characterized by lower refractive indices and faster etch rates. Similarly, faster deposition rates will result in less density, larger strains, lower refractive indices, and faster etch rates. Although SiO$_2$ films were studied in most detail, the same results were found with various silicate glasses.

In conclusion it can be said that, by the combined use of infrared spectroscopy, refractive index, and etch rate, various similar glass and oxide insulating films can be compared and evaluated with respect to composition, structure, and water and chemical stability.

IV. Electrical Properties of Glass Films

1. ELECTRICAL REQUIREMENTS FOR PASSIVATION

A number of electrical properties may be listed for glass films which determine their usefulness in device passivation. In general, a low dielectric constant is desired for the reduction of capacitance between metallic interconnection lands and the semiconductor substrate. The relative dielectric constant is easily measured, and for common glasses falls into the range of 4 (pure SiO$_2$) to 20 (high lead content lead silicate). A high dielectric strength is an obvious requirement since voltages of 100 volts may be applied across a 1-μ film (field equals 10^6 volts/cm). The breakdown strength of a film is frequently limited by defects in the film rather than by the bulk dielectric strength. The most critical requirement for a passivation film is that it forms a suitable surface potential at the insulator-semiconductor interface, and that this surface potential is stable during the operating life of the device.

The surface potential (or, more properly, interface potential) determines the conductivity type and carrier density at the insulator-semiconductor interface. Surface potential u_s and bulk potential u_B are defined in Fig. 16, which shows an electron-energy band diagram of an insulator-semiconductor interface for the very general case of an applied field E in the insulator normal to the surface, space-charge Q_I per unit area in the insulator near the interface, and charge Q_{SS} in interface states. The carrier concentrations at any point in the semiconductor are given by

$$n_e = n_i \exp(u), \qquad n_h = n_i \exp(-u) \qquad (2)$$

where n_e and n_h are electron and hole concentrations, n_i is the intrinsic carrier concentration, and u is the distance of the Fermi level $\mathscr{E}_F$ above the intrinsic Fermi level $\mathscr{E}_i$ (measured in units of kT/q). Bulk and surface concentrations are given by substitution of u_B and u_s, respectively, into Eq. (2). The semiconductor space-charge per unit area Q_S is uniquely determined by u_s and u_B for any particular semiconductor (*109*). If $u_s = u_B$, there is no semiconductor band-bending (the flat-band condition) and $Q_S = 0$. Application of Gauss's law to the structure of Fig. 16 gives

$$-\epsilon E = Q_I + Q_{SS} + Q_S \qquad (3)$$

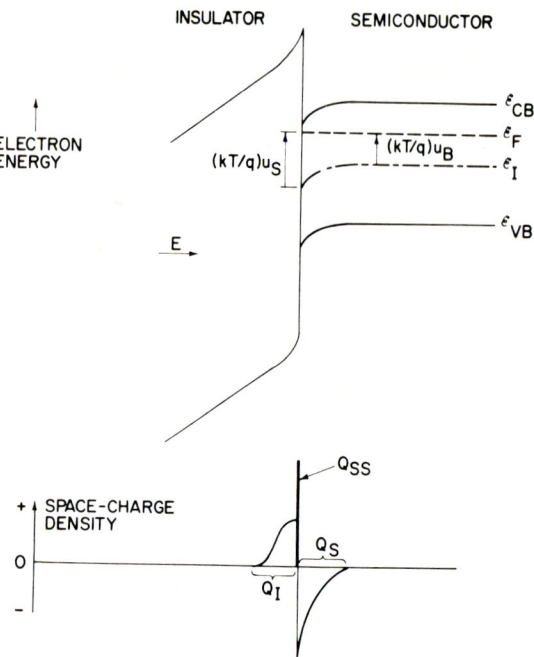

FIG. 16. Energy-band diagram and space-charge distribution at an insulator-semiconductor interface.

where ϵ is the dielectric constant of the insulator. We see that Q_S (and thus u_s) is determined both by the applied field and by charge in the insulator or in interface states.

The primary instability mechanism in glass passivated surfaces is the migration of cations through the insulator to accumulate in a space charge layer Q_I. If one assumes that the insulator obeys Ohm's law with all conduction being due to ionic migration and also assumes no ionic neutralization at the interface (a blocking electrode), the ΔQ_I (or ΔN_I) caused by a field E applied normal to the surface for a time t is

$$\Delta Q_I = q\,\Delta N_I = Et/\rho \qquad (4)$$

where ρ is the resistivity, and q is the electronic charge. The operating fields and allowable ΔN_I are widely variable between devices. The gate insulation of a field-effect transistor may have $E = 10^6$ volts/cm with $\Delta N_I = 10^{11}/\text{cm}^2$ being a serious instability (causing 0.4-volt shift of the turn-on voltage with 1000 A of SiO_2). On the other hand, planar bipolar transistors usually have fields less than 10^5 volts/cm in the passivation film over the base, with $\Delta N_I = 10^{12}/\text{cm}^2$ being below the inversion threshold for the diffused base region. For a rough calculation let us assume a device operating life of 3.2×10^8 sec (~ 10 years) and obtain from Eq. (4) the required resistivities:

$$\rho = 2 \times 10^{20} \text{ ohm-cm} \quad \text{for} \quad E = 10^5 \text{ volts/cm}, \quad \Delta N_I = 10^{12}/\text{cm}^2$$
$$\rho = 2 \times 10^{22} \text{ ohm-cm} \quad \text{for} \quad E = 10^6 \text{ volts/cm}, \quad \Delta N_I = 10^{11}/\text{cm}^2 \quad (5)$$

These are extremely high resistivities for glasses at room temperature and are more difficult to realize at slightly elevated temperatures. Methods of measuring ionic polarization in passivation films will be described in Section IV,2.

Two approaches may be taken to obtain electrical stability in passivation films. One may form a film with such a tight glassy structure that only a very small fraction of the cation impurities (e.g., sodium) can migrate to or away from the interface region. High-resisitivity fused glasses are an example. A second approach is to form a film which is so free of mobile ions that migration of all the ions gives a ΔN_I which is still acceptable. This type of passivation must be protected from contamination on its outer surface. Carefully grown thermal SiO_2 forms a passivation film of this type on Si. As described in Section IV,5 a phosphosilicate layer formed over the SiO_2 will prevent contamination by sodium.

There are particular advantages to using multilayer passivation. The case of SiO_2 covered by a glass with much lower ionic resistivity has been analyzed

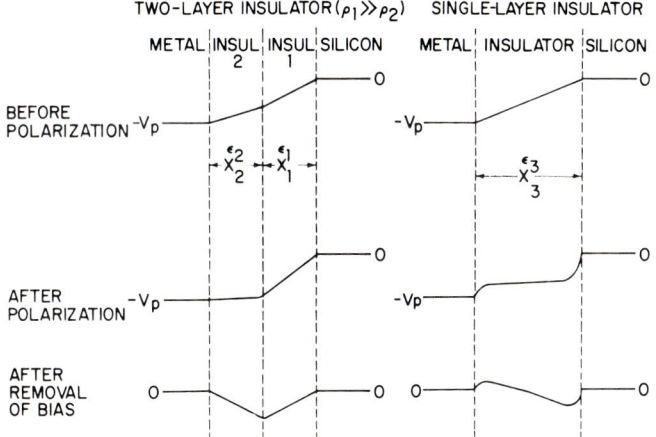

FIG. 17. Potential profiles in MIS structures with two-layer and single-layer insulators. The three cases illustrated are: (a) after application of an applied bias $-V_P$, but before any ionic polarization of the insulators; (b) after ionic polarization of the insulators has reached equilibrium; (c) after returning bias to zero, but before relaxation of ionic space-charge. For clarity, the surface potential changes in the silicon are not shown.

by Snow and Dumesnil (110). Fig. 17 compares potential profiles for metal-insulator-silicon (MIS) structures with single- and double-layer insulators before and after polarization of the films to equilibrium under applied bias V_p at elevated temperature. At equilibrium there is zero field in the central region of the low-resistivity glass and current flow ceases. We see in the two-layer structure that the field outside the Si surface approaches V_p/x_1 after polarization; that is, all the voltage is dropped across the high-resistivity insulator. In the case of a single low-resistivity layer the space-charge layer drops are much higher before equilibrium occurs, and extremely high fields at the interface can result. The difference between the two cases is clear when we compare the charge levels in the silicon after returning the applied bias to zero. In the two-layer case (110)

$$\Delta N_s = \frac{\Delta Q_s}{q} = \frac{C_1 V_p}{q(1 + C_2/C_1)} \quad \text{(two-layer)} \tag{6}$$

where C_1 and C_2 are the capacitances per unit area of the high- and low-resistance layers, respectively. If we assume for the single-layer structure that the cathode space-charge drop is caused by a depletion of cations which leave behind a uniform density n of negatively charged sites, then one can easily show by integration of Poisson's equation that

$$\Delta N_s = (2n\epsilon_3 V_A/q)^{1/2} - \epsilon_3 V_P/qx_3 \quad \text{(single-layer)} \tag{7}$$

where V_A is voltage drop across the anode space-charge region, and x_3 is the film thickness. V_A will be greater than $0.5V_p$ since cations reaching the cathode will accumulate with a density greater than n. However, for the sake of comparison let $V_p = 2V_A = 20$ volts, $x_3 = 2x_1 = 2x_2 = 10^{-4}$ cm, $n = 10^{19}/\text{cm}^3$, $\epsilon_1 = \epsilon_2 = \epsilon_3 = 50 \times 10^{-14}$ F/cm. Substituting into Eqs. (6) and (7) gives

$$\begin{aligned}\Delta N_s &= 6.2 \times 10^{11}/\text{cm}^2 \quad \text{(two-layer)} \\ \Delta N_s &= 2.5 \times 10^{13}/\text{cm}^2 \quad \text{(single-layer)}.\end{aligned} \tag{8}$$

We see that the two-layer structure gives a ΔN_s level which is acceptable for many applications even when the outer insulator (2 in Fig. 17) is not of extremely high resistivity. If the first insulator is free of ionic migration, then the resisitivity requirement of $> 10^{20}$ ohm-cm may be decreased for the outer insulator, and its other properties such as expansion coefficient, chemical and water stability, and ease of application become of major importance. The major electrical requirements then fall on the insulator which is applied directly to the semiconductor surface.

2. Methods of Measuring Ionic Polarization

As discussed in Section IV,1, ionic conduction in passivation films can lead to space-charge accumulations at the insulator-semiconductor interface which degrade device operation. This section will discuss methods for measuring ionic flow in glass films. A clear objective is to predict by relatively short-term measurements the ionic flow which will occur over a long-term period in a typical device at operating stress condition. Such a prediction is made possible by the fact that temperature dependence of resistivity due to ionic motion in glasses usually is described by the Arrhenius relation

$$\rho(T) = \rho_0 \exp[\Phi/kT] \text{ ohm-cm} \quad (9)$$

where ρ_0 is a constant dependent on the glass (ohm-cm), Φ is the activation energy (electron-volt), k is Boltzmann's constant (8.615×10^{-5} electron-volt/°K), and T is the absolute temperature (°K). If this equation holds, the ratio of resistivities at any two temperatures T_1 and T_2 is then

$$\rho(T_1)/\rho(T_2) = \exp \frac{\Phi}{k}\left[\frac{1}{T_1} - \frac{1}{T_2}\right] \quad (10)$$

To illustrate the strong temperature dependence of resistivity, the ratio $\rho(T_1)/\rho(300°K)$ is plotted in Fig. 18 for $T > 300°K$ (27°C) and for several activation energies. Most high-resistivity glasses have $\Phi > 1$ eV. Taking the $\Phi = 1$ eV curve in Fig. 18 for, example, one observes, referring to Eq. (4), that a charge flow occurring in 10^8 sec at 27°C will be observed in 70 sec at 200°C due to the great reduction in ρ. The approach for evaluation of passivation films then is to raise temperature to a range where resistivity is low enough for accurate measurement. Measurement of resistivity and its activation energy in this range then permits an extrapolation of resistivity to the device operating temperature.

The electrical properties of glass have been studied by many workers over the past 50 years. Most of these measurements have been made on bulk glass samples with thickness of 1 mm or greater. However, there are a number of reasons why electrical evaluation of passivation glasses should be done on the thin-film MIS structure formed by depositing a film of glass on a semiconductor substrate and then evaporating a contact metal electrode. (An evaporation of an ohmic contact to the backside of the wafer completes the structure as shown in Fig. 19.) Not only can many devices be formed on a single semiconductor wafer for better statistical test information, but—more important—a film may exhibit properties quite different from bulk material. Furthermore, the high fields of 10^5 to 10^6 volts/cm applied to passivation films are difficult to reach in bulk samples. Another advantage of the MIS structure is that space-charge accumulation in the insulator can be

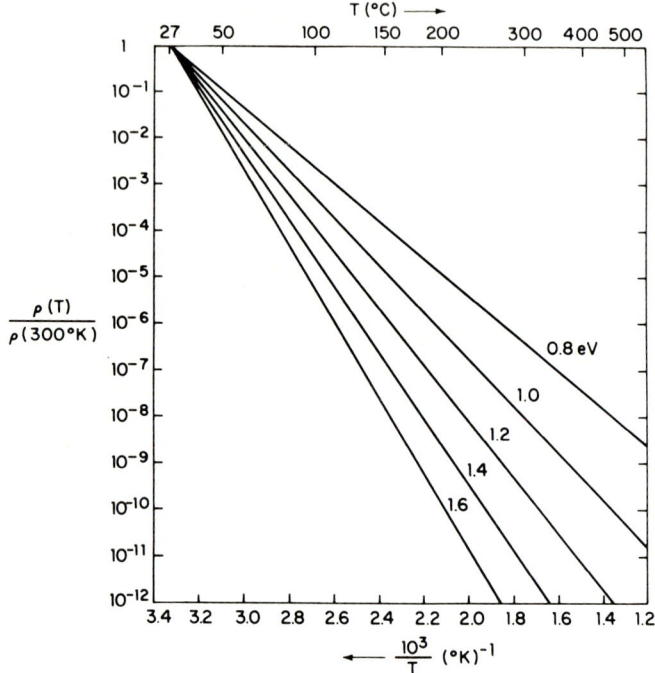

FIG. 18. The ratio of elevated-temperature resistivity to room-temperature resistivity versus temperature for materials having an Arrhenius behavior [Eqs. (9) and (10)]. The activation energies φ are given on the curves.

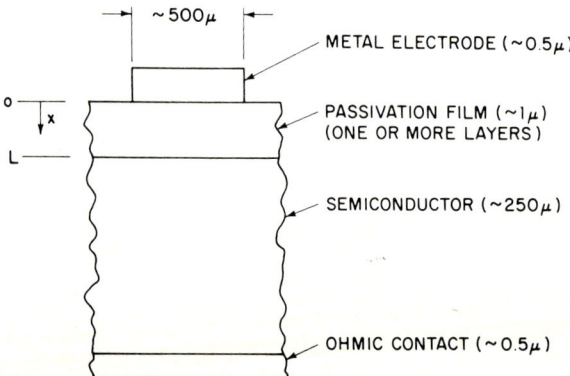

FIG. 19. Schematic cross section of an MIS structure. The dimensions given are merely illustrative and may be widely varied.

detected directly by its effect on the semiconductor surface charge and the resultant shift in the capacitance-voltage (C-V) characteristic.

Since the C-V characteristic of the MIS structure has been discussed in the literature recently by a number of authors (*111–113*), only a qualitative review of the theory will be given here. The simplest equivalent circuit for such a device is a fixed capacitance per unit surface area C_I, corresponding to the insulator layer, in series with a variable capacitance C_S due to the space-charge layer of the semiconductor surface. The behavior of such a device in terms of the semiconductor band structure may be qualitatively understood by referring to Fig. 20. The illustration is for *n*-type silicon with a uniform

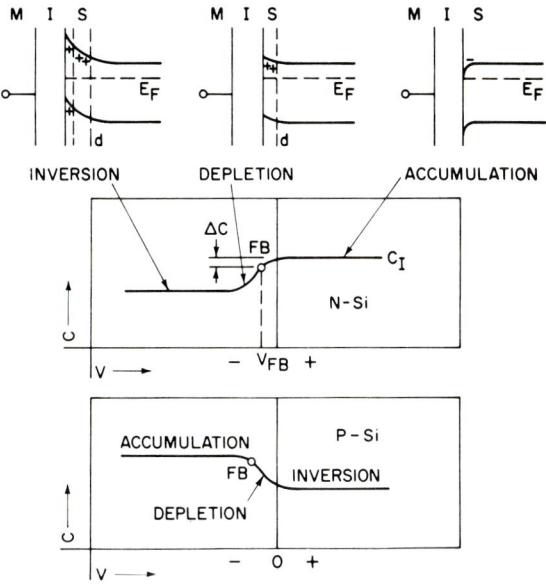

FIG. 20. Silicon energy-band diagram for three regions of the C-V characteristic of an MIS capacitor. The band diagrams and the upper C-V curve are for *n*-type silicon, and the lower C-V curve is for *p*-type silicon, $\mathscr{E}_F$ is the Fermi level, and d indicates the depletion layer edge.

donor impurity concentration. When the bias on the metal electrode is varied, the majority carrier concentration near the insulator-silicon interface can be accumulated above the concentration in the bulk of the silicon, depleted below the bulk concentration, or inverted (giving a *p*-type surface in this example). A band diagram is given for each of these conditions. Bias polarity is defined as the potential of the metal electrode with respect to the bulk of the silicon. Considering first the diagram for accumulation, the electron charge induced lies very close to the interface, and the device capacitance reaches a maximum level determined by the thickness and permittivity of the insulator. As bias is decreased, the surface is depleted. The high-frequency-induced charge fluctuation occurs at the edge of the depletion region, and the increased distance between the electrode and the induced ac charge results in a capacitance decrease. As the bias is made more negative, the silicon surface inverts. The hole charge induced by the bias now occurs in a very thin layer near the interface, but this layer has a charging time constant sufficiently long that charge fluctuations at frequencies of 1 kc or higher generally occur at the inner depletion layer edge. Since charge induced by the dc bias goes into the hole layer, the position of the depletion layer edge is now nearly independent of bias, and the capacitance saturates at a low value as shown. Similar reasoning for *p*-type silicon leads to a complementary characteristic as shown in the lower curve of Fig. 20.

When the conduction and valence bands are flat out to the insulator-silicon interface, there is zero space-charge within the silicon. The capacitance per unit area of the silicon surface at this "flat-band" point is given by

$$C_{SFB} = q(\epsilon_s n_D/kT)^{1/2} \qquad (11)$$

where ϵ_s is the permittivity of silicon, and n_D is the dopant atom concentration *(111)*. This capacitance in series with the insulator capacitance C_I gives a fractional decrease of device capacitance:

$$\frac{\Delta C}{C_I} = \frac{C_I}{q(\epsilon_s n/k_D T)^{1/2} + C_I} \qquad (12)$$

in going from the maximum capacitance of the accumulation region to the flat-band point. This point is indicated by *FB* in Fig. 20, and the bias required is denoted V_{FB}. The number of charges per cm^2 which are applied in going from zero bias to V_{FB} is then given by

$$N_{FB} = C_I V_{FB}/q \qquad (13)$$

Let us now examine the relationships between V_{FB} and space-charge in the insulator. Insulator space-charge will induce image charges (of the opposite sign) in the silicon and the metal electrode. Assuming that the surface-state charge and the metal-semiconductor work-function difference are zero, one may easily show that the image charge induced in the silicon with zero applied bias is

$$Q_{SO} = -Q_I' = -\frac{1}{L}\int_0^L x\,\eta(x)\,dx \qquad (14)$$

where $\eta(x)$ is the space-charge density per cm^3 in the insulator of thickness L. The distance x is defined in Fig. 19. Because of the factor x in the integral we see that any space-charge near the electrode will induce very little charge in the silicon, while a space-charge near the silicon has most of its image charge in the silicon. Eq. (14) then defines Q_I' as the "effective" space-charge in the insulator. If bias is applied so that the flat-band condition occurs (i.e., $Q_S = 0$), the additional charge supplied to the electrode is identical to Q_{SO}. This yields the simple relation

$$Q_{SO} = C_I V_{FB} = q N_{FB} \tag{15}$$

Any migration of ions through the insulator will change the effective insulator space-charge and cause a corresponding shift of V_{FB}. The measurement of ionic flow by C-V shift then involves three steps: (1) initial C-V traces are made after formation of the MIS structure; (2) the device is bias-temperature stressed at an appropriate temperature, field, and time (e.g., 200°C, + 10^5 volts/cm, 60 min) and then quickly cooled to room temperature while bias is being maintained; (3) the C-V trace is repeated and the shift of V_{FB} determined. The change in effective insulator space-charge is then

$$\Delta Q_I' = q \, \Delta N_I' = - C_I \, \Delta V_{FB} \tag{16}$$

If there are active surface states which are charged during the application of the flat-band bias, then Eq. (15) will not hold, and $C_I V_{FB}$ will be somewhat larger than Q_{SO}. However, ionic motion in the insulator generally does not change surface-state densities, and Eq. (16) may still be used to measure changes in ionic space charge. One characteristic of this measurement is that V_{FB} shifts in the direction opposite in sign to the stress bias V_p. For example, positive V_p will drive positive ions toward the silicon and causes $\Delta Q_I'$ to be positive. This, in turn, produces according to Eq. (16) a negative ΔV_{FB}. For some insulators in which ionic motion is negligible, ΔV_{FB} values are observed with the same sign as V_p (88). This is normally ascribed to electron transfer and trapping at the insulator-silicon interface. This measurement method offers several advantages over a direct measurement of charge flow by ammeter, but the primary advantage is that charge accumulation is measured directly at the termination of the stress period rather than by a continuous measurement during the bias-temperature stress. Thus, small leakages in the bias cell or along the insulator surface do not influence the result, and many devices can be stressed simultaneously for long periods of time. The high sensitivity of the method is demonstrated by the following calculation. A typical glass of 1 μ thickness may have a capacitance C_I of 5×10^{-9} F/cm^2. A $\Delta N_I'$ of 10^{10} charges/cm^2 will then [using Eq. (16)] give a C-V shift of 0.32 volts, which is easily measured. The maximum resistivity measurable depends on the time under stress as seen from Eq. (4). For example, if the above shift occurred after 1000 hr (3.6×10^6 sec) with a field of 10^5 volts/cm, then Eq. (4) gives $\rho = 2.25 \times 10^{20}$ ohm-cm. This corresponds to a current of about 5×10^{-16} A/cm^2 which is too small for direct measurement on an electrometer (assuming an electrode area on the order of 10^{-3}

to 10^{-2} cm^2). The maximum $\Delta N_I'$ measurable is limited by the breakdown strength of the film during C-V tracing. For example, with a breakdown field of 5×10^6 volts/cm, the maximum $\Delta N_I'$ measurable in the above film would be $\sim 1.6 \times 10^{13}$/cm^2. For a lower limit on measurable resistivity let us assume that this $\Delta N_I'$ occurs in 100 sec at a field of 10^5 volts/cm. These values give a ρ of 4×10^{12} ohm-cm. Obviously the C-V shift measurement is useful over a wide range of resistivities.

There are occasions when the direct measurement of ionic current flow is preferred over the C-V shift measurement. The determination of charge buildup rates as a function of temperature, for instance, requires many tedious heating and cooling periods when the C-V method is used. Also, the time dependence of charge buildup is difficult to measure with the C-V method for short time periods. It is simple, however, to measure it directly at the elevated temperature. Thus, resistivity can be measured to a lower range, and dependence on bias polarity and magnitude can easily be determined by the direct ion current measurement.

This measurement is typically made (114) on one device at a time in a cell in which the temperature of the wafer is controlled. A selected bias is applied to the silicon by means of the backside ohmic contact, and current is measured with an electrometer which is connected to the MIS electrode by a low-leakage probe. The current flowing into the electrometer is converted to a voltage by its input resistor. By using a capacitor instead of a resistor, charge can be measured directly. It is generally advisable to connect these components in the feedback loop of the electrometer since this reduces the input voltage to a few millivolts and gives a fast time response. The output of the electrometer is fed to a recorder to give a current-time or charge-time trace.

The advantage of the charge-time measurement over the current-time measurement is illustrated in Fig. 21. When a bias step is applied, a sharp current spike can be observed which is the displacement current in the dielectric ($\partial D/\partial t \to \infty$). In a current-time measurement the meter must be shorted out during this spike and a portion of the ionic current following it can thus easily be missed. However, if the charge is measured, the displacement current merely causes a step $C_I A \Delta V$ and is easily separated from the ionic charge which follows. A second advantage of the charge measurement is that it correlates with the C-V measurement, as will be discussed later.

Any current due to surface leakage may be eliminated by using a grounded guard ring around the dot being measured. In many cases this precaution is not necessary since the path along the insulator surface is more than 1000 times the distance through the film. Also, since surface conduction is known to be a strong function of the ambient humidity (115, 116) such effects are minimized by flushing the cell with a dry gas.

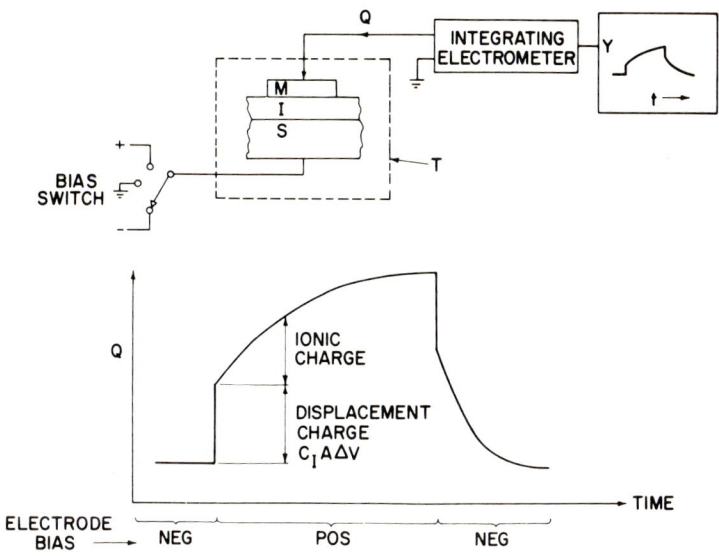

FIG. 21. Schematic circuit used for measurement of charge versus time in MIS devices, with a typical trace [Kerr (114)].

One can easily show the conditions under which a correlation between the C-V shift and the direct charge-time measurement will exist. Let us assume a one-dimensional current flow through the MIS structure. The externally measured current I_{EXT} will then be the sum of three internal components given by

$$I_{EXT}/A = i_I + i_E + i_D \qquad (17)$$

where i_I, i_E, i_D are the ionic, electronic, and displacement current densities, respectively. The right-hand side of Eq. (17) will be the same for any plane through the structure at any instant of time, although the contributions of the three components will vary. For example, $i_I = i_D = 0$ in the metal or in the bulk of the silicon, while i_E may be zero in the insulator. Let us now evaluate Eq. (17) at the insulator-semiconductor interface where $i_I = 0$, and let us assume for the moment that $i_E = 0$ at this point. Then

$$I_{EXT} = A i_D \Big]_{x=L} = A \frac{\partial D}{\partial t} \Big]_{x=L} \qquad (18)$$

and

$$\Delta Q_{EXT} = A \int i_D \, dt = A \, \Delta D \Big]_{x=L} \qquad (19)$$

If the bias is not changed during this integration, ΔD will be equal to the change in the effective insulator space-charge. From Eq. (16) we have, under this condition,

$$\Delta Q_{\text{EXT}} = A\ \Delta D = A\ \Delta Q_I' = -C_I A\ \Delta V_{FB} \tag{20}$$

where ΔV_{FB} is obtained from a C-V measurement. This correlation does not hold if electrons cross the insulator-semiconductor interface to neutralize positive ions or to travel through the insulator. In either case $\Delta Q_{\text{EXT}} > -C_I A\ \Delta V_{FB}$. Lack of correlation is thus evidence for either ion neutralization or electronic conduction in the insulator.

3. Films of Major Interest

Since introduction of the planar process for semiconductor device fabrication, thermally grown SiO_2 has been almost universally used for first-level passivation on silicon devices. In the last three years, development of the insulated-gate field-effect transistor has stimulated much experimental work on interface charge and stability of the Si-SiO$_2$ system. Section IV,4 will review the electrical properties of thermal SiO_2 films. Particular emphasis will be given to the current understanding of instability mechanisms.

During the diffusion of junctions, phosphosilicate and borosilicate glasses (for the most common diffusants) may form over the SiO_2. In some cases these glasses are retained as part of the passivation film. The electrical properties of these glasses, and the stabilizing effect of phosphosilicate in particular, are discussed in Section IV,5.

A variety of glasses may be applied after the first-level passivation to protect device surfaces and metallurgy from ambient contamination and moisture effects. Electrical measurements on such glasses are reviewed in Section IV,6.

4. Thermal SiO$_2$

The use of thermal SiO_2 in stabilizing the surface of silicon was first discussed by Atalla et al. ([117](#)). By combining the diffusion-masking ([118](#)) and passivation properties of SiO_2, the planar fabrication process ([119](#)) was developed to yield silicon diodes and transistors of reduced leakage, higher gain, lower noise, and reduced sensitivity to ambient gases. Under certain conditions instabilities were still observed and were attributed to ionic drift over the SiO_2 in the junction fringing fields ([120](#)). The development of the insulated-gate field-effect transistor (IGFET) ([121, 122](#)), in which SiO_2 is used as the gate insulator, has stimulated a large amount of study of the Si-SiO$_2$ system in recent years. The requirements on surface charge magnitude and stability are much more critical for the IGFET than for planar diodes or transistors. Although thermal SiO_2 is very simple to form and has the simplest of glass structures, the wide range of properties reported by various workers has shown that the electrical bulk and interfacial properties of this material depend on a number of processing factors (some of which are very subtle).

A detailed review of the extensive work on thermal SiO_2 is obviously beyond the scope of this article. The reader is referred to several reviews in the literature (*123–125*) as well as journal issues devoted particularly to surface properties (*126*). What will be given here is a brief review of the present understanding of the Si-SiO_2 system with emphasis on instability mechanisms under bias-temperature stress. Instabilities occurring in SiO_2 passivation films in the presence of ionizing radiation have been recently reviewed by Mitchell and Wilson (*127*) and will not be discussed.

There is general agreement among workers that oxidation of silicon tends to make the silicon surface more *n*-type than the bulk of the silicon. That is, negative bias must be applied to a gate electrode to achieve the flat-band condition, and N_{FB} is a negative number. The reported magnitude of N_{FB} has varied widely, but most reported values fall into the range of $10^{11}/cm^2$ to $2 \times 10^{12}/cm^2$. It has been shown that N_{FB} and the density of active surface states are influenced by the oxidizing gas (O_2 or steam) (*25, 128, 129*), the oxidation temperature (*25*), the oxidation rate prior to termination of the oxidation (*130, 131*), annealing at the oxidation temperature in an inert ambient (*130, 131*), the crystal orientation of the silicon (*18–25*), and the cooling rate (*25*). These conditions are easily controllable, but it has also been shown (*22*) that sodium impurities in the film increase the surface charge. Elimination of all sodium from the oxidizing atmosphere is difficult and may explain some of the differences in charge levels reported. Annealing experiments as a function of gas and temperature have shown that both N_{FB} and surface state densities can be reduced by annealing at temperatures below 500°C. Gases containing hydrogen or water are most effective, and annealing effects are generally accepted as involving the diffusion of hydrogen to the interface region (*128*). The cause of N_{FB} values resulting from oxidation in a system free of sodium is not clearly understood, but it has been proposed that it is due to excess silicon (*25*). Etch-back experiments have shown that the source of this charge is located very near to the Si-SiO_2 interface (*25, 132, 133*).

Under carefully controlled processing conditions, the Si-SiO_2 system can have very low surface charge ($<2 \times 10^{11}/cm^2$), low active state densities ($<10^{11}/cm^2$ eV), very low surface recombination velocity (~ 5 cm/sec) (*134*), and a high breakdown strength ($>6 \times 10^6$ volts/cm). The relative dielectric constant is 3.9 ± 0.1 (*113, 117, 135*). A disadvantage of the Si-SiO_2 system is that sodium is fairly mobile at device operating temperatures, and this can lead to instabilities unless all sodium contamination is prevented from reaching the SiO_2. Instability mechanisms in the Si-SiO_2 system will be discussed in the remainder of this section.

By slowly sweeping bias and measuring current through a Au-SiO$_2$-Si device, Yamin and Worthing (*136*) showed that a large amount of charge ($\sim 10^{13}$/cm^2) could be stored by applying positive bias to the gold at temperatures as low as 150°C. Kerr *et al.* (*137*) showed that application of 0.5×10^6 volts/cm at 150°C for 60 min to Al-SiO$_2$-Si structures could cause $-N_{FB}$ surface charge increases (from C-V data) on the order of 10^{13}/cm^2 with positive bias. Negative bias had much smaller effect and N_{FB} could not be driven to positive values. Direct measurement of charge flow at elevated temperature confirmed the magnitude and asymmetries observed in the C-V measurements. The source of these instabilities was not clear at first. The migration of oxide vacancies from the metal-SiO$_2$ to the SiO$_2$-Si interface was proposed (*138, 139*), but this model was discounted after Snow *et al.* (*140*) showed that stable devices could be obtained if contamination was avoided in all processing steps. They also showed that instabilities with magnitudes and asymmetries mentioned above resulted if the surface of a "clean" oxide was sodium contaminated before evaporation of the aluminum

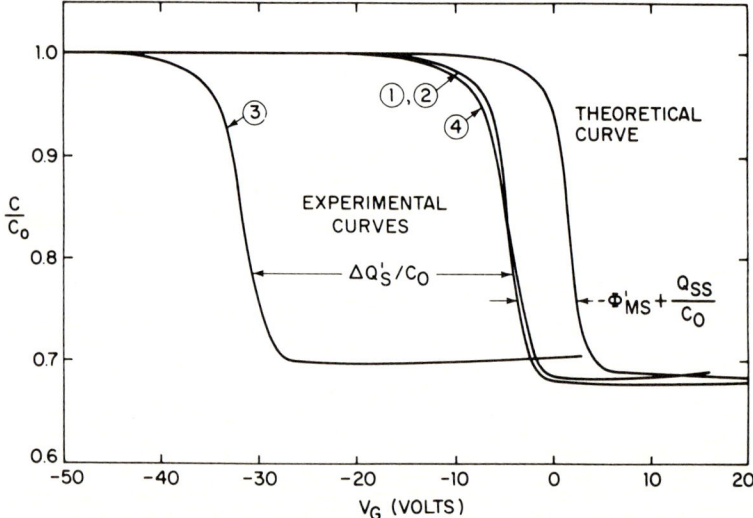

FIG. 22. Effect of applying a bias to a sodium-contaminated MOS structure at elevated temperature: (1) original curve; (2) after 5 min at -10 volts, 150°C; (3) after 5 min at $+10$ volts, 150°C; (4) after 5 min shorted at 150°C. The SiO$_2$ thickness is 2000 Å [Snow *et al.* (*140*)].

electrodes. As shown in Fig. 22 negative bias had little effect and a short-circuited dot recovered fairly rapidly at 150°C after shifting with positive bias.

Logan and Kerr (*141*) evaporated sodium, lithium, and potassium onto clean SiO$_2$ films ($\approx 10^{13}$ ions/cm^2) and studied the migration rates with positive bias as a function of temperature after evaporating aluminum electrodes. C-V shifts saturated at the levels expected if all contaminant ions migrated through the SiO_2. The Na^+ and Li^+ rates were quite similar while K^+ rate was about 10^3 less at any temperature. This is undoubtedly due to larger ionic radius of K^+ (1.33 A) compared to Na^+ (1.00 A) and Li^+ (0.70 A). With Na^+ and Li^+ the "forward drift" time constant (positive bias) was much longer than the "recovery" time constant (negative bias after drifting with positive bias). Hofstein (142) made a detailed study of charge motion in dry O_2-grown SiO_2 used as the gate insulation of FET's. He observed that forward drift time constants were orders-of-magnitude longer than recovery time constants, and he attributed this asymmetry to trapping of the positive ions near the metal-SiO_2 interface. The instability was enhanced by exposure to water, and the recovery time constants were several orders-of-magnitude faster than expected from data on sodium mobility in bulk fused silica. Consequently, Hofstein proposed that the highly mobile ion is the hydrogen ion.

Recent work (114), however, has indicated that motion of sodium in thermal SiO_2 is much more rapid than predicted from bulk measurements on fused silica. Figure 23 shows ionic charge transported through SiO_2 contaminated with sodium ($\sim 10^{13}$ ions/cm^2) before evaporation of clean aluminum. The charge flow at 150°C is measured versus time for a bias cycle of -30 volts,

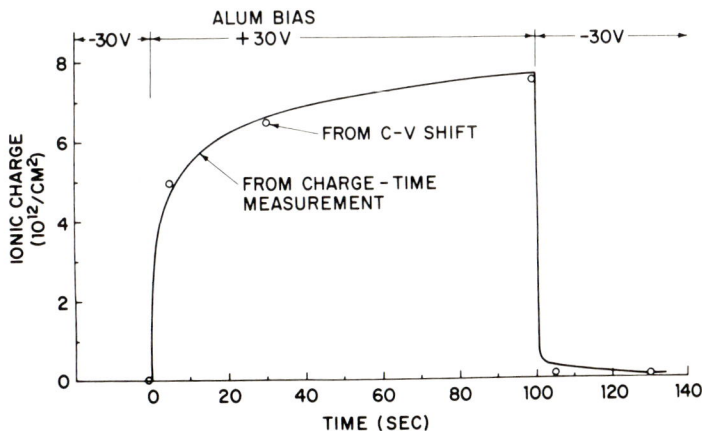

FIG. 23. Charge versus time data for sodium-contaminated thermal SiO_2 under positive and negative bias at 150°C [Kerr (114)].

+30 volts, −30 volts. Note that transport is quite rapid at 150°C and that the forward drift (+30 volts) is slower than the recovery drift (−30 volts). Since this cycle can be repeated indefinitely, the circuit was interrupted at different points and the C-V shift measured after quenching to room temperature. Figure 8 shows the excellent agreement between the two measurements as also found by Snow et al. (*140*). More recently this rapidly moving species has been positively identified (*143*) as being sodium by using radiotracer sodium ($Na^{22}Cl$) as the contaminant. The sample of Fig. 23 was cycled at 140°C at bias of ±26 volts. A series of devices were open circuited at various points in the cycle (similar to points used for C-V shift data of Fig. 23). Location of the sodium in these devices was then determined by etch-sectioning and making autoradiograms. In general, the sodium was always concentrated at either or both the Al-SiO_2 or the Si-SiO_2 interfaces (within 1000 Å). The amount of sodium near the Si-SiO_2 interface correlated with the charge flow measured electrically. For example, on dots heated with positive bias for several minutes, all added sodium was found near the Si-SiO_2 interface. When the positive bias was followed by 0.5 sec of negative bias at 140°C, the amount of sodium near the Si-SiO_2 interface was an order-of-magnitude less. The transit time for sodium under these conditions is therefore less than 0.5 sec.

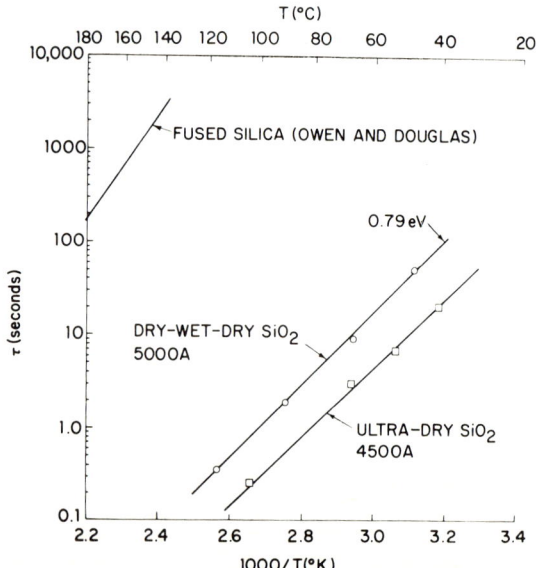

FIG. 24. Recovery time-constant versus $1/T$ for sodium contaminated ($10^{13}/cm^2$) thermal oxides. The applied field is -6.0×10^5 volts/cm. The τ calculated from data on fused silica [Owen and Douglas (*144*)] is also shown [Kerr (*143*)].

Defining the recovery time constant as the time measured for one half of the charge to be transferred upon switching to negative bias, this time constant is shown in Fig. 24 versus reciprocal temperature for two wafers with different oxide preparation. Note that the dry-wet-dry (O_2-steam-O_2) oxide and the ultradry O_2-grown oxide do not differ greatly in τ and that both have activation energies on the order of 0.8 eV. These time constants are similar to those of the highly mobile species studied by Hofstein (*142*). The much greater τ expected from measurements on fused silica is also shown in Fig. 24. This is obtained from data by Owen and Douglas (*144*) who found a linear relation between sodium content and conductivity. It is thus possible to calculate ion mobility versus temperature (for example, $\mu = 2.7 \times 10^{-14}$ cm^2/volt-sec at 140°C). The transit time for a 5000 A film at a field of 0.5×10^6 volts/cm can then be calculated and is shown in Fig. 24. Owen and Douglas found an activation energy of ~ 1.4 eV. The great difference shown in Fig. 24 between fused silica and thermal SiO_2 with respect to sodium migration is quite remarkable since the two materials are so similar in other physical properties. The reason for this difference may be related to the fact that most of the sodium in fused silica is bound to O^- atoms and any sodium ion moving through the glass is easily retrapped by O^- ions. In thermal SiO_2 the ions move through a film essentially free of negatively charged trapping sites. As discussed by Hofstein (*142*), interface trapping can then dominate the charge transfer kinetics. A number of workers have shown by neutron activation analysis (*22, 145, 146*) that thermally grown SiO_2 films typically have sodium levels in the range of 10^{16} to 10^{17}/cm^3 in the bulk of the film. This sodium is apparently tightly bound as Si-O-Na and does not migrate easily at low temperatures where surface contaminated sodium is quite mobile.

5. Glasses Formed during Diffusion

The most common diffusants for silicon planar devices are phosphorus (*n*-type) and boron (*p*-type). When P_2O_5 and B_2O_3 are used as diffusant sources, phosphosilicate and borosilicate glasses, respectively, are formed on the surface (see Section II,1). Since these glasses may be left on the completed devices to form part of the passivation film, the electrical characteristics of these glasses are of interest and will be discussed in this section.

Phosphosilicate glass has received considerable study since Kerr *et al.* (*137*) showed that formation of phosphosilicate resulted in great improvement of bias-temperature stability. Both *npn* planar transistors and MOS capacitors with phosphosilicate were shown to have better stability when bias-temperature stressed at temperatures of 100°C or higher. Figure 25 shows the shift in V_{FB} measured on MOS capacitors with and without phosphosilicate after heating to various temperatures with +30 volts bias for 60 min. Data is shown for five stabilized wafers with variations in the phosphorus

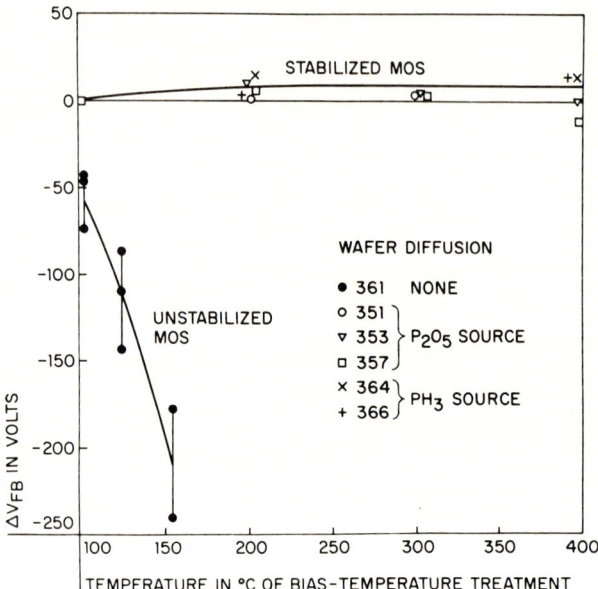

FIG. 25. Shift in V_{FB} versus temperature of $+30$ volt, 60-min bias-temperature stress for MOS devices with and without stabilization of the oxide by phosphorus diffusion. Silicon was n-type, 5.3 ohm-cm, and contacts were aluminum [Kerr et al. (137)].

diffusion step. The thickness of the phosphosilicate layers was varied from 700 to 4300 A, and both P_2O_5 and PH_3 (O_2 ambient) diffusion sources were used. As seen in Fig. 25, these variations did not cause large variations in the stability. The phosphosilicate layer resulted in a large reduction in ionic conduction measured with positive bias at elevated temperatures and a reduction in initial surface charge ($-N_{FB} \approx 2 \times 10^{12}/cm^2$ without P_2O_5, $-N_{FB} \approx 0.6 \times 10^{12}/cm^2$ after P_2O_5). Yamin (147) reported that converting the upper 600 A of a 6000-A thermal oxide to phosphosilicate glass completely eliminated the charge storage normally seen in thermal SiO_2 with cyclic bias applied at 400°C. The mechanism of stabilization by phosphosilicate was not at first clear since the cause of large instabilities in SiO_2 was not then known. Thomas and Young (138) and Seraphim et al. (139) proposed that P_2O_5 reduces the concentration of oxide vacancies and thus prevents their migration. However, the demonstration by Snow et al. (140) that sodium is the source of large instabilities suggested that phosphosilicate getters or blocks movement of contaminant alkali ions.

Snow and Deal (148) demonstrated that phosphosilicate prevents migration of sodium by rinsing a wafer with 2000 A of thermal SiO_2 and 700 A of phosphosilicate in NaCl solution before applying the electrodes. Under bias of $+10$ volts at 300°C for 5 min the C-V shift was about -1 volt, whereas contaminated wafers without phosphosilicate shifted more than −60 volts. The C-V shift occurred under positive or negative bias on phosphosilicate samples with or without sodium contamination and was attributed to a dipolar polarizability of the phosphosilicate glass. This polarization phenomenon was studied on phosphosilicate films formed by depositing P_2O_5 at 1020°C onto thermal SiO_2. The drift ΔV saturates at a value proportional to the polarizing bias V_P and is fairly rapid, having a time constant of about 1 min at 80°C, with a 1.0 eV activation energy. The magnitude of saturation shift is given by

$$\Delta V_{\text{SAT}} = \frac{-K_0 X_g \lambda V_P}{K_g[(K_g + \lambda)X_0 + K_0 X_g]} \tag{21}$$

where K_0 and K_g are the relative dielectric constants of the oxide and phosphosilicate glass, respectively, X_0 and X_g are the corresponding thicknesses, and λ is the polarizability of the phosphosilicate. Snow and Deal found that the value $\lambda = 0.75$ fits the data for their phosphosilicate. Equation (21) shows that this instability can be minimized by using a phosphosilicate layer much thinner than the SiO_2 layer. Snow and Deal also reported a dielectric constant of $K_g = 4.00$–4.10 and a dielectric strength of 1.2–1.4 × 10^7 volts/cm for phosphosilicate glass.

Kerr (114, 149) studied sodium migration through phosphosilicate layers as a function of temperature and phosphosilicate thickness. The phosphosilicate was formed by P_2O_5 deposition on SiO_2 at 1000°C followed by a steam-oxygen reoxidation cycle at 970°C. This reoxidation cycle lowers the phosphorus content, and considerably lowers the etch rate of the phosphosilicate (see Section III,3). Different amounts of phosphosilicate were then etched off to give thicknesses ranging from 0 to 730 Å. After evaporating ~10^{13} sodium ions/cm^2 and aluminum electrodes, the MOS devices were stressed at +30 volts for 30 min at various temperatures up to 400°C. Figure 26 shows flat-band voltage after bias-temperature. Note that the gross instability due to the sodium contaminant below 200°C is largely eliminated by only an 80 Å thick phosphosilicate layer. At temperatures above 200°C, the sodium appears to migrate through to the $Si-SiO_2$ interface. However, the temperature required for such migration increases with phosphosilicate thickness. Evidence for strong trapping in the phosphosilicate was obtained by cycling bias at elevated temperature and observing charge transfer rates. If the structural "tightness" of the phosphosilicate glass were responsible for its resistance to sodium migration, then sodium could be rapidly driven back and forth through the SiO_2 after the initial migration through the phosphosilicate. However, the "redrift" time constant was observed to be more than 10^3 greater than the "recovery" time constant (negative bias). The redrift time constant is independent of time under negative bias, indicating

MOS C-V STABILITY AS FUNCTION OF PHOSPHOSILICATE THICKNESS

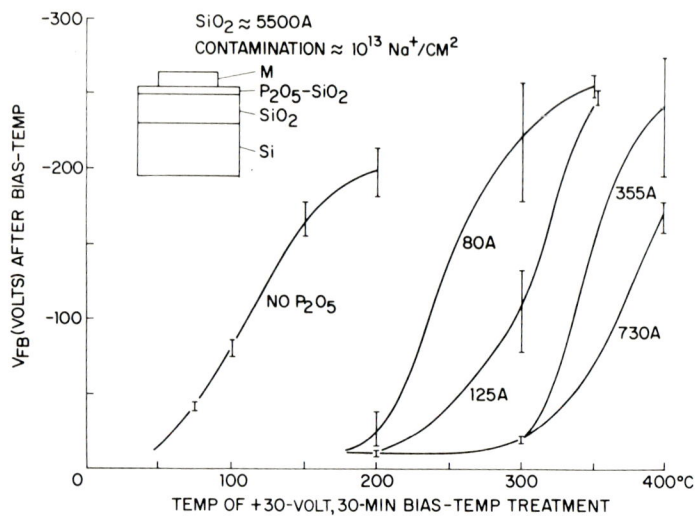

FIG. 26. V_{FB} after stress versus temperature of +30-volt, 30-min bias-temperature stress for sodium-contaminated oxides with varied phosphosilicate layer thicknesses. The phosphosilicate thicknesses for each wafer are given on the curves, and the data scatter for three identically stressed devices is shown at each point [Kerr (149)].

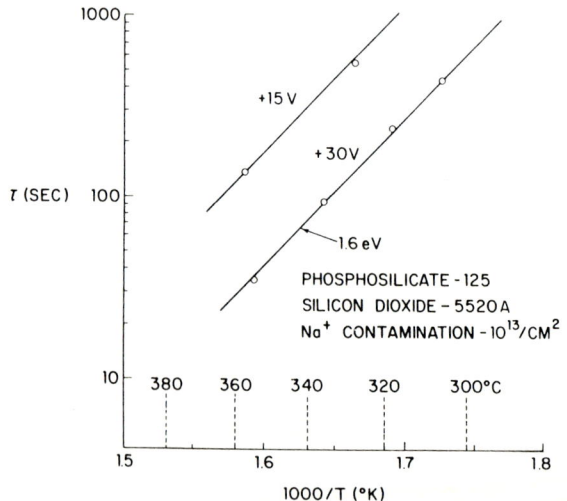

FIG. 27. Redrift time-constant versus $1/T$ for a sodium-contaminated, phosphosilicate-SiO_2 structure. These data are from charge-time measurements taken after drift of the sodium to the SiO_2-Si interface (positive bias) and then recovery for a few seconds (negative bias) [Kerr (149)].

that the sodium ions are trapped as soon as they reach the phosphosilicate. The temperature dependence of the redrift time constant for one of the samples is shown in Fig. 27. The 1.6 eV activation energy may be interpreted as the trap depth. A proposed model for the trapping mechanism is that a phosphorus atom in the phosphosilicate structure is surrounded by three bridging oxygens and one nonbridging oxygen. The phosphorus atom and the nonbridging oxygen form a charge dipole. As a sodium ion migrates past this site, it would experience an ion-dipole attraction and be trapped.

Carlson et al. (145) showed by neutron activation of phosphosilicate-SiO_2 double layers that sodium is strongly segregated in the phosphosilicate. Typical sodium concentrations were $10^{17}/cm^3$ in the phosphosilicate and $<10^{16}/cm^3$ in the underlying SiO_2. Yon et al. (146) found similar gettering effects after forming phosphosilicate glass on an oxide which had been intentionally contaminated with radiotracer sodium. Buck and Dalton (150) diffused (at 600°C) and field-drifted (at 400°C) radiotracer sodium into phosphosilicate-over-SiO_2 layers and could detect the sodium only in the phosphosilicate.

Borosilicate glass has received considerably less study than phosphosilicate since it apparently does not block migration of impurity alkali ions. Seraphim et al. (139) compared bias-temperature effects on thermal SiO_2, borosilicate over SiO_2, and phosphosilicate over SiO_2 (all on p-type silicon). Only the phosphosilicate failed to show a large negative C-V shift after positive bias at 325°C for 30 min. After -30 volts bias at 325°C for 30 min the borosilicate sample exhibited a positive surface charge at the silicon interface and a C-V minimum shifted from -17 to $+30$ volts. Since the borosilicate layer was thicker than the SiO_2 layer in this sample, it is not clear whether this shift is due to a polarization of the borosilicate glass or to negative space-charge accumulation in the SiO_2 near the Si-SiO_2 interface.

Yamin (151) studied the interaction of boron and phosphorus in stabilizing SiO_2 films by using boron tribromide and phosphorus tribromide sources and diffusing at 1050°C. He found that diffusing phosphorus after boron gave a film showing no evidence of ionic charging peaks under cyclic bias at 400°C. Diffusion of boron over phosphorus stabilized film, however, gave a film showing ionic charge storage. The model postulated is that a surface layer richer in boron than phosphorus will contain oxygen anion vacancies. The vacancies permit protons to migrate into the film and free alkali ions.

6. Deposited Glasses

The electrical properties of glasses have been investigated by many workers over the past 50 years. Recent reviews of this large body of literature have been given by Sutton (152, 153) and by Holland (116). Most of the electrical measurements on glass have been made on bulk (~1 mm or greater thickness) samples, and relatively little has been published on electrical properties of thin glass films for semiconductor device passivation. White (*154*) has reviewed the various techniques and materials used in forming thin-film dielectrics. One of the earliest methods of passivating silicon devices with glass involved dip coating the completed, unpassivated devices in low-melting (< 400°C) glasses of the arsenic-sulphur system (*155, 156*). However, since the development of the planar technology for silicon devices, glass has been primarily used for "second-level" passivation over the thermal SiO_2 or a SiO_2-phosphosilicate composite layer. As discussed in Section IV,1, such multilevel passivation, in which the "first-level" insulator is free of ionic conduction, permits glasses to be used which would be too unstable for direct application to the semiconductor surface. Ionic conduction properties of the glass are still very important, however, in cases where the underlying oxide is much thinner than the glass film, or when a device structure is particularly sensitive to surface fields.

Kerr (*157*) studied the space-charge buildup in thin glass films when they were subjected to electric bias at elevated temperature. Several glasses in the lead-aluminoborosilicate and zinc-aluminoborosilicate families were studied, and were deposited on bare silicon by sedimentation and fusing of glass powder (*68*). Film thicknesses varied from 1.6 to 3.8 μ. All measurements were made on aluminum-glass-silicon structures, which are very sensitive to space-charge buildup in the glass, since any space-charge will cause a shift of the capacitance-voltage characteristic along the voltage axis. Initial surface charge levels were quite low ($N_{FB} < 2.7 \times 10^{11}/cm^2$) indicating that this technique of applying glass causes a very low density of surface states or charge density in the insulator. Application of bias at temperatures in the range 100–350°C induced large C-V shifts as shown in Fig. 28. It was proposed that these shifts were due to mobile cations (probably sodium) which are initially uniformly distributed throughout the glass and neutralized by fixed anions. Positive electrode bias leads to an accumulation of sodium ions near the silicon, and the resulting positive space-charge causes a negative C-V shift. Negative bias, on the other hand, moves sodium away from the glass-silicon interface, leaving a negative space-charge due to the unneutralized anions, and giving a positive C-V shift. Figure 28 shows that the temperature required for a given C-V shift is quite reproducible on each wafer but varies widely for different glass compositions. The wide range of glass resistivities was also found by direct measurements of current versus temperature (at 10 volts bias). These resistivity differences did not correlate with the sodium content of the glasses (all had 10^{19} sodium atoms/cm^3 or greater) and were undoubtedly due to structural differences. The asymmetry seen in Fig. 28, where negative bias causes larger C-V shifts, was not observed in the

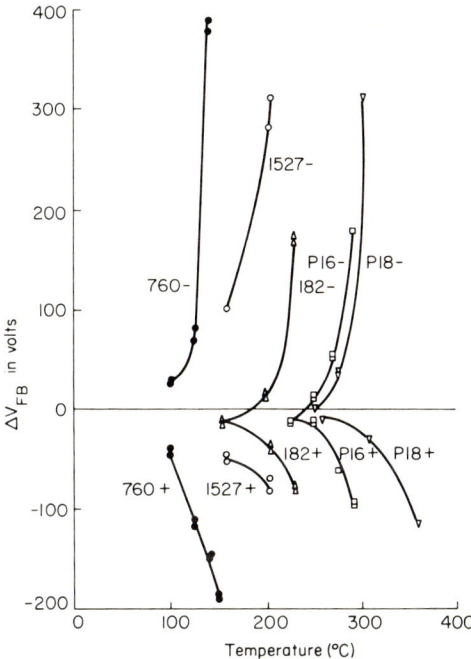

FIG. 28. Shifts in V_{FB} versus temperature of ± 10-volt, 60-min bias-temperature stress for metal-glass-silicon devices. The glasses are lead-aluminoborosilicates and zinc-aluminoborosilicates deposited by sedimentation and fusing. Polarity of the applied bias is indicated on each curve [Kerr (157)].

conduction measurements, and is interpreted as being caused by a partial neutralization of ions at the glass-silicon interface.

Snow and Dumesnil (110) studied space-charge polarization in glass-over-oxide structures by means of C-V measurements. The equilibrium space-charge and kinetics of space-charge formation in this structure were analyzed after assuming an initially uniform distribution of mobile ions in the glass. All experimental work involved a lead borosilicate glass (75% PbO, 12% SiO_2, 10% B_2O_3, 3% TiO_2 by weight) which was sedimented onto the thermal SiO_2 and fused at 530–550°C. In cases where the space-charge width in the glass is much less than the glass thickness, the theoretical C-V shift at equilibrium is given by

$$\Delta V_{\text{SAT}} = -(K_0 X_g / K_g X_0) V_P \qquad (22)$$

where K_0 and K_g are the oxide and glass relative dielectric constants (4 and 16 in this case), X_0 and X_g are the oxide and glass thicknesses, and V_P is the polarizing bias. By varying X_g, X_0, and V_P, Eq. (22) was verified experimentally for negative V_P, as shown in Fig. 29. Measurements of the polarization

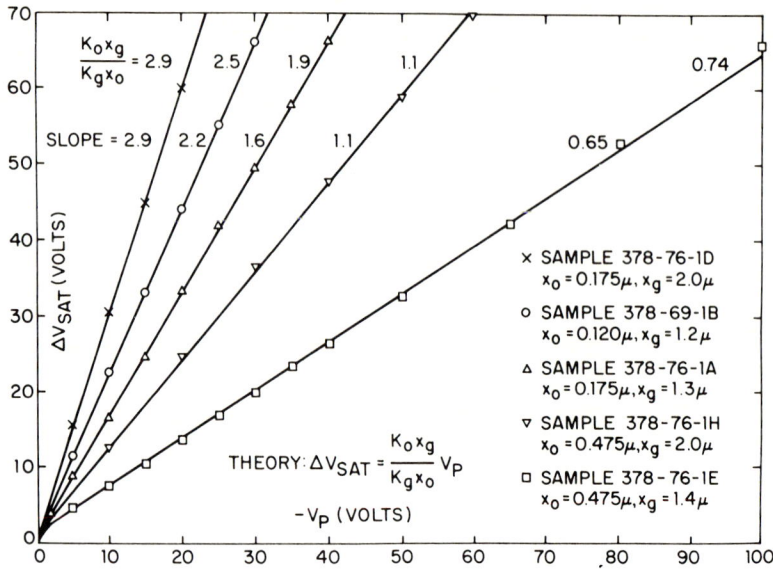

FIG. 29. The saturation C-V shift versus the applied negative polarizing bias for glass-over-SiO$_2$ samples with various X_g/X_0 ratios. The theoretical and measured slopes are given on each curve [Snow and Dumesnil (110)].

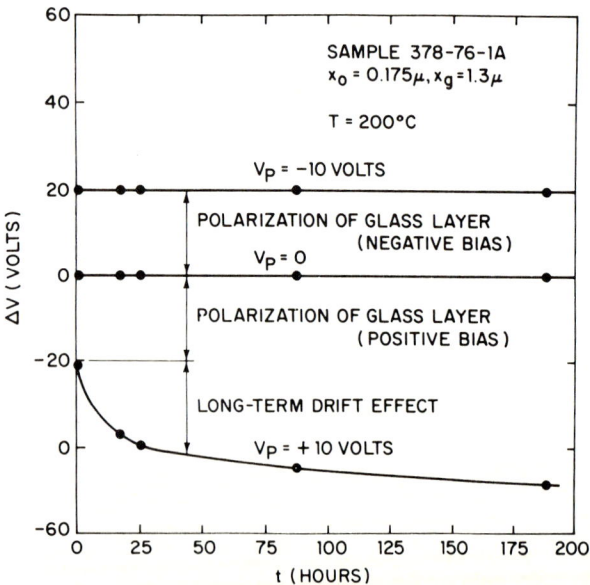

FIG. 30. C-V shift versus time under positive, negative, and zero bias for a glass-over-SiO$_2$ sample. Note long-term drift in addition to rapid initial polarization under positive bias [Snow and Dumesnil (110)].

time constant as a function of temperature gave an activation energy of 1.05 eV and indicate a glass resistivity of $\sim 5 \times 10^{12}$ ohm-cm at 120°C. Equation (22) did not hold for positive V_P. As shown in Fig. 30, an additional long-term drift effect was observed and interpreted as being due to sodium from the glass moving through the oxide. The rapid polarization of the glass, however, was independent of the sodium content and was attributed to the migration of Pb^{++} ions.

Recent work by Kerr (158) indicates that sodium is the dominant mobile species in a lead-aluminoborosilicate glass containing significantly less PbO (about 30 wt%) and illustrates the importance of phosphosilicate glass in multilevel passivation. A sedimented glass film was fused onto bare silicon, onto thermal SiO_2, and onto a phosphosilicate stabilized SiO_2 film. After evaporating aluminum electrodes, MIS devices of each type were biased at +10 volts, 200°C, and charge flow was directly measured as a function of time. Charge versus time curves for the three samples are shown in Fig. 31.

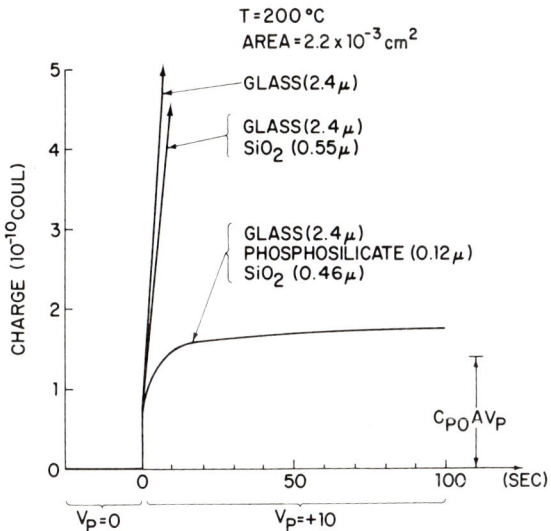

FIG. 31. Charge versus time with positive bias at 200°C for glass-on-silicon, glass-over-SiO_2, and glass-over-phosphosilicate-SiO_2 [Kerr (158)].

As expected, the glass over the phosphosilicate polarizes rapidly until all the applied bias is across the phosphosilicate-SiO_2 layer. One expects a saturation charge of $C_{PO}AV_P$, where C_{PO} is the capacitance per cm^2 of this layer, A is the electrode area, and V_P is the applied bias. As shown in Fig. 16, the measured saturation level is close to this value, indicating that there is little transport of the ionic species through the phosphosilicate-SiO_2 layer.

No such saturation is observed, however, in the glass-over-SiO_2 sample (charge reaching 3.6×10^{-9} C at 100 sec). The charge flow in this sample is nearly as rapid as in the specimen in which the glass was applied to bare silicon. It is obvious that mobile ions reaching the glass-SiO_2 interface have no difficulty in moving through the SiO_2, suggesting that the mobile ion is sodium. Figure 31 demonstrates the necessity of the phosphosilicate layer (or equivalent blocking layer) when using, in multilevel passivation, a glass which conducts by sodium ion migration.

Pyrolytic aluminosilicate glass films deposited at temperatures below 400°C have been used for capacitors (59) and as protective overcoats for oxide passivated planar silicon devices (60, 61). High dielectric strength ($>6 \times 10^6$ volts/cm) and high room-temperature resistivity ($>3 \times 10^{16}$ ohm-cm) are reported (59) for these films. Data on space-charge generation (indicated by C-V stability) has not been given. Eversteijn (64) studied electrical properties of aluminosilicate formed by pyrolysis of tetraethylorthosilicate and triisobutyl aluminum at low temperatures. At 400°C the optimum atomic ratio of Si : Al was found to be 5–6.5 : 1 which gave a relative dielectric constant of 4–4.3, a dielectric strength of $\sim 1.5 \times 10^7$ volts/cm, and a room-temperature resistivity of $\sim 10^{14}$ ohm-cm (at 4×10^6 volts/cm).

Although pyrolytic SiO_2 has been deposited by a variety of reactions (see Section II,3), relatively little has been published on the electrical stability of such films. Rand and Ashworth (33) made MOS measurements on pyrolytic oxide formed in the carbon dioxide process (850°C) and found surface charge and dielectric strength to be comparable to steam-grown oxide. Rand (36) reported that the nitric oxide process produces on Si an SiO_2 film with a surface charge, dielectric strength, and bias-temperature stability comparable to those of steam-grown oxide. Miura et al. (65) found that the stabilizing property of phosphosilicate glass also occurs when the phosphosilicate is formed pyrolytically over pyrolytic SiO_2 ($SiCl_4$ process, 900°C). Tokuyama (44) showed that formation of a lead silicate layer over pyrolytic SiO_2 improves bias-temperature stability.

Davidse and Maissel (84) have deposited a variety of glass compositions by rf-sputtering. Films greater than 1000 Å were shown to have low pinhole densities and high dielectric strength ($3-5 \times 10^6$ volts/cm). Under proper sputtering conditions, the ionic stability of these glasses is probably equal or superior to equivalent glass compositions obtained by sedimentation or thermal oxidation.

Amorphous films of silicon nitride have received recently considerable interest as passivation layers. Hu (88) reported physical properties of silicon nitride films prepared by pyrolytic reaction of SiH_4 and NH_3 (87) and by reactive sputtering of a silicon cathode in N_2. He reported a dielectric constant of 6.2–6.5, a dielectric strength of $\sim 10^7$ volts/cm, and low field resistivities of 10^{15} ohm-cm at 400°C and 2×10^{13} ohm-cm at 500°C. Current-voltage loop measurements showed no detectable ionic conductivity below 400°C. Tombs et al. (*159*) replaced the SiO_2 on planar silicon devices with silicon nitride and found that metal-nitride-silicon capacitors were stable to bias-temperature stress after the nitride surface had been contaminated by sodium. Kerr (*114*) showed that silicon nitride is a barrier to sodium by evaporating $Na^{22}Cl$ ($\sim 10^{13} Na/cm^2$) onto a pyrolytic silicon nitride film before evaporating aluminum electrodes. The MIS devices were then given a sequence of bias-temperature treatments between C-V measurements. The results (Fig. 32) show C-V shifts at 400 and 500°C which are in the wrong

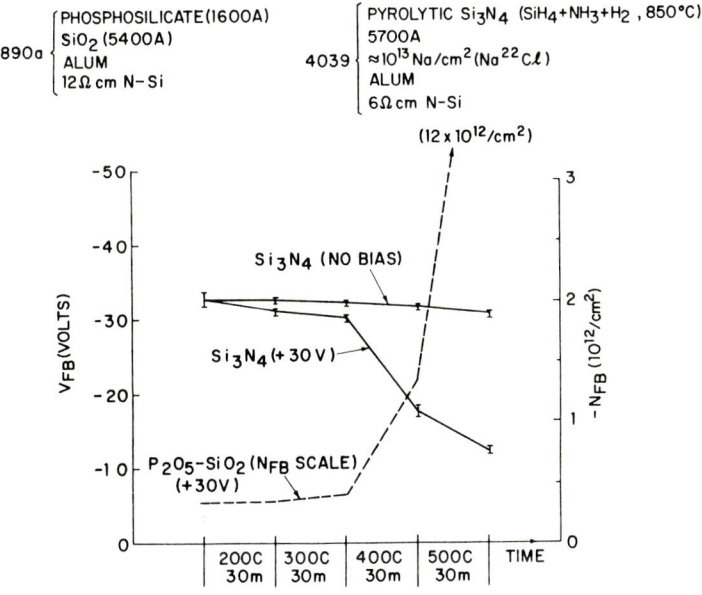

FIG. 32. V_{FB} and N_{FB} versus time with sequence of bias-temperature stress treatments applied to a sodium-contaminated pyrolytic silicon nitride and a phosphosilicate-SiO_2 composite film (no intentional contamination). The phosphosilicate data refer only to the N_{FB} scale [Kerr (*114*)].

direction to be explained by sodium migration. These shifts are probably due to electron transfer and trapping at the nitride-silicon interface. For comparison, Fig. 32 shows N_{FB} for a phosphosilicate stabilized oxide sample, which exhibits ionic polarization at 400 and 500°C. After the 500°C treatment of the nitride sample, the aluminum electrodes were etched off and an autoradiogram was made. The absence of any images in the autoradiogram showed that the sodium had never left the aluminum-nitride interface. Dalton (*160*) investigated sodium drift and diffusion by evaporating $Na^{22}Cl$ ($\sim 10^{14}$

Na/cm^2) onto pyrolytic silicon nitride surfaces. Autoradiograms indicated that fields of $\sim 10^5$ volts/cm at 400°C drove no sodium into the films. Diffusion for 22 hr at 600°C caused measurable diffusion of sodium only into the outer 1000 A of the nitride films. Chu et al. (*161*) showed that the instabilities due to electron transfer at the nitride-silicon interface can be greatly reduced by separating the nitride and the silicon by a thin SiO$_2$ layer. Hu et al. (*162*) gave evidence that instabilities in reactively sputtered silicon nitride films are due to hole injection and trapping. Schneer et al. (*163*) have demonstrated that silicon nitride can be used as a junction seal over oxide passivated planar devices. Devices with this protection were shown to have low failure rates even when highly contaminated with sodium ($\sim 10^{17}$ Na/cm^2) and operated at 300°C. The large number of papers presented at a recent symposium (*164*) on silicon nitride films demonstrates the growing interest in this material for device passivation.

V. Applications of Glass Films to Semiconductor Devices

1. General Advantages

Until recently, the major application of glass films to semiconductor surfaces has been for the purpose of achieving the passivation and protection of discrete planar silicon devices. At the present time, glass films are also used as insulators in the multilayer wiring of monolithic silicon circuits. Future extension to other semiconductor materials is probable at least on a limited scale. In this section we will confine ourselves to silicon applications due to the great predominance of this material in semiconductor device technology.

From a device design and fabrication point of view, the major advantages of glass films are:

(a) Elimination of the need for bulky and expensive hermetically sealed packages.

(b) Protection of the metal interconnecting lands from corrosion and mechanical abrasion. This allows bulk, mechanized handling techniques and more freedom of choice of interconnection methods to the next packaging level.

(c) Excellent-quality insulation for multilevel wiring of monolithic circuits on the chip level. This is essential in order to take advantage of the inherent high device density capabilities of silicon planar technology.

2. Special Considerations For Each Method of Application

The methods of formation of glass films covered in this article can be reduced to three broad classifications: (1) fusing of a glass frit, (2) pyrolytic decomposition and/or reaction of volatile compounds of the glass constituents at the wafer surface, and (3) vacuum deposition, including evaporation and sputtering. Each of these methods offers advantages and disadvantages, and, depending on the particular endproduct one is trying to fabricate, good reasons can usually be found for using one method over the others.

The ideal process is one in which complete compatibility with the device and its metal interconnections is achieved. Generally, as low a deposition temperature as possible is desired consistent with good quality. The net effect is that of striking a compromise between the deposition conditions and the quality of the insulator.

The major advantages and disadvantages of the broad deposition methods mentioned above are:

a. Fusion of Glass Frit

(1) Advantages

(a) Compositional control—the glass that is deposited is the glass selected. The chemical complexity of the glass and compositional variations during firing are not primary factors.

(b) Fusion tends to cover pinholes, gives excellent chemical bonding to the underlying substrate and the glass acts as a flux which dissolves inorganic contaminants, and it pins them down or, in other words, it is "freezing" them.

(c) Simplicity of equipment and process lends itself to low-cost mass production techniques.

(2) Disadvantages. The major disadvantage is that of the firing temperature. The restrictions imposed by this affects the choice of glass and becomes the dominant factor. Thus, from the point of chemical stability and coefficient of thermal expansion the most desirable glasses are high-temperature glasses with high firing temperatures. Some of the boundary conditions are outlined below:

(a) The presence or absence of metal lands under the glass;

(b) The maximum temperature which the metal lands and the metal-semiconductor contacts can stand;

(c) The presence or absence of gold for lifetime control in the silicon.

In most high-speed transistor and monolithic structures the necessity for etching very small, closely spaced emitter and base contact holes, and the necessity for fanning out to conveniently spaced terminals, dictates the use of metal lands under the glass. In this case, the maximum firing temperature of the glass is basically determined by the metallurgy. For example, if aluminum lands are used, the aluminum-silicon eutectic temperature of approximately 577°C forms the upper boundary. In the case of diodes, since the single terminal can be placed directly on the desired contact area of the silicon, metal lands are not required under the glass, and these restrictions are thus removed. If gold is used for lifetime control, however, the glass firing temperature must be compatible with the gold activation temperature which is approximately 1050°C. That is to say the device cannot be glassed at a temperature at which the gold will be deactivated unless one is willing and able to reactivate. Fortunately this is not a serious restriction since there are several glasses which will fire at or near the gold activation temperature or, alternatively, sufficiently low to avoid any problem.

When all the above considerations are taken into account, one can appreciate that the glass layer applied by this method cannot be added to a device as an afterthought, but it must be incorporated into the device design from the beginning.

b. Pyrolytic Decomposition
(*1*) *Advantages*

(a) In principle, a high-temperature glass can be deposited at relatively low temperatures.

(b) Relatively high deposition rates of the order of 1000 A/min can be achieved.

(*2*) *Disadvantages*

(a) Compositional control is relatively difficult and depends both on the vapor phase composition and on the temperature uniformity of the substrate. This would also influence thickness control.

(b) The reaction products or reactants include water and decomposed organics which can be trapped or occluded in the glass layer. This will be greater the lower the formation temperature.

(c) The glasses formed are restricted to the simpler glasses. Although this may not be a serious drawback, it does imply a limiting choice.

(d) Temperature limitations occur here, similarly as in the fusion method. The same ground rules apply.

(e) Obviously, the choice of reactants are such that neither these nor the reaction products should attack the semiconductor structure including the metallurgy.

c. Vacuum Methods
(*1*) *Rf sputtering*

(a) *Advantages*

    (i) A wide range of glasses can be rf sputtered, and the glass deposited closely resembles the starting material.
    (ii) Rates of deposition are relatively high; up to 2000 A/min.

(iii) Deposition temperature can be maintained low, so that compatibility problems, previously mentioned, are negligible.
(iv) Compositional control is easily maintained.
(v) The properties of the deposited film closely resemble those of fused glass films.
(vi) Good thickness uniformity.

(b) *Disadvantages*

(i) To obtain various glasses it is necessary to obtain or fabricate cathodes of these glasses in reasonably large size and free of coarse defects.
(ii) Equipment is complex.
(iii) Substrate temperature control is difficult because of its location in the plasma.

(2) *Reactive sputtering.* The major advantages this offers over rf sputtering is that very-high purity SiO_2 can be formed using a semiconductor grade silicon cathode. Extension to more complex glasses is cumbersome and deposition rates and quality are generally lower.

(3) *Evaporation.* Major advantages over rf sputtering is relative simplicity of equipment and deposition rate.

Major disadvantages are compositional control and relatively poor glass quality.

3. Illustrations of Applications

a. Fused Frit Method. The major commercial application of this method is IBM's Solid Logic Technology (*3, 4, 10*) which is incorporated in IBM's System 360. In this application, discrete and multiple silicon diodes and transistors are passivated and protected by a fused borosilicate-type glass film approximately 1.5 μ thick. Contact holes are etched through the film either to silicon itself (in the case of diodes) or to metal lands (in the case of transistors), and solder terminations are subsequently applied. These "device chips" can then be mechanically handled and attached, by reflow joining, to ceramic modules containing resistors and/or capacitors. The modules are then loosely capped for mechanical protection, but they are not hermetically sealed.

b. Chemical Decomposition. Motorola has developed a major commercial application of this method in which borosilicate and/or aluminosilicate glasses are being deposited onto joined device chips prior to hermetic sealing for added protection (*52–63*), and the Bell Laboratories (*165*) have developed a process using silicon nitride. Bell has incorporated relatively thin ($\sim 0.1\ \mu$) silicon nitride films over the thermal oxide, but under their gold

"Beam-Lead" metalization to form an inert system which does not require further environmental protection.

c. RF Sputtering. IBM has recently reported the use of this method for depositing SiO_2 films for passivation and protection of silicon monolithic circuits and for multilayer wiring of monolithic circuits (*4, 166–168*).

REFERENCES

1. J. A. Perri, H. S. Lehman, W. A. Pliskin, and J. Riseman, *Electrochem. Soc. Meeting, Detroit*, October 1961.
2. J. L. Langdon, W. E. Mutter, R. P. Pecoraro, and K. K. Schuegraf, *Electron Devices Meeting, Washington, D.C.*, October 1961.
3. J. A. Perri, *Semicond. Prod.* **8**, 21 (1965).
4. J. A. Perri and J. Riseman, *Electronics* **39**, 108 (1966).
5. L. Holland, "The Vacuum Deposition of Thin Films." Wiley, New York, 1956.
6. N. Schwartz and R. W. Berry, *Phys. Thin Films* **2**, 363 (1964).
7. L. V. Gregor, *Phys. Thin Films* **3**, 131 (1966).
8. L. I. Maissel, *Phys. Thin Films* **3**, 61 (1966).
9. R. Glang, *J. Vacuum Sci. Technol.* **3**, 37 (1966).
10. E. M. Davis, W. E. Harding, R. S. Schwartz, and J. J. Corning, *IBM J. Res. Develop.* **8**, 102 (1964).
11. W. A. Pliskin, *Proc. IEEE* **52**, 1468 (1964).
12. W. A. Pliskin, *Am. Ceram. Soc. Meeting, Washington, D.C., May 1966*; also published as IBM preprint MP 22.0078.
13. B. E. Deal and A. S. Grove, *J. Appl. Phys.* **36**, 3770 (1965).
14. W. A. Pliskin, *IBM J. Res. Develop.* **10**, 198 (1966).
15. P. J. Burkhardt and L. V. Gregor, *Trans. AIME* **234**, 299 (1966).
16. P. J. Burkhardt, *J. Electrochem. Soc.* **114**, 196 (1967).
17. F. C. Collins and T. Nakayama, *J. Electrochem. Soc.* **114**, 167 (1967).
18. J. F. Delord, D. G. Hoffman, and G. Stringer, *Bull. Am. Phys. Soc.* [2], **10**, 546 (1965).
19. P. Balk, P. J. Burkhardt, and L. V. Gregor, *Proc. IEEE* **53**, 2133 (1965).
20. Y. Miura, *Japan. J. Appl. Phys.* **4**, 958 (1965).
21. P. V. Gray and D. M. Brown, *Appl. Phys. Letters* **8**, 31 (1966).
22. E. Kooi, *Philips Res. Rept.* **21**, 477 (1966).
23. N. Kawamura and H. Iwasaki, *Electrochem. Soc. Meeting, Philadelphia*, October 1966, Abstr. 180.
24. A. G. Revesz, K. H. Zaininger, and R. J. Evans, *J. Phys. Chem. Solids* **28**, 197 (1967).
25. B. E. Deal, M. Sklar, A. S. Grove, and E. H. Snow, *J. Electrochem. Soc.* **114**, 266 (1967).
26. W. A. Pliskin and R. P. Esch, *J. Appl. Phys.* **36**, 2011 (1965).
27. W. A. Pliskin and H. S. Lehman, *Symp. Manufacturing In-Process Control Measuring Tech. Semicond., Phoenix, March 1966*; also published as IBM Tech. Rept. TR 22.279.
28. R. J. Archer, *J. Opt. Soc. Am.* **52**, 970 (1962).
29. W. A. Pliskin and H. S. Lehman, *J. Electrochem. Soc.* **112**, 1013 (1965).
30. R. M. Valletta, J. A. Perri, and J. Riseman, *Electrochem. Technol.* **4**, 402 (1966).
31. J. Klerer, *J. Electrochem. Soc.* **112**, 503 (1965).
32. S. K. Tung and R. E. Caffrey, *Trans. AIME* **233**, 572 (1965).
33. M. J. Rand and J. L. Ashworth, *J. Electrochem. Soc.* **113**, 48 (1966).
34. L. A. Murray and N. Goldsmith, *J. Electrochem. Soc.* **113**, 1297 (1966).

35. W. A. Pliskin, *Electrochem. Soc. Meeting, San Francisco, May 1965*; W. A. Pliskin and P. P. Castrucci (to be published).
36. M. J. Rand, *J. Electrochem. Soc.* **114**, 274 (1967).
37. W. A. Pliskin, P. D. Davidse, H. S. Lehman, and L. I. Maissel, *IBM J. Res. Develop.* (to be published).
38. S. Krongelb and T. O. Sedgwick, *Electrochem. Soc. Meeting, Cleveland, May 1966*, Abstr. 54.
39. W. A. Pliskin, *Electrochem. Soc. Meeting, Philadelphia*, October 1966, Abstr. 140; to be published in "Measurement Techniques for Thin Films," by Electrochem. Soc.
40. J. R. Ligenza, *J. Appl. Phys.* **36**, 2703 (1965).
41. D. A. Kallander, S. S. Flaschen, R. J. Gnaedinger, Jr., and C. M. Duffy, *Electrochem. Soc. Meeting, Indianapolis, May 1961*.
42. S. S. Flaschen and R. J. Gnaedinger, *Met. Soc. Conf.* **16**, 15 (1961).
43. T. Tokuyama, *Proc. IEEE* **52**, 723 (1964).
44. T. Tokuyama, *Electrochem. Soc. Meeting, San Francisco, May 1965*, Abstr. 92.
45. W. A. Pliskin and R. P. Gnall, *J. Electrochem. Soc.* **111**, 872 (1964).
46. E. Kooi, *J. Electrochem. Soc.* **111**, 1383 (1964).
47. W. J. Armstrong and M. C. Duffy, *Electrochem. Technol.* **4**, 475 (1966).
48. G. Siddall, *Vacuum* **9**, 274 (1959).
49. B. Lewis, *Microelectron. Reliability* **3**, 109 (1964).
50a. W. A. Pliskin, *Trans. Nat. Vacuum Symp., 13th, San Francisco, October 1966*, Abstr. 8-1. Am. Vacuum Soc.
50b. H. Schwarz and H. A. Tourtellotte, *Trans. Nat. Vacuum Symp., 13th, San Francisco, October 1966*, Abstr. 5-4. Am. Vacuum Soc.
51. E. L. Jordan, *J. Electrochem. Soc.* **108**, 478 (1961).
52. J. Klerer, *J. Electrochem. Soc.* **108**, 1070 (1961).
53. W. Steinmaier and J. Bloem, *J. Electrochem. Soc.* **111**, 206 (1964).
54. H. S. Lehman, R. M. Valletta, and R. A. Leonard, Private Communication (1965).
55. E. L. MacKenna, W. H. Legat, and W. P. Cox, *Electrochem. Soc. Meeting, Cleveland, May 1966*, Abstr. 53.
56. L. L. Alt, S. W. Ing, Jr., and K. W. Laendle, *J. Electrochem. Soc.* **110**, 465 (1963).
57. D. R. Secrist and J. D. Mackenzie, *Solid-State Electron.* **9**, 180 (1966).
58. D. R. Secrist and J. D. Mackenzie, *J. Electrochem. Soc.* **113**, 914 (1966).
59. D. Peterson, *IEEE Trans. Component Pt.* **10**, 119 (1963).
60. D. R. Peterson, H. B. Bell, and A. L. Epstein, *Electrochem. Soc. Meeting, Washington, D.C., October, 1964*, Abstr. 135.
61. D. L. Tolliver, H. C. Evitts, and A. L. Epstein, *Electrochem. Soc. Meeting, Washington, D.C., October 1964*, Abstr. 136.
62. H. W. Cooper and J. J. LaBrie, *Electrochem. Soc. Meeting, Washington, D.C., October 1964*, Abstr. 127.
63. H. C. Evitts, D. L. Tolliver, and K. R. Mackenzie, Final Tech. Rept. TR-65-285 (ASTIA Report AD 473939). Air Force Materials Lab., August 1965. Previous ASTIA reports in this series: 423632 and 430280 by S. S. Flaschen, H. C. Evitts, and J. R. Black; 439885 and 443200 by H. C. Evitts, D. R. Peterson, D. L. Tolliver, and A. L. Epstein; 457070 and 462743 by H. C. Evitts, D. L. Tolliver, and K. R. Mackenzie.
64. F. C. Eversteijn, *Philips Res. Rept.* **21**, 379 (1966).
65. Y. Miura, S. Tanaka, Y. Matukura, and H. Osafune, *J. Electrochem. Soc.* **113**, 399 (1966).
66. W. A. Pliskin, *Appl. Phys. Letters* **7**, 158 (1965).
67. G. Hetherington and K. H. Jack, *Phys. Chem. Glasses* **3**, 129 (1962).

68. W. A. Pliskin and E. E. Conrad, *Electrochem. Technol.* **2**, 196 (1964).
69. W. A. Pliskin *J. Electrochem. Soc.* **114**, 620 (1967).
70. L. Holland and G. Siddall, *Vacuum* **3**, 245 (1953).
71. W. R. Sinclair and F. G. Peters, *J. Am. Ceram. Soc.* **46**, 20 (1963).
72. E. E. Smith and D. R. Kennedy, *Proc. Inst. Elec. Engrs. (London) Pt B.* **109**, *Suppl. 22*, 504 (1962).
73. E. Bjorck, *Le Vide* **19**, 262 (1963).
74. C. R. Fuller and S. S. Baird, *Electrochem. Soc. Meeting, Pittsburgh, April 1963*, Abstr. 65.
75. R. G. Frieser, *J. Electrochem. Soc.* **113**, 357 (1966).
76. W. R. Sinclair and F. G. Peters, *Rev. Sci. Instr.* **33**, 744 (1962).
77. J. C. Williams, W. R. Sinclair, and S. E. Koonce, *J. Am. Ceram. Soc.* **46**, 161 (1963).
78. J. I. Lodge and R. W. Stewart, *Can. J. Res.* **A26**, 205 (1948].
79. G. K. Wehner, *Advan. Electron. Electron Phys.* **7**, 239 (1955).
80. G. S. Anderson, W. N. Mayer, and G. K. Wehner, *J. Appl. Phys.* **33**, 2991 (1962).
81. G. V. Jorgenson and G. K. Wehner, *J. Appl. Phys.* **36**, 2672 (1965).
82. P. D. Davidse and L. I. Maissel, *Proc. Trans. Intern. Vacuum Congr., 3rd, 1965*, **2**, p. 651. (1966).
83. P. D. Davidse and L. I. Maissel, *Insulation*, April 1966.
84. P. D. Davidse and L. I. Maissel, *J. Appl. Phys.* **37**, 574 (1966).
85. P. D. Davidse, *Symp. Deposition Thin Films Sputtering, Univ. of Rochester, Rochester, New York, June 1966*.
86. H. F. Sterling and R. C. G. Swann, *Solid-State Electron.* **8**, 653 (1965).
87. V. Y. Doo, D. R. Nichols, and G. A. Silvey, *J. Electrochem. Soc.* **113**, 1279 (1966).
88. S. M. Hu, *J. Electrochem. Soc.* **113**, 693 (1966).
89. A. R. Janus and G. A. Shirn, *J. Vacuum Sci. Technol.* **4**, 37 (1967).
90. C. Shaeffer, F. Matossi, and K. Wirtz, *Z. Physik* **89**, 210 (1934).
91. F. Matossi and H. Kruger, *Z. Physik* **99**, 1 (1936).
92. V. A. Florinskaya and R. S. Pechenkina, *Dokl. Acad. Nauk SSSR* **91**, 59 (1953).
93. P. E. Jellyman and J. P. Procter, *J. Soc. Glass Technol.* **39**, T173 (1955).
94. V. A. Kolesova, *Opt. Spectr. (USSR)* (English Transl.) **6**, 20 (1959).
95. W. A. Pliskin and E. E. Conrad, *J. Phys.* **25**, 17 (1964).
96. W. A. Pliskin and E. E. Conrad, *IBM J. Res. Develop.* **8**, 43 (1964).
97. E. A. Corl, S. L. Silverman, and Y. S. Kim, *Solid-State Electron.* **9**, 1009 (1966).
98. G. Hass, *J. Am. Ceram. Soc.* **33**, 353 (1950).
99. G. Hass and C. D. Salzberg, *J. Opt. Soc. Am.* **44**, 181 (1954).
100. A. P. Bradford and G. Hass, *J. Opt Soc. Am.* **53**, 1096 (1963).
101. J. T. Cox, G. Hass, and J. B. Ramsey, *J. Phys.* **25**, 250 (1964).
102. E. Ritter, *Opt. Acta* **9**, 197 (1962).
103. A. P. Bradford, G. Hass, M. McFarland, and E. Ritter, *Appl. Opt.* **4**, 971 (1965).
104. L. F. Drummeter and G. Hass, *Phys. Thin Films* **2**, 305 (1964).
105. P. White, *Vacuum* **12**, 15 (1962).
106. J. R. Priest, H. L. Caswell, and Y. Budo, *J. Appl. Phys.* **34**, 347 (1963).
107. D. B. York, *J. Electrochem. Soc.* **110**, 27 (1963).
108a. O. Ruff and P. Schmidt. *Z. Anorg. Allgem. Chem.* **117**, 172 (1921).
108b. C. B. Alcock, *Trans. Brit. Ceram. Soc.* **60**, 147 (1961).
109. R. H. Kingston and S. F. Neustadter, *J. Appl. Phys.* **26**, 718 (1955).
110. E. H. Snow and M. E. Dumesnil, *J. Appl. Phys.* **37**, 2123 (1966).

111. D. R. Frankl, *Solid-State Electron.* **2**, 71 (1961).
112. R. Lindner, *Bell System Tech. J.* **41**, 803 (1962).
113. A. S. Grove, B. E. Deal, E. H. Snow, and C. T. Sah, *Solid-State Electron.* **8**, 145 (1965).
114. D. R. Kerr, *Electrochem. Soc. Meeting, Cleveland, May 1966*, Abstr. 14.
115. W. Shockley, W. W. Hooper, H. J. Quiesser, and W. Schroen, *Surface Sci.* **4**, 299 (1966).
116. L. Holland, "The Properties of Glass Surfaces." Wiley, New York, 1964.
117. M. M. Atalla, E. Tannenbaum, and E. J. Scheibner, *Bell System Tech. J.* **38**, 749 (1959).
118. C. J. Frosch and L. Derick, *J. Electrochem. Soc.* **104**, 547 (1957).
119. J. A. Hoerni, *IRE Electron Devices Meeting, Washington, D.C., 1960.*
120. M. M. Atalla, A. R. Bray, and R. Lindner, *Proc. Inst. Elec. Engrs.* (*London*) *Pt. B* **106**, 1130 (1959).
121. D. Kahng and M. M. Atalla, *IRE-AIEE Solid-State Device Res. Conf., Pittsburgh, 1960.*
122. S. R. Hofstein and F. P. Heiman, *Proc. IEEE* **51**, 1190 (1963).
123. R. P. Donovan, Integrated silicon device technology, Vol. 7. ASD-TDR-63-316. Res. Triangle Inst., Durham, North Carolina, (1965).
124. B. E. Deal, E. H. Snow, and A. S. Grove, *Semicond. Prod.* **9**, No. 11, 25 (1966).
125. A. Goetzberger, *Arch. Elek. Übertr.* **20**, 241 (1966).
126. *IBM J. Res. Develop.* **8**, No. 4 (1964); *Trans. AIME* **233**, No. 3 (1965); *IEEE Trans. Electron Devices* **12**, No. 3 (1965); *IEEE Trans. Electron Devices* **13**, No. 2 (1966).
127. J. P. Mitchell and D. K. Wilson, *Bell System Tech. J.* **46**, 1 (1967).
128. P. Balk, *Electrochem. Soc. Meeting, San Francisco, May 1965*, Abstr. 109.
129. E. Kooi, *IEEE Trans. Electron Devices* **13**, 238 (1966).
130. K. H. Zaininger and A. G. Revesz, *Appl. Phys. Letters* **7**, 108 (1965).
131. A. G. Revesz and K. H. Zaininger, *IEEE Trans. Electron Devices* **13**, 246 (1966).
132. H. S. Lehman, *IBM J. Res. Develop.* **8**, 422 (1964).
133. J. Olmstead, J. Scott, and P. Kuznetzoff, *IEEE Trans. Electron Devices* **12**, 104 (1965).
134. A. S. Grove and D. J. Fitzgerald, *Solid-State Electron.* **5**, 894 (1966).
135. J. L. Sprague, J. A. Minahan, and O. J. Wied, *J. Electrochem. Soc.* **109**, 94 (1962).
136. M. Yamin and F. L. Worthing, *Electrochem. Soc. Meeting, Toronto, May 1964*, Abstr. 75.
137. D. R. Kerr, J. S. Logan, P. J. Burkhardt, and W. A. Pliskin, *IBM J. Res. Develop.* **8**, 376 (1964).
138. J. E. Thomas, Jr. and D. R. Young, *IBM J. Res. Develop.* **8**, 368 (1964).
139. D. P. Seraphim, A. E. Brennemann, F. M. d'Heurle, and H. L. Friedman, *IBM J. Res. Develop.* **8**, 400 (1964).
140. E. H. Snow, A. S. Grove, B. E. Deal, and C. T. Sah, *J. Appl. Phys.* **36**, 1664 (1965).
141. J. S. Logan and D. R. Kerr, *IEEE Solid-State Device Res. Conf., Princeton, June 1965.*
142. S. R. Hofstein, *IEEE Trans. Electron. Devices* **13**, 222 (1966).
143. D. R. Kerr, *Silicon Interface Specialists Conf., Las Vegas, March 1967.* To be published.
144. A. E. Owen and R. W. Douglas, *J. Soc. Glass Technol.* **43**, 159 (1959).
145. H. G. Carlson, G. A. Brown, C. R. Fuller, and J. Osborne, "Physics of Failure in Electronics," Vol. 4. Rome Air Develop. Center, 1966.
146. E. Yon, W. H. Ko, and A. B. Kuper, *IEEE Trans. Electron. Devices* **13**, 276 (1966).
147. M. Yamin, *IEEE Trans. Electron. Devices* **12**, 88 (1965).
148. E. H. Snow and B. E. Deal, *J. Electrochem. Soc.* **113**, 263 (1966).
149. D. R. Kerr, *Silicon Interface Specialists Conf., Las Vegas, November 1965.*
150. T. M. Buck and J. V. Dalton, *Silicon Interface Specialists Conf., Las Vegas, November 1965.*

151. M. Yamin, *IEEE Trans. Electron Devices* **13**, 256 (1966).
152. P. M. Sutton, The dielectric properties of glass, *in* "Progress in Dielectrics" (J. B. Birks and J. H. Schulman, eds.), Vol. 2. Wiley, New York, 1960.
153. P. M. Sutton, *J. Am. Ceram. Soc.* **47**, 188, 219 (1964).
154. P. White, *Insulation* **9**, 57 (1963).
155. S. S. Flaschen, A. D. Pearson, and I. L. Kalnins, *J. Appl. Phys.* **31**, 431 (1960).
156. A. D. Pearson, Sulphide, selenide and telluride glasses, *in* "Modern Aspects of the Vitreous State" (J. D. Mackenzie, ed.), Vol. 3. Butterworths, London and Washington, D.C., 1964.
157. D. R. Kerr, *IBM J. Res. Develop.* **8**, 385 (1964).
158. D. R. Kerr, Unpublished data.
159. N. C. Tombs, H. A. R. Wegener, R. Newman, B. T. Kenney, and A. J. Coppola, *Proc. IEEE* **54**, 87 (1966).
160. J. V. Dalton, *Electrochem. Soc. Meeting, Cleveland, May 1966*, recent newspaper Abstr. 23.
161. T. L. Chu, J. R. Szedon, and C. H. Lee, *Electrochem. Soc. Meeting, Philadelphia, October 1966*, Abstr. 158.
162. S. M. Hu, D. R. Kerr, and L. V. Gregor, *Appl. Phys. Letters* **10**, 97 (1967).
163. G. H. Schneer, W. vanGelder, V. E. Hauser, and P. F. Schmidt, *IEEE Electron Devices Meeting, Washington, D.C., October 1966*.
164. *Electrochem. Soc. Meeting, Philadelphia, October 1966*, Abstr. 146–163 and recent news abstracts 1, 2, 4–6.
165. *Bell Lab. Record* **44**, 290–346 (1966) (entire October-November 1966 issue).
166. B. Agusta, P. Bardell, and P. P. Castrucci, *IEEE Electron Devices Meeting, Washington, D.C., October 1965*.
167. O. Bilous, I. Feinberg, and J. L. Langdon, *IBM J. Res. Develop.* **10**, 370 (1966).
168. V. A. Dhaka, *Intern. Elektron. Arbeitskreis Ev, Munich, Germany, October 1966*.

Hot-Electron Transport and Electron Tunneling in Thin Film Structures

C. R. Crowell*

*Departments of Materials Science and Electrical Engineering,
University of Southern California, Los Angeles, California*

and

S. M. Sze

*Bell Telephone Laboratories, Incorporated,
Murray Hill, New Jersey*

I. Introduction	325
II. Hot-Electron Scattering Processes in Metals	327
1. Hot-Electron and Electrical Conductivity Mean-Free Paths	327
2. Electron-Electron Mean-Free Paths	328
III. Collection of Hot Electrons	330
1. Electron-Phonon Scattering	330
2. Quantum-Mechanical Reflection	338
IV. Photoemission Experiments	341
1. Methods of Analysis	341
2. Attenuation Length Measurements	345
V. Tunnel Emission	350
1. Emitter Characteristics	351
2. Base Transport	353
VI. Schottky (Thermionic) Emission	354
1. Emitter Characteristics	356
2. Experimental Measurements	360
VII. Discussion and Summary	368
References	369

I. Introduction

Much interest has recently been expressed in the characteristics and potential applications of transistor-like three-terminal structures composed of alternating layers of metal and insulator or semiconductor. Historically, the first of these structures, a metal-insulator-metal-insulator-metal structure in which current flow through the insulator layers occurred by tunneling, was made by Mead (*1*). Spratt *et al.* (*2*) pointed out that the current gain of such structures could be greatly improved by replacing the collector insulator by

---

* Supported by the Technical Committee of the Joint Services Electronics Program under Grant No. AF-AFOSR-496-66.

a Schottky barrier semiconductor layer. Rose (3), Atalla and Kahng (4), and Geppert (5) continued the process of development by suggesting that the tunnel emitter be replaced by a Schottky barrier emitter. As originally envisaged, all three structures had close relationships with the bipolar transistor. All three were radically different from the bipolar transistor, however, in the use of a thin metal "base" region of the order of 100 A thick. This region was postulated to be essentially transparent for electrons injected from the emitter towards the collector and gave these structures three advantages over the bipolar transistor: First, the fact that electrons with only a fraction of an electron volt of energy relative to the Fermi energy in metals have transit times of the order of 10^{-14} sec for a 100-A film ensured that the base transit time would be negligible in comparison with that of a bipolar transistor. Secondly, since scattering in such a film would virtually preclude subsequent collection of excited carriers in the above structures, minority carrier storage in the base would also be eliminated. The high base conductance of even a 100-A metal film relative to that of the base of a high-frequency transistor was the third advantage of these structures over the bipolar transistor (6, 7).

We have placed the material in this article within the context of the above structures, but with the focus mainly on one problem of intrinsic interest that is common to all three, namely that of the transport of excited charge carriers or "hot" electrons through metal films. Thus we have not discussed many aspects of tunneling in metal-insulator-metal structures. Attention has also been mainly directed to the transport of electrons near the Fermi energy with energies typically less than the metal work function, though we have also discussed experiments in which one or more of the insulator or semiconductor regions are in effect replaced by a vacuum.

Section II contains a short review of the approach and conclusions resulting from some of the existing theoretical treatments of scattering processes in metals. Section III contains an outline of theoretical treatments of the problem of collection of hot electrons, a problem common to a development of a quantitative understanding of all hot-electron transport measurements. In Section IV experimental analysis and results are presented from studies of electrons photoexcited in metal films and subsequently collected either at a vacuum electrode or over a metal-semiconductor (Schottky) barrier on one side of a film. Electron transport properties deduced from experiments using tunnel emitters are reviewed in Section V. Section VI contains experimental analysis and data deduced from structures using Schottky emitters. We have not sought to discuss in detail the relative merits of the structures from the viewpoint of device applications. Current-gain limitations demonstrate that even the most promising structure of the three, that with a Schottky emitter and Schottky collector, appears to have difficulty in competing successfully with the bipolar transistor for wide-band high-frequency applications (8). We have also not presented an organized consideration of a class of superficially similar devices, the metal-edge amplifier and related structures which depend on space-charge-limited current flow through pinholes in metal films or around the edges of such films. Lavine (9) has reviewed the properties of these structures. In the experimental evidence we have considered, however, we have attempted to assess the possibility that the observed current transport may have been inadvertently dominated by phenomena associated with such pinhole or other film defects.

II. Hot-Electron Scattering Processes in Metals

The processes which lead to the scattering of hot electrons in metals are qualitatively similar to those which determine the electrical conductivity. Electron-defect, electron-impurity, and electron-phonon scattering all occur. Strong effects from surface scattering, however, should not occur since the measurements which we consider involve electron transport through rather than parallel to the surface of thin films. In contrast, electron-electron scattering is more important for hot electrons than for electrons near the Fermi energy. This is apparent from density-of-states arguments to be discussed later. Electron-electron interactions degrade the energy of hot electrons, but do not change the flux of electrons at all in the free-electron case, since momentum is conserved within the electron distribution. For electrons several electron-volts above the Fermi energy, the possibility of plasma excitations exists as an additional scattering mechanism.

We have considered the above scattering processes in two groups. The first group comprises defect, impurity, and phonon scattering processes closely related to those involved in electrical conductivity. Electron-electron and electron-plasma scattering make up the second group.

1. Hot-Electron and Electrical Conductivity Mean-Free Paths

Defects and charged impurities introduce essentially temperature-independent contributions to the scattering associated with electrical conductivity, as is evidenced by Matthiessen's observations [Matthiessen and Vogt (10)]. Thus these mechanisms should not provide a strongly energy-dependent contribution to the scattering of hot electrons. This is also suggested by Mott's calculation of the energy dependence of the electron scattering produced by temperature-independent local deviations of the electron potential energy from that of a periodic lattice (11). A mean-free path proportional to the square of the electron kinetic energy was predicted. Mott used the Born approximation, which is valid for the case where the electron kinetic energy is large in comparison with the coulomb potential energy perturbation, a condition easily satisfied in monovalent metals. Approximately the same results are obtained from the Conwell–Weisskopf treatment of essentially unscreened coulomb scattering (*12*), and from the calculations made for a coulomb potential screened by free carriers by Dingle (*13*) and by Brooks (*14*). These approaches have been compared by Smith (*15*).

Electron-phonon scattering is a much more temperature-dependent process than defect and impurity scattering because of the temperature dependence of the amplitude of the lattice vibrations. The energy dependence of the electron mean-free path for electron-phonon scattering is, however, the same as that for defect and impurity scattering since all have essentially a shielded coulomb origin. The electron-phonon portion of this scattering problem has been calculated theoretically by Wilson (*16*) for free electrons. Thus when carriers in only a single parabolic band are involved, we can combine Wilson's and Mott's result to relate the hot-electron mean-free path for lattice-related scattering mechanisms, λ_c, to the electron mean-free path for electrical conductivity, λ_σ. Then

$$\lambda_c = \lambda_\sigma (E/E_f)^2 \qquad (1)$$

where E is the hot-electron kinetic energy, and E_f is the Fermi kinetic energy, both measured from the bottom of the conduction band. This relationship permits us to compare data obtained from hot-electron measurements with that from studies of electrical conductivity.

2. Electron-Electron Mean-Free Paths

The calculation of the mean-free path for electron-electron scattering in a real metal is a problem of considerable difficulty. On the other hand, the approximate energy dependence of the electron-electron mean-free path, $\lambda_{e\text{-}e}$, can be predicted very simply from density-of-states considerations. The relaxation time for electron-electron scattering is inversely proportional to the square of the difference between the electron energy and the Fermi energy, since this difference determines both the number of states with which an electron can interact and the number of states to which electrons can be excited. Since the mean-free path equals the product of the relaxation time and carrier velocity, then

$$\lambda_{e\text{-}e} \propto E^{1/2}(E - E_f)^{-2} \qquad (2)$$

This relationship also holds for the mean-free path of holes.

Quinn (*17*) used a self-consistent dielectric approach to estimate values of λ_{e-e} for a hot electron interacting with a free-electron gas. His result is

$$\lambda_{e\text{-}e} = \frac{14.5(E_f \beta)^{3/2} E}{(m^*)^{1/2}[\tan^{-1} \beta^{-1/2} + \beta^{1/2}/(1 + \beta)]} (E - E_f)^{-2} \qquad (3)$$

where $\lambda_{e\text{-}e}$ is in angstroms, m^* is the electron effective mass in units of the free-electron mass, the energies are measured in electron-volts, and

$$\beta = (4/9)^{1/3}(r_s/\pi) \tag{4}$$

r_s (measured in units of the Bohr radius) is the radius of a sphere equal in volume to the volume per electron. From the Born approximation and a phenomenological Yukawa potential, Motizuki and Sparks (18) obtained results equivalent to Quinn's in the limit of high free-electron densities. Adler (19) used a random phase approximation dielectric approach with a one OPW model for aluminum.[1] When his initial results are corrected for a computational error, the effects of Umklapp processes and local field corrections are predicted to be small. Adler also deduced the possibility of significant anisotropic scattering effects and enhanced hot-electron scattering associated with flattened Fermi surfaces. Quinn later pointed out that when d-band contributions to the dielectric constant are present, the theoretical mean-free path values (17) should be appreciably increased (20). Ritchie and Ashley (21) have considered electron exchange interactions, and predict an increase of approximately 70% for the $\lambda_{e\text{-}e}$ of monovalent noble metals relative to the mean-free paths, neglecting exchange. If both Quinn's correction factor for the d-band dielectric shielding and Ritchie and Ashley's exchange corrections are superimposed on the predictions of Eq. (3), an increase of a factor of approximately three is expected for the $\lambda_{e\text{-}e}$ values of the monovalent noble metals.

Quinn (17) has also estimated the mean-free path for hot-electron-plasma interactions. For a free-electron model, the threshold energy for this interaction in aluminum is $E \approx 25$ eV. Krolikowski and Spicer (22) have seen no evidence of plasma interactions in photoemission from copper for electron energies as large as 10 eV above the Fermi level. Similar results have been observed for gold (22). It thus appears that for the hot-electron energies we consider here, namely $E \lesssim 2E_f$, from both theoretical and experimental evidence, plasma interactions will not make appreciable contributions to hot-electron scattering.

In summary, the relative importance of the scattering processes characterized by the mean-free paths $\lambda_{e\text{-}e}$ and λ_c depends strongly on the experimental situation for two reasons. In the first place, $\lambda_{e\text{-}e}$ has a strong energy dependence relative to that of λ_c that makes $\lambda_{e\text{-}e}$ dominant for electrons with a large excitation energy. Secondly, the average energy loss associated with electron-electron scattering is approximately half the excitation energy (21), whereas the loss associated with λ_c is typically a few tens of millivolts. In Sections IV, V, and VI, we discuss cases in which the above distinctions are of major importance in the interpretation of experimental results.

[1] Orthogonalized plane wave model.

III. Collection of Hot Electrons

To permit a more comprehensive interpretation of experimental measurements, in this section we review theoretical work on the energy and temperature dependence of the collection efficiency for hot electrons. Hot-electron transport in metal films can be observed in the neighborhood of a metal-semiconductor, metal-insulator, or metal-vacuum interface but the efficiency of injection and collection across the interface must be appreciable. The dominant processes which affect the efficiencies of collection and injection are generation and absorption of phonons by hot electrons in the semiconductor or insulator regions, and quantum-mechanical reflection of the excited charge carriers at the potential energy barrier in the neighborhood of the interface. The shape of the barrier is of considerable importance in both scattering processes. We consider first the effect of electron-phonon scattering, in which the shape of the barrier near the potential energy maximum is most important, and second the effect of quantum-mechanical reflection in which all features of the barrier shape are important.

1. Electron-Phonon Scattering

Hall (23) has suggested that the problem of backscatter of hot electrons at a metal-semiconductor interface should be analogous to that of the backscatter of thermal neutrons at a vacuum-diffuser interface, where the reflection coefficient is of the order of one half. This should be a reasonable approximation if the hot-electron energy is large in comparison with both the phonon energy and the potential energy drop across the collector barrier.

For low-energy electrons, Crowell and Sze (24, 25) have developed two theoretical treatments of the collection problem. In their initial approach (24) they assumed that generation of optical phonons of a single energy, E_{op}, was the dominant backscatter process, and that the electron mean-free path was a constant for electron kinetic energies in excess of E_{op}. An electron was then collected in the bulk of the collector semiconductor or reflected depending on where the optical-phonon scattering event occurred which reduced the electron energy below that required to surmount the barrier. An analytic solution to the problem of two scattering events was obtained. Because phonon absorption was not considered, this theory can only be applied at low temperatures ($kT \lesssim E_{op}$). In the subsequent approach (25) allowance was made for phonon absorption and for energy dependence of the mean-free path. In one sense, however, the first theory was more sophisticated than the second in that in the latter only one scattering event was considered: i.e., if, after the first phonon scattering, the electron was within the cone of acceptance for passage into the body of the collector semiconductor, then the electron was assumed to be collected (cf. Fig. 1). The agreement between

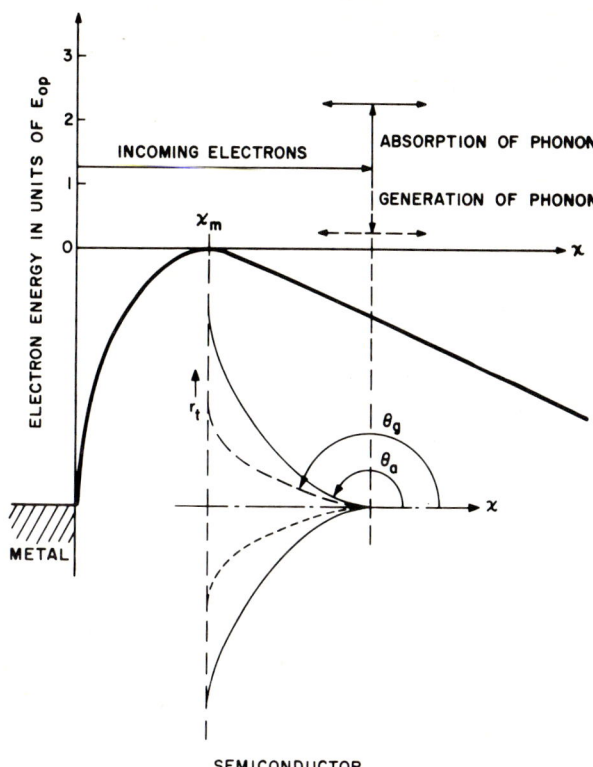

FIG. 1. Electron potential energy versus distance from a metal-semiconductor interface. x_m is the position of the potential maximum, E_{op} is the optical-phonon energy. θ_a and θ_g are the limiting angles for collection after absorption or generation, respectively, of an optical phonon. The subsequent electron trajectories (transverse displacement r_t versus x) are also shown (24).

both approaches at low temperatures, however, suggests that the second approach is also a good approximation in the temperature range where the first approach is not valid. The second theory is summarized here. Before the final results are presented, two underlying factors affecting the collection problem are considered: the hot-electron mean-free path in the collector and the potential barrier shape.

a. Electron-Optical-Phonon Mean-Free Path. If a parabolic electron energy versus crystal momentum relationship exists, the mean distance in the x direction, L_{ax}, for an electron to absorb an optical phonon can be expressed in the form (26, 27)

$$L_{ax} = \frac{L_0}{N}\left[\frac{E_x}{E_x + E_t + E_{op}}\right]^{1/2} \tag{5}$$

N is the expectation value of the number of optical phonons per mode [$N = 1/(\exp(E_{op}/kT) - 1)$]. E_x is the energy associated with x-directed momentum of the electron and E_t is the energy associated with transverse momentum. L_0 is the high-energy low-temperature asymptotic value of the mean-free path. L_{gx}, the mean travel distance in the x direction for an electron to generate an optical phonon is infinite if $(E_x + E_t) < E_{op}$. If $(E_x + E_t) \geq E_{op}$,

$$L_{gx} = \frac{L_0}{N+1}\left[\frac{E_x}{E_x + E_t - E_{op}}\right]^{1/2} \quad (6)$$

The term $E_x^{1/2}$ in Eqs. (5) and (6) arises because L_{ax} and L_{gx} are proportional to the x-directed velocity of the electron. The terms $(E_x + E_t \pm E_{op})^{1/2}$ arise from the density of states available for the electron after absorption or generation, respectively, of an optical phonon. An energy-independent mean-free path, L, for optical-phonon scattering, whether from absorption or generation, at high electron energies is predicted from Eqs. (5) and (6):

$$L = L_0 \tanh(E_{op}/2kT) \quad (7)$$

If the transverse momentum distribution of the electrons is essentially Maxwellian with the same temperature as the lattice, the first-order effect of the distribution on the mean-free paths in the x direction can be approximated by equating E_t to kT. Figure 2 shows plots of L_{ax}/L_0 and L_{gx}/L_0 as a function of E_x/E_{op} for selected values of E_{op}/kT. It is apparent that for $E_x > E_{op}$, the mean-free paths vary only slowly with energy.

The values of L_0 are, of course, of great interest. Conwell's (27) treatment of relaxation times from a deformation potential approach could be used to calculate L_0. One of the most direct sources, however, is from secondary ionization data. Room-temperature secondary ionization rates for electrons and holes have been measured by Miller in Ge (28), Lee et al. in Si (29), Logan and White in GaP (30), and Logan and Sze in GaAs and Ge (31). Crowell and Sze (32) have shown that the dependence of charge carrier ionization probability per unit distance traveled on the electric field and on the lattice temperature can be expressed in terms of a modification of Baraff's (33) three-parameter theory. The parameters are: L, as described above; E_i, the ionization threshold energy; and $\langle E_{op} \rangle$, the average energy loss per phonon scattering. The E_i values for best fit are approximately three halves the band-gap energy. Baraff's theory was originally developed in terms of E_{op}, i.e., without allowing for absorption of optical phonons. Since the number of collisions per unit path length in which generation of optical phonons occurs is proportional to $(N + 1)$ and the corresponding number of collisions associated with absorption of optical phonons is proportional to N [cf. Eqs. (5) and (6)], the actual net loss of electron energy per unit path

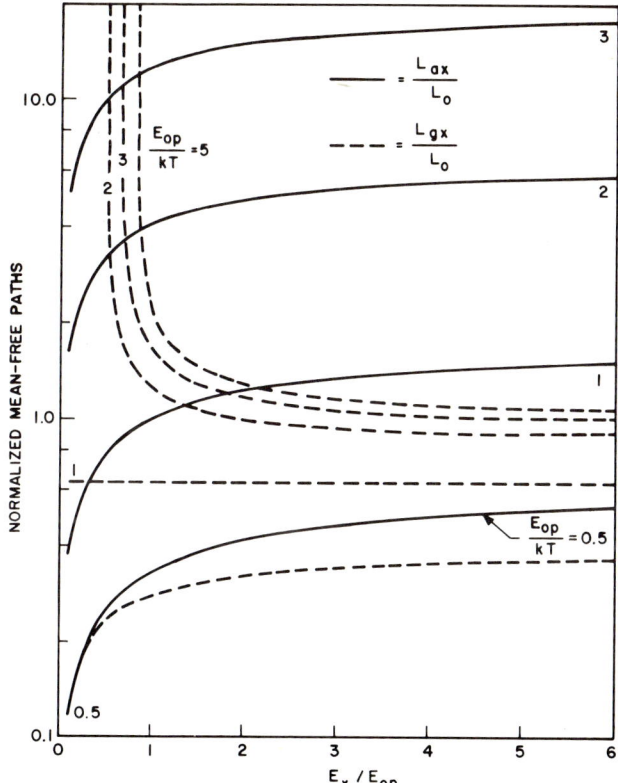

FIG. 2. Normalized mean-free paths for generation, L_{gx}/L_0, and absorption, L_{ax}/L_0, for electron travel in the x direction as a function of E_x/E_{op}, where L_0 is the high-energy low-temperature asymptotic value of the optical-phonon mean-free path, and E_x is the energy associated with momentum in the x direction. The energy associated with transverse momentum is kT. E_{op} is the optical-phonon energy (25).

length, which is proportional to $(N + 1 - N)$, is independent of the temperature. Thus

$$\langle E_{op}\rangle/E_{op} = L/L_0 = \tanh(E_{op}/2kT) \qquad (8)$$

Experimental values of L at room temperature, and L_0 values for Ge, Si, GaAs, and GaP are listed in Table I. The distinction between L and L_0 is important for Ge and GaAs because both semiconductors have E_{op} values only slightly larger than kT at room temperature.

b. Potential Barrier Shape. Figure 1 shows the approximate potential energy for an electron in a metal-semiconductor barrier as a function of the distance, x, from the metal-semiconductor interface. The potential energy maximum arises from the combined action of the electric field, $\mathscr{E}$, near the

TABLE I

Hot Carrier Mean-Free Paths for Optical-Phonon Scattering

	Ge	Si Hole	Si Electron	GaAs	GaP
E_{op} (eV) (34, 35)	0.036	0.062	0.062	0.036	0.050
L_{300}(A)	65	38	62	35	32
L_0 (A)	105	47	76	58	42

interface and an image force due to charge induced on the metal surface by the approach of the electron. Since hot electrons must travel beyond the potential energy maximum to reach the bulk of the semiconductor, the barrier shape is of considerable importance in affecting the probability of collection. The electron potential energy, $V(x)$, relative to the potential energy maximum is

$$V(x) = -q^2/16\pi\varepsilon_d x - q\mathscr{E}x + q\,\Delta\varphi \tag{9}$$

where q is the charge of the electron, ε_d is the image force permittivity of the semiconductor, and $q\Delta\varphi$ is the amount by which the barrier is lowered from its value at zero field.

$$\Delta\varphi = (q\mathscr{E}/4\pi\varepsilon_d)^{1/2} \tag{10}$$

The barrier maximum occurs at

$$x_m = (q/16\pi\varepsilon_d\mathscr{E})^{1/2} \tag{11}$$

Sze et al. (36) have shown from photoemission measurements that Eq. (10) described the barrier height lowering in a gold-silicon Schottky barrier if the image force dielectric constant of silicon is 12 (cf. Fig. 3). This is consistent with the semiconductor dielectric constant at frequencies just below those at which band-to-band transitions occur, and is the expected result if the hot-electron transit time available for polarization of the dielectric is considered.[2]

Equation (9) thus describes the barrier in the neighborhood of the potential energy maximum. For values of x of the order of a few angstroms, the potential profile rises rapidly in a distance very small in comparison with the electron mean-free path. Thus the exact shape of the barrier is not important for small x if only phonon scattering is considered. Two more-detailed models for the barrier shape are considered in Section III, 2 where the problem of quantum-mechanical reflection is treated.

---

[2] Thus far Eq. (10) has not been checked for a semiconductor in which there is an appreciable difference between the high- and low-frequency dielectric constants.

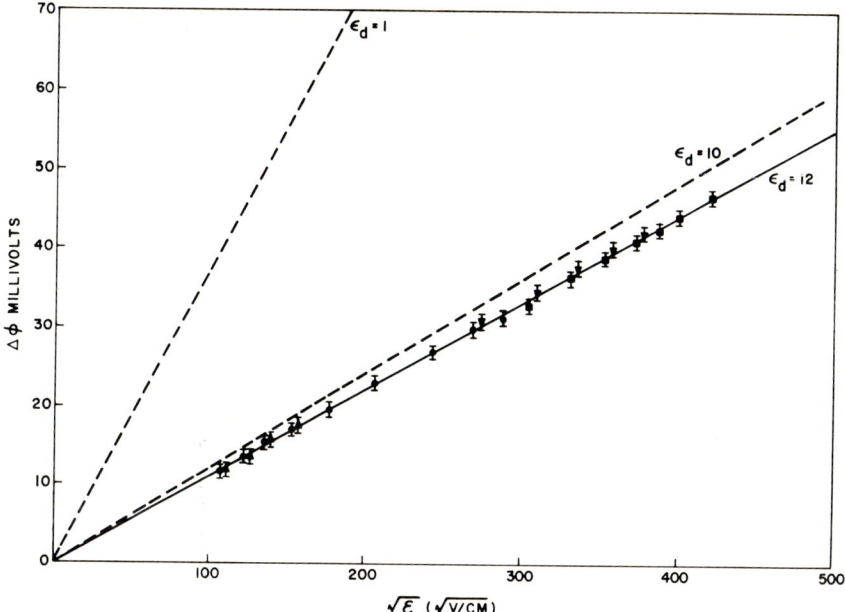

FIG. 3. Relationship between total Schottky-barrier lowering, $\Delta\varphi$, and the electric field at a gold n-type silicon interface. The lines are determined by Eq. (10) for various dielectric constants. 8.2 ohm-cm Si: ●, ▲, 0.2 ohm-cm Si: ■, ▼ (36).

c. *Collector Efficiency.* The information summarized above with respect to the energy dependence of the electron mean-free path and the shape of the barrier now makes possible a calculation of the probability, $T(x)$, that an electron normally incident on the barrier reaches a given value of x without undergoing a collision. Even though $T(x)$ must be considered as changing with the angle of electron incidence, the normal-incidence theory can still provide semiquantitative predictions for conditions where there is an appreciable distribution of angles of incidence.

$$T(x) = \exp -\int_0^x (1/L_{ax} + 1/L_{gx})\, dx \qquad (12)$$

where the electron kinetic energy, E_x, implicit in the expressions for L_{gx} and L_{ax} is

$$E_x = E_e - V(x) \qquad (13)$$

E_e is the electron energy relative to the barrier maximum if the transverse momentum is zero. Even electrons which do not reach a given x without being scattered do not necessarily return to the metal region and thus escape being collected. The scattering angles θ_a and θ_g which, after absorption or generation, respectively, of an optical phonon, will still permit collection (if no further scattering occurs) are determined by

$$\cos \theta_a = \frac{x_m - x}{|x_m - x|}\left[\frac{-V(x)}{E_x + kT + E_{op}}\right]^{1/2} \quad (14)$$

and

$$\cos \theta_g = \frac{x_m - x}{|x_m - x|}\left[\frac{-V(x)}{E_x + kT - E_{op}}\right]^{1/2} \quad (15)$$

Figure 1 shows representative limiting trajectories for collection of electrons scattered from a point beyond the potential energy maximum. If the electrons are isotropically scattered and the second and subsequent collisions are neglected, the probability that an electron will eventually reach x is then

$$C(x) = T(x) + \int_0^x \frac{T(u)}{2}\left[\frac{(1 - \cos \theta_a)}{L_{au}} + \frac{(1 - \cos \theta_g)}{L_{gu}}\right] du \quad (16)$$

For $x > x_m$, $C(x)$ is a slowly varying function of x because the contribution of $T(x)$ to $C(x)$ decreases with increasing x and is almost compensated by the fact that θ_a and θ_g approach π for large x. If we choose a distance s greater than x_m such that $T(x_m)/T(s) = e$, i.e. $(s - x_m)$ is one effective mean-free path, $C(s)$ is a better approximation to the probability of collection than $C(\infty)$ because there is little likelihood of electrons being backscattered from $x > s$ if the possibility of subsequent collisions is considered. Figure 4

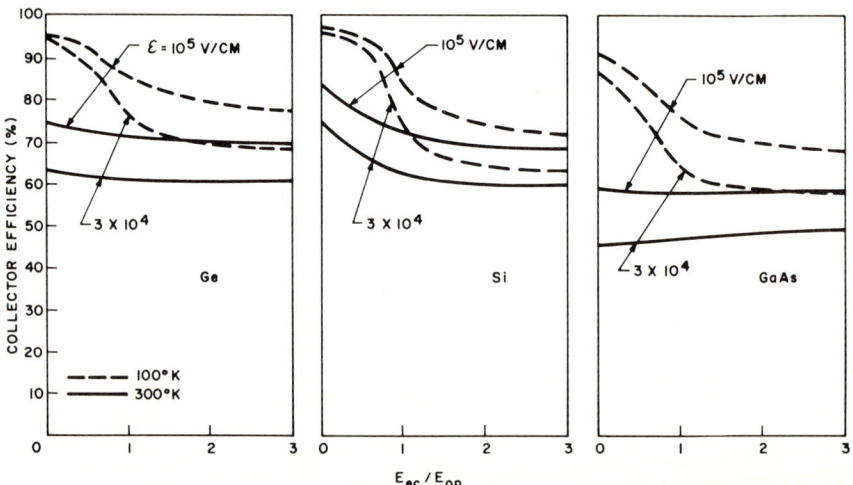

FIG. 4. Collector efficiency after electron-phonon scattering versus initial electron energy, E_{ec}, measured (in units of E_{op}) from the potential energy maximum of metal-semiconductor barriers in Ge, Si, and GaAs. The image force dielectric constants are 16, 12, and 11.6 for Ge, Si, and GaAs, respectively. The optical-phonon mean-free paths are given in Table I.

shows the collection efficiency for Ge, Si, and GaAs, respectively, at 100 and 300°K for collector electric fields of 3×10^4 and 1×10^5 volts/cm as a function of the energy of the incident electrons, E_{ec}, relative to the barrier height. To be more precise, the collection efficiency, α_c, is defined as $C(s)$ averaged over a Maxwellian distribution of electrons emitted from some source, where E_{ec} is the potential energy at the point of emission relative to the collector potential energy maximum:

$$\alpha_c = \int_{E_{ec}}^{\infty} C(s, E_e) \exp(-E_e/kT) \, dE_e/kT \tag{17}$$

The predicted values of α_c are relatively independent of electron energy and temperature for $E_{ec} > E_{op}$, and lower than those for $E_{ec} < E_{op}$. The results are not critically dependent on the values of the electron mean-free path. Figure 5 shows the collection efficiency for Ge using the mean-free path as a parameter. The dotted lines in Fig. 5 ($\exp - x_m/L$) give for comparison a

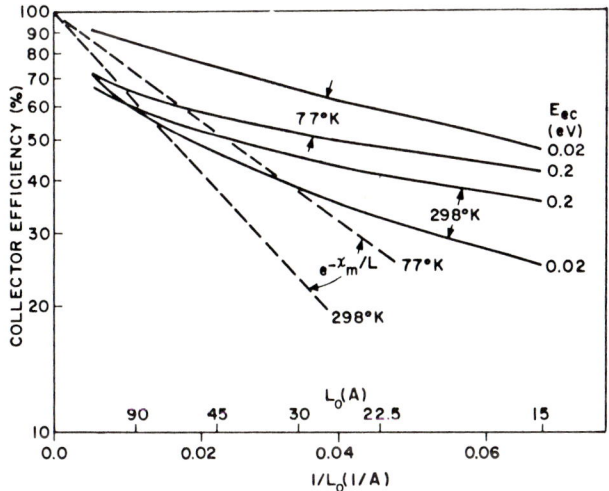

FIG. 5. Collector efficiency at 77 and 298°K for selected values of E_{ec} (in electron-volts) as a function of the high-energy low-temperature mean-free path L_0 and with a collector field of 3×10^4 volts/cm. The dashed lines give the approximate probability that an electron reaches the barrier potential maximum without being scattered (25).

rough estimate of the probability that an electron reaches the potential energy maximum without a collision. The changes in L are not strongly reflected in α_c because there is appreciable compensation between forward and backward scattering near the potential energy maximum.

The above treatment is based on an energy dependence of the mean-free path for electrons which interact with optical modes of lattice vibration in nonpolar crystals. The present calculations should thus be applicable to collector efficiencies in the case of Ge and Si. The results for GaAs are probably optimistic since the mean-free path for interaction with optical modes in polar crystals increases with energy (37), and the calculations have contained an effective high-energy mean-free path from avalanche multiplication data. On the other hand the avalanche multiplication analysis does not consider the possibility of electrons scattering into energy minima above the conduction band. Since the electron-phonon coupling in any event is stronger in polar than in nonpolar crystals, from theoretical considerations the collection efficiency in GaAs is not expected to exceed that of Si or Ge.

2. Quantum-Mechanical Reflection

Crowell and Sze (38) have used numerical methods to solve the Schroedinger equation for the quantum-mechanical reflection coefficient (QMR) of electrons at metal-semiconductor barriers. Since these calculations are the most pertinent ones for the systems we discuss, this approach is outlined here. The calculations were carried out for a "MacColl" and a "Thomas–Fermi" barrier. These represent expected extremes for smooth and abrupt potential energy transitions. Figure 6 shows the two approximations, which differ from that in Fig. 1 only for small values of x. MacColl (39) calculated the QMR in the absence of an electric field for a "metal-vacuum" barrier in which the potential energy is equal to W_B, the potential energy characteristic of the bottom of the conduction band in the metal, for all values of x such that $-V(x) > W_B$. This is indicated by the dotted line in Fig. 6. Unlike the MacColl barrier, the Thomas–Fermi barrier does not have a discontinuity in electric displacement. In the Thomas–Fermi barrier the image force and applied field terminate exponentially with the Thomas–Fermi characteristic screening length λ (40). The value of x at which the match to the image force must be made is X_{tf}, where

$$X_{tf} = X_{mc}[1 + (1 + 4\lambda X_{mc}\varepsilon_d/\varepsilon_m)^{1/2}]/2 \qquad (18)$$

$$X_{mc} = q^2/16\pi\varepsilon_d W_B \qquad (19)$$

is the matching point for the MacColl case, and ε_m is the lattice permittivity of the metal.

The matching procedure used in the "Thomas–Fermi" case is reasonable since the region in which the electrostatic field penetration is exponential commences very close to the point where the Fermi energy in the metal equals the potential energy due to the image force. A still more rigorous Thomas–Fermi approach would use a varying screening length characteristic of the local carrier density (40). Little added physical significance would be

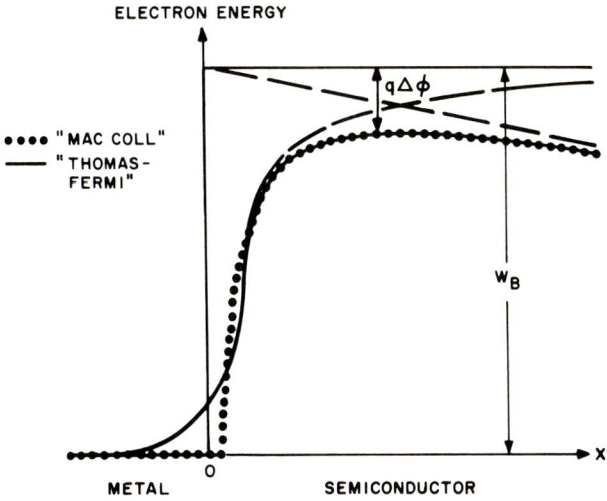

FIG. 6. Potential energy versus distance for "Thomas–Fermi" and "MacColl" metal-semiconductor barriers. W_B is the total barrier height measured from the bottom of the conduction band of the metal, $q\,\Delta\emptyset$ is the barrier lowering due to the image force (38).

expected from this approach, since λ would vary appreciably only over a small fraction of a lattice spacing.

The Thomas–Fermi barrier assumed by Crowell and Sze exhibits a slightly different Schottky lowering from the MacColl barrier since the appropriate expression for the potential barrier $V(x)$ for $x > X_{tf}$ [cf. Eq. (9)] is

$$V(x) = -q\mathscr{E}x + q\mathscr{E}(X_{tf} - \lambda\varepsilon_d/\varepsilon_m) - q^2/16\pi\varepsilon_d x \qquad (20)$$

Crowell and Sze (38) assumed that any mass discontinuity between the electron effective mass in the metal and in the semiconductor occurred effectively at X_{tf} for the Thomas–Fermi model and at X_{mc} for the MacColl model. The precise location of such a change and the rate of change of the effective mass are unimportant if the total change occurs within a small fraction of an electron wavelength.

For the metal-vacuum case, the two models give potential barriers which are essentially similar to those deduced from several other one-dimensional approaches. Bardeen (41) has calculated a Hartree–Fock self-consistent potential for the metal-vacuum case with a free-electron metal. A similar situation has been considered by Juretschke (42). Sachs and Dexter (43) have deduced a corrected image potential with an additional term proportional to x^{-2} in Eq. (9). Loucks and Cutler (44) have used a Bohm–Pines formalism to calculate the effect of the Coulomb correlations on the exchange portion of the surface potential. Belford et al. (45) have recently used the Sachs–Dexter model, and Cutler and Davis (46) a variety of the above models to calculate the field dependence of the reflection coefficient for the metal-vacuum case. The above treatments generally predict smaller reflection coefficients the smoother the potential transition between the metal and the vacuum.

The approach used by Crowell and Sze (38) consisted of a numerical fifth-order Taylor series calculation of two independent wave function solutions of the Schroedinger equation and their derivatives over the regions where a WKB solution was not a good approximation. The Wronskian was monitored to check the accuracy of the calculations. The appropriate linear combination of the two independent solutions was then determined by matching the solutions to WKB solutions at large distances from the metal-semiconductor interfaces. The general matching conditions of continuity of wave function, Ψ, and continuity of $(d\Psi/dx)/m^*$ were used both at the WKB matching points and throughout the region where the computer solution was obtained.

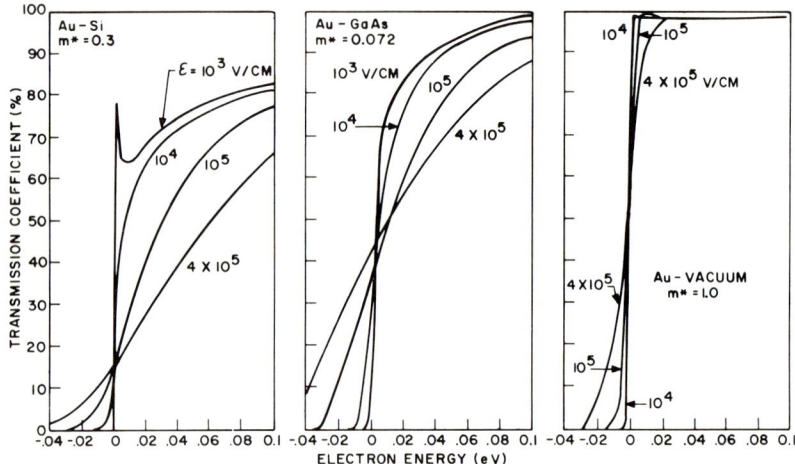

FIG. 7. Quantum-mechanical transmission coefficients for normal incidence as a function of electron energy measured from the potential maximum for Au-Si, Au-GaAs, and Au-vacuum systems. The image force dielectric constants are the same as in Fig. 4. The assumed effective electron masses are 0.3 in Si (47), 0.072 in GaAs (48), and 1.0 in Au.

Figure 7 shows representative values of the quantum-mechanical transmission (QMT) for the Thomas–Fermi barriers as a function of electron energy relative to the barrier potential energy maximum for a selection of electric fields for Au-Si, Au-GaAs, and Au-vacuum barriers. The results from the MacColl barrier are very similar. The effective mass in the case of the Au-Si barrier is that of the principle component of the electron effective mass of Si in the $\langle 111 \rangle$ direction (47). The QMT for the Au-semiconductor barriers is considerably less than that for the Au-vacuum barrier because the dielectric shielding of the image force in the semiconductors makes the barrier much more abrupt than the metal-vacuum barrier.

The predicted spike in transmission for the Au-Si barrier for $\mathscr{E} = 10^3$ volts/cm is the result of constructive interference of reflection from the base of the barrier (near $x = X_{tf}$) and from the potential energy maximum. This result is analogous to that observed in the periodic deviation of the Schottky effect in thermionic emission. This subject has been reviewed by Herring and Nichols (49). Such a spike should be very difficult to observe in practice because to reach the potential energy maximum and be coherently reflected an electron must travel several mean-free paths for optical phonon scattering without a collision with the lattice. The data at 10^3 volts/cm for the metal-semiconductor case are thus of somewhat academic interest except possibly at very low temperatures.

The results in Fig. 7 have all been calculated for normal incidence. Crowell and Sze (38) have discussed the case of oblique incidence and indicated that, if conservation of transverse momentum is assumed, the present results should apply if the effective electron energy is appropriately reduced. This generally reduces the transmission.

In summary, from theoretical considerations a large energy ($\gtrsim 0.05$ eV) of normally incident electrons is necessary to overcome the major effects of quantum-mechanical reflection. When the problem of optimizing the condition for best over-all collector efficiency is considered, however, an energy as large as 0.05 eV for incident electrons leads to appreciable electron-optical phonon scattering ($\gtrsim 40\%$ at room temperature at electric fields somewhat smaller than those for avalanche breakdown). When the electron energy is decreased, the quantum-mechanical transmission reduces the collector efficiency more rapidly than it is raised by the effect of decreased phonon scattering. Thus, at best, there is of the order of, or somewhat less than, a 50% chance of collection of a hot electron incident on a Schottky-barrier collector.

IV. Photoemission Experiments

1. METHODS OF ANALYSIS

Photoemission experiments are among the most useful tools for a study of factors which affect the transport of hot electrons in thin film structures. Photothreshold analysis gives one of the most direct means of measuring metal-semiconductor (50, 51) and metal-insulator-semiconductor barrier heights (52), and has been used to determine the image force dielectric constant of a metal-semiconductor barrier (cf. Section III, 1, b).

When monochromatic light of frequency v is incident upon a thin metal film in a metal-semiconductor system (Fig. 8a), electrons excited in the metal can be collected in the body of the semiconductor; i.e., a photocurrent can

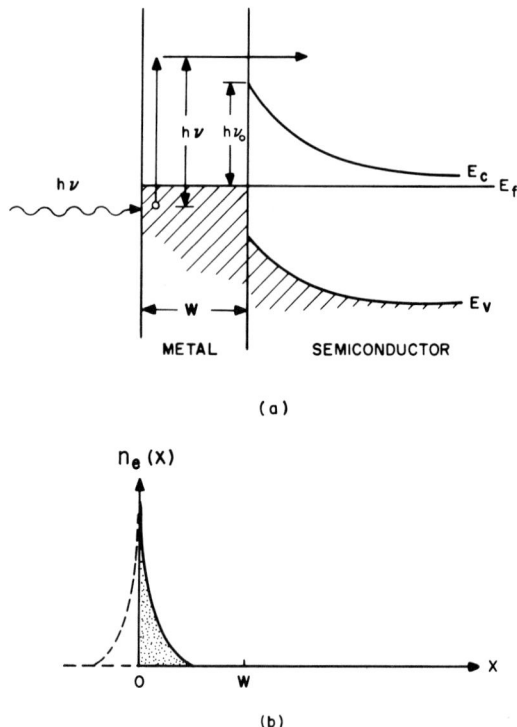

FIG. 8. (a) Energy-band diagram for photoexcited electrons in a Schottky barrier. hv_0 is the metal-semiconductor barrier height, and W is the thickness of the metal film. (b) Photo-excited electron density distribution $n_e(x)$ versus distance. Reflection of electrons at $x = 0$ makes the effective distribution approximately symmetrical about $x = 0$.

be generated. If hv is less than the semiconductor energy band-gap, the electrons can also be excited by light which has passed through the body of the semiconductor. According to Fowler's analysis (53), the photoresponse per absorbed photon is proportional to $(v - v_0)^2$ if $E_f > h(v - v_0) > kT$, where hv_0 is the potential barrier height measured from the Fermi level in the metal and E_f is the Fermi kinetic energy.

For "front" illumination as in Fig. 8a, the photoresponse per absorbed photon, R_f, as a function of metal film thickness, W, can be described in terms of an electron attenuation length or range, λ_a, from a simple one-dimensional model proposed by Spitzer et al. (50). In this model the radiation is assumed to be attenuated in the metal according to $\exp(-\alpha x)$ where α is the optical absorption constant, or $1/\alpha$ the photon penetration depth, and the probability of collection of an electron generated at x is assumed to be proportional to $\exp[-(W-x)/\lambda_a]$. These conditions are tantamount to also assuming that optical reflections and multiple reflections of the photo-excited electrons within the metal film can be neglected. Then

$$R_f = \left[\frac{K}{1-(\alpha\lambda_a)^{-1}}\right]\left[\frac{\exp(-W/\lambda_a)-\exp(-\alpha W)}{1-\exp(-\alpha W)}\right] \quad (21)$$

where K is a constant of proportionality. If $\lambda_a > 1/\alpha$, and $\alpha W > 1$, then Eq. (21) approaches

$$R_f = \frac{K}{1-(\alpha\lambda_a)^{-1}}\exp(-W/\lambda_a) \quad (22)$$

When $\alpha\lambda_a < 1$ and $\alpha W > 1$, the response tends toward

$$R_f = \frac{K}{1-(\alpha\lambda_a)^{-1}}\exp(-\alpha W) \quad (23)$$

The reflection of electrons at $x = 0$ will in practice make R_f vary more nearly exponentially with W since the effective electron source is more symmetrical and located at $x = 0$ (cf. Fig. 8b).

Crowell *et al.* (*51*) have also shown that if λ_a varies essentially linearly with electron energy in the range between $h\nu$ and $h\nu_0$, the effective electron energy is $h\nu_0 + \frac{2}{3}h(\nu - \nu_0)$ relative to the Fermi energy in the metal.

From the above assumptions, again neglecting reflections, Sze *et al.* (*54*) have shown that the back response R_b, i.e., the photocurrent per absorbed photon with light incident upon the semiconductor side, is

$$R_b = \left[\frac{K}{1+(\alpha\lambda_a)^{-1}}\right]\left[\frac{1-\exp(-(\alpha+1/\lambda_a)W)}{1-\exp(-\alpha W)}\right] \quad (24)$$

From Eqs. (21) and (24),

$$\frac{R_f}{R_b} = \left[\frac{1+\alpha\lambda_a}{1-\alpha\lambda_a}\right]\left[\frac{\exp(-\alpha W)-\exp(-W/\lambda_a)}{1-\exp(-(\alpha+1/\lambda_a)W)}\right] \quad (25)$$

This ratio is independent of K and is useful for analyzing cases where α is comparable to $1/\lambda_a$.

The measured attenuation length, λ_a, is actually the result of various energy loss and scattering processes. The most important contributions to the measured λ_a values are the electron-phonon interaction and the electron-electron interaction discussed in Section II. Two different approaches to separate these two contributions have been given in the literature.

Stuart et al. (55) used a Monte Carlo calculation. They considered cases in which specular or diffuse reflections of the photoexcited electrons occurred at both surfaces of the metal films. For $\lambda_{e-e} = 1000$ A, $\lambda_c = 400$ A, an average acoustic phonon energy loss of 0.001 eV per phonon collision, $1/\alpha = 130$ A, and $h(v - v_0) = 0.225$ eV, R_f, the number of electrons collected at a Au-Si barrier per absorbed photon was computed as a function of film thickness. The attenuation length was obtained from the slope of a semilog plot of $\ln R_f$ versus thickness at a thickness of the order of 600 A. λ_a was 395 A for the case of specular reflection and 350 A for diffuse reflection. λ_a is shown in Fig. 9 as a function of λ_{e-e} for $\lambda_c = 100$ and 400 A for both specular and diffuse reflections.

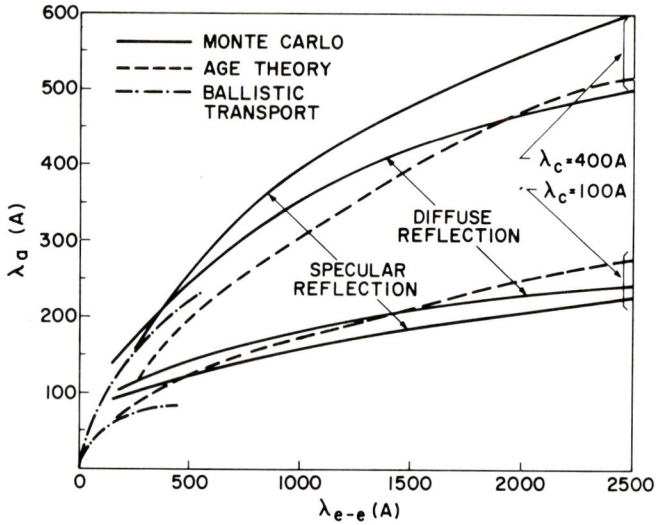

FIG. 9. Attenuation length, λ_a, as a function of the electron-electron mean-free path, λ_{e-e}, from a Monte Carlo analysis (55), Age theory [cf. Eq. (26)], and for ballistic transport [λ_a given by Eq. (31)]. λ_c is the mean-free path for lattice-related scattering processes.

Values of λ_a from Fermi Age Theory (54, 56) are also shown in Fig. 9. This approach (54) gives the following asymptotic relationship between λ_a, λ_{e-e}, and λ_c:

$$\lambda_a(E) = [\lambda_{e-e}^2 \lambda_c / 3(\lambda_{e-e} + \lambda_c)]^{1/2} \qquad (26)$$

This expression is valid if the initial source is located many attenuation lengths from the surface, the electron-phonon interaction is elastic, and $\lambda_{e-e} \gg \lambda_c$. Although the above conditions are difficult to satisfy in most experimental situations, from Fig. 9 it is apparent that Eq. (26) gives λ_{e-e} values within a factor of two of the results obtained from the Monte Carlo calculation (55).

When λ_{e-e} is smaller than λ_c, one scattering tends to trap the electron in the metal. λ_a should then be very nearly equal to $\lambda_c \lambda_{e-e}/(\lambda_c + \lambda_{e-e})$.

2. Attenuation Length Measurements

The first attenuation length measurements were made by Thomas (57), who observed the saturation of vacuum photoresponse in thin films of potassium as they were being deposited on a quartz substrate. The saturation was determined by inspection. Thomas' results are shown in Fig. 10.

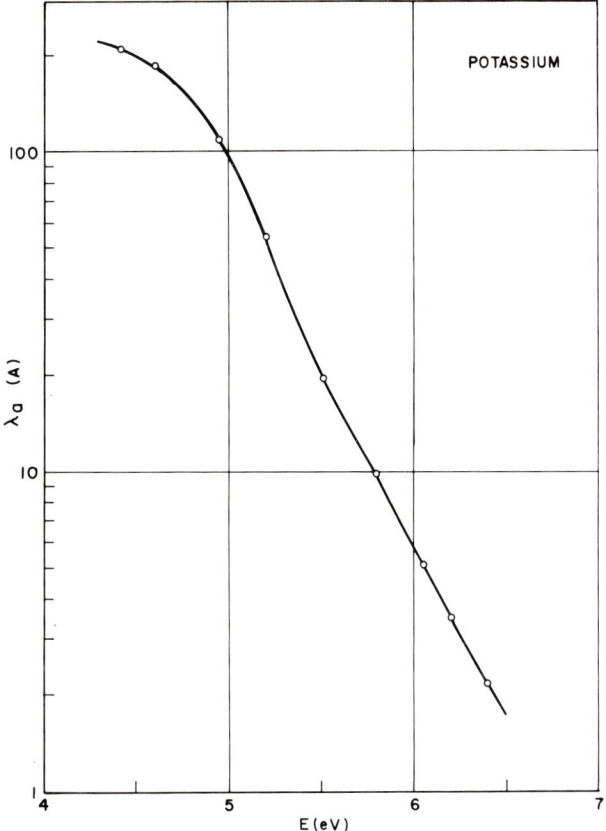

Fig. 10. Attenuation length in potassium versus electron energy measured from the bottom of the conduction band (57).

Spitzer et al. (50) reported the first attenuation length measurements on a metal-semiconductor system. They used front illumination on Au-Si Schottky barriers prepared by evaporation of Au films on Si surfaces freshly cleaved in vacuum. Crowell et al. (51) subsequently reported additional similar measurements on Ag, Cu, and Pd. Crowell *et al.* (*58*) also reported λ_a measurements for photoexcited holes in Au in Au-*p*-type GaP barriers. Sze *et al.* (*54*) extended the measured range of energy and temperature effects on λ_a for hot electrons in Au.

Soshea and Lucas (*59*) have completed a study of gold films deposited slowly in a vacuum $\approx 10^{-9}$ Torr on specially prepared smooth-cleaved surfaces. We will use their results to illustrate the details of the experimental approach to λ_a. Figure 11 shows Soshea and Lucas' data for Au-Si barriers

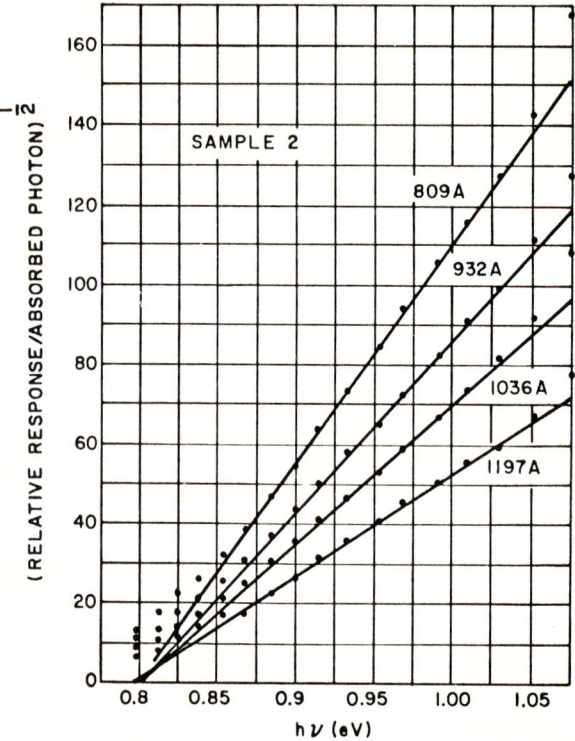

FIG. 11. Square root of the relative photoresponse at room temperature per absorbed photon versus photon energy for Au-Si barriers with four gold film thicknesses (*59*).

fitted to a simplified Fowler plot ($R_f^{1/2}$ versus $h\nu$). Note that for $(h\nu - 0.8 \text{ eV}) \geq 3kT$, the data points for any thickness can be fitted by a straight line as predicted by the Fowler analysis. The lines define a consistent photothreshold energy of 0.80 ± 0.01 eV for all gold thicknesses.

The photoresponse per absorbed photon as a function of Au thickness for several sets of Au-Si diodes is shown in Fig. 12 for $h\nu = 0.952$ eV. A least-squares fit gives 360 A for λ_a. Soshea and Lucas (*59*) also showed that the

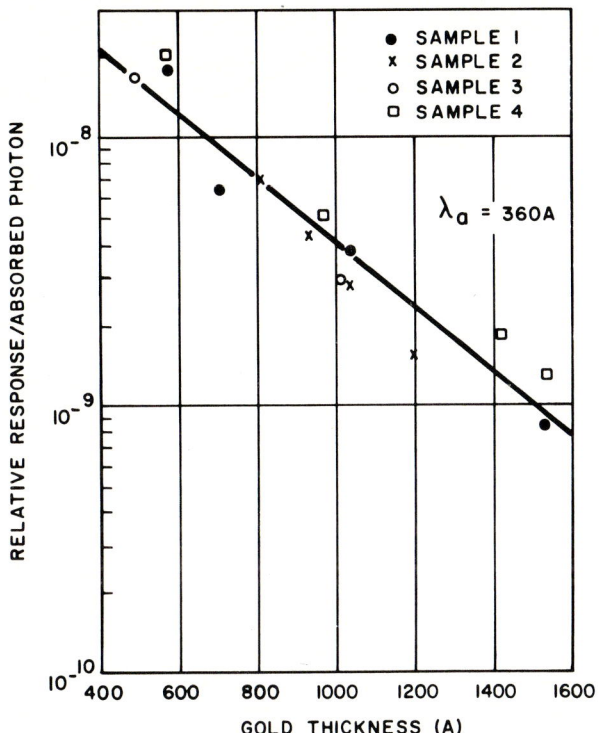

FIG. 12. Relative photoresponse per absorbed photon as a function of the gold film thickness for $hv = 0.952$ eV (59).

earlier measurements by Spitzer et al. (50) are consistent with this value (≈ 330 A) when appropriate corrections are applied for the effect of the substrate on photon absorption in thin films. Soshea and Lucas avoided the necessity of making this correction by working only with films that were thick enough that the photon absorption was essentially a constant (cf. Fig. 11). This is a technique which can only be used if the hot-electron mean-free path is reasonably large in comparison with the photon penetration depth.

The metal-semiconductor system is more suitable for a study of the attenuation length of hot electrons with electron energies less than the band gap of the semiconductor. When hv is greater than the band gap, photoexcitation of carriers in the semiconductor can easily become significant, and mask the photoresponse from the metal. For electron energies larger than the band gap, photoemission into vacuum should be used whenever possible. An example (54) of vacuum photoemission is shown in Fig. 13 where R_f/R_b is plotted against the gold film thickness for $hv \simeq 4.8$ eV. Because of the neglect of multiple reflections in the analysis, the fit is not good at small thicknesses.

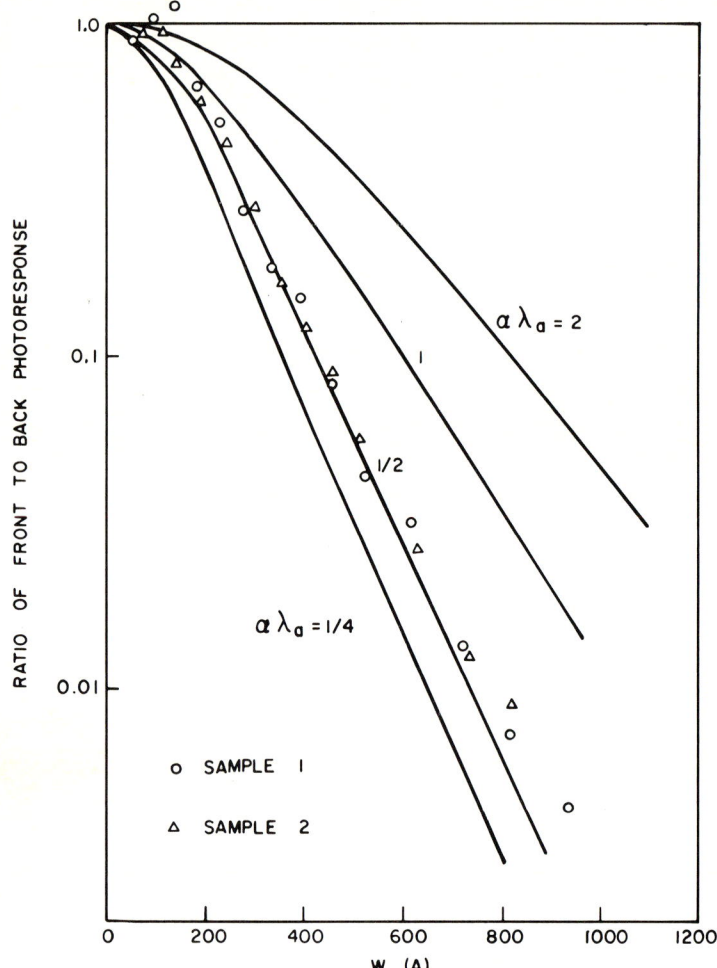

FIG. 13. Ratio of front to back photoresponse versus gold film thickness. The solid lines are from Eq. (25). α is the photon absorption coefficient ($= 1/130$ Å^{-1}). $\lambda_a = 70 \pm 10$ Å for $hv = 4.8$ eV (54).

For thicker films, however, $\alpha \lambda_a \simeq \frac{1}{2}$, and λ_a is 70 ± 20 Å for electrons of approximately 4.8 eV energy relative to the Fermi energy (54).

A summary of the measured attenuation lengths in gold films is shown in Fig. 14. The experimental data for electron energies greater than 5 eV were all obtained from tunnel-emitter structures which are discussed in the next section.

Results for other metals and for photoexcited holes are summarized in Table II.

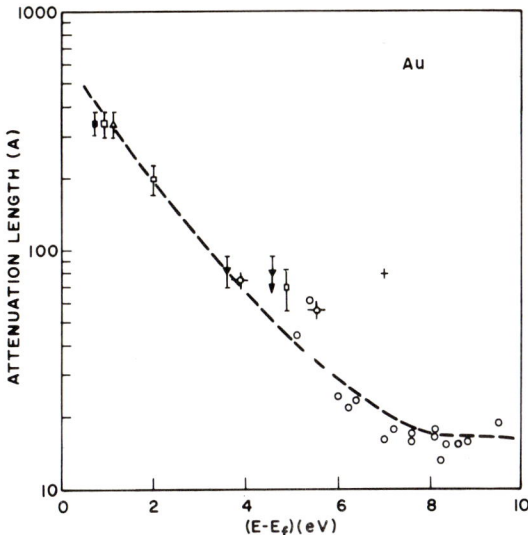

FIG. 14. Attenuation length in gold films as a function of electron energy above the Fermi energy. Experimental data for electron energies greater than 5 eV were all obtained from measurements on tunnel-emitter structures (Section V). Legend: ■, Crowell et al. (51); □, Sze et al. (54); △, Soshea and Lucas (59); ▼, Katrich and Sarbei, (60); , Kanter (61); +, Mead (62); O, Steele and Feist (63).

TABLE II

HOT-ELECTRON AND HOT-HOLE ATTENUATION LENGTHS FROM PHOTOEMISSION EXPERIMENTS

Metal	Electrons		Holes	
	λ_a (Å)	$(E - E_f)$(eV)	λ_a (Å)	$(E - E_f)$(eV)
Au	(cf. Fig. 14)		250	0.80 (58)[a]
Ag	440	0.83 (51)		
	450	0.65 (64)		
Cu	50 ∼ 200	0.79 (51)		
	70 ∼ 110	0.927 (64)		
	280	0.61 (65)		
Pd	170	0.85 (51)		
Al			< 50	0.927 (64)

[a] This result has been corrected for the optical absorption energy versus gold film thickness determined by Soshea and Lucas (59).

V. Tunnel Emission

A tunnel-emission thin-film triode was first proposed by Mead (1). The energy band diagram for this structure is shown in Fig. 15a. In such a structure electrons tunnel from the Fermi level in the emitter metal film to the conduction band in the insulator which separates the emitter and base metal layers. The electrons which do not suffer subsequent scattering can then reach the collector metal film if the Fermi energy in the emitter is greater than the potential energy maximum of the collector barrier. Electron emission into vacuum can occur if the insulator-metal collector of Fig. 15a is replaced

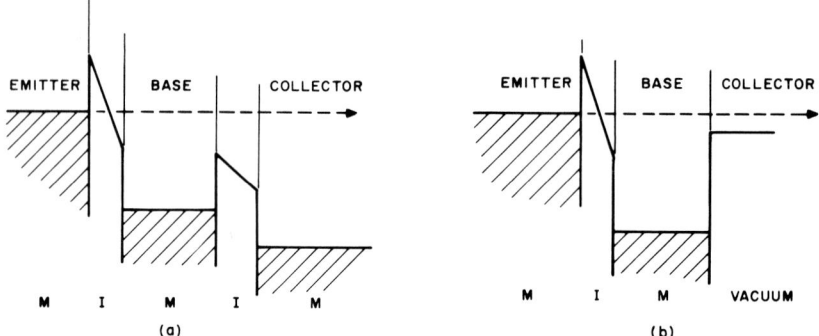

FIG. 15. (a) Energy band diagram of a thin-film tunnel-emission triode (1). (b) Energy band diagram of a tunnel emission diode (66).

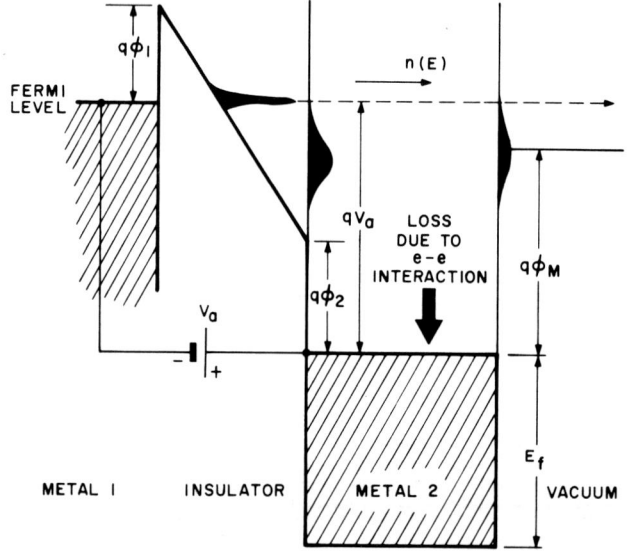

FIG. 16. Schematic electron energy distribution in a tunnel emission diode (66).

by a vacuum as shown in Fig. 15b, and if the metal-vacuum work function, $\emptyset_M$, is less than the bias voltage applied between the metal and the base (V_a in Fig. 16). The configuration in Fig. 15b has been investigated extensively because of its potential application as a replacement for thermionic emitters. Both structures have been used to study the transport of hot electrons. Initially we review some of the evidence relevant to a description of current transport in the regions other than the metal film or base. The information concerning base transport is then considered.

1. Emitter Characteristics

In the experimental results from structures of the type shown in Fig. 15b, typically less than 1% of the electrons which reach the metal base escape into vacuum. Thus the process of hot-electron emission is extremely inefficient. In structures with the configuration shown in Fig. 15a, or structures with a Schottky barrier collector (2), any pinholes in the metal base which permit the emitter and collector semiconductors or insulators to touch will provide paths through which space-charge-limited current can flow [cf. the metal-edge and related amplifying structures (9)]. This difficulty almost precludes the use of thin-film triodes for fundamental studies of hot-electron transport in metal films.

The hot-electron transport process can be divided into the following parts: tunneling from the emitter Fermi level into the conduction band of the emitter insulator; drift caused by the electric field in the insulator and scattering therein associated with phonons, impurities, and other insulator defects; transport in the metal "base" film, where the dominant loss appears to be due to electron-electron interaction; and collection at the collector "electrode" (a collector in the vacuum is implicitly required in Fig. 15b).

The tunnel emission between electrodes separated by a thin insulating film was first studied by Sommerfeld and Bethe (67). Holm (68) extended the theory to include the intermediate voltage range between the near-ohmic behavior at low voltages and the high voltage range where the Fowler-Nordheim (69) theory of field emission applies. Simmons (70) considered in addition effects of the barrier shape when the image-force potential energy is considered. Hartman (71) has used an "equivalent trapezoidal barrier" approach which performs much the same function. In practice, the bias voltages needed to produce appreciable tunnel emission into vacuum are large enough compared with the barrier φ_2 (cf. Fig. 16) that the Fowler-Nordheim analysis applies.[3] From this theory the predicted half-width of the total energy

---

[3] The major difficulty that the structure faces when competing with a bipolar transistor is determined by this tunneling process: for comparable current densities, the emitter-base transconductance is much lower than that of a transistor unless the insulator thickness is so small that pinholes are almost a certainty.

distribution of the electrons at the point of emergence from the tunneling region is very narrow in comparison with any observed energy distribution of emitted electrons: for $q\varphi_1 = 2$ eV, an electric field of 10^7 volts/cm, and a free electron effective mass in the emitter metal and insulator, the energy half-width at emergence is 0.005 eV at 0°K and 0.15 eV at 300°K (66). This distribution is shown schematically in Fig. 16.

Once electrons have tunneled to the conduction band in the insulator, the generation of optical phonons occurs as the electrons gain kinetic energy from the electric field. Thus, as shown in Fig. 16, the electron energy distribution spreads as electrons traverse the insulator. From studies of the energy distribution of electrons emitted into vacuum from structures with similar base thicknesses and varying emitter insulator thicknesses, Handy (66) has reported that the peak energy of the electron distribution decreases

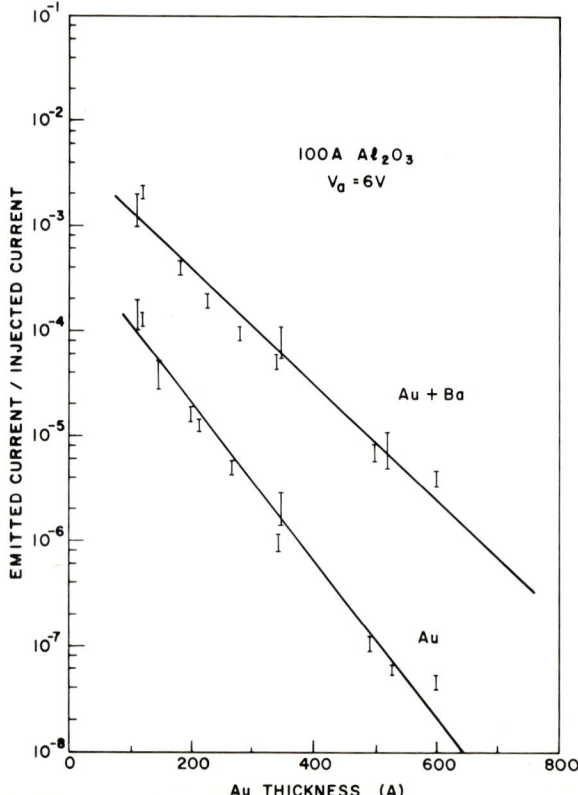

FIG. 17. Ratio of the current emitted into vacuum to the current injected into the gold film as a function of film thickness for an Al-Al$_2$O$_3$ (100-A)-Au tunnel emission diode. The applied voltage, V_a, is 6 volts (61).

by ≈ 0.03 eV/A in Al_2O_3. Since the Debye temperature of aluminum oxide is 1200–1500°K (72), the optical-phonon energy should be ≈ 0.1 eV. Handy (66) consequently suggests that the mean hot-electron interaction distance is ≈ 4 A in the oxide. From measurements on Al-Al_2O_3-Al tunnel cathodes, Collins and Davis (73) deduced a similar value of 5 ± 1 A.

A triode structure of Al-Al_2O_3-Al-Al_2O_3-Al film was studied by Nelson and Anderson (74). Current transfer was measured as a function of collector-oxide thickness and collector bias at 77 and 300°K. The mean-free path in Al_2O_3 was deduced to be 12 A. This is in reasonable agreement with the values found in tunnel cathodes, since the average interaction distance in the direction of the electric field is then ≈ 3 A (66).

The above type of scattering causes a rapid degradation of energy in the electron distribution and tends to randomize the electron momentum distribution before the electrons are injected into the metal base. This makes it very difficult for electron emission to occur with appreciable efficiency since the electron energy associated with momentum normal to the collector barrier must exceed the barrier energy. Note the strong increase in emitter efficiency (Fig. 17) observed by Kanter (61) in Al-Al_2O_3-Au structures when the deposition of the order of a monolayer of barium on the gold surface lowered the work function of the emitting surface by approximately 2.1 eV.

Aside from the limitations imposed on the emitter efficiency by the height of the collector barrier (limitations which appear to be intrinsically due to the emitter insulator), the collector has only a minor additional effect on the probability of emission of a hot electron. For a vacuum collector, quantum-mechanical reflection as discussed in Section III, 2, will be only a few per cent. For an insulator-metal collector, the additional reduction in emitter efficiency should be a factor ≈ 0.5 (cf. Sections III, 1 and 2).

2. Base Transport

Since hot electrons in tunneling structures appear to be nearly isotropically distributed before they are injected into the metal base, hot-electron transport through the base should be governed by conditions similar to those that apply to the photoemission studies considered in Section IV. In one respect the results from tunnel emission studies appear inferior in comparison with those from photoemission experiments: the energy distribution of the injected electrons is less well defined in the former. A tunnel emission experiment, however, does not require the separation of effects associated with the penetration depth of illumination from effects due to the electron mean-free path. In practice the above advantage associated with the tunnel structure is of critical importance in the high energy range when $\lambda_{e\text{-}e} \ll \lambda_c$. Then a single hot-electron-electron collision in the metal film causes the hot electron to lose enough energy that emission into vacuum will not occur. This has been shown by Kanter (61) who found that the energy distribution of emitted electrons was unaffected by the metal base thickness. The attenuation length for high-energy hot electrons is thus effectively λ_{e-e}. If a tunnel emission study is confined to voltages near the threshold bias for emission, the energy at which λ_{e-e} is measured is essentially the threshold energy. At higher bias voltages, however, unless the total energy of the emitted electrons is monitored as Kanter (61) has done with a hemispherical collector, the energy to be assigned to a measured attenuation length is in doubt.

Attenuation lengths reported for hot electrons in gold are shown in Fig. 14 for both photoemission measurements (51, 54, 59, 60), and for hot electrons emitted into vacuum from tunnel cathodes (61–63). No reliable attenuation length measurements have been reported for structures using insulator-metal collectors. The tunnel emitters were produced by evaporation of a metal and subsequent oxidation of a portion of the metal followed by a deposition of the metal base. Thermal oxidation in a controlled atmosphere or anodic oxidation were used to produce oxides of controlled thicknesses. Mead (62) used a Be-BeO-Au structure. Kanter (61) and Steele and Feist (63) investigated Al-Al$_2$O$_3$-Au structures. The tunnel emission results shown in Fig. 14 have been assigned to the "normal" electron energy, which is associated with the momentum normal to the emitter surface. A portion of the intrinsic dependence of λ_{e-e} on energy must thus be assumed to be suppressed.

In summary, the scattering which tends to randomize the hot-electron momentum distribution in the emitter insulator before electrons are injected into the metal base of tunnel cathodes provides some difficulties when transport measurements are to be interpreted. This phenomenon has much more serious implications, however, when the application of such structures as electron emitters is contemplated: the scattering strongly decreases the emitter efficiency and strongly increases the emitter noise temperature. At present this appears to be an intrinsic limitation imposed by the requirement of electron transport through an insulator.

VI. Schottky (Thermionic) Emission

In the previous sections, the transport of hot electrons produced by photoexcitation and tunneling was considered. In this section we will discuss the process of Schottky (or thermionic) emission, another method of generating electrons for subsequent study of the transport of hot electrons. Figure 18 shows the band diagrams for two representative structures, a semiconductor-metal-semiconductor transistor (SMST) structure, and a vacuum triode. In the structure of Fig. 18a, electrons are injected over the emitter barrier, $q\varphi_e$, and into the metal as nonequilibrium (or hot) electrons. If the height of the subsequent barrier, $q\varphi_c$, is less than that of the emitter, and if the metal

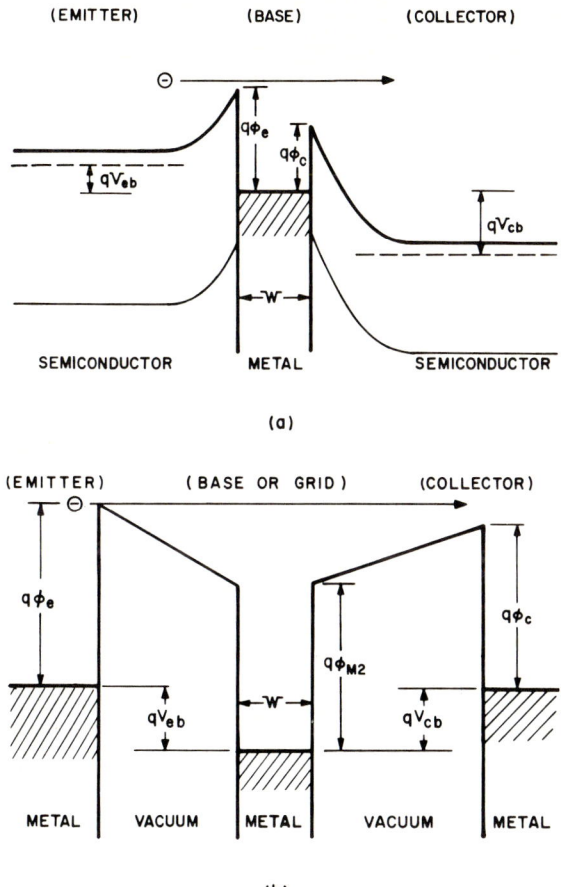

FIG. 18. (a) Energy band diagram for a semiconductor-metal-semiconductor structure with a forward-biased emitter (voltage V_{eb}), and reverse-biased collector (voltage V_{cb}) (4). (b) Energy band diagram for a thermionic triode. Electrons from the emitter which are not scattered in the base are subsequently collected (82).

thickness is comparable to the hot-electron mean-free path in the base, then hot electrons can be collected over the second Schottky barrier. In the triode structure shown in Fig. 18b, an electron beam is thermionically emitted into the vacuum and injected into the metal thin-film base or control grid. The electrons which emerge from the far side then proceed towards the collector electrode.

The triode measurement is confined to electron energies above the control grid work function. The SMST measurement is confined to essentially the emitter barrier energy, which is almost independent of emitter-base bias and is always less than the base work function.[4] Thus to cover a wide range of hot-electron energy, it is necessary to use both types of structure and to perform the SMST measurements with a variety of emitter semiconductors. An energy analysis of the transmitted electron beam is possible in the triode, while in the SMST structure no analogous measurement can be made. Thus for base-transport studies it is more important to have a detailed theoretical understanding of the effect of the emitter and collector semiconductors on current transport in the SMST structure than in the vacuum triode. The following treatment accordingly is concentrated mainly on the emitter and collector efficiencies of the SMST structure as a necessary preliminary to a study of hot-electron transport in the base region. Furthermore we will consider only triode experiments in which the electron energy is low enough that secondary-electron emission is absent.

1. EMITTER CHARACTERISTICS

The processes involved in current transport in SMST structures are qualitatively analogous to those in tunnel-emitter structures. For example, when an electron passes over the emitter potential energy maximum (cf. Fig. 19), the injection of the electron into the metal base is almost assured, as is the case

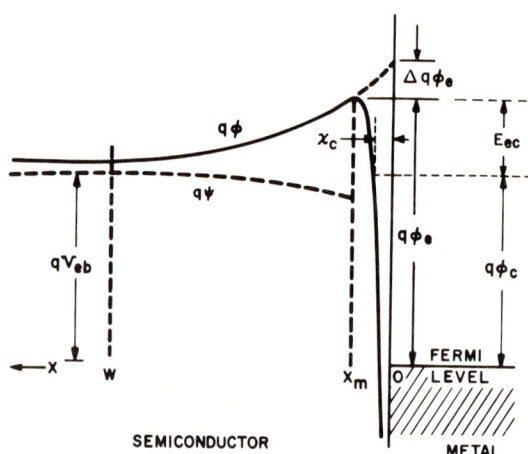

FIG. 19. Electron potential energy $q\phi$ and imref $q\psi$ as a function of distance in a metal-semiconductor barrier. $q\phi_e$ is the barrier height, and $\Delta q\phi_e$ is the emitter barrier lowering due to the electric field and the image force. x_c is the point where an electron at rest in the emitter has enough energy to surmount a collector barrier of height $q\phi_c$. E_{ec} is the energy difference between the emitter and collector barriers (75).

[4] No exception to this case has yet been observed in which appreciable emission of electrons into vacuum could be obtained. Such a structure, the Schottky analog of the tunnel cathode, would be an extremely desirable alternative to thermionic emitters.

when tunneling to the emitter insulator conduction band occurs (cf. Fig. 16). Similarly electron scattering between the potential energy maximum and the metal-semiconductor interface is analogous to (though far less important than) scattering in the emitter insulator. Base transport is analogous in the two cases, but has some important distinctions which are discussed in this section. Collector backscatter has analogous effects on current transfer, but percentagewise is much more important in the SMST structure than in the tunnel emitter.

Let us consider first the process of generating hot electrons. Crowell and Sze (75) have recently presented a detailed theoretical consideration of the current density-voltage characteristic (J versus V_{eb}) of ideal Schottky barriers which might be used as the emitter base combination in SMST structures. The results appear to be in good agreement with experimental measurements. Crowell and Sze's treatment combines Bethe's thermionic emission theory (76), Schottky's diffusion theory (77), and theoretical calculations of the effect on the electron recombination velocity at the potential energy maximum of phonon-induced backscattering and quantum-mechanical tunneling through (or reflection from) the barrier. Most of the basically new elements of the treatment have been derived from the material outlined in Section III. The $J - V_{eb}$ characteristic is

$$J = \frac{f_P f_Q A^* T^2 \exp(-q\varphi_e/kT)}{1 + f_P f_Q A^* T^2 / q N_c v_d} [\exp(qV_{eb}/kT) - 1] \qquad (27)$$

where A^* is the effective Richardson constant for the semiconductor interface orientation (78), N_c is the effective density of states in the conduction band to the emitter semiconductor, f_P is the probability (averaged over a Maxwellian distribution) that an electron from the body of the emitter semiconductor is backscattered between x_m and the metal surface by phonon scattering, f_Q is the ratio of current density in the presence of a quantum-mechanical transmission coefficient, $\tau(E)$, integrated over a Maxwellian distribution of the current density if only classical transmission occurred, and v_d is the effective diffusion velocity associated with the transport of electrons through the space-charge region between the neutral body of the semiconductor and the potential energy maximum.

$$f_Q = \int_{-\infty}^{\infty} \tau(E) \exp(-(E - E_f)/kT) \, dE/kT \qquad (28)$$

and

$$v_d = \left[\int_{x_m}^{W} \frac{q}{\mu kT} \exp(V(x)/kT) \, dx \right]^{-1} \qquad (29)$$

where μ is the electron mobility in the semiconductor, and $V(x)$ is determined by Eq. (9).

Typical values of f_p for Ge-, Si-, and GaAs-Au Schottky barriers are $\gtrsim 0.8$ at 300°K (75) if the electric field, $\mathscr{E}$, at the metal-semiconductor interface exceeds 10^4 volts/cm. f_Q is plotted in Fig. 20 for Au-Si and Au-GaAs

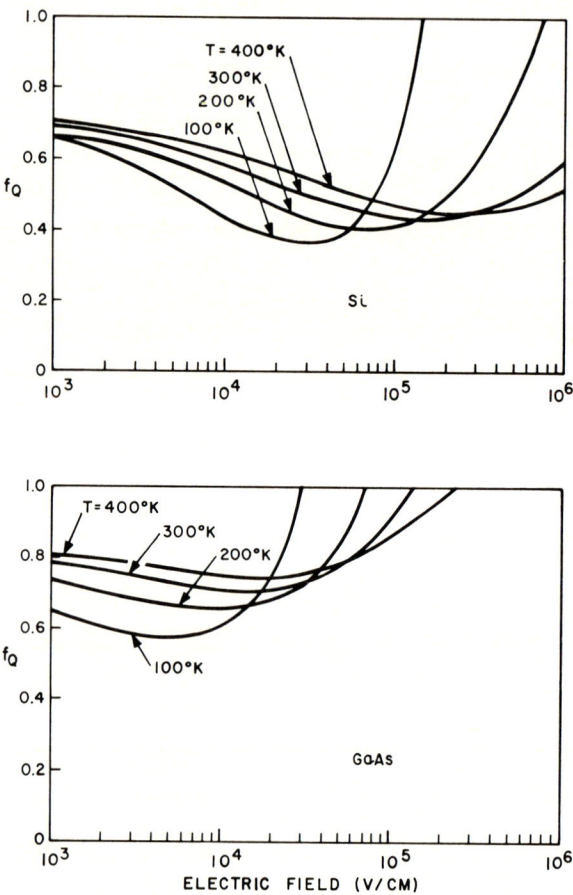

FIG. 20. Quantum-mechanical transmission coefficient averaged over a Maxwellian distribution of electrons incident on the potential energy maximum of Au-Si and Au-GaAs Schottky barriers as a function of electric field for selected temperatures (75).

"Thomas–Fermi" barriers as a function of $\mathscr{E}$ for selected temperatures. The values of $\tau(E)$ in Eq. (28) are based on data similar to that in Fig. 7. The term f_Q rises at lower electric fields more rapidly for the Au-GaAs system than for the Au-Si system because the lower conduction-band electron effective mass in GaAs (48) facilitates tunneling at these fields. Even when the effect of the image force on v_d is considered, $\frac{2}{3} < v_d/\mu\mathscr{E} < 1$ in most practical cases (75). The term which contains v_d in Eq. (27) then varies slowly with the applied bias and has a magnitude between one quarter and one half.

The above treatment outlines the conditions under which a Schottky barrier behaves essentially as a thermionic rather than a tunnel emitter as far as the magnitude of electron flow into the metal base is concerned. In the emitter semiconductor it is quite possible to have phonon-induced scattering, just as in the tunnel cathode case. This scattering does not prevent an electron from reaching the metal, but even in the absence of further scattering it can prevent the electron from crossing the collector barrier. The range of x over which such scattering can occur is $x_c > x > 0$ in Fig. 19, where x_c is the point at which the electron potential energy equals the collector potential energy maximum. Scattering between x_m and x_c can lead to electrons being scattered over the emitter potential energy maximum. Such electrons effectively are never emitted. Any other electron scattered between x_m and x_c must subsequently receive enough momentum from the barrier that the collector barrier can be surmounted if no further collision occurs. There is a finite angle of acceptance at the collector for electrons scattered between x_c and the metal surface. Crowell and Sze (25) have defined the emitter efficiency as the ratio of the current which is collectable in the above sense to the total current which is actually injected into the metal. In Fig. 21 the theoretical values of the emitter efficiency are shown as a function of E_{ec} in units of E_{op} for selected

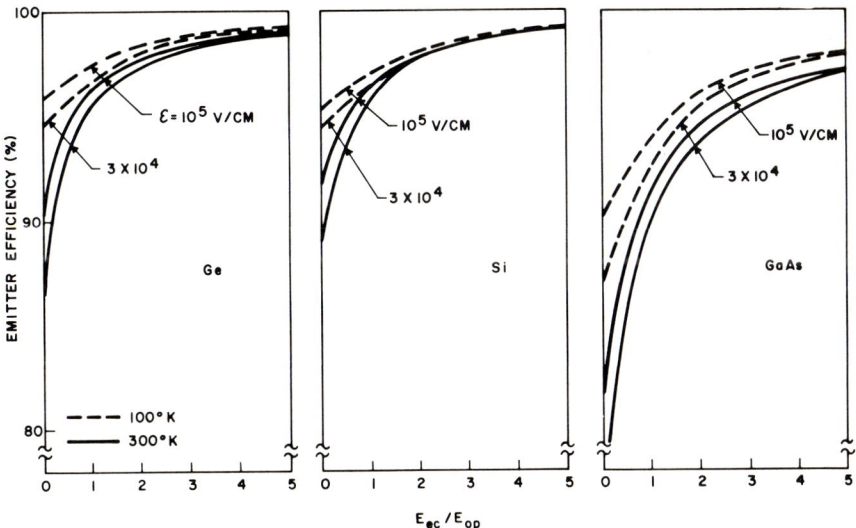

FIG. 21. Emitter efficiency as a function of the electron energy, E_{ec}, measured from the potential energy maximum for metal-Ge, Si, and GaAs barriers. The parameters used are the same as in Fig. 4.

emitter temperatures and electric fields. The calculations are based on assumptions and methods similar to those described in Section III, 1. Note that the emitter efficiency generally exceeds 90% if $E_{ec} > E_{op}$. This result gives added support to the conclusion at the end of Section III that the condition $E_{ec} > E_{op}$ is desirable for efficient current transport in SMST structures. The emitter efficiencies of SMST structures are much greater than those of tunnel emitters for three reasons:

(1) In SMST structures the electrons are emitted much closer to the metal base than in tunnel emitters;

(2) the collector barrier is smaller than the emitter barrier; and

(3) the electron-phonon mean-free paths are an order of magnitude greater for Si, Ge, and GaAs than for Al_2O_3.

Since scattering in the emitter semiconductor can be arranged to play only a small role in SMST structures by making $E_{ec} > E_{op}$, the interpretation of base transport measurements then becomes straightforward. All the electrons injected into the metal essentially take trajectories normal to the metal-semiconductor interface. If we neglect scattering in the emitter, the injected hot electrons in the metal have average energies $(E_f + q\varphi_e + kT)$ and kT associated with normal and transverse momenta, respectively. Since the hot-electron kinetic energy is very much greater than E_{ec}, any scattering event in the metal base will virtually preclude the subsequent collection of a hot electron. The same is true of the vacuum triode structures if the collector is biased to provide a collector barrier which nearly matches the emitter barrier. Thus the hot-electron attenuation in the base metal films of SMST and triode structures is essentially $\exp(-W/\lambda_B)$, where λ_B is the ballistic mean-free path.

$$\lambda_B = \frac{\lambda_{e\text{-}e}\lambda_c}{\lambda_{e\text{-}e} + \lambda_c} \tag{30}$$

The collector efficiency of metal-semiconductor and metal-vacuum barriers has been considered in Section III from a point of view which is directly applicable to SMST and triode structures since the theory summarized there is formulated for the case of normal incidence.

2. Experimental Measurements

a. SMST Structures. Atalla and Kahng (4) and Geppert (5) reported the first SMST structures. These structures, however, were not sufficiently stable or reproducible to use for more than semiquantitative studies. Crowell and Sze (79) used a cantilever beam (Fig. 22) as a stable micromanipulator capable of incremental adjustments of the order of 10 A to make nondestructive contact between a smoothly pointed and freshly cleaned semiconductor needle and a thin metal film evaporated on electromechanically polished

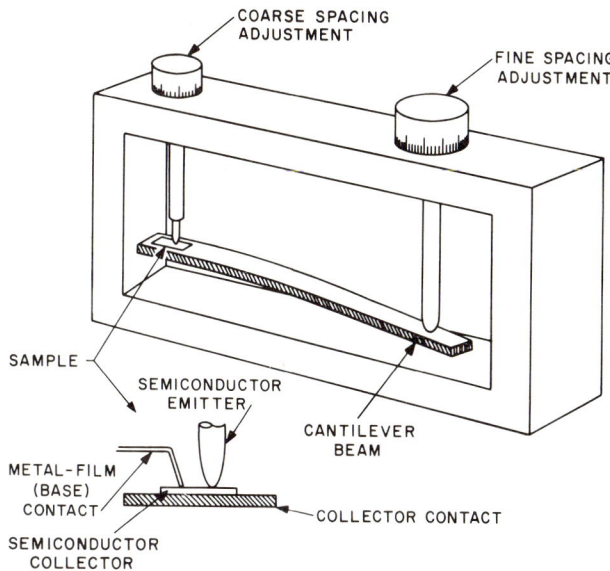

FIG. 22. Cantilever for making nondestructive contact of semiconductor-emitter and metal-base. Insert: geometrical configuration of SMST structure (80).

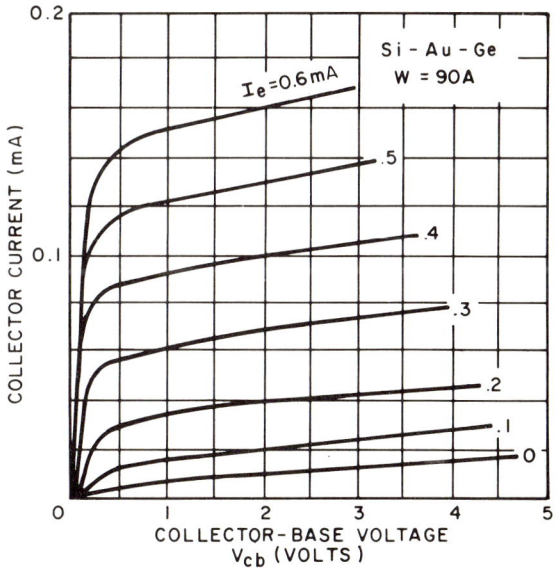

FIG. 23. Common-base collector current-voltage characteristics of a Si-Au-Ge transistor structure. Emitter current steps: 0.1 mA (80).

semiconductor substrates. The substrate served as the collector semiconductor, the metal film as the base, and the needle as the emitter semiconductor (cf. Figs. 18a and 22). While for device applications an all-thin-film structure is almost mandatory, the point contact structure has the merit of being made with semiconducting material of desirable bulk properties. In addition, when the base film is greater than 100 A thick, the emitter and collector semiconductors are not as likely to come into contact through pinholes in the metal film (and thus to form a metal-edge amplifier) as might be the case with evaporated or epitaxially deposited emitter semiconductor layers.

A typical collector current-voltage characteristic for selected emitter currents is shown in Fig. 23, as reported by Sze et al. (80). The dynamic common base current transfer ratio, α_0, is a constant for emitter currents larger than 0.5 mA. The electrical characteristics satisfy three of the criteria necessary to eliminate the possibility of appreciable current transfer through pinholes in the metal base:

(1) α_0 does not decrease appreciably with increasing emitter current: if most of the current were passing through pinholes there would be a tendency for the current to saturate.

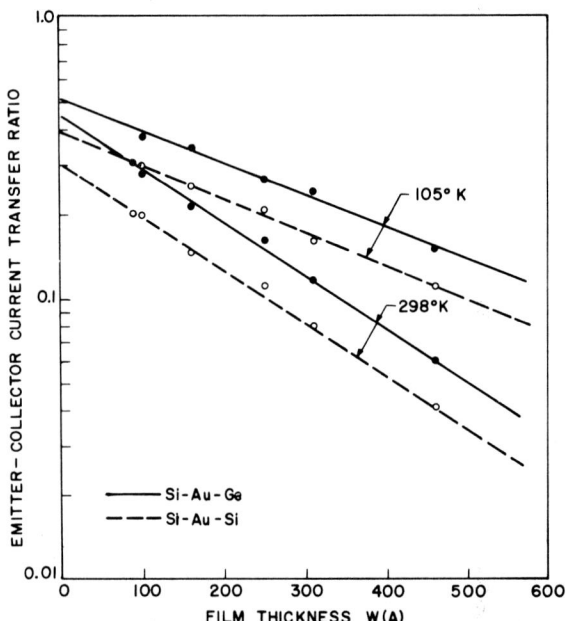

FIG. 24. Emitter-to-collector incremental current transfer ratios in Si-Au-Si and Si-Au-Ge structures as a function of Au-film thickness at 298 and 105°K with a collector electric field of 3×10^4 volts/cm (79).

(2) There is no appreciable α_0 when the polarity of the emitter drive is reversed, whereas current through pinholes would be injected in both directions.

(3) There is no appreciable inverse α_0 as can be expected because the emitter-base contact area is much smaller than the collector-base contact area, and the emitter barrier height is normally greater than the collector barrier height.

The results obtained at 105 and 300°K by Crowell and Sze (79) for a Si point emitter in contact with Au-Si and Au-Ge Schottky diodes with varying metal film thicknesses are shown in Fig. 24. As expected, there is a linear relationship between $\ln \alpha_0$ and W. The slope can be used to determine λ_B:

$$\alpha_0 = \alpha^* \exp(-W/\lambda_B) \tag{31}$$

where α^* is the value of α_0 when W is extrapolated to zero thickness.

TABLE III

COMPARISON OF THEORETICAL AND EXPERIMENTAL VALUES OF
α^* (298°K) AND α^* (105°K)/α^* (298°K)

Structure	α^* (298°K)		α^* (105°K)/α^* (298°K)	
	Theory	Expt.	Theory	Expt.
Si-Au-Si	0.37 ± 0.10	0.31 ± 0.03	1.25 ± 0.03	1.28 ± 0.05
Si-Au-Ge	0.40 ± 0.10	0.46 ± 0.03	1.09 ± 0.03	1.08 ± 0.05

The data in Table III show that the values of α^* and the temperature dependence of α^* from Fig. 24 are in reasonable agreement with the theoretical values deduced from the approaches outlined in Section III. From Table IV

TABLE IV

MEAN-FREE PATH VALUES FOR $\approx$ 0.85-eV ELECTRONS IN AU

Structure	λ_B (Å)			λ_e (Å)
	298°K	105°K	105°K (predicted)	
Si-Au-Si	229 ± 7	357 ± 20	362 ± 14	525 ± 36
Si-Au-Ge	228 ± 11	387 ± 27	362 ± 28	520 ± 57

it is apparent that the λ_B values deduced from Fig. 24 also agree for both structures since the same emitter structure is used. In addition the temperature dependence of λ_B is as expected if the mean-free path of the temperature-dependent portion of λ_B is the same as the mean-free path for phonon scattering in bulk gold, λ_p ($\lambda_p = 406$ A at 298°K (80) and 1150 A at 105°K). The λ_e values in Table IV give the combined hot-electron mean-free paths for impurity, defect, and electron scatterings. α^* and λ_B values consistent with theoretical expectations were also obtained from the data shown in Fig. 25 (80) for a GaP point on Au-Ge, -Si, -GaAs, -CdSe, and -CdS barriers.

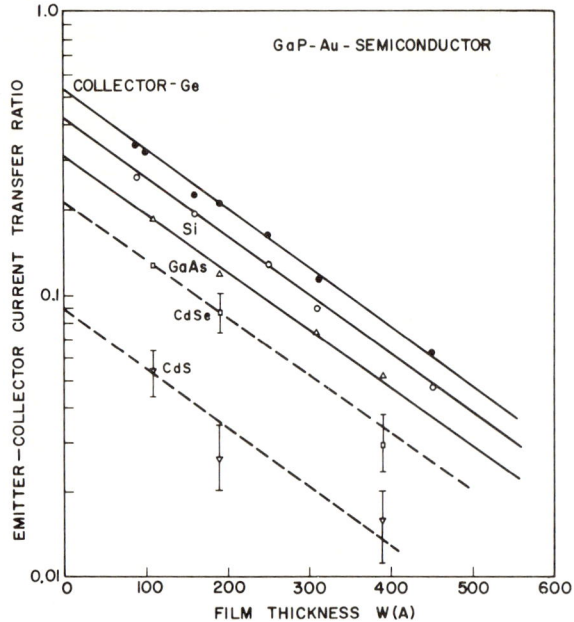

FIG. 25. Emitter-to-collector incremental current transfer ratios versus film thickness for GaP-Au-semiconductor structures with a 2-volt collector reverse bias (80).

The mean-free paths reported by Sze et al. (80) for GaP, GaAs, Si, and Ge point emitters on Au films and GaP, Si, and Ge point emitters on Ag and Pd films are presented in Fig. 26 in a manner designed to facilitate a determination of λ_c and λ_{e-e}. From Eqs. (1) and (3) it is anticipated that a plot of $(1/\lambda_B)(E/E_f)^2$ versus $(E_f/E)(E - E_f)^2$ should be linear if Quinn's theory (17) correctly predicts at least the form of the energy dependence of λ_{e-e} [E, the average energy of the hot electrons injected in the metal base is $(E_f + q\emptyset_e + 2kT)$ if no scattering occurs between the emitter potential energy maximum and the metal surface]. The λ_B and λ_{e-e} values deduced from the parameters of best

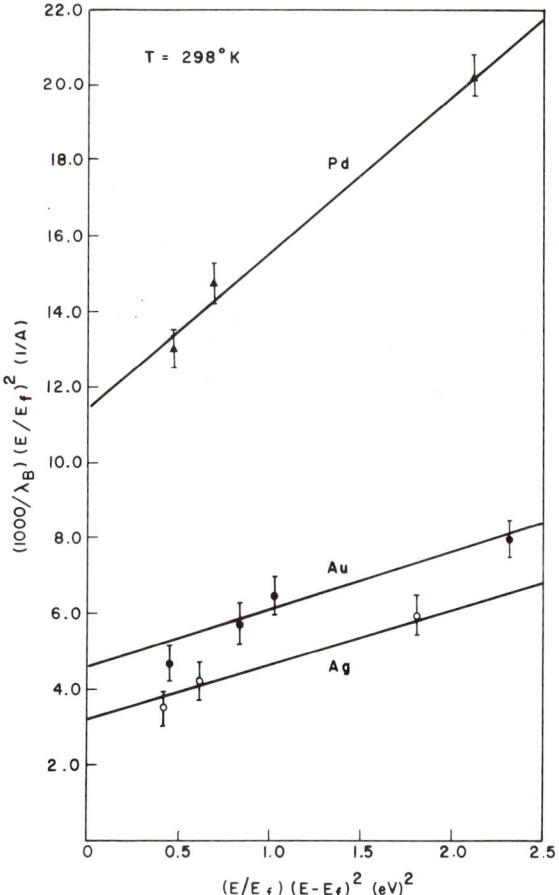

FIG. 26. Relationship between ballistic mean-free path and electron energy for Ag, Au, and Pd at 298°K.

fit for electrons 1 eV above the Fermi level are listed in Table V. The results are not strongly affected by the value of E_f used in the analysis. The quantity λ_σ ($= \lambda_c(E_f)$) should be comparable to the mean-free path determined from studies of the electrical conductivity. A comparison of the λ_σ and λ_p values (81) in Table V leads to the conclusion that the measurements were made on films with appreciable defects and impurities, since $\lambda_\sigma < \lambda_p$ in every case. The correlation between the measured values of λ_{e-e} and Quinn's theoretical prediction (17) multiplied by a factor of three to allow for d-band dielectric shielding (20) and exchange effects (as discussed in Section II) (21) appears to be very good.

TABLE V

Electron Mean-Free Paths (Å)

Metal	$E = E_f + 1$ eV			$E = E_f$	
	λ_B	λ_{e-e}	λ_{e-e} (theory)	λ_σ	λ_p
Ag	265	880	930	310	570
Au	220	910	990	220	406
Pd	87	300	420	88	110

The λ_{e-e} value for Pd was calculated assuming 0.6 free electrons per atom (81) to obtain E_f for the plot in Fig. 26. The theoretical value of λ_{e-e} obtained from these parameters contains no allowance for the possibility of d-band scattering of hot electrons.

b. Triode Structures. Kanter (82) has recently reported measurements of the transmission of hot electrons through free-standing thin gold films in a triode structure (cf. Fig. 18b). Electrons from a thermionic emitter, a simple

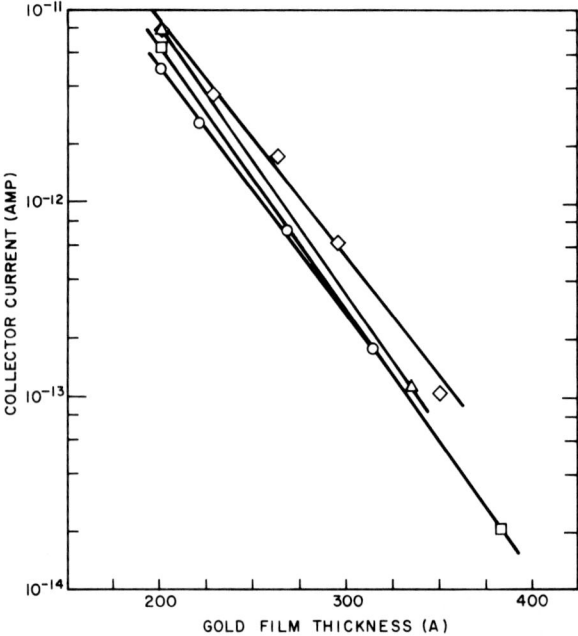

FIG. 27. Collector current of a thermionic triode with gold film "grid" as a function of gold film thickness. The hot-electron energy in the gold film is 5.25 eV relative to the Fermi level (82).

diode electron gun, were restricted to near-linear trajectories in the vacuum regions by an axial magnetic field of 200 gauss. Only those electrons which passed through the metal film without scattering were collected. The collector current in the structure is shown in Fig. 27 at selected stages in the growth of evaporated gold films. The incremental thickness of the films, which were ≈ 200 A when originally mounted, was monitored during the deposition. The electron energies were determined from the applied bias, the contact potentials as obtained from the current-voltage characteristics, and the

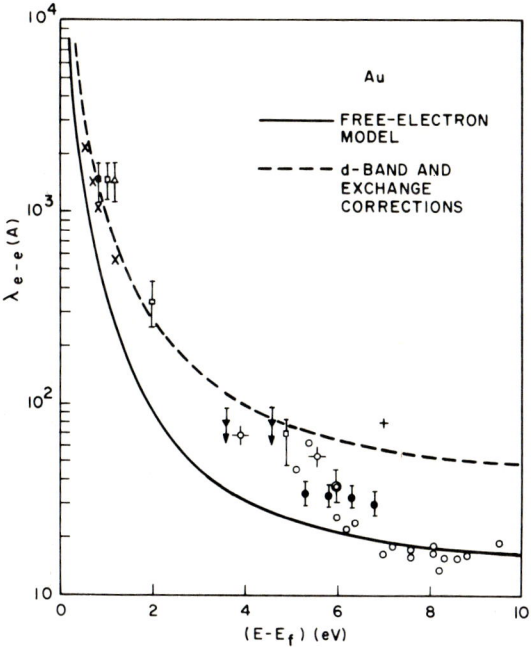

FIG. 28. Electron-electron mean-free paths versus electron energy in gold. The solid line is from Eq. (3), the dotted line corresponds to values of λ_{e-e} three times larger than those from the free-electron model (cf. Section II, 2). Experimental photoelectric and tunnel emission data correspond to those in Fig. 14 and use the same legend. The λ_{e-e} values were obtained from Fig. 9. Legend: ■, Crowell et al. (51); □, Sze et al. (54); △, Soshea and Lucas (59); ▼, Katrich and Sarbei (60); ⌀, Kanter (61); +, Mead (62); ○, Steele and Feist (63); ×, Sze et al. (80); ●, Kanter—320°K (82); ◉, Kanter—140°K (82).

assumption that the work function of the gold film was 4.7 eV. The mean-free paths determined by Kanter at 140 and 320°K are plotted as λ_{e-e} in Fig. 28 since $\lambda_c \ll \lambda_{e-e}$ at these energies. Note also that, as expected, the temperature difference does not produce a significant change in mean-free path.

VII. Discussion and Summary

We have outlined the results of theoretical and experimental studies of hot-electron transport in metals in a variety of thin-film structures. These observations permit a discussion of the device potentialities of such structures and of promising areas for further research.

The results shown in Fig. 28 indicate that there is general agreement between the electron-electron mean-free paths deduced from photoemission, tunnel emission, and thermionic emission measurements of hot-electron transport in gold films. At low energies the measurements are also in general agreement with the theoretical expectations, but the theoretical results cannot be expected to reflect the details of the band structure far from the Fermi level. Most of the existing measurements appear to have been made on films with a conductivity of from 50 to 75% of the conductivity of the bulk metal. There is need for further transport studies in more perfect films and films of a variety of other metals.

For high-energy electrons (of energy greater than the work function) the most reliable mean-free path measurements have been obtained from experiments which use the most difficult technique—the observation of hot-electron transport through free-standing films. The measurements in which tunnel emission cathodes were used and the energy of the emitted electrons analyzed are the next most reliable. Of the techniques discussed, the use of photoemission requires the discrimination of the electron mean-free path from the optical penetration depth and thus is the least satisfactory at high energies.

In the low-energy range the use of the point contact SMST structure offers the best means of studying hot-electron mean-free paths because the hot-electron energy is clearly defined. It is unfortunate, however, that a different semiconductor point emitter is required for each electron energy investigated. Photoemission measurements are more complex to make and to interpret and thus are more prone to error, especially with very thin films, since the optical absorption is not constant when the film thickness is varied. When the electron-electron mean-free path greatly exceeds the conductivity mean-free path, however, the photoemission measurement may be desirable since it will yield a larger attenuation length than the ballistic mean-free path [this occurs when $\lambda_{e-e} \gg 2\lambda_c$—cf. Eqs. (26) and (30)]. Photoemission measurements also remain the most reliable single method of measuring metal-semiconductor, metal-insulator, and metal-vacuum barrier heights. Thin-film tunnel-emission triodes have not been used successfully to measure hot-electron mean-free paths in metal films.

The above studies indicate that hot-electron mean-free paths are long enough in several metals so that the attenuation of the hot-electron current in metals is not a forbiddingly severe bar per se to the operation of hot-electron thin-film devices, but the grounded-base current gain of three-terminal thin-film transistor-like structures with a metal base appears to be limited to $\lesssim 0.5$ from a consideration of the collection efficiency at metal-insulator and metal-semiconductor barriers. Such devices exhibit no net current gain in the grounded emitter configuration; thus, for a general replacement of transistors, these devices do not appear to be promising.

It may, however, still be possible to use hot-electron diodes as substitutes for thermionic emitters, and even for the grid and cathode assembly of a vacuum tube. This requires either (1) that the metal-vacuum interface of a Schottky diode be treated (possibly by cesiation) to have a lower work function than the height of a Schottky barrier at the metal-semiconductor interface, or (2) that an insulator be found or perfected which has a long enough mean-free path for phonon scattering that a tunnel-emission cathode can have a considerably enhanced efficiency.

REFERENCES

1. C. A. Mead, *Proc. IRE* **48**, 359 (1960).
2. J. P. Spratt, R. F. Schwarz, and W. M. Kane, *Phys. Rev. Letters* **6**, 341 (1961).
3. A. Rose, Interim Rept., No. 6A, RCA, June 1960; Govt. Contract Rept No. bsr 77523 supported in part by the U.S. Navy, September, 1960.
4. M. M. Atalla and D. Kahng, *I.R.E. Trans. Electron. Devices* **9**, 507 (1962).
5. D. V. Geppert, *Proc. IRE* **50**, 1527 (1962).
6. M. M. Atalla and R. W. Soshea, *Solid-State Electron.* **6**, 245 (1963).
7. J. L. Moll, *IEEE Trans. Electron Devices* **10**, 299 (1963).
8. S. M. Sze and H. K. Gummel, *Solid-State Electron.* **9**, 751 (1966).
9. J. M. Lavine, *SCP Solid-State Technol.* **7**, 17 (1964).
10. A. Matthiessen and C. Vogt, *Ann. Phys. Chem.* **122**, 19 (1864).
11. N. F. Mott, *Proc. Cambridge Phil. Soc.* **32**, 281 (1936); also N. F. Mott and H. Jones, "The Theory of the Properties of Metals and Alloys," p. 290. Dover, New York, 1958.
12. E. M. Conwell and V. F. Weisskopf, *Phys. Rev.* **77**, 388 (1950).
13. R. B. Dingle, *Phil. Mag.* **46**, 831 (1955).
14. H. Brooks, *Advan. Electron. Electron Phys.* **8**, 85 (1955).
15. R. A. Smith, "Semiconductors," Chapter 5. Cambridge Univ. Press, London and New York, 1961.
16. A. H. Wilson, "Theory of Metals," p. 264. Cambridge Univ. Press, London and New York, 1955.
17. J. J. Quinn, *Phys. Rev.* **126**, 1453 (1962).
18. K. Motizuki and M. Sparks, *J. Phys. Soc. Japan* **19**, 486 (1964).
19. S. L. Adler, *Phys. Rev.* **130**, 1654 (1963); also *Phys. Rev.* **141**, 814 (1966).
20. J. J. Quinn, *Appl. Phys. Letters* **2**, 167 (1963).
21. R. H. Ritchie and J. C. Ashley, *J. Phys. Chem. Solids* **26**, 1689 (1965).
22. W. F. Krolikowski and W. E. Spicer, *Bull. Am. Phys. Soc.* [2] **11**, 916 (1966); Private communication (1967).
23. R. N. Hall, *Solid-State Electron.* **3**, 320 (1961).
24. C. R. Crowell and S. M. Sze, *Solid-State Electron.* **8**, 673 (1965).

25. C. R. Crowell and S. M. Sze, *Solid-State Electron.* **8**, 979 (1965).
26. C. Herring, *Bell System Tech. J.* **34**, 237 (1955).
27. E. M. Conwell, *Phys. Rev.* **135**, A1138 (1964).
28. S. L. Miller, *Phys. Rev.* **99**, 1234 (1955).
29. C. A. Lee, R. A. Logan, R. L. Batdorf, J. J. Kleimack, and W. Wiegmann, *Phys. Rev.* **134**, A761 (1964).
30. R. A. Logan and H. G. White, *J. Appl. Phys.* **36**, 3945 (1965).
31. R. A. Logan and S. M. Sze, *J. Phys. Soc. Japan* **21** (*Suppl.*), 434 (1966).
32. C. R. Crowell and S. M. Sze, *Appl. Phys. Letters* **9**, 242 (1966).
33. G. A. Baraff, *Phys. Rev.* **128**, 2507 (1962).
34. R. A. Logan and J. M. Rowell, *Phys. Rev.* **136**, A1751 (1964).
35. R. N. Hall, J. H. Racette, and H. Ehrenreich, *Phys. Rev. Letters* **4**, 456 (1960).
36. S. M. Sze, C. R. Crowell, and D. Kahng, *J. Appl. Phys.* **35**, 2534 (1964).
37. H. Frolich, *Proc. Roy. Soc.* **A160**, 230 (1937).
38. C. R. Crowell and S. M. Sze, *J. Appl. Phys.* **37**, 2683 (1966).
39. L. A. MacColl, *Phys. Rev.* **56**, 699 (1939); also *Bell System Tech. J.* **30**, 888 (1951).
40. N. F. Mott and H. Jones, "Theory of the Properties of Metals and Alloys," p. 86. Dover, New York, 1958.
41. J. Bardeen, *Phys. Rev.* **49**, 653 (1936).
42. H. J. Juretschke, *Phys. Rev.* **92**, 1140 (1953).
43. R. G. Sachs and D. L. Dexter, *J. Appl. Phys.* **21**, 1307 (1950).
44. T. Loucks and P. H. Cutler, *J. Phys. Chem. Solids* **25**, 105 (1964).
45. G. G. Belford, A. Kuppermann, and T. E. Phipps, *Phys. Rev.* **128**, 524 (1962).
46. P. H. Cutler and J. C. Davis, *Surface Sci.* **1**, 194 (1964).
47. J. C. Hensel, H. Hasegawa, and M. Nakayama, *Phys. Rev.* **138**, A225 (1965).
48. R. N. Dexter, B. Lax, A. F. Kip, and G. Dresselhaus, *Phys. Rev.* **96**, 222 (1964).
49. C. Herring and M. H. Nichols, *Rev. Mod. Phys.* **21**, 185 (1949).
50. W. G. Spitzer, C. R. Crowell, and M. M. Atalla, *Phys. Rev. Letters* **8**, 57 (1962).
51. C. R. Crowell, W. G. Spitzer, L. E. Howarth, and E. E. Labate, *Phys. Rev.* **137**, 2006 (1962).
52. R. Williams, *Phys. Rev.* **140**, A569 (1965).
53. R. H. Fowler, *Phys. Rev.* **38**, 45 (1931).
54. S. M. Sze, J. L. Moll, and T. Sugano, *Solid-State Electron.* **7**, 509 (1964).
55. R. Stuart, F. Wooten, and W. E. Spicer, *Phys. Rev.* **135**, A495 (1964).
56. E. Fermi, "Nuclear Physics," p. 187. Univ. of Chicago Press, Chicago, Illinois, 1950.
57. H. Thomas, *Z. Physik* **147**, 395 (1957).
58. C. R. Crowell, W. G. Spitzer, and H. G. White, *Appl. Phys. Letters* **1**, 3 (1962).
59. R. W. Soshea and R. C. Lucas, *Phys. Rev.* **138**, A1182 (1965).
60. G. A. Katrich and O. G. Sarbei, *Soviet Phys-.Solid State* (*English Transl.*) **3**, 1181 (1961).
61. H. Kanter, *J. Appl. Phys.* **34**, 3629 (1963).
62. C. A. Mead, *Phys. Rev. Letters* **8**, 56 (1962); **9**, 46 (1962).
63. S. R. Steele and W. Feist, Rept. No. 11, June–September 1965, Contract No. DA 28–043–AMC–0035 (E). Raytheon Co., Waltham, Massachusetts, for USAEL, Fort Monmouth, New Jersey.
64. L. B. Leder, M. E. Lasser, and A. C. Rudolph, *Appl. Phys. Letters* **5**, 215 (1964).
65. P. H. Bardell, Jr., Hot electron transport in thin copper films, Rept. No. 5059–1. Stanford Electron. Labs., Stanford Univ. Press, Stanford, California, August 1964.
66. R. M. Handy, *J. Appl. Phys.* **37**, 4620 (1966).

67. A. Sommerfeld and H. Bethe, *in* "Handbüch der Physik," H. Geiger and K. Scheel, eds.), Vol. 24/2. Springer, Berlin, 1933.
68. R. Holm, *J. Appl. Phys.* **22**, 569 (1951).
69. R. H. Fowler and L. Nordheim, *Proc. Roy. Soc.* **A119**, 173 (1928).
70. J. G. Simmons, *J. Appl. Phys.* **34**, 1793 (1963).
71. T. E. Hartman, *J. Appl. Phys.* **35**, 3283 (1964).
72. A. Goldsmith, T. Waterman, and H. Hirshorn, "Handbook of Thermophysical Properties of Solid Materials," Vol. III, p. 35. Macmillan, New York, 1961.
73. R. E. Collins and L. W. Davis, *Appl. Phys. Letters* **2**, 213 (1963).
74. O. L. Nelson and D. E. Anderson, *J. Appl. Phys.* **37**, 66, 77 (1965).
75. C. R. Crowell and S. M. Sze, *Solid-State Electron.* **9**, 1035 (1966).
76. H. A. Bethe, Rept. 43/12. M.I.T. Radiation Lab., Cambridge, Massachusetts, 1942.
77. W. Schottky, *Physik. Z.* **32**, 833 (1931).
78. C. R. Crowell, *Solid-State Electron.* **8**, 395 (1965).
79. C. R. Crowell and S. M. Sze, *Phys. Rev. Letters* **15**, 659 (1965).
80. S. M. Sze, C. R. Crowell, G. P. Carey, and E. E. Labate, *J. Appl. Phys.* **37**, 2690 (1966).
81. N. F. Mott and H. Jones, "The Theory of the Properties of Metals and Alloys," pp. 199, 268. Dover, New York, 1958.
82. H. Kanter, *Appl. Phys. Letters* **10**, 73 (1967).

Author Index

Numbers in parentheses are reference numbers and are included to assist in locating references where the author's name is not mentioned in the text. Numbers in italics refer to the page of the article on which the reference is listed.

Abelès, F., 77 (192, 193, 194), 78 (194), *95*
Adamson, Peggy L., 139, *187*
Adler, S. L., 329, *369*
Agusta, B., *320* (166), *324*
Albert, L., 199 (55), 200 (55), 201 (55), 202 (55, 78), 203 (55), 204 (55), 206 (55), 233 (55), *252*
Alcock, C. B., 283 (108b), *322*
Alexander, L. E., 218 (97), 222 (97), *253*
Alfano, R. R., 83 (211), *96*
Allinson, D. L., 149 (34), 156 (34), 171 (34, 122), 172, 173, 175 (34), *188*, *190*
Allison, R., 68 (163), *94*
Allpress, J. G., 152 (71, 72), 161, 180 (71, 72), *189*
Alt, L. L., 263 (56), 264, 319 (56), *321*
Amelincky, S., 144 (26), 155 (26), 162 (94), 182 (26), 184 (26), *187*, *189*, 195 (21), 199 (69), 225 (129), *251*, *252*, *254*
Anderson, D. E., 353, *371*
Anderson, G. S., 269 (80), *322*
Andrade, E. N. Da C., 120, *135*, 152 (68), *189*
Angel, D. W., 6 (16), 50 (101), *91*, *93*
Archer, R. J., 79 (200, 201), 84 (216), *95*, 261, *320*
Armstrong, W. J., 262 (47), *321*
Ashley, E. J., 3 (9), 11 (9, 35), 26 (30), 39 (74), 46 (82), *90*, *91*, *92*
Ashley, J. C., 329, 365 (21), *369*
Ashworth, J. L., 261 (33), 263 (33), 314, *320*
Atalla, M. M., 300 (120, 121), 301 (117), *323*, 326, 341 (50), 342 (50), 345 (50), 347 (50), 360, *369*, *370*
Atkinson, R. H., 245, *255*
Averback, B. L., 221, 230, *253*

Bachmann, L., 120, 136 (51), *136*
Baer, E., 121 (54), *136*
Baez, A. V., 50 (117), *93*
Bailey, A. I., 3 (5), *90*
Baird, S. S., 267 (74), *322*
Balk, P., 260 (19), 301 (19, 128), *320*, *323*

Ballard, S. S., 75 (188), *95*
Baltz, A., 159 (88), 171 (121), 186, *189*, *190*
Banerjee, B. C., 212, *253*
Baraff, G. A., 332, *370*
Barakat, N., 86 (227), *96*
Bardeen, J., 339, *370*
Bardell, P., 320 (166), *324*
Bardell, P. H., Jr., *370*
Barlett, J. T., 152 (70), *189*
Barnes, S. C., 199 (58, 60), 200, 204 (58, 60), 206, 209, 210, 211, 228, 233 (58, 84), *252*, *253*, *254*
Barrell, H., 85 (221), *96*
Barrett, C. S., 142 (20), *187*, 227, *253*
Barrett, M. A., 84 (217), *96*
Barton, J. L., 200 (76), *252*
Bashara, N. M., 39 (70), *92*
Bassett, G. A., 118, 119 (42, 43), 120, 128 (69), 133 (43), *135*, *136*, 144 (28), 150 (4, 38, 42, 61), *152* (42), 155, 156 (38), 160, 165, 166, 169, 175 *187*, *188*, *189*, 226 (133), *254*
Batdorf, R. L., 332 (29), *370*
Bauer, E., 223, *253*
Baumeister, P., 50 (102), *93*
Beattie, J. R., 84 (212), *96*
Beaumont, D., 60 (140), *94*
Becker, R., 98 (11), 99 (11), *134*, 193, *251*
Behrndt, K. H., 11, 21, 23 (36), *91*
Belford, G. G., 339, *370*
Belk, R., 26 (62), *92*
Bell, H. B., 265 (60), 314 (60), 319 (60), *321*
Bennett, H. E., 4 (10, 13), 9 (26) 10 (32), 11 (35), 12 (10, 32), 13, 16 (32), 17, 18 (40), 19 (10), 38 (69), 39 (69, 74), 41 (69), 46 (10, 82), 48 (88), 49 (88), 50 (13, 26, 98), 58 (127), 60 (37, 127), 62 (98), 64 (32, 88), 81 (69), 84 (69), 62 (127), *91*, *92*, *93*, *94*
Bennett, J. M., 2 (3), 3 (3), 6 (15), 9 (26), 10 (32), 12 (32), 16 (32), 25 (60, 61), 26 (15, 30), 28 (15), 34 (15, 60, 61), 36 (15), 39 (74), 46 (82), 50 (26), 55 (123), 64 (32), 85 (15), 86 (15, 60, 61), 88 (15, 60, 61), 89 (15), *90*, *91*, *92*

373

AUTHOR INDEX

Berning, P. H., 39 (72), 40 (72), *92*
Berry, R. W., 258, 282, *320*
Bertaut, F., 222, 224 (111), *253*
Bethe, H., 351, 357 (76), *371*
Bethge, H., 150 (46), 152 (46), *188*
Bevans, J. T., 60 (153), *94*
Bicelli, L. P., 199 (65, 66, 67, 68), 200 (65, 66, 67, 68), 204, 207, 209 (65, 67, 68), 210, 211 (68), 228, 236 (66), *252*
Bicknell, R. W., 150 (59), *188*
Bilous, O., *320* (167), *324*
Biondi, M. A., 60 (139), *94*
Birchenall, C. E., 123 (59), 127 (59), *136*
Bjorck, E., 267 (73), *322*
Blackwell, H. E., 68 (165), *94*
Bloem, J., 263 (53), 264, 319 (53), *321*
Blevin, W. R., 60 (137, 149), *94*
Blum, W., 192, 227 (137), *251*, *254*
Bockris, J. O'M., 191, 192, 195 (2), 196, 197 (24, 25, 40), 198, 199 (36, 39, 64), 200 (36, 39, 76), 201 (36), 202, 203 (2), 204 (36, 39, 64), 206 (36, 39, 64), 209 (36, 39, 64), 210 (64), 211 (36, 64), *251*, *252*
Booker, G. R., 150 (60), 169 (108, 110, 111), 172, 186, *188*, *190*
Boettner, E. A., 47 (86), *92*
Bolle, H. J., 86 (231), *96*
Borie, B., 40, *92*, 144 (27), *187*, 230, *254*
Bottka, N., 58 (128), *94*
Bouillon, F., 150 (55), *188*
Bousquet, P., 85 (226), *96*
Bradford, A. P., 39 (71), *92*, 282 (100, 103), *322*
Bragg, W. L., 140 (19), *187*
Brandenberg, W. M., 60 (138, 148), *94*
Brandes, H., 198, *252*
Bray, A. R., 300 (120), *323*
Brenneman, A. E., 302 (139), 306 (139), 309 (139), *323*
Brenner, A., 192, *251*
Brenner, S. S., 118 (40), *135*
Bronco, C. J., 50 (119), *93*
Brooks, H., 139, *187*, 328, *369*
Brown, D. M., 260 (21), 301 (21), *320*
Brown, G. A., 305 (145), 309 (145), *323*
Brown, W. J., 60 (149), *94*
Bruce, C. F., 85 (219), *96*
Bruck, L., 159 (85), *189*
Buck, T. M., 7 (18), *91*, 309, *323*
Budewski, E., 202 (79), 203 (79), *252*

Budo, Y., 282 (106), *322*
Burbank, R. D., 171, *190*
Burge, D. K., 38 (69), 39 (69), 41 (69), 68 (160), 81 (69), 84 (69), *92*
Burkhardt, P. J., 260, 301 (19), 302 (137), 305 (137), 306 (137), *320*, *323*
Burns, J., 68 (163), *94*
Burton, W. K., 192, 193, 194, 195, *251*
Buttner, F. H., 139 (13), *187*

Cabrera, N., 138 (6), 146, 147, 157, 158, 160 (29), 161, 162 (29), 174, *187*, 192, 193, 194 (16), 195 (16), 202 (80), 207, 231, *251*, *252*, *253*, *254*
Caffrey, R. E., 261 (32), 263 (32), 264, *320*
Cahn, J. W., 108, *135*
Canfield, L. R., 41 (78), 60 (135), 68 (78), *92*, *94*
Carlson, H. G., 305 (145), 309, *323*
Carey, G. P., 361 (80), 362 (80), 364 (80), 367 (80), *371*
Castrucci, P. P., 284, 320 (166), *321*, *324*
Caswell, H. L., 282 (106), *322*
Cathcrart, J. V., 144 (27), *187*
Catlin, A., 171 (123), 181, *190*
Chakraverty, B. K., 111, 112 (31), 120, 127 (31), *135*, 152, *189*
Charig, J. M., 150 (59), *188*
Chasmer, R. P., 50 (111, 112, 113, 114, 115), *93*
Childs, C. B., 50 (104), *93*
Chirigos, J. N., 113 (32), 120, *135*
Chopra, K. L., 166, *189*
Chow, E. T-K., 22, 23, *91*
Chu, T. L., 316, *324*
Ciddor, P. E., 85 (219), *96*
Clausen, O. W., 60 (138), *94*
Coblentz, W. W., 60 (145), *94*
Cochrane, W., 223, 232, 234 (149), 235 (149), 236 (149), *253*, *254*
Cockcroft, J. D., 122, 123 (58a), 127 (58a), *136*
Cohen, J. B., 222 (112), 228 (141), *253*, *254*
Cohen, M., 223 (116), *253*
Collins, F. C., 260 (17), *320*
Collins, R. E., 353, *371*
Colson, J. P., 79 (202), 84 (202), *95*
Conjeand, P., 150 (43), 152 (43), *188*

Conrad, E. E., 266 (68), 267 (68), 270 (68), 271 (95, 96), 310 (68), *322*
Conrady, A. E., 55, *93*
Conway, B. E., 196, 197 (24, 25, 41), *251, 252*
Conwell, E. M., 328 (12), 331 (27), 332, *369, 370*
Cook, H. C., 212, *253*
Cooper, H. W., 265 (62), 319 (62), *321*
Coppola, A. J., 315 (159), *324*
Corl, E. A., 274, *322*
Corning, J. J., 258 (10), 319 (10), *320*
Cosslett, V. E., 224 (123), *253*
Cottrell, A. H., 147 (30), *187*
Courtney-Pratt, J. S., 3 (5), *90*
Cox, J. T., 9 (24), *91*, 282 (101), 285 (101), *322*
Cox, W. P., 263 (55), 264 (55), 319 (55), *321*
Crawford, J. L., 185 (144), 186, *190*
Croce, P., 23 (57), 24, *92*
Crowell, C. R., 330, 331 (24), 332, 333 (25), 334 (36), 335 (36), 337 (25), 338, 339, 340, 341, 342 (50), 343, 345, 346, 347 (50), 349, 354 (51), 356 (75), 357, 358 (75), 359, 360, 361 (80), 362 (79, 80), 363, 364 (80), 367, *369, 370, 371*
Cullity, B. D., 218 (98), *253*
Cutler, P. H., 339, *370*

Dalton, J. V., 309, 315, *323, 324*
Damjanovic, A., 191, 192, 195 (2), 196 (2, 34, 35, 36, 37, 38, 39), 198, 199 (36, 38, 39, 64), 200 (36, 38, 39), 201, 202, 203 (2), 204, 206, 207 (38), 209 (36, 38, 39, 64), 210, 211, 233 (38), *251, 252*
Dash, W. C., 169 (107), *190*
Davidse, P. D., 261 (37), 269, 271 (37), 272 (37), 275 (37), 277 (37), 280 (37), 285, 288 (37), 314, *321, 322*
Davis, E. M., 258 (10), 319 (10), *320*
Davis, J. C., 339, *370*
Davis, L. W., 353, *371*
Deal, B. E., 260, 261, 295 (113), 301 (25, 113, 124), 302 (140), 304 (140), 306, *320, 323*
Dekeyser, W., 195 (21), *251*
Delavignette, P., 162, *189*
Deleuil, R., 85 (226), *96*
Delord, J. F., 260 (18), 301 (18), *320*
Derick, L., 300 (118), *323*

Despic, A. R., 196 (33), 198 (33), *251*
Devanathan, M. A. V., 196 (40), 197, *252*
Dexter, D. L., 339, *370*
Dexter, R. N., 340 (48), 358 (48), *370*
Dhaka, V. A., 320 (168), *324*
Dickson, E. W., 150 (40, 63), 156 (40), 173, *188*, 223 (121), 235 (155), 243, 244, *253, 254*
Dietz, R. W., 2 (3), 3 (3), *90*
Dingle, R. B., 328, *369*
Donovan, T. M., 3 (8, 9), 7 (8), 8, 11 (9, 35), *90, 91*
Donovan, R. P., 301 (123), *323*
Doo, V. Y., 270 (87), 314 (87), *322*
Döring, W., 98 (11), 99 (11), *134*, 193, *251*
Douglas, R. W., 304, 305, *323*
Dresselhaus, G., 340 (48), 358 (48), *370*
Drum, C. M., 169 (115), *190*
Drummeter, L. F., 282, *322*
Duffy, C. M., 261 (41), 262 (47), *321*
Dumesnil, M. E., 292, 311, *322*
Dunkle, R. V., 60 (151, 153), *94*
Dunn, S. T., 60 (150), *94*
Dyson, J., 22 (46), *91*

Eberstein, A., 2 (1), *90*
Economou, N. A., 199 (56, 61), 200 (56, 61), 204 (56, 61), 206, 209, 242 (61), *252*
Edwards, D. K., 60 (144, 152), *94*
Ehrenreich, H., *370*
Ehrlich, G., 107 (24), *135*
Eichkorn, G., 219 (107), 228 (107), 231, *253*
Eisner, E., 86 (228), *96*
Ellis, T., 218, 219, 232 (103), *253*
Ellis, W. C., 174, *190*
Emberson, R. M., 83 (207), *95*
Engelsrath, A., 73 (172), *95*
Ennos, A. E., 4 (4), *90*
Enyo, M., 196 (29, 30), 198 (29), *251*
Epstein, A. L., 265 (60, 61), 314 (60, 61), 319 (60, 61), *321*
Erb, R. A., 120, *136*
Erdey-Gruz, T., 199 (49), 204 (49), *252*
Esch, R. P., 261 (26), 271 (26), 288, *320*
Estermann, I., 121, *136*
Evans, R. J., 260 (24), 301 (24), *320*
Eversteijn, F. C., 265 (64), 266, 314, *321*
Evitts, H. C., 265 (61, 63), 314 (61), 319 (61, 63), *321*

Eyring, E. M., 107 (23), *135*
Eyring, H., 107 (23), *135*

Fahrenfort, J., 75 (176), *95*
Fankuchen, I., 23 (56), *92*
Farnsworth, H. E., 143, *187*
Faust, J. W., 153, 156 (75), *189*
Faust, R. C., 86 (232), 87 (232), *96*
Feder, J., 98 (12), 99 (12), *134*
Feinberg, I., *320* (167), *324*
Feist, W., 349, 354, 367, *370*
Fermi, E., 344 (56), *370*
Ficker, J., 238 (160), *254*
Finch, G. I., 234 (152), 235 (153), *254*
Finch, R. H., 169 (106), *190*
Finegan, J. D., 230 (142), *254*
Fischer, H., 199 (52, 55, 56), 200 (52, 55, 56), 201 (55), 202 (55, 78), 203 (55), 204 (52, 55, 56), 206, 211, 219 (107), 227, 228 (107), 231, 233 (55), *251*, *252*, *253*
Fisher, J. C., 192, 203 (81), *252*
Fitzgerald, D. J., 301 (134), *323*
Flaschen, S. S., 261 (41, 42), 310 (155), *321*, *324*
Fleischmann, M., 191, 233 (3), 235 (3), *251*
Fletcher, N. H., 139, *187*
Florinskaya, V. A., 271 (92), *322*
Foreman, W. T., 50 (96), 68 (96), *93*
Forty, A. J., 152 (69), *189*, 195, *251*
Fowler, R. H., 342 (53), 351, *370*, *371*
Frank, F. C., 139, 142 (22), 152 (69), 157 (15), 162 (15), 166, 175 (15), 184 (22, 134), *187*, *189*, *190*, 193, 194 (16), 195, 203, 207, 208 (86), *251*, *253*
Frankl, D. R., 295 (111), 296 (111), *323*
Fray, S. J., 60 (136), *94*
Freeman, G. H. C., 67 (158), *94*
Frenkel, J., 110, *135*, 192, *251*
Friedman, H. L., 302 (139), 306 (139), 309 (139), *323*
Friedmann, G., 87 (239), *96*
Frieser, R. G., 267 (75), *322*
Frolich, H., 338 (37), *370*
Frosch, C. J., 300 (118), *323*
Fryer, R. E., 53 (122), 54, *93*
Fujita, F. E., 238 (161), 239 (161), *254*
Fuller, C. R., 267 (74), 305 (145), 309 (145), *322*

Fullman, R. L., 203 (81), *252*
Funk, E. R., 139 (12a), *187*

Gallagher, P. C. J., 167 (104a), *190*
Gandais, M., 23 (57), 24 (57), *92*
Garmon, L. B., 150 (58), 153, *188*, 212, 213, 233 (95), 234 (156), 238 (162, 163), 238 (156, 162, 163), 240 (162), 242 (95), 243 (156, 163), 245 (156, 163), *253*, *254*
Gastaud, A., 85 (226), *96*
Gates, D. M., 60 (140), *94*
Genzel, L., 50 (103), *93*
Geppert, D. V., 326, 360, *369*
Gesser, H., 211 (90), *253*
Gibbs, J. W., 100 (17), 113 (17), 119 (17), *134*, 138 (5), 150 (5), *187*, 192, *251*
Gier, J. T., 60 (144, 153), *94*
Giron, I., 199 (62), 204 (62), 227, *252*
Glang, R., 258, *320*
Glocker, R., 327, *254*
Glossop, A. B., 243, *255*
Gnaedinger, R. J., Jr., 261 (41, 42), *321*
Gnall, R. P., 262 (45), 270 (45), 272 (45), 273 (45), 288, *321*
Gobeli, G. W., 79 (201), *95*
Goetzberger, A., 301 (125), *323*
Goldsmith, A., *371*
Goldsmith, N., 261 (34), 263 (34), 274, *320*
Good, A., 200 (72), *252*
Goodwin, A. R., 60 (136), *94*
Gorbunova, K., 199 (51), 204 (51), *252*
Gore, G., 191 (1), *251*
Gottsche, H., 156 (79), 159 (79), 175 (79), *189*
Gradmann, U., 143, *187*
Gradmann, V., 249 (171), *255*
Grant, J., 50 (105), *93*
Gray, P. V., 260 (21), 301 (21), *320*
Greenland, K. M., 21, *91*
Gregor, L. V., 258, 260, 301 (19), 316 (162), *320*, *324*
Gretz, R. D., 100 (18), 106 (18), 110 (29), 111 (29), 115, 117, 118 (18, 37), 122 (58), 124 (58), 125 (58), 127 (18, 37), 128, *134*, *135*, *136*
Grove, A. S., 260, 261, 295 (113), 301 (25, 113, 124, 134), 302 (140), 304 (140), 306 (140), *320*, *323*

Grünbaum, E., 131, *136*, 138, 140 (9), 159, 160 (9), 161 (92), 162, 176 (88a), 178, 179, *187*, *189*, *190*
Gummel, H. K., 327 (8), *369*
Gwathmey, A. T., 227, *254*

Hackerman, N., 210 (89), *253*
Hacskaylo, M., 78, *95*
Hall, C. E., *253*
Hall, M. J., *190*
Hall, R. N., 330, *369*, *370*
Hammad, F. H., 239 (166), *255*
Handy, R. M., 350 (66), 352 (66), 353, *370*
Hansen, W. N., 75 (177, 178, 179, 180, 181), *95*
Haque, C. A., 143, *187*
Harding, W. E., 258 (10), 319 (10), *320*
Hardy, A. C., 50 (89), 75 (174), *92*, *95*
Hardy, S. C., 117 (38), 118 (38), *135*
Harrick, N. J., 75 (182, 183, 184, 185), 76 (189), *95*
Harrison, G. R., 50 (94), *93*
Hartman, T. E., 23 (53), *91*, 351, *371*
Hasegawa, H., 340 (47), *370*
Hashimoto, H., 155, *189*, 212, *253*
Hass, G., 9 (24), 10 (33, 34), 39, 40, 50 (106, 107), 60 (34), 84 (215), *91*, *92*, *93*, *96*, 282, 285 (101), 286 (99), *322*
Hauser, V. E., 316 (163), *324*
Heavens, O. S., 21, 22 (48), 25, 26 (48), 77 (195), 78 (196, 198), 86 (238), *91*, *95*, *96*
Heidenreich, R. D., 171, *190*, 225 (128), *254*
Heiman, F. P., 300 (122), *323*
Henderson, G., 85 (225), 86 (225), *96*
Hensel, J. C., 340 (47), *370*
Herring, C., 331 (26), 341, *370*
Hess, R. B., 58 (128), *94*
Hetherington, G., 266 (67), *321*
d'Heurle, F. M., 302 (139), 306 (139), 309 (139), *323*
Hill, R. M., 86 (235), *96*
Hinson, D. C., 67, *94*
Hintermann, H. E., 238, *255*
Hinton, R. W., 228 (141), *254*
Hirsch, P. B., 142 (21), 182 (21), *187*, 225, 226 (130), *254*
Hirshorn, H., *371*

Hirth, J. P., 97 (3, 4, 5, 6, 8), 99 (13), 100 (4, 5, 6, 8), 102 (3), 103, 104 (20), 106 (3, 6, 20), 107 (3), 108 (3, 27), 109 (3, 4, 6), 110, 113, 114 (33), 117 (5), 119 (3, 48), 120, 121, 122 (58), 123 (3, 27), 124 (58), 125 (27, 58), 127 (27), 131 (3, 6), 133 (4), *134*, *135*, *136*, 137 (3), 150, 151, 152, 154 (63a), 155 (3, 63a), 159, 160, 164, 184, 193, *187*, *188*, *189*, *190*, *251*
Hofer, E., 219 (105, 106), 228 (105, 106), 230, *253*
Hoerni, J. A., 300 (119), *323*
Hoffman, D. G., 260 (18), 301 (18), *320*
Hoffman, R. W., 230 (142), *254*
Hofstein, S. R., 300 (122), 303, 305, *323*
Hogaboom, G. B., 192, *251*
Holden, J., 87 (241), 88, *96*
Holland, L., 9 (23), 22 (49), *91*, 258, 267, 298 (116), 309, *320*, *322*, *323*
Holm, R., 351, *371*
Hooper, W. W., 298 (115), *323*
Hopkins, B. E., 37 (66), *92*
Horton, J. A., 75 (178), *95*
Hosokawa, N., 218 (103), 219 (103), 232 (103), *253*
Hothersall, A. W., 227 (136), *254*
Howarth, L. E., 341 (51), 343 (51), 345 (51), 349 (51), 354 (51), 367 (51), *370*
Howie, A., 142 (21), 169 (110), 182 (21), *187*, 225 (130), 226 (130), *254*
Hruska, S. J., 97 (6), 100 (6), 106 (6), 108 (26), 109 (6, 28), 123, 124 (28, 63a), 131 (6), *134*, *135*, *136*, 151 (67a), *189*
Hu, S. M., 270 (88), 297 (88), 314, 316, *322*, *324*
Hudson, J. B., 123, 124 (61), 127 (60, 61), *136*
Hulburt, E. O., 60 (132), *94*
Humphreys-Owen, S. P. F., 69, *94*
Hunter, W. R., 10 (33, 34), 50 (101), 60 (34), 68 (164), 69 (167), 70, 72, 73, 74, 75, *91*, *93*, *94*, *95*
Hutchinson, T. E., 156 (82), *189*

Imura, T., 218, *253*
Ing, S. W., Jr., 263 (56), 264 (56), 319 (56), *321*
Inman, M. C., 160 (91a), *189*
Inn, E. C. Y., 68 (161), *94*

Ino, S., 150 (49), 156 (49, 81), 159 (81), 160 (81), 164 (49), 165, 172, 175 (49), 178 (49), *188*
Isebeck, K., 150 (52), *188*
Iwasaki, H., 260 (23), 301 (23), *320*

Jaccodine, R. J., 169 (115), *190*
Jack, K. H., 266 (67), *321*
Jackson, C. S., 122, 124 (58), 125 (58), *136*
Jacobs, M. H., 118 (45, 46), 119 (45), 120 (45), 132 (75), 133, *135*, 150 (41, 62, 63), 155 (41), 156 (41), 165, 167, 168, 170, 171 (102), 174, 175, *188*, *189*, *190*, 235 (155), 243 (155, 168), 243 (155), *254*, *255*
Jaffe, J. H., 86 (237), *96*
Janus, A. R., 270 (89), *322*
Jardinier-Offergeld, M., 150 (55), *188*
Javet, P., 219 (105, 106)), 228 (105, 106), 230 *253*
Jellyman, P. E., 271 (93), *322*
Jesser, W. A., 139, 145, 146, 150 (12), 158, 162, 235 (154), 243 (154), 245, *187*, *254*
Johnson, F. A., 60 (136), *94*
Johnson, G. R., 199 (70), 200 (70), 206 (70), *252*
Johnston, A. R., 82 (205), *95*
Johnston, R. G., 16 (39), 65 (39), *91*
Jones, F. E., 50 (111, 112, 113, 114, 115), *93*
Jones, H., 338 (40), 365 (81), 366 (81), *370*, *371*
Jordan, E. L., 263, *321*
Jorgenson, G. V., 269 (81), *322*
Joyce, B. A., 150 (59), *188*
Juenker, D. W., 74 (173), *95*
Juretschke, H. J., 339, *370*

Kahng, D., 300 (121), *323*, *326*, 334 (36), 335 (36), 360, *369*, *370*
Kaischew, R., 202, 203, *252*
Kallander, D. A., 261 (41), *321*
Kalnins, I. L., 310 (155), *324*
Kamiya, Y., 171, *190*
Kane, W. M., 325 (2), 351 (2), *369*
Kanter, H., 349, 352 (61), 353, 354, 355 (82), 366, 367, *370*, *371*
Katrich, G. A., 349, 354 (60), 367, *370*

Kaupp, E., 227, *254*
Kawamura, N., 260 (23), 301 (23), *320*
Kay, D. H., *253*
Kaye, Wilbur, 46 (85), *92*
Kehoe, R. B., 156 (80), 159 (80), 175 (80), *189*
Kelly, J. C., 26 (63), 78 (196), *92*, *95*
Kelly, P. M., 225, *254*
Kennedy, D. R., 267 (72), *322*
Kenney, B. T., 315 (159), *324*
Kenty, J. L., 126 (65), *136*
Kerr, D. R., 298 (114), 299, 302, 303, 304, 305, 306, 307, 308, 310, 311, 313, 315, 316 (162), *323*, *324*
Kierstead, F. H., 60 (143), *94*
Kim, Y. S., 274 (97), *322*
Kingston, R. H., 289 (109), *322*
Kip, A. F., 340 (48), 358 (48), *370*
Kirchner, F., 171 (119), *190*
Kita, H., 196 (30, 32), 198 (32), *251*
Kleimack, J. J., 332 (29), *370*
Klerer, J., 261 (31), 263, 319 (52), *320*, *321*
Klug, H. P., 218 (97), 222 (97), *253*
Knudsen, M., 121 (55), *136*
Ko, W. H., 305 (146), 309 (146), *323*
Koehler, W. F., 2 (1), 4 (11, 12), 25 (60), 34 (60, 64), 58 (127), 60 (127), 62 (127), 65, 86 (60), 88 (60, 64), *90*, *92*, *94*
Koester, C. J., 85 (218), *96*
Kohlschütter, V., 199 (48, 50), 200 (72), 204 (48, 50), *252*
Kolesova, V. A., 271 (94), *322*
Koller, L. R., 47 (87), 50, *92*
Kooi, E., 260 (22), 262 (46), 301 (22, 129), 305 (22), *320*, *321*, *323*
Koonce, S. E., 267 (77), *322*
Koop, S. A., 123 (61), 124 (61), 127 (61), *136*
Koppelmann, G., 78 (197), *95*
Koutsky, J. A., 121, *136*
Kozawa, S., 83, *92*
Krebs, K., 78 (197), *95*
Krolikowski, W. F., 329, *369*
Krongelb, S., 261 (38), 263 (38), 264 (38), *321*
Kruger, H., 271 (91), *322*
Kruger, J., 37, 38, *92*
Kubaschewski, O., 37 (66), *92*
Kuhlmann-Wilsdorf, D., 139, 158 (86), 162 (86), *187*

Kuhn, H., 60 (133), *94*
Kunin, L. L., 139 (14), 156 (14), *187*
Kuper, A. B., 305 (146), 309 (146), *323*
Kuppermann, A., 339 (45), *370*
Kuznetzoff, P., 301 (133), *323*

Labate, E. E., 341 (51), 343 (51), 345 (51), 349 (51), 354 (51), 361 (80), 362 (80), 364 (80), 367 (51, 80), *370, 371*
LaBrie, J. J., 265 (62), 319 (62), *321*
Laendle, K. W., 263 (56), 264 (56), 319 (56), *321*
Lander, J. J., 40 (77), *92*
Langdon, J. L., 257 (2), 320 (167), *320, 324*
Lasser, M. E., *370*
Lavine, J. M., 327, 351 (9), *369*
Law, T. J., 118 (45, 46), 119 (45), 120 (45), 133 (45), *135*, 150 (41), 155 (41), 156 (41), 165 (41), 175, *190*, 243 (168), *255*
Lawless, K. R., 150 (54, 58), 153, 180 (130), 181 (131), *188, 190*, 199 (63), 204 (63), 212, 223 (115), 233, 234 (63, 156), 238, 239, 240 (162), 243, 245, 249, *252, 253, 254, 255*
Lax, B., 340 (48), 358 (48), *370*
Leder, L. B., *370*
Lee, C. A., 332 (29), *370*
Lee, C. H., 316 (161), *324*
Legat, W. H., 263 (55), 264 (55), 319 (55), *321*
Lehman, H. S., 257 (1), 261 (27, 29, 37), 263 (29, 54), 264, 269 (37), 271 (27, 37), 272, 273 (27, 29), 274, 275 (29, 37), 277 (29, 37), 280 (37), 282 (29), 283, 284 (29), 285 (37), 286, 287, 288, 301 (132), 319 (54), *320, 321, 323*
Leidheiser, H., Jr., 227, 238 (162), 239 (162), 240 (162), *254*
Lenham, A. P., 84 (214), *96*
Leonard, R. A., 263 (54), 264 (54), 319 (54), *321*
Lettington, A. H., 84 (211a), *96*
Lewis, B., 263 (49), 285, *321*
Liddell, H. M., 78 (198), *95*
Ligenza, J. R., 261, *321*
Lighty, P. E., 199 (71), 200 (71), 209 (71), 218, 220, 231, *252, 253*
Lincke, R., 50 (97), *93*
Lindner, R., 295 (112), 300 (120), *323*

Lindsay, R. B., 23 (55), *92*
Lighthill, M. J., 207, *253*
Lodge, J. I., 268, *322*
Loewenstein, E. V., 73 (172), *95*
Logan, J. S., 302, 305 (137), 306 (137), *323*
Logan, R. A., 332 (29, 30), *370*
Lohmann, A., 86 (230), *96*
Loofbourow, J. R., 50 (94, 109), *93*
Lord, R. C., 50 (94), *93*
Lorenz, W., 198, *252*
Lothe, J., 97 (9), 98 (12), 99 (12, 14), 103, 109 (9, 14), *134*
Loucks, T., 339, *370*
Lowenheim, F. A., 192, *251*
Lucas, R. C., 346, 347 (59), 349, 354 (59), 367, *370*

McAlister, E. D., 60 (155), *94*
McBride, W. R., 46 (81), 50 (98), 62 (98), *92, 93*
McCarroll, B., 107 (24), *135*
McCarthy, D. W., 50, *92*
McCarthy, K. A., 75 (188), *95*
MacColl, L. A., 338, *370*
McCrackin, F. L., 79 (202), 83, 84 (202), 84 (206), *95*
McFarland, M., 282 (103), *322*
MacKenna, E. L., 263 (55), 264, 319 (55), *321*
MacKenzie, J. D., 263 (57, 58), 264, 319 (57, 58), *321*
MacKenzie, J. K., 164, *189*, 265 (63), 319 (63), *321*
McKeown, D., 60 (138), *94*
McLauchlan, T. A., 22 (50), *91*
Macleod, J. E. S., 86 (235), *96*
MacRae, A. U., 150 (57), *185*
Madden, R. P., 16 (39), 37, 39 (72), 40 (72), 41 (78), 50 (108, 116), 60 (135), 65 (39, 67, 156, 157), 68, *91, 92, 93, 94*
Mader, S., 138 (7), *187*
Maissel, L. I., 9 (21), *91*, 258, 261 (37), 267, 269, 271 (37), 272 (37), 275 (37), 277 (37), 280 (37), 285, 288 (37), 314, *320, 321, 322*
Malinowski, S., 202 (79), 203 (79), *252*
Marraud, A., 23 (57), 24 (57), *92*
Martindale, J. G., 120, *135*, 152 (68), *189*
Matossi, F., 271 (90, 91), *322*
Matthews, H. I., 200 (75), *252*

AUTHOR INDEX

Matthews, J. W., 128, 131, 133, *136*, 139 (11, 12), 143, 144 (11), 145, 146, 147 (11), 148, 149 (31, 34), 150 (12, 35, 36, 47, 50, 52), 152 (47, 50), 153, 155, 156 (34, 35, 36, 50), 157, 158, 159, 160 (47, 50, 91), 161, 162 (11, 86, 96), 163, 164 (35, 47, 50), 167, 169, 171 (34, 36, 52, 122), 172, 173, 174, 175 (34, 35), 176 (47, 50, 88a), 177 (47), 178, 179, 180 (50, 91), 182 (11, 12, 96), 183, 184 (138, 139), 185 (11, 138, 139, 144), 186, *187*, *188*, *189*, *190*, 195, *251*
Matthiessen, A., 327, *369*
Mattson, E., 196 (28), *251*
Matukura, Y., 265 (65), 314 (65), *321*
Maurer, R. D., 46 (84), *92*
Mayer, W. N., 269 (80), *322*
Mead, C. A., 325, 349, 350, 354, 367, *369*, *370*
Mehl, W., 196 (26, 27), 198 (26), *251*
Meissner, K. W., 85 (220), *96*
Mendelson, S., 169 (112, 113), 173, 186, *190*
Menter, J. W., 128 (69), *136*, 144 (25, 28), 155 (25, 28, 78), 160 (28), 166 (4), 182 (25), 184 (25), *187*, *189*, *254*
Menzer, G., 171, *190*
Mertens, F. P., 83 (210), *96*
Michel, E., 50 (105), *93*
Miedler, L. J., 47 (86), *92*
Miller, D. P., 169 (109), *190*
Miller, S. L., 332 (28), *370*
Minahan, J. A., *323*
Mitchell, D. F., 150 (54), *188*, 223 (115), *253*
Mitchell, J. P., 301, *323*
Mitchell, J. W., 152 (70), 162, *189*
Mitsuishi, A., 50 (95), *93*
Mitzumo, J., 238 (161), 239 (161), *254*
Miura, Y., 260 (20), 265 (65), 301 (20), 314, *320*, *321*
Moazed, K. L., 97 (8), 103 (20), 104 (20), 106 (20), 108 (27), 115, 118 (35, 39, 41), 123 (27), 125 (27), 127 (27, 35), *134*, *135*, 150, 151 (63a), 152, 154 (63a), 155 (63a), 159, 160, *188*
Mokhtar, S., 86 (227), *96*
Moll, J. L., 326 (7), 343 (54), 344 (54), 346 (54), 347 (54), 348 (54), 349 (54), 354 (54), 367 (54), *369*, *370*
Moore, A. J. W., 164 (99), *189*
Moore, C. R., 169 (109), *190*
Motizuki, K., 329, *369*

Mott, N. F., 197, *252*, 327 (11), 338 (40), 365 (81), 366 (81), *369*, *370*, *371*
Müller, K., 196 (40), 197 (40), *252*
Mullins, W. W., 111 (30), *135*
Murr, L. E., 160 (91a), *189*
Murray, L. A., 261 (34), 263 (34), 274, *320*
Mutter, W. E., 257 (2), *320*
Mutucumarana, T. de S., 200 (75), *252*

Nagasawa, A., 149 (32), 171 (32), *188*
Nagel, M. R., 52 (121), *93*
Nakayama, M., 340 (47), *370*
Nakayama, T., 260 (17), *320*
Nanni, L. F., 218 (103), 219 (103), 232 (103), *253*
Nawata, S., 86 (233), *96*
Neher, R. T., 60 (152), *94*
Nelson, K. E., 60 (144), *94*
Nelson, O. L., 353, *371*
Neustadter, S. F., 289 (109), *322*
Newman, R., 315 (159), *324*
Newman, R. C., 138, 140 (8), 223 (114), *187*, *253*, *254*
Nicholas, J. F., 142 (22), 164 (99), 184 (22), *187*, *189*
Nichols, D. R., 270 (87), 314 (87), *322*
Nichols, M. H., 341, *370*
Nicholson, R. B., 225 (130), 226 (130), *254*
Nordheim, L., 351, *371*
Nosulenko, N. A., 87 (240), *96*
Nutting, J., 225, *254*
Nye, J. F., 140 (19), *187*

Odencrantz, F. K., 34 (64), 88 (64), *92*
Ogawa, M., 68 (165), *94*
Ogawa, S., 149 (32), 156 (81), 159 (81), 160 (81), 171 (32), *188*, *189*, 238, 239, 240, *254*
Ogburn, F., 199 (62), 204 (62), 227, *252*
Olmstead, J., 301 (133), *323*
Olsen, A. L., 46 (81), *92*
Orem, T. H., 227, *254*
Osafune, H., 265 (65), 314 (65), *321*
Osborne, J., 305 (145), 306 (145), *323*
Owen, A. E., 304, 305, *323*

Packer, D. M., 60 (143), *94*

Padawer, G. E., 218 (103), 219 (103), 232 (103), *253*
Palumbo, G., 50 (97), *93*
Paschen, F., 60 (146), *94*
Pashley, D. W., 118, 119 (45, 47), 120, 128, 131 (47), 132 (75), 133 (44, 45, 75), *135, 136,* 137, 138 (10), 144 (28), 150 (2, 39, 40, 41, 61, 62, 63), 155, 156 (1, 10, 40, 41), 160 (28), 164 (10), 165, 166 (4), 167 (102), 168 (102), 170 (102), 171, 172, 173, 174 (102), 175, 176, 180, 186, *187, 188, 189, 190,* 223 (114, 121), 224, 225 (130), 226 (130, 133), 235 (155), 242 (122), 243, 244 (155), *253, 254, 255*
Passaglia, E., 75 (186), 83 (206), 84 (206), *95*
Paterson, M. S., 230 (143), *254*
Paunovic, M., 196 (36, 37, 39), 199 (36, 39), 200 (36, 39), 201 (36), 204 (36, 39), 206 (36, 39), 209 (36, 39), 211 (36), *251, 252*
Pearson, A. D., 310 (155, 156), *324*
Pechenkina, R. S., 271 (92), *322*
Pecoraro, R. P., 257 (2), *320*
Perri, J. A., 257 (1, 3, 4), 261 (30), 267 (30), 268 (30), 285 (30), 288 (30), 319 (3, 4), *320*
Perrin, F. H., 50 (89), 75 (174), *92, 95*
Peters, F. G., 267, *322*
Peterson, D., 265 (59), 314 (59, 60), 319 (59), *321*
Peterson, D. R., 265, 319 (60), *321*
Peterson, D. W., 39 (70), *92*
Pfund, A. H., 77, 78 (191), *95*
Philip, R., 86 (234), *96*
Phillips, V. A., 154, 181, *189, 190*
Phipps, T. E., 339 (45), *370*
Pick, H. J., 199 (54, 57, 58), 200 (58), 202, 204, 205 206, 207, 209, 211 (57, 58), 233 (58), *252*
Pinsker, Z. G., 223, *253*
Pivovonsky, M., 52 (121), *93*
Pliskin, W. A., 257 (1), 259 (11, 12), 260, 261, 262 (45), 263 (29, 35, 39, 50a), 265 (66), 266 68), 267 (68, 69), 269, 270 (39, 45, 68), 271 272, 273, 274, 275, 276, 277, 278, 279, 280, 281, 282 (12, 29), 283, 284, 285, 286, 787, 288, 302 (137), 305 (137), 306, (137) 310 (68), *320, 321, 322, 323*
Plumb, R. C., 83 (209, 210), *96*
Poli, G., 199 (65, 66, 67, 68), 200 (65, 66, 67, 68), 204, 207, 209 (65, 67, 68), 210, 211 (68), 228, 236 (66), *252*

Poppa, H., 165, *189*
Porteus, J. O., 4 (10), 12 (10), 13, 17, 18, 19 (10), 46 (10), *90, 91*
Potter, R. F., 71, *94, 95*
Pound, G. M., 97 (1, 3, 5, 6, 9), 98 (12), 99 (12, 14, 16), 100 (5, 6), 102 (3), 103, 106 (3, 6), 107 (3), 108 (3, 26), 109 (3, 6, 9, 14), 111, 112 (31), 113, 114, 115, 117, 118 (35, 37), 119 (3), 120, 121, 122, 123 (3, 59, 63), 127 (31, 33a, 35, 37, 59), 131 (3, 6), *134, 135, 136,* 137 (3), 150, 151 (67a), 152, 155 (3), 159, 160 (3), 164, *187, 189,* 193, *251*
Price, P. B., 200 (74), *252*
Pride, G. E., 59 (129), *94*
Priest, J. R., 282 (106), *322*
Procter, J. P., 271 (93), *322*
Prussin, S., 184 (136), *190*

Quarrington, J. E., 60 (136), *94*
Queisser, H. J., 143 (23), 169 (106), 184 (23, 135, 137, 140), 185 (23), *187, 190,* 298 (115), *323*
Quinn, J. J., 328, 329, 364 (17), 365 (17, 20), *369*

Rabinovitch, K., 41 (78), 68 (78), *92*
Racette, J. H., *370*
Raether, H., 223, *253*
Ramsey, J. B., 9 (24), *91,* 282 (101), 285 (101), *322*
Rand, M. J., 261 (33, 36), 263 (33, 36), 264, 265, 314, *320, 321*
Rang, O., 185 (145), *190*
Rank, D. H., 55, 56 (126), *93*
Rausch, D. W., 118 (39), *135*
Rawdon, H. S., 227 (137), *254*
Read, H. J., 238, 239, 240, *254*
Reames, J. P., 6 (14), *90*
Reid, C. D., 60 (155), *94*
Reimer, L., 224 (126), 225, 238, *254*
Reiss, H., 151 (67), *189*
Renk, K. F., 50 (103), *93*
Revesz, A. G., 260 (24), 301 (24, 130, 131), *320, 323*
Rhodin, T. N., 97 (7), 100 (7), 109 (7), 110, 124 (64), 126, 133 (7), *134, 136,* 150, 151, 152 (45), 154, 155, 160, *188*
Rideout, V. L., 75 (187), *95*

Riseman, J., 257 (1, 4), 261 (30), 267 (30), 268 (30), 285 (30), 288 (30), 319 (4), *320*
Ritchie, R. H., 329, 365 (21), *369*
Ritter, E., 282, 286 (102), *322*
Robbins, J. L., 150 (51), 152, 154, 155, *188*
Roberts, R. W., 9 (28), 84 (28), *91*
Roberts, S., 84, *96*
Robins, J. L., 126, *136*
Roddick, R. D., 60 (144), *94*
Rollins, R. W., 124 (64), 126 (64), *136*, 150 (45), 151 (45), 152, 160 (45), *188*
Rose, A., 326, *369*
Rouard, P., 85 (222), 86, *96*
Rowell, J. M., *370*
Royds, T., 60 (147), *94*
Rudee, M. L., 239 (166), *255*
Rudiger, O., 164 (97), 171 (119), *189*, *190*
Rudolph, A. C., *370*
Ruff, O., 283 (108a), *322*
Russell, K. C., 98 (12), 99 (12, 14), 109 (14), *134*
Rustgi, O. P., 50 (99), *93*
Ruth, V., 108 (27), 123, 125 (27), 127 (27), *135*

Sachs, R. G., 339, *370*
Sah, C. T., 295 (113), 301 (113), 302 (140), 304 (140), 306 (140), *323*
Salzberg, C. D., 282 (99), 286 (99), *322*
Samuels, L. E., 7 (17), *91*
Sanders, J. V., 152 (71, 72), 171, 180 (71, 72), *189*
Sanderson, R. B., 60 (141), *94*
Sandhu, H. S., 87 (239), *96*
Sarbei, O. G., 349, 354 (60), 367, *370*
Sard, R., 238 (164), *255*
Sato, H., 156 (83a), *189*
Sauro, J., 23 (56), *92*
Sawyer, R. A., 50 (110), *93*
Scharf, P. T., 50 (100), *93*
Scheibner, E. J., 85 (224), *96*, 301 (117), *323*
Schlotterer, H., 149 (33), 156 (83), 171 (33), 186, *188*, *189*, *190*
Schmidt, P., 283 (108a), *322*
Schmidt, P. F., 316 (163), *324*
Schneer, G. H., 316, *324*
Schoening, F. R. L., 171 (121), 186, *190*
Schottky, W., 357 (77), *371*
Schroen, W., 298 (115), *323*
Schuegraf, K. K., 257 (2), *320*
Schulz, L. G., 23 (54), 85 (223, 224), 86 (229), *91*, *96*, 150 (37, 53), *188*
Schuster, A., 55 (125), *93*
Schwartz, C. D., 238 (164), *255*
Schwartz, H., 263, *321*
Schwartz, L. H., 228 (141), *254*
Schwartz, N., 258, 282, *320*
Schwartz, R. F., 325 (2), 351 (2), *369*
Schwartz, R. S., 258 (10), 319 (10), *320*
Schwuttke, G. H., 184 (137), *190*
Scott, G. D., 22 (50), *91*
Scott, J., 301 (133), *323*
Scott, L. L., 50 (119), *93*
Scott, N. J., 40 (76), *92*
Sears, G. W., 108, 120, *135*, *136*, 203 (81), 204 (82), *252*
Secrist, D. R., 263 (57, 58), 264, 319 (57, 58), *321*
Sedgwick, T. O., 261 (38), 263 (38), 264 (38), *321*
Seiter, H., 199, 200, 201, 202, 203, 204 (55), 206 (55), 233 (55), *252*
Sella, C., 150 (43, 44), 152 (43, 44), *188*
Sennett, R. S., 22 (50), *91*
Seraphim, D. P., 302 (139), 306, 309, *323*
Seraphin, B. O., 3 (8), 7 (8), 8, 58 (128), *90*, *94*
Setty, T. H. V., 196 (35), 199 (64), 204 (64), 206 (64), 209 (64), 210 (64), 211 (64, 91), 236, 238, *251*, *252*, *253*, *254*
Sewell, P. B., 223 (116), *253*
Shaeffer, C., 271 (90), *322*
Shanefield, D., 199 (71), 200 (71), 209 (71), 218 (99), 220 (99), 231 (99), *252*, *253*
Shaw, C. C., 60 (140), *94*
Shaw, C. H., 50 (96), 68 (96), *93*
Shaw, J. E., 60 (137), *94*
Shearer, J. N., 55 (123), *93*
Shin, J. J., 120, 136 (51), *136*
Shinozaki, S., 156 (83a), *189*
Shipp, G. S., 68 (165), *94*
Shirn, G. A., 270 (89), *322*
Shklyarevski, I. N., 87 (240), *96*
Shockley, W., 298 (115), *323*
Shrier, A., 218 (99, 103), 219 (103), 220 (99), 231 (99), 232 (103), *253*
Siddall, G., 263 (48), 267, *321*, *322*
Siegel, B. M., 126, *136*
Sigsbee, R. A., 114, 122, 127 (33a), *135*

AUTHOR INDEX

Silver, M. D., 22, 23, *91*
Silverman, S. L., 274 (97), *322*
Silvey, G. A., 270 (87), 314 (87), *322*
Simmons, G. W., 223 (115), *253*
Simmons, J. G., 351, *371*
Simnad, M. T., 99 (16), 103 (16), 122 (16), 123 (59), 127 (59), *134*, *136*
Simpson, N. H., 210 (89), *253*
Sinclair, W. R., 267, *322*
Sinsheimer, R. L., 50 (109), *93*
Sklar, M., 260 (25), 301 (25), *320*
Slade, J. J., 218 (102), *253*
Slavin, W., 91, *92*
Sloope, B. W., 131 (71, 72), *136*, 169, 171 (105), *190*
Smith, A., 60 (131), *94*
Smith, E. E., 267 (72), *322*
Smith, H. M., 9 (27), *91*
Smith, R. A., 50, *93*, (111, 112, 113, 114, 115), 328, *369*
Smith, R. S., 219 (104), 228 (104), *253*
Snow, E. H., 260 (25), 292, 295 (113), 301 (25, 113, 124), 302, 304, 306, 311, 312, *320*, *322*, *323*
Sommerfeld, A., 351, *371*
Soonpaa, H. H., 3 (6), *90*
Soshea, R. W., 326 (6), 346, 347 (59), 349, 354 (59), 367, *369*, *370*
Sparks, C. J., 40, *92*, 144 (27), *187*, 230, *254*
Sparks, M., 329, *369*
Spicer, W. E., 329, 344 (55), *369*, *370*
Spitzer, W. G., 341 (50, 51), 342, 343 (51), 345, 346 (58), 347, 349 (51), 354 (51), 367 (51), *370*
Sprague, J. L., *323*
Spratt, J. P., 325, 351 (2), *369*
Srivastava, R. D., 211 (90), *253*
Sroka, R., 199 (52), 200 (52), 204 (52), *252*
Steele, S. R., 349, 354, 367, *370*
Steinberg, H. L., 83 (206), 84 (206), *95*
Steinemann, S., 238, *255*
Steinmaier, W., 263 (53), 264, 319 (53), *321*
Sterling, H. F., 270 (86), *322*
Stewart, R. W., 268, *322*
Stickler, B. A., 150 (60), *188*
Stickler, R., 169 (108), *190*
Stirland, D. J., 150 (59), *188*
Stoebe, T. G., 239, *255*
Stone, D. E., 23 (55), *92*

Storey, G. G., 199 (57, 58, 60), 200 (58, 60), 204 (57, 58, 60), 205 (57), 206 (57, 58, 60), 207 (57), 209 (57, 58, 60), 211 (57, 58), 233 (58), *252*
Stowell, M. J., 118, 119 (45), 120 (45), 132 (75), 133 (44, 45, 75), *135*, 150 (39, 41), 155 (41), 156 (41), 165, 167 (102), 168 (102), 170 (102), 171 (102), 172, 174, 175, 176, *188*, *189*, *190*, 224, 242 (122), 243 (168), *253*, *255*,
Stringer, G., 260 (18), 301 (18), *320*
Stromberg, R. R., 75 (186), 83 (206), 84 (206), *95*
Strong, J., 9 (25), 50 (118), 60 (130), 83 (208), *91*, *93*, *94*, *96*
Stuart, R., 344, *370*
Sugano, T., 343 (54), 344 (54), 346 (54), 347 (54), 348 (54), 349 (54), 354 (54), 367 (54), *370*
Sumner, G. G., 150 (48), 155 (48), *188*
Sun, C. H. 235 (153), *254*
Sundquist, B. E., 164, *189*
Sutton, P. M., 309, *324*
Swann, R. C. G., 270 (86), *322*
Sze, S. M., 327 (8), 330, 331 (24), 332, 333 (25), 334, 335 (36), 337 (25), 338, 339, 340, 341, 343, 344 (54), 346, 347 (54), 348 (54), 349, 354 (54), 356 (75), 357, 358 (75), 359, 360, 361 (80), 362, 363, 364, 367, *369*, *370*, *371*
Szedon, J. R., 316 (161), *324*

Tanaka, S., 265 (65), 314 (65), *321*
Tannenbaum, E., 301 (117), *323*
Taylor, A. H., 60 (142), *94*
Taylor, N. J., 161, *189*
Teasdale-Buckell, P., 85 (221), *96*
Thielen, J., 50 (105), *93*
Thirsk, H. R., 191, 233 (3), 235 (3), *251*
Thomas, D. J. D., 169 (114), *190*
Thomas, G., 143 (23), 184 (23, 140), 185 (23), *187*, *190*, 225 (127), *254*
Thomas, H., 345, *370*
Thomas, J. E., Jr., 302 (138), 306, *323*
Thompson, E. R., 143, 144 (24), *187*, 213, 214, 219 (96), 228 (96), 229 (96), 231, 234 (96), 235 (96), 242, 243, 249, *253*, *255*
Thompson, M. W., *190*
Thompson, N., 159 (84), *189*

Thomson, G. P., 223, 232, 236 (113), *253*
Thurnau, D. H., 68 (162), *94*
Tiller, C. O., 131 (71, 72), *136*, 169, 171 (105), *190*
Tiller, W. A., 184, *190*
Tokuyama, T., 262, 314, *321*
Tolansky, S., 2 (2), 3 (7), 20, 22 (47), 25 (58, 59), 26 (59, 62), 86 (236), *90*, *91*, *92*, *96*
Tolliver, D. L., 265 (61, 63), 314 (61), 319 (61, 63), *321*
Tombs, N. C., 315 (159), *324*
Torricelli, A., 199 (50), 204 (50), *252*
Tournier, J., 162 (94), *189*
Tourtellotte, H. A., 263, *321*
Tousey, R., 10 (33, 34), 50 (101), 60 (34), 68 (164), *91*, *93*
Treherne, D. M., 84 (214), *96*
Trent, H. M., 23 (55), *92*
Treuting, R. G., 174, *190*
Trillat, J. J., 150 (43, 44), 152 (43, 44), *188*
Trivich, D., 199 (56, 61), 200 (56, 61), 204 (56, 61), 206, 209, 242 (61), *252*
Tronstad, L., 82 (203), *95*
Tung, S. K., 261 (32), 263 (32), 264, *320*
Turnbull, A., 26 (62), *92*
Turnbull, D., 97 (2), 106, *134*, *135*
Turner, A. F., 9 (27), *91*
Turner, D. R., 199 (70), 200 (70), 206 (70), *252*
Tuzzolino, A. J., 68 (163), *94*

Ubersax, F., 199 (48), 204 (48), *252*
Udin, H., 139 (12a, 13), *187*
Unvala, B. A., 169 (111), 172 (111), *190*
Uyeda, R., 155, 171, *189*, *190*

Valdre, U., 186, *190*
Valletta, R. M., 261 (30), 263 (54), 264 (54), 267, 268, 285, 288, 319 (54), *320*, *321*
Van der Merwe, J. H., 107 (22), 128 (22), *135*, 139, 142, 157 (15), 162 (15, 16, 17, 18), 174, 184, 185 (143), *187*, *190*, 231, *254*
Vanderslice, T. A., 9 (28), 84 (28), *91*
Van Gelder, W., 316 (163), *324*
Vaughan, T. B., 199 (57), 204, 205 (57), 206 (57), 207 (57), 209 (57), 211 (57), *252*
Verma, A. R., 195, *251*

Vermaak, J. S., 184, 185 (143), *190*
Vermilyea, D. A., 198, 200 (74), 206, 207, *252*, *253*
Vissner, W. M., 75 (176), *95*
Vogt, C., 327, *369*
Volmer, M., 99, *134*, 150 (66), *189*, 192, 198, 199 (47, 49), 204 (47, 49), *251*, *252*
Vonnegut, B., 106, *135*

Wainfan, N., 23 (56), *92*
Wakramian, A. T., 199 (51), 204 (51), *252*
Walker, P. L., Jr., 212, *253*
Walker, W. C., 50 (99), 72, *93*, *95*
Walker, W. P., 181 (131), *190*
Walton, A. G., 121, (54) *136*
Walton, D., 97 (7), 100 (7, 19), 109 (7, 19), 110, 124, 126 (64), 130, 133 (7), *134*, *136*, 150, 151, 152, 155 (64, 65), 160, *188*
Wanlass, F. M., 107 (23), *135*
Warren, B. E., 221, 222 (109), 230, *253*
Washburn, J., 143, 169 (106), 184 (23), 140, 185 (23), *187*, *190*
Watanabe, D., 156 (81), 159 (81), 160 (81), *189*, 238 (161), 239 (161), *254*
Watanabe, K., 68 (161), *94*
Watelski, S. B., 169 (109), *190*
Waterman, T., *371*
Watts-Tobin, R. J., 197, *252*
Waylonis, J. E., 84 (215), *96*
Weaver, C., 85 (225), 86 (225, 235), *96*
Webb, M. B., 200 (74), *252*
Weeks, R. F., 60 (134), *94*
Wegener, H. A. R., 315 (159), *324*
Wehner, G. K., 269, *322*
Weil, R., 212, 238, 239, 240, *253*, *254*, *255*
Weingart, J. M., 82 (205), *95*
Weisskopf, V. F., 328 (12), *369*
Weissler, G. L., 50 (99), 68 (165), *93*
Weissmann, S., 218 (99, 103), 219 (103), 220 (99), 231 (99), 232 (103, 148), *253*, *254*
Wemple, S. H., 75 (187), *95*
Whelan, M. J., 142 (21), 182 (21, 133), *187*, *190*, 225 (130), *254*
White, H. G., 332 (30), 346 (58), *370*
White, J. U., 50 (120), *93*
White, P., 282 (105), 282 (105), 310, *322*, *324*
White, W. C., 4 (12), *90*
Whitham, G. B., 207, *253*

Widmer, H., 169 (116), *190*
Wied, O. J., *323*
Wiegmann, W., 332 (29), *370*
Wilcock, J., 199 (53, 54), 202, 204 (53, 54), 206 (54), *252*
Williams, J. C., 267 (77), *322*
Williams, R., 341 (52), *370*
Wills, J. M. M., 126 (66a), *136*
Wilman, H., 200 (75), 211 (91), 234 (152), 236, 238, *252*, *253*, *254*
Wilson, A. H., 328, *369*
Wilson, B. A., 60 (133), *94*
Wilson, D. K., 301, *323*
Winterbottom, A. B., 82 (204), *95*
Wirtz, K., 271 (90), *322*
Wolfe, W. L., 75 (188), *95*
Wolter, A. R., 23 (52), *91*
Wood, R. W., 121 (56), *136*
Wood, W. A., 227, *254*
Woodruff, W. H., 83 (211), *96*
Wooten, F., 344 (55), *370*
Worthing, A. G., 60 (154), 71 (170), *94*, *95*
Worthing, F. L., 302, *323*

Wranglen, G., 199 (59), 200 (59, 73), 202, 204 (59), *252*
Wulff, J., 139 (12a, 13), *187*

Yamada, Y., 50 (95), *93*
Yamin, M., 302, 306, 309, *323*, *324*
Yang, L., 99 (16), 103 (16), 122 (16), 123 (59), 127 (59), *134*, *136*, 234 (152), *254*
Yarwood, J., 9 (22), *91*
Yeh, G. S., 126 (66a), *136*
Yolken, H. T., 37, 38, *92*
Yon, E., 305 (146), 309, *323*
York, D. B., 282 (107), *322*
Yoshinaga, H., 50 (95), *93*
Young, D. R., 302 (138), 306, *323*
Young, F., 153, *189*
Young, L., 9 (20), *91*

Zaininger, K. H., 260 (24), 301 (24, 130, 131), *320*, *323*
Zeldovich, J. B., 98 (10), 99 (10), *134*

Subject Index

Abbé resolution criterion, 55
Abelès–Brewster angle measurement of refractive index, 77–78
Accommodation of misfit
 between nuclei and substrate, 161–163
 between overgrowth and substrate, 139–149
Aluminosilicate glass films, pyrolytic, 314
Aluminum oxide, electron gun evaporation, 283–285
Annealing of thin films, 186
Attenuation length measurements, 345–350

Bandwidth, spectrometer, 55–57
Birefringence, 47
Boundary formation between doubly positioned nuclei, 173–174
Brewster angle measurement, 76–78
Bunching, 209

Cleaning of glass substrates, 5–7
 glow discharge, 6
Coalescence of nuclei, 165–175
 liquid-like behavior, 165
Condensation coefficient effects on nucleation, 107–108
Corning
 191 CP glass, 276
 7050 glass, 277–279
Cross-slip, 147–149
Crystal growth
 by screw dislocation step advancement, 193–195
 from vapor, 192–195
Current flow, ionic, in glass films, 293–300

Defect(s)
 in films, 149–150, 180–182
 formation, 165–175
Defocusing effect of thick samples, spectrometer, 45–46
Detectors, vacuum ultraviolet, 68–69
Diffusion flux in size space, 98–99

Dislocation(s)
 formation, 169–171
 misfit, 142–143, 182–186
  during diffusion across interface between crystals, 184–186
 generation, 146–147
Double-positioning, 156
Dust particle prevention, 6

Electrodeposition on thin metal films, 243–248
Electrodeposits, 191–255
 difference from vapor deposition, 195–196
 impurity effects, 210–212
 influence of substrate metal, 212–217
 morphology, 199–217
 nucleation rate, 198
 results of structure studies, 226–250
 screw dislocation mechanism, 203–204
 structure, 217–250
 temperature effects, 210–212
 thickness effects, 210–212
 two-dimensional surface nucleation, 198–199
Electron
 diffraction study of electrodeposit structure, 223–224, 232–238
 microscope study of electrodeposit structure, 224–226, 238–250
  copper, 238–239
  nickel, 239–243
 tunneling in thin film structures, 325–371
  collector efficiency, 335–338
Ellipsometer measurement, 79–84
Emission, thermionic, 354–367
 experimental measurements, 360–367
Emittance, spectral, 10
Emitter characteristics, 356–360
Entropy of mixing, 102
Epitaxy and heterogeneous nucleation, 128–134
 role of contact angle, 130–131
 role of temperature, 129–130
 theory, 129–131
Etching techniques for evaluating glass films, 272–273

Feco interferometric method, 31–37
  absolute phase change measurement, 88–90
  accuracy, 36–37
  alignment, 33–34
  coating of plates, 31–32
  interferogram analysis, 34–36
  measurement of surface roughness, 20–21
Fermi age theory, 344
Film formation, 8–12
  by generation, growth and coalescence of nuclei, 150–186
  modes, 138
  nucleation processes, 97–136
Fizeau interferometric method, 24–31
  alignment, 27
  coating of flats, 26
  conditions for producing sharp fringes, 24–27
  measurement of surface roughness, 19–20
  sensitivity to surface roughness, 29–31
Flux
  diffusion, in size space, 98–99
  impingement, 101, 09
Free energy
  of formation, nuclei, 101–102
  minimum, configurations, 157–158
  total, of substrate system, 102–103, 111

Gas, residual, effect on film properties, 9–10
General Electric GSC-1 glass, 274–276
Glass films, 257–324
  application to semiconductor devices, 316–320
  boiling water and humidity tests, 277–279
  borosilicate, 309
  deposited, 309–316
  electrical properties, 289–316
  evaluation of physical and chemical properties, 270–289
  formed during diffusion, 305–309
  frit fusion, 317–318, 319
  fused
  and RF sputtered, structural differences, 274–277
  from sedimented glass powders, 266–267
  phosphosilicate, 262, 305–309

  preparation, 259–270
    by pyrolytic decomposition, 263–266, 318
    radio-frequency sputtered, 268–269, 318–319
    reactively sputtered, 267–268
    space-charge buildup in, 310–311
    vacuum evaporated, 263
Gold
  growth on silver, 142–143
  growth on sodium chloride, 176–180
  (111) nuclei, rapid growth, 164–165
Grating equation, Littrow mounting, 56

Hot-electron
  collection, 330
  generation, 357–359
  transport, 325–371

Image charge in silicon, 296–297
Interface structure, 106–107
Interferometer, basic equation, 28, 35–36

Lattice disorder effect on optical properties, 11
Layer
  growth, 204–209
  structure, block-or cubic, 206–207
Lead growth on (111) surface of silver, 138–139

Mean free paths
  electron-electron, 328–329
  electron-optical-phonon, 331–333
  hot-electron and electrical conductivity, 327–328
  for hot-electron-plasma interactions, 328–329
Microscopy, interference, 271–272
MIS structure, 293ff
Moiré fringe patterns, 226
  of nuclei misalignment, 156–157
Monolayer growth mechanism, 196–199
Monte Carlo calculation of attenuation length, 344

Nickel deposited on copper, surface structure, 212–214
Nucleation in thin film formation, 97–136, 150–186
  data, analysis, 122–124
  effect of deposition rate, 154
  effect of substrate temperature, 155
  of electrodeposits, 192–217
    two-dimensional surface, 198–199
  epitaxial, theory, 129–131
  experimental results, 114–127
  heterogeneous, 98–114
    classical theory, 98–103
    contact angle modification, 103–106
    and epitaxy, 128–134
    high substrate temperature modifications, 108–109
    impurity effects, 113
    interface structure, 106–107
    low substrate temperatures, 109–111
    substrate imperfections, 111–113
  influence of substrate perfection and purity, 152–154
  rate, 151–152
    direct measurement, 124–126
  role of imperfections and impurities, 120–121
  at surface steps, 152
Nuclei
  alignment, effect of contaminants, 161
  coalescence, 165–175
  free energy of formation, 101–102
  growth, 163–165
  misalignment, 156–157
  orientation, 156–161
  perfection, 155
  shape, 100–101, 161
Nucleus radius, critical, 198

Optics, thin film, precision measurement in, 1–96
Orientation of nuclei, 156–161
  changes in, 175–180
  influence of deposition rate, 160
  influence of substrate temperature, 158–160
  at surface steps, 160–161
Oxidation of silicon, 260–262

Oxide
  film thickness, 37–41
    capacitance measurement, 39–40
    x-ray measurement, 40–41
  growth in vacuum, 37

Passivation, electrical requirements, 289–292
Pemco S 1117 glass, 279
Phase change
  absolute, on reflection measurement, 84–90
    Feco interferometric method, 88–90
    methods of measurement, 85–86
    sources of error, 86–88
  due to nonabsorbing film on absorbing substrate, 38
Phosphor, sodium salicylate, 68–69
Phosphosilicate glasses, 262, 305–309
  in multilevel passivation, 313–314
  sodium migration through, 307–309
Photoemission experiements, 341–350
  methods of analysis, 344–350
Photoresponse per absorbed photon, 342–343
Platinum growth on gold, 143–144
Polarimeter measurements, 69–74
Polarization
  effects in reflection measurements, 66–67
  ionic, 293–300
  space-charge, in glass-over-oxide structures, 311–313
Polishing techniques, bowl-feed, 3–5
Positioning, double, 223–224
Potential barrier shape, 333–335
Purity, evaporated material, 10–11
Pyramidal growth forms, 200–204

Reflectance, specular
  correction for surface roughness, 17–18
  relation to surface roughness, 13–16
Reflection
  attenuated total, 74–76
  measurement
    absolute phase change on, 84–90
    non-normal incidence, 69–78
    normal incidence, 57–69
    using polarized light, 70–72
    unpolarized light, 72–74
    quantum-mechanical, 338–341

Reflectometers
  double-reflection spherical mirror, 61–65
  single-reflection movable detector, 65–69
  types, 59–60
Replica techniques, 224–225
Ridge-type deposits, 209–210

Scattering
  electron-phonon, 330–338
  hot-electron, processes in metals, 327–329
  of light in spectrometers, 46, 49–51
Schottky emission, 354–367
Silane decomposition, 263–264
Silicon dioxide films
  etch rate, 286–289
  evaporated, 282–285
  oxygen deficiency in, 285–286
  pyrolytic, 314
  refractive index, 286–289
  RF sputtered, 277
  sodium in, 301–305
  thermal 300–305
Silicon monoxide films, evaporated, 282–285
Silicon nitride
  amorphous, 314–316
  pyrolytic and sputtered, 269–270
Single-crystal films
  evaporated, 137–190
  monolayer growth, 138–150
Slitwidth, spectrometer spectral, 55–57
SMST structures, experimental measurements, 360–366
Space-charge
  buildup in thin glass films, 310–311
  polarization in glass-over-oxide structures, 311–313
Spectra, infrared transmission and reflection, 273–274
Spectrometer
  photometric nonlinearity, 47–49
  sample and shutter emission, 51–52
  scattered light, 49–51
  spectral slitwidth, 55–57
  wavelength calibration error, 52–55
Spectroscopy, infrared, evaluation of glass films, 270–271
Spirals, growth, 202
Sputtered glass films, 267–269
  effect of moisture, 279–282

Stacking fault formation, 166–169
Strain
  equilibrium, of an epitaxially aligned film, 139–140
  generation, 174–175
Substrate
  imperfections, effect on nucleation, 111–113
  preparation, 2–8
    crystalline, 7–8
    glass, 3–7
  temperature
    high, 108–109
    low, 109–111
Supersaturation, critical, 121–127
Surface
  roughness, 12–31
    correction of reflectance measurement for, 17–18
    effect on Fizeau thickness measurement, 29–31
    Gaussian, 13–17
    measurement, 18–21
    non-Gaussian, 17
    relation to specular reflection, 13–16
  steps
    nucleation at, 152
    orientation of nuclei at, 160–161

Thickness, film, 21–41
  Feco method, 31–37
  Fizeau method, 24–31
  methods of measurements, 21–24
  oxide films, 37–41
  quartz crystal oscillator method, 23
  x-ray measurement, 23–24
Transmission measurement, optical, 41–57
  commercial spectrometers, 41–42
  instrumental sources of error, 47–57
  systematic errors caused by sample, 44–47
Transmittance of thin film on nonabsorbing substrate, 42–44
Triode structures, 366–367
Tunnel-emmission triode, thin film, 350–354
  base transport, 353–354
  emitter characteristics, 351–353

Tunneling, electron, 325–371
Twin formation, 171–173

Vamfo, 271–272
Vapor deposition, chemical, 113–114

Wavelength calibration errors, 52–55
Wave velocity, kinematic, 208

X-ray
    diffraction measurement of electrodeposit
        structure, 218–222, 226–232
        gold and nickel on copper, 229–230
        thick copper on copper, 231–232
        line profile analysis, 218–222
    thickness measurement
        metal film, 23–24
        oxides, 40–41

Zeldovich nonequilibrium factor, 99